D1093444

Smart Buildings Digitalization

Smart Buildings Digitalization

IoT and Energy Efficient Smart Buildings Architecture and Applications

Edited by
O.V. Gnana Swathika, K. Karthikeyan, and
Sanjeevikumar Padmanaban

CRC Press is an imprint of the
Taylor & Francis Group, an **informa** business

First edition published 2022
by CRC Press
6000 Broken Sound Parkway NW, Suite 300, Boca Raton, FL 33487-2742

and by CRC Press
4 Park Square, Milton Park, Abingdon, Oxon, OX14 4RN

First edition published by CRC Press 2022

CRC Press is an imprint of Taylor & Francis Group, LLC

ISBN: 978-1-032-06177-1 (hbk)
ISBN: 978-1-032-06178-8 (pbk)
ISBN: 978-1-003-20106-9 (ebk)

DOI: 10.1201/9781003201069

Typeset in Times
by codeMantra

Contents

Preface

A smart building is a state-of-the-art building with features that facilitate individuals making informed decisions about the buildings based on the data through smart metering and Internet-of-things (IoT) sensors. IoT and big data analytics is conglomerated with IoT and digital sensors in a web-based system where the building can be monitored, controlled, and acted upon in a real-time scenario. Various artificial intelligence (AI) and machine learning (ML) applications are discussed concerning smart buildings. This book discusses further how renewable energy sources are integrated into smart buildings using suitable power electronic devices. Advanced technologies with monitoring, protection, and energy management features are deployed in smart buildings. A case study on automation is a crucial feature that is elaborately discussed concerning smart buildings.

Five Salient Features:

1. Smart buildings for the 21st century
2. Role of IoT and big data analytics in smart buildings
3. AI- and ML-based applications in smart buildings
4. Monitoring, protection, load balancing, and energy management in smart buildings
5. A case study on automation in smart buildings

Editors

O.V. Gnana Swathika (Member '11–Senior Member '20, IEEE) earned a BE in Electrical and Electronics Engineering at Madras University, Chennai, Tamil Nadu, India, in 2000; an MS in Electrical Engineering at Wayne State University, Detroit, MI, USA, in 2004; and a PhD in Electrical Engineering at VIT University, Chennai, Tamil Nadu, India, in 2017. She completed her postdoc at the University of Moratuwa, Sri Lanka in 2019. Her current research interests include microgrid protection, power system optimization, embedded systems, and photovoltaic systems.

K. Karthikeyan is an electrical and electronics engineering graduate with a master's in personnel management from the University of Madras. With two decades of rich experience in electrical design, he has immensely contributed toward the building services sector comprising airports, Information Technology Office Space (ITOS), tall statues, railway stations/depots, hospitals, educational institutional buildings, residential buildings, hotels, steel plants, and automobile plants in India and abroad (Sri Lanka, Dubai, and the UK). Currently, he is Chief Engineering Manager – Electrical Designs for Larsen & Toubro (L&T) Construction, an Indian multinational Engineering Procurement Construction (EPC) contracting company. Also, he has worked at Voltas, ABB, and Apex Knowledge Technology Private Limited. His primary role involved the preparation and review of complete electrical system designs up to 110kV. Detailed engineering stage covering by various electrical design calculations, design basis reports, suitable for construction drawings, and Mechanical Electrical Plumbing (MEP) design coordination. He is the point of contact for both client and internal project team, lead and manage a team of design and divisional personnel, day-to-day interaction with clients, peer review, managing project deadlines, Project time estimation, assisting in staff appraisals, training, and recruiting.

Sanjeevikumar Padmanaban (Member '12–Senior Member '15, IEEE) earned a bachelor's degree in electrical engineering at the University of Madras, Chennai, India, in 2002; a master's (Hons) in electrical engineering at Pondicherry University, Puducherry, India, in 2006; and a PhD in electrical engineering at the University of Bologna, Bologna, Italy, in 2012. He was an Associate Professor at VIT University from 2012 to 2013. In 2013, he joined the National Institute of Technology, India, as a faculty member. In 2014, he was invited to be a visiting researcher at the Department of Electrical Engineering, Qatar University, Doha, Qatar, funded by the Qatar National Research Foundation (Government of Qatar). He continued his research activities with the Dublin Institute of Technology, Dublin, Ireland, in 2014. Further, he served as an Associate Professor in the Department of Electrical and Electronics Engineering, University of Johannesburg, Johannesburg, South Africa, from 2016 to 2018. From 2018 to 2021, he has been a faculty member in the Department of Energy Technology, Aalborg University, Esbjerg, Denmark. He is currently at Aarhus University, Herning, Denmark. He has authored over 300 scientific papers. Dr. Padmanaban was the recipient of the Best Paper cum Most Excellence Research Paper Award from IET-SEISCON '13, IET-CEAT '16, IEEE-EECSI '19, and IEEE-CENCON '19 and five best paper awards from ETAEERE '16-sponsored Lecture Notes in Electrical Engineering – Springer. He is a fellow of the Institution of Engineers, India; the Institution of Electronics and Telecommunication Engineers, India; and the Institution of Engineering and Technology, UK. He is an editor/associate editor/editorial board member for refereed journals, including the *IEEE Systems Journal*, *IEEE Transactions on Industry Applications*, *IEEE Access*, *IET Power Electronics*, *IET Electronics Letters*, and *Wiley-International Transactions on Electrical Energy Systems*. He is the subject editorial board member of *Energy Sources – Energies Journal*, *MDPI*, and the subject editor for the *IET Renewable Power Generation*, *IET Generation, Transmission and Distribution*, and *FACTS Journal* (Canada).

Contributors

S. Angalaeswari
School of Electrical Engineering
Vellore Institute of Technology
Chennai, India

Morteza Azimi Nasab
CTIF Global Capsule
Herning, Denmark

V. Berlin Hency
School of Electronics Engineering
Vellore Institute of Technology
Chennai, India

S. Charles Raja
Department of Electrical and Electronics Engineering
Thiagarajar College of Engineering
Madurai, India

C.T. Chidambaram
EDRC, B&F
L&T Construction
Mumbai, India

Jayakumar Chinnappan
Department of Computer Science and Engineering
Sri Venkateswara College of Engineering
Pennalur, India

Vaishnavi Chirravuri
School of Electrical Engineering
Vellore Institute of Technology
Chennai, India

Vidhi Choudhary
School of Electronics Engineering
Vellore Institute of Technology
Chennai, India

Luke Gerard Christie
School of Social Science and Languages
Vellore Institute of Technology
Chennai, India

Faazila Fathima S
School of Electrical Engineering
Vellore Institute of Technology
Chennai, India

O.V. Gnana Swathika
School of Electrical Engineering
Vellore Institute of Technology
Chennai, India

K.T.M.U. Hemapala
Department of Electrical Engineering
University of Moratuwa
Moratuwa, Sri Lanka

K. Jamuna
School of Electrical Engineering
Vellore Institute of Technology
Chennai, India

J. Jeslin Drusila Nesamalar
Department of Electrical and Electronics Engineering
Kamaraj College of Engineering and Technology
Virudhunagar, India

T. Karthick
Department of Electrical and Electronics Engineering
Thiagarajar College of Engineering
Madurai, India

Karthik G
School of Electronics Engineering
Vellore Institute of Technology
Chennai, India

K. Karthikeyan
Larsen & Toubro Pvt. Ltd.
Mumbai, India

Mohammad Khoobani
Young Researchers and Elite club
Shahrood University of Technology
Shahrud, Iran

Rubia Ramesh Kumar
School of Electronics Engineering
Vellore Institute of Technology
Chennai, India

M Mahesh
Department of Electrical and Electronics Engineering
New Horizon College of Engineering
Bengaluru, India

Priyank Mehra
School of Electronics Engineering
Vellore Institute of Technology
Chennai, India

G Naveen Kumar
Department of Electrical and Electronics Engineering
Andhra Loyola Institute of Engineering and Technology
Vijayawada, India

J. Nishanthy
Department of Electrical and Electronics Engineering
Thiagarajar College of Engineering
Madurai, India

Sanjeevikumar Padmanaban
CTIF Global Capsule
Herning, Denmark

Aadyasha Patel
School of Electrical Engineering
Vellore Institute of Technology
Chennai, India

M Prabhakar
School of Electrical Engineering
Vellore Institute of Technology
Chennai, India

Prasanna Venkatesh S
EDRC, B&F
L&T Construction
Mumbai, India

Premalatha L
School of Electrical Engineering
Vellore Institute of Technology
Chennai, India

R. Ramesh
EDRC, B&F
L&T Construction
Mumbai, India

D.H. Ranasinghe
Department of Electrical Engineering
University of Moratuwa
Moratuwa, Sri Lanka

Reena Monica P
School of Electronics Engineering
Vellore Institute of Technology
Chennai, India

Aayush Sharma
School of Electrical Engineering
Vellore Institute of Technology
Chennai, India

Saloni Sharma
School of Electronics Engineering
Vellore Institute of Technology
Chennai, India

Siva Sankari Subbiah
Department of Information Technology
Kingston Engineering College
Vellore, India

Swetha KK
School of Electronics Engineering
Vellore Institute of Technology
Chennai, India

P. Tejaswi
School of Electrical Engineering
Vellore Institute of Technology
Chennai, India

Ralph Thangaraj
School of Electronics Engineering
Vellore Institute of Technology
Chennai, India

K Vinoth Kumar
Department of Electrical and Electronics Engineering
New Horizon College of Engineering
Bengaluru, India

A.C. Vishnu Dharssini
Department of Electrical and Electronics Engineering
Thiagarajar College of Engineering
Madurai, India

Suren Senadheera Wewalage
Department of Electrical Engineering
University of Moratuwa
Moratuwa, Sri Lanka

Mohammad Zand
CTIF Global Capsule
Herning, Denmark

1 Building Smart Cities and Smarter Data Centers for the 21st-Century Global Citizen

A Brief Study

Luke Gerard Christie and Ralph Thangaraj
Vellore Institute of Technology

CONTENTS

1.1 INTRODUCTION: A BACKDROP OF ACCESSIBILITY TO ENERGY GLOBALLY AND ALSO WITH INDIA IN PERSPECTIVE: THE NEED FOR SMART CITIES

Global economies when competing require high levels and increasing supply of energy to ensure that the cities are electrified; organizations and industrial units are powered; and household is receiving electricity supply. The increase in sufficient, rapid, uninterrupted energy production and distribution leads to a sustainable economy. Low levels of energy supply *stultifies* an economy, and the bigger the economy, the more the electricity powered by nuclear-powered plants, coal-powered plants, and renewable energy. Schools, hospitals, universities, organizations, and people's lives are run on the amount of accessibility electricity. In fact, due to high levels of pollution, a few countries like Germany, Sweden, Nicaragua, Scotland, China, Uruguay, Denmark, Kenya, and to an extent, the United States of America are looking toward shifting to a low

DOI: 10.1201/9781003201069-1

carbon economy. The actual newest objective of the United Nations is that every individual has access to electricity in the new Sustainable Development Goal (SDG) Plan, which ensures that by 2030 everyone must have access to reliable, affordable energy. Upon ratification at the Paris Climate Accord, countries have been asked to come on board to work on newer policies in their respective countries to shift to cleaner, smarter, reliable energy that conserves the biosphere and prevents global warming and climate change. In this manner, it is important to expand energy efficiency and to shift to renewable energy. Governments across the globe are being asked to tweak their policies to shift to a low carbon economy, where the biggest economies have been making relevant in-roads in global integration and in global relevance. However, for a country like India, despite the challenges, she has taken the initiative to embed new technologies in the energy grid. Countries with a sophisticated network controlling their electricity supply have a robust, cutting-edge grid and an infrastructure that saves energy when not used and further changes are being initiated to keep saving energy. Unlike India, it is impossible to save energy in a sophisticated manner, which will be discussed in the latter section of this chapter. Third-world countries must resort only to common-sense attitude like switching of the mains when not in use or switch of appliances when not in use, so on and so forth, to save energy. If energy levels are saved extensively, these countries can reduce their debt-level ratio.

1.2 THE NEED FOR SMART CITIES

1.2.1 Brief Synopses on India's Utilization of Energy Supply and Challenges

In India, an emerging economy has the same burdens of ensuring that she competes with the rest of the bigger economies now running as the seventh largest economy in the world. The major question is, "Can India reduce her costs in energy supply, which runs the bulk of her massive expenditure to run the economy?" India's formal economy contributes almost 7% to the GDP and 93% comes from the informal economy. Her entire contribution to the global economy is based only on the consumption of energy – electricity and fossil fuels and electricity powered by fossil fuel. Three major costs on energy consumption are plant costs used at big industrial units, multilateral organizations, and grid-level costs disseminated across India's households in India's 4000 cities and towns and her 664,369 villages, of which more than half do not receive electricity. It is quite recently the government's policy initiative to electrify all her villages, a massive ongoing project. Besides, there are serious capital costs that cut through the length and breadth of India's organizational and household spaces, both formally and informally, which in turn contribute to the GDP. Capital costs, maintenance and operation, and fueling costs vary for nuclear-powered plants, coal-powered plants, and the complementation of renewable energy, all of which need immense energy that are driven by huge loads of electricity. The sad yet bitter truth is unlike the top five economies, India's economy cannot do without her huge loads of electricity supply and its generational capacity. The constant yet consistent supply can power the economy brimming with the potential of traversing in the direction of being a global leader in the years to come. The challenge for India is also that due to her complex geography, the supply of energy remains unreached to all contours, resulting in unequal distribution, but the reach is there and there's been much effort to ensure that in order to compete with the globe, India must be suffused with energy (fossil fuel and renewables) supply all around the clock. With her vast challenges, she remains to be one of the leading economies. All countries have a sophisticated energy grid that can be contained or controlled accordingly and has saved high or increasing levels of energy, *unlike* India. As of now being integrated to the global economy, India is changing to equal the energy mindset of the developed world by shifting to smarter cities and cleaner, renewable energy sources like wind and solar.

1.3 THE COST OF ELECTRICITY

Consumers receive electricity through a grid with the significant amounts of investment laid down by a distributor. Upon buying electricity supply from the generator, the distributors multiply or add distribution and transmission costs. The first cost is to recover technical losses, operating expenses, and profit to determine the tariff to be charged from a consumer. The harsh reality in India is that when several generators are connected to the grid, unstructured grid-management policies and the many interactions with the grid influence the working of a generator and its supply of electricity supply. An even worse reality is that with the complex interactions with the generator, electricity markets are not assigned to any price to system effect. In recent years with governments pushing for renewable energy or alternate supplies of energy to be used or to shift to a low carbon economy, renewable energy is presently connected to the grid where grid-level costs have different components.

In the Economic Survey 2016–17 (Volume 2), an attempt has been made to estimate the grid-level costs. The "social cost of carbon" represents economic cost of greenhouse gas emissions adding health costs, costs of irregularity, cost of land, cost of government incentives according to global parity, and cost arising from unused assets. All energy grids adopt system cost and other costs as well. Countries that have shifted to alternate sources of energy have managed to bring down consumption costs when compared to costs when fossil fuels or coal has been earlier used. With the complexity of newer and advanced businesses that rely heavily on technology and electricity with more healthcare facilities and hospitals surfacing to cater to burgeoning populations, more supply of electricity is required. The dilemma is if governments can curb losses by controlling inflated costs and save unutilized power. The traditional or earlier pattern of assessing and determining the cost of electricity cannot be used as a framework in the 21st century to assess intermittent and distributable electric supply options but fresh policies need to be chalked out. Energy supply that is reliable, affordable, resilient, flexible, and climate-friendly is the need of the hour across the globe, and it the first best policy of all governments that have taken the initiative of shifting to alternate sources of energy that will eventually become climate resilient by incorporating all low-carbon-energy technologies. With this goal in mind in new city planning and shift to new infrastructure framework, countries that are speeding up their goals in catering to their diverse population have smart building, smart technologies, and robust smart cities that are closely aligned to the United Nations "Sustainable Development Goals."

1.4 THE *NEW NORMAL* AS COUNTRIES SHIFT TO SMART TECHNOLOGY AND SMART CITIES POWERED BY INTELLIGENT DATA CENTERS

As countries have ratified the Paris Climate Accord in their policies, the desire is to build smart cities and to incorporate smart technologies that are highly resilient and state of the art to contain and save unused energy. Smart cities that are coming up are only to shift from the old normal where energy did run amok with rampant expenditure to saving capital costs and transforming into being more climate-friendly. The ultimate and comprehensive plan of smart cities is to be more sustainable and improve social services that are constantly aligned to the SDGs. The development of adopting the SDGs is relayed on all areas from institutional, social, economic, and physical structures that accommodate citizens in a social setting, in which new policies are framed. It is understood that the 21st century with its infusion of technology has to shift to smart cities, and where especially in the distribution and consumption of electricity, data centers will be installed to ensure that unused energy is either contained or distributed elsewhere and put to constructive use for economic development. The data and digital technology, being laid out for better decision making and improving the quality of life, is a prerogative for not only saving time but cost and revenue when we look at GDP equivalence. All of this is accomplished with sophisticated and comprehensive, real-time data that have been harvested on a real-time basis and customized data offering data agencies the competency and capabilities to observe and study events as they unfold, or to understand how demand patterns are changing, and respond with faster and lower-cost solutions. It is these initiatives that stimulate the foundation for smarter cities that will go to being more pollution-free, energy-efficient, cost-efficient, economic, and sustainable and where ecosystems are protected. The data that have been efficiently harvested is collected by analyzing and studying the following for implementation. The entire concept of smart cities is to rely on the IoT (Internet of Things) integrating Information and Communication Tools optimizing efficiency and services to citizens by first analyzing their behavioral patterns in an ecosystem and where data is also customized. The entire logic of smart cities is to only improve how we interact with our environment and to build a sustainable environment through efficient real-time process seen through impact on footprint analyses. This framework builds a clearer pathway for interaction between citizens in a smart city and its policy makers that will enable effective and new policies that benefit all stakeholders in an environment where in actual reality becomes transactional as it becomes easier to respond to newer challenges on a real-time basis centered around previous information gained or customized data already collected from history of living in an urban environment by analyzing the following:

a. Device utilization in buildings and amount utilization
b. Behavioral patterns of citizens using devices and patterns of behavior in a building
c. Hours of electricity supply used in a building in a regulated manner by looking at random behavior over a stipulated period of time

d. Technology supply and use in education facilities, office spaces, healthcare facilities and hospitals, and other community environs
e. Infrastructure plans and green policies being adopted
f. High intensity and low intensity of lighting used in buildings and offices with digital interface

The data collected upon the observation of citizen's behavioral patterns and devices is analyzed and monitored to manage areas in a smart city from transport, to power plants, water supply, waste management, information systems, traffic, crime, healthcare, education to other community areas. All of this is driven by data centers massively ingesting Artificial Technology and the smart IoT to observe, to analyze, and to save energy efficiently or where working and living in a smart societal environment is easier to do business and to process information as the highly efficient data systems that are run on advanced technology are updated and have comprehensive information of citizens in a city or information of weather patterns or changing weather patterns based on previous data of the past 10 or 15 years that is fed into these systems to predict weather and climatic changes. With the help of data centers, a smart city that learns and innovates constantly responds in a real-time basis with the timely intervention of smart IoT and e-governance measures. In all smart cities, the infrastructure and interaction stays efficient and reliable. The evolution of cognitive computing and engagement with cloud computing and Artificial Intelligence powers data centers to operate accordingly with better or smart efficiency. We have to keep in mind the following that holistically make up the data centers in offices, apartment complexes, and buildings that integrate and engage with all stakeholders in general:

i. Digital *telecommunication networks*
ii. Ubiquitous *embedded intelligence* systems
iii. Sensors and *tags*
iv. *Software* (knowledge competence)

These complex yet sophisticated combinations of diverse technology infrastructure form the assortment for communication and engagement at different levels between technological systems and humans, thus making a cohesive and coherent pattern to carry out structured responses in an efficient manner with the human framework of analyzing behavioral patterns infiltrated with cognitive potentials such as creativity and intellectual curiosity, learning curves and education, humanity consciousness, and empathy and knowledge. The blend of technology with advanced philosophical thought patterns drives the smart city initiative with data centers playing a prominent role in its facilitation. All smart cities with data centers aim to improve quality of life and to conserve energy by involving all stakeholders by harnessing technology. The smart cities that have already taken shape in a few countries like Sweden, Germany, and Norway have worked on, ensuring that land is used to its optimum level and being more inclusive in order to expand housing opportunities for all with its intelligent systems of applications and systems does optimize well-being reducing energy congestion, carbon-dioxide levels by fully engaging technology to its maximum potential. The enhanced support communication and transparency with all stakeholders fully accessing open data guarantee cross-collaboration: if problems do crop up, the relevant technical support can be reined in order to address the issue at hand providing insightful data to all on an ongoing basis. The community remains analyzed and studied, which helps the data centers to assess and deliberate citizen needs and their changing preferences. It is observed that smart cities are the newest policies being framed and implemented by well-meaning governments of the day as the idea of a sustainable, inclusive environment is more a need of the hour after the severe ecological deficit in the last decade, or so this policy initiative seems to be more scientifically and technologically appropriate to ameliorate global warming and climate change levels. The penultimate goal of smart cities is to provide a safer, cleaner, more sustainable, and environmentally green planet that is healthy for all despite the costs involved in electricity or energy supply, or in transportation networks and other sectors girded with sophisticated electronic sensors and methods. A few of the contemporary and current realities of smart cities with the data center initiatives have become a fact of life in a smart, secure, safe city. They are:

a. Smart city citizens' smartphone becomes their mobile driver's license, ID card, bank, insurance with digital credentials that simplifies local government services and access to basic services, which is common in most countries
b. Connected traffic in a smart system network receives data from sensors informing drivers of traffic congestion offering a different route, thereby reducing road congestion and all of this in real time or informing of weather patterns
c. Connected traffic in a smart system network can communicate with parking meters at toll gates
d. Waste management companies prepare a pickup of garbage when the cans are filled as they receive a message from the cans with a preplanned schedule based on the customized data
e. Street lighting that is solar-powered can be used accordingly and with relevant purpose, i.e., switching on and off as the need arises

1.5 DATA CENTERS THAT KEEP SMART CITIES GOING – *THE BRAINS BEHIND*

Intelligent computer systems that drive telecommunications and storage systems do require large repositories of data to take decisions with the co-opting with smart IoT. All data centers function on a robust telecommunications network amplified with the internet in close interaction with multiple internet loops to keep information coming or stored for future use. The major component of the data centers is to carry out information and to harvest information from customers who are in sync and connected with the system via the internet as these intelligent systems adopt a step-by-step approach to arrive and relay information. The primary functions of data centers are to:

a. Homogenize the entire framework in an intelligent manner, creating the facility of replacing aging data systems or technology
b. Reduce and lower capital and energy consumption
c. Involve automated technology that has already been programmed with customized data and updation or upgradations, which can be re-booted at will
d. Prevent data mishap and data security

These intelligent systems called data centers vary in sizes based on the organizational capacity and the digitalization of the business ecosystem that they adhere to. Although in these days, for a fact, data centers consume a lot of energy, governments have preferred to adopt data centers as smart cities cannot be achieved without these advanced data centers, which facilitate as the brains (owing to their being dynamic, making it easier to offload or shift or provision data or migrate information) in real time over the cloud for enhancing performance. All smart cities require the routinized mechanization to ensure that systems are in place and glitches are wiped out to avoid unnecessary scrimmage to enhance performance of all systems interaction and interfacing with each other, or else if a system crashes, the entire infrastructure grinds to a halt. Data centers run the infrastructure, on the one hand, and, on the other, keep carrying out automated tests to ensure that the required checks and balance are in place and also adhering to a dynamic reconfiguration as and when required, which is more progressive and evolutionary functioning as a singular cell with a mind of its own known as a modular solution used for quick deployment or for *disaster recovery*, which is installed and made operational in very short time. Data centers in organizations and offices or financial institutions facilitate business continuity and availability through the grid operate via cloud computing mechanisms, thereby reducing huge costs when compared to achieving these operations manually that can take time and days to complete, which in this case, takes a matter of hours as all communications take place over networks centered around the IP protocol complementation. The complex and dynamic data that is routed between sensors and switches transporting information to the outside world from these servers is accomplished with a double-time pathway.

Data centers are the nucleus and transmit information by containing and controlling the flow reducing wastage and keeping systems functioning at an all-time-efficient manner working to its fullest potential. When energy consumption is used on this architecture rather than the traditional manner, consumption in organizations and office spaces is reduced drastically and intelligent decisions are taken by the system. A country's contribution to the GDP is entirely based on how intelligent our technological systems have become and the controlling of surplus of energy used for other economic purposes that pay high dividends elsewhere. When an electric grid of an economy is codified and computed to a data center, costs can be kept down and performance in operations and database management can be accelerated to stimulate growth to enhance prospects. The increasing number of internet users across the globe who consume exponentially for purposes of entertainment and shopping to commerce and media has developed a formidable competition in the marketplace of work and technology. With the pandemic, governments, offices, and educational institutions have relied on the internet, which has been equally controlled by data centers to keep the engine of operations working and moving at an all-time high. The new policies in all countries have propelled the idea for more space in data and cloud initiative and proposals that initiate comprehensive digitalization. The pandemic has only warranted that data centers mature in the technology ecosystem with network modernization, expansive fiber optics, 5G, increase in data center investments, and enhanced power infrastructure. This has not only accentuated the market activity in data center space but ensured that all market players across the globe are more tightly knit in their competitive environs by increasing footprint furthering new ideas and new competitors.

In today's world of massive reliance of technology, countries and governments are forced to aim for digital sovereignty in an ever-connected world where data centers are most critical to the functioning of the internet. Today, all governments and multi-lateral organizations are affirmative of data center ecosystem gaining more traction, where in a year's time from now, the intelligent data centers will facilitate new revolutionary footprints in the functioning of markets and business spaces. The future has been transformed in the technology space in fast-forward mode with the excessive intervention of data centers that have brought on unbridled growth and space for conducting business, policy and addressing healthcare and educational needs in the past 1 year. All governments are in a re-think mode of creating and building empowered data care facilities that co-opt all other sectors in an updated standardized digital and dynamic platform to doing business and carrying out policy as embedded in the SDGs.

BIBLIOGRAPHY

[1] A. Brown, and D. A. Patterson. Embracing failure: a case for recovery-oriented computing (ROC). In High Performance Transaction Processing Symposium, 2001.

[2] A. Greenberg, et al., VL2: a scalable and flexible data center network, *ACM SIGCOMM Comput. Commun. Rev.*, vol. 39, no. 4, pp. 51–62, 2009.

[3] A. Greenberg, P. Lahiri, D. A. Maltz, P. Patel, and S. Sengupta. Towards a next generation data center architecture: scalability and commoditization. In Proceedings of the ACM Workshop on Programmable Routers for Extensible Services of Tomorrow, pp. 57–62, 2008.

[4] Amazon Web Services. URL: http://aws.amazon.com.

[5] B. Bimber. Three faces of technological determinism. In M. R. Smith & L. Marx (Eds.), *Does Technology Drive History? The Dilemma of Technological Determinism.* Cambridge MA: MIT Press, pp. 79–100, 1994.

[6] C. Kopparapu. *Load Balancing Servers, Firewalls, and Caches.* US: John Wisely & Sons Inc., ISBN: 978-0-471-42128-3, 2002.

[7] Cisco Systems. *Data Center: Load Balancing Data Center Services*, US: Cisco systems, Cisco Data Center, 2004.

[8] Cisco. Data Center Ethernet. http://www.cisco.com/en/US/-netsol/ns783/networking solutions package.html.

[9] D. Daniel. *Michel Foucault Lectures on the Will to Know and Oedipal Knowledge.* UK: Palgrave Macmillan, 2011.

[10] P. Durbin. *A Guide to the Culture of Science, Technology, and Medicine.* New York: Free Press, 1980.

[11] H. I. Ansoff. *Corporate Strategy: An Analytic Approach to Business Policy for Growth and Expansion.* New York: McGraw-Hill, 1965.

[12] M. Heidegger. The question concerning technology, In D. Krell (Ed.), *Martin Heidegger: Basic Writings*. New York: Harper & Row, 1976.
[13] E. Husserl. Philosophy and the crisis of European man. In Q. Lauer (Trans.), *Phenomenology and the Crisis of Philosophy*. New York, NY: Harper and Row, pp. 149–192, 1965b.
[14] K. Church, J. Hamilton, and A. Greenberg. On delivering embarassingly distributed cloud services. In *Hotnets VII*, Washington, USA, 2008.
[15] T. Kuhn. *The Structure of Scientific Revolutions*. Chicago: University of Chicago Press, 1962.
[16] L. A. Barroso, and U. Hlzle. The case for energy-proportional computing. *IEEE Comput.*, vol. 40, 2007.
[17] M. L. J. Abercrombie. The Anatomy of Judgment: An Investigation into the Processes of Perception and Reasoning, Posted: 1960.
[18] M. Al-Fares, A. Loukissas, and A. Vahdat. A scalable, commodity data center network architecture. In *SIGCOMM*, Seattle, Washington USA, Proceedings of the ACM SIGCOMM 2008 Conference on Data Communication, Seattle, 17–22 August, 63–74, 2008.
[19] K. Mathur. *From Government to Governance: A Brief Survey of the Indian* experience. New Delhi: National Book Trust, 2009.
[20] W. Sellars. Philosophy and the scientific image of man, In *Science, Perception and Reality*. London: Routledge & Kegan Paul, 1963.
[21] The Green Grid. URL: http://www.thegreengrid.org.
[22] The Uptime Institute. URL: http://uptimeinstitute.org.
[23] W. Myron. Social science research and public policy in India. *Econ. Political Weekly*, vol. 14, no. 37, 1581–158, 1979.

2 Big Data for SMART Sensor and Intelligent Electronic Devices – Building Application

Mohammad Zand, Morteza Azimi Nasab, and Sanjeevikumar Padmanaban
CTIF Global Capsule

Mohammad Khoobani
Shahrood University of Technology

CONTENTS

DOI: 10.1201/9781003201069-2

ACRONYM

AHU	Air Handler Unit
AP	Access Point
BACnet	Building Automation and Control (BAC) Networks
BANs	Body Area Networks
CCF	Cross-Correlation Function
CSD	Cross-Spectral Density
DAC	Data Acquisition Systems
DOF	Degrees of Freedom
DRAM	Dynamic Random-Access Memory
ERA	Eigen Realization Algorithm
FEM	Finite Element Model
FFT	Fast Fourier Transform
HVAC	Heating Ventilation Conditioning
IoT	Internet of Things
LED	Light-Emitting Diode
Li-Fi	Light Fidelity
LSWT	Lifting Scheme Wavelet Transform
LANs	Local Area Networks
MANs	Metropolitan Area Networks
NAT	Network Address Translator
OOK	On-Off Keying
PAM	Pulse Amplitude Modulation
PANs	Personal Area Networks
PSD	Power Spectral Density
PLC	Power Line Communication
RDT	Random Decrement Technique
RFID	Radio Frequency Identification
RFP	Rational Fraction Polynomial
RSSI	Received Signal Strength Indicator
SDN	Software-Defined Network
SHM	Structural Health Monitoring
SVD	Singular Value Decomposition
TCP	Transmission Control Protocol
TEG	Thermal Electrical Generation
TSV	Through Silicon Via
UDP	User Datagram Protocol
WPT	Wavelet Packet Transform
WSN	Wireless Sensor Network
WANs	Wide Area Networks
WT	Wavelet Transform

2.1 INTRODUCTION

Big Data is a new concept in today's control systems that works with massive information in a short period. This information can be structured (regular and classified data) or non-structured (irregular and random volume data). Although the volume of information seems paramount, it is the type of use and exploitation of a division or all this information by users that is the matter of discussion. Big Data is indeed a comprehensive approach for control systems and smart buildings to make better decision-making via information collected by smart sensors. Essential features and definitions in smart homes and management energy based on Big Data are as follows [1–13]:

Volume: The first feature of Big Data is the volume accumulated from smart sensors embedded in a control process.

Velocity: The second characteristic of Big Data is the speed of its processes so that information exchanges must be carried out at high speed at different levels.

Variety: Format and type of information are not always the same. This information can be text, a voltage, a current, or different types of digital signals.

Complexity: Since information might be made of multiple sources and be diverse in nature, the process of relating and coordinating them together has been complicated; so to prevent this, a comprehensive system is needed to be considered.

Due to the above-mentioned features, the developed technologies in the buildings are termed smart building and building management. Although the notion of such ideally smart homes that many activities are included is impossible, many companies and providers of telecommunications-related technologies offer their products for smart buildings according to concepts of the IoTs. In the subsequent sections, different elements of a smart building will be elaborated.

2.2 THE EMERGENCE AND CONSIDERING BIG DATA TOWARD BUILDING APPLICATION

Big Data is not utilized in this field exclusively because of the challenges with a large amount of information, but this is the purpose of utilizing this procedure and how to exploit this information that makes it beneficial. Generally, since various types of sensors and data loggers are used in a smart home, it can be agreed that Big Data solutions are a good way of dealing with the acquired information. By investigating and analyzing the data received from sensors, data is categorized, and decisions are made based on a predefined intelligent control algorithm [13–18].

The most important targets of a smart building based on smart sensors are expressed as follows:

- Leveling up of welfare for the residents of the building
- Increasing the quality of life by reaching desired humidity and temperature based on an intelligent controller
- Considering the IoT for equipment control
- Activation and non-activation of the equipment according to the planning
- Decreasing energy usage along with enhancing efficiency
- Controlling the lighting, heating, ventilation, and air conditioning in an intelligent manner

- Identifying fast-powered equipment
- Power consumption reduction
- Smart management of building equipment
- Increased security in buildings by employing smart sensors
- Building safety with traffic control systems
- Powering off electric equipment in case of an earthquake
- Increasing safety by using intelligent fire systems and fire declaration
- To achieve the targets mentioned earlier, we need to exchange information among innovative units in a building.

2.3 THE PRINCIPLE OF SMART BUILDINGS

A smart building can be designed as a programmable system to be naturally intelligent and integrated. The electric utilities of a building cover the subsequent terms: movement-sensitive CCTV, cooling components, alarms, the detector of the fire, irrigation and watering systems, water/electricity measures, monitoring of elevator, and utilized systems at the entrance of the building. Traditional systems have been designed based on the independent performance of these elements so that each element has corresponded with a monitoring indicator, such as a control diagram, equipment, executive maps, and diagnostic procedures to satisfy the desired strategies. The goal of designing a smart building is to use an integrated intelligent system as a management core to control and monitor all aforementioned independent elements as a whole and to secure interactions and communication among all these parts. Other terms related to these kinds of control systems are as follows:

- SCADA, which is an abbreviation of Supervisory, Control, Data, and Acquisition
- PLC, Programmable Logic Controllers [19].
- EMS, Energy Management System
- DGP, which stands for Data Gathering Panel
- Communication protocols such as Modbus, Lon works, and BACnet
- BMS Operator Workstation represented by terms like “Front End”

2.4 WHAT IS THE PURPOSE OF DESIGNING SMART BUILDINGS?

1. Allow users or operators to set operational plans for intelligent electronic devices to perform energy saving provided an area in the smart building is empty.
2. The ability to monitor energy consumption, including measuring the electric services, natural gas, hot water, and fuel.
3. The capability to convey a warning via making a telephone call, email, or text message to inform managers of intelligent buildings and technicians about the problems and failures of the system.

4. The capability of correction and accountability must be included according to the duty. For instance, the cooling or heating facilities vary regarding the setpoints from different zones.
5. Employ BAS control algorithms like re-regulation of a static pressure regulator, heating power plants, and other operations that can be implemented regarding such predictive strategies of energy conservation.
6. Along with the appropriate mechanical system, the economic settings should be carried out based on the enthalpy and control point of the CO_2 setting.
7. Enabling the system to balance the air handling units and other equipment capabilities so that the equipment can be rearranged at the right time to guarantee that the setpoints of the desired zone are reached before residents arrive.
8. Communication capabilities can be integrated into other facilities of automated control systems and TCP/IP. The open-source communication protocol is an advantage with BACnet or other positive items.

2.5 APPLICATION DOMAIN

Systems that are associated with smart buildings use smart sensors and intelligent devices to understand better how buildings are operated and let them adjust the systems to their desired points. While working with extensive data, BMS can be regarded as a functional approach for operators and users. In this case, reports are generated automatically, and warnings are sent if measures have passed a threshold, breakdown, or fault. Smart building management systems collect information and control signals related to several systems that work simultaneously using a wide range of different software programs, allowing them to use a single interface. They can also compare spaces, buildings, and metrics; this makes it more accessible, more comprehensive and allows information to be classified from one system to another. The most common primary function of a smart building is controlling of heating systems, ventilation, and air conditioning of buildings, including [20,21]:

- Air handling units
- Cooling towers
- Chilled water plant
- Tenant condenser water
- Heating water plant
- Computer room AC
- Exhaust systems
- Zone controls

A smart building system may also be used to supervise and control power distribution, energy consumption, and uninterrupted power supplies (UPS) and may be known as smart building energy management systems (SBEMS) that cover the following duties [22]:

- Control of building systems and services
- Control application programming

- Graphic user interface (GUI)
- Logging and trending concerning operation and performance of building
- Observing the performance and building operation online
- Time scheduling of building systems
- Fault management and alarming
- Energy management and reporting
- User event management

Regarding how reputable are signals from the sensors and a strategy to employ the collected data determines the efficiency of a smart building. For illustration, to manage the level of heating expected to enable the plant to be initiated and the building is pre-warmed before the occupants' arrival, information on the external conditions is needed. The foremost benefits of smart buildings also involve [23–28]:

- Flexibility and ease of change
- Integration with other building services
- Operator interaction, feedback, and control
- Customized control strategies
- Scalability

2.6 THE BIG DATA CHALLENGES AND BENEFITS IN BUILDINGS

There will be some challenges in smart buildings because of different characteristics of information mentioned under the term "Big Data" as follows:

- Computing, storage (memory systems and grids), and networking smart sensors for data accusation, transmission, processing, building management
- Planning and change the settings
- Complexity in use
- Securing against cyber-attacks
- The challenges associated with implementing the platform
- The file systems and database: parallel SQL databases to take care of the high complexity of Big Data. In addition to that, the databases are NoSQL and NewSQL.

The application of intelligent sensors in a building has the following advantages [2]:

- High security and parameters control
- Optimal utilization of resources using innovative sensor programming
- Eliminating the need of re-wiring
- Power consumption reduction due to intelligent control
- Returning the costs of implementing an intelligent building by energy saving

2.7 THE IMPORTANT PROCESS IN SMART BUILDINGS

2.7.1 Technology and Protocols

There are two necessities: making a plausible link and a communication network among sensors in an intelligent manner. The first is allocated with connecting smart buildings with sensors, and the second is with the connection of smart buildings with the environment outside them. As it is presented in Figure 2.1, different area networks can be categorized as follows [3]:

1. WANs, typically involves satellites and antennas that connect to a wide area
2. MANs, one that serves the area
3. LANs, answer the needs of the person who is responsible for managing the network
4. PANs, looking at the needs of a consumer with close equipment
5. BANs, for the continuity of a personal network

A protocol is a sum of rules that regulate the way innovative equipment is connected to a building. The role of the protocol in a smart building is similar to the role of language daily life of humans. There are many protocols for smart buildings. Most of these protocols were first restricted to a firm and were gradually developed into a standard. In general, the data transfer of the equipment in a smart building is done through the following three methods [4]:

- Low-voltage wires and typically DC
- PLC, where data are transferred onto power circuits
- Wireless, normally, through the electromagnetic waves

KNX: The best way to work with a smart building is taking advantage of products with a KNX protocol. KNX is a communication protocol in smart buildings using information technology to connect devices such as smart sensors, controllers, and actuators. It is one of the few international standards ISO/IEC 14543-3 in the context of a smart building.

Zigbee: It is a class of high-level communication protocols that use a standard-based digital transmitter-receiver according to wireless networks with low data rates based on the IEEE802 standard. Initially, it was defined as a more straightforward and cheaper technology than Bluetooth for

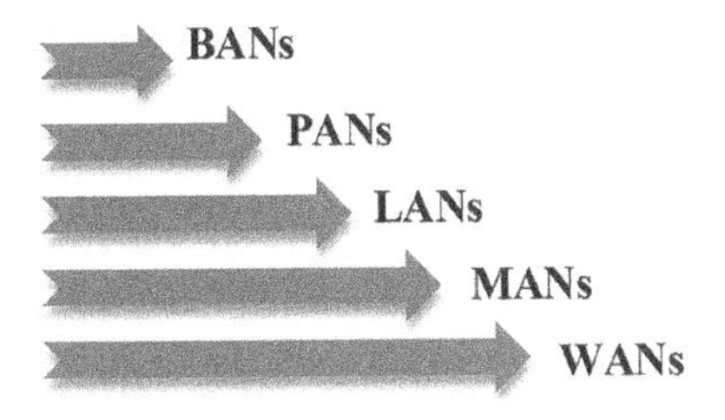

FIGURE 2.1 Different area networks in smart building based on smart sensors.

personal wireless networks. According to this protocol, products that are designed can be connected to more than 64,000 other units via a network.

X10: The main characteristic of this protocol is to send the control command to devices via a power supply network. Therefore, there is no need for re-wiring. It is sufficient to connect an electric vehicle (or smart sensors) through an interface to the smart building electric grid. It is also possible to communicate with the Internet through a remote converter. This protocol can be connected to more than 256 other units via a network [4].

BACnet: One of the most common protocols in mechanical devices is BACnet, a standard data transmission protocol for use in automation and management projects associated with intelligent buildings (or multiple buildings) that allow the transmission of information among intelligent sensors. This protocol dedicated the ISO 16484 – 5 in 2003 in the international standards [5].

2.7.2 Data Acquisition and Storage

Data is obtained and sent to a data service, for instance, data captured in CCTV, data captured in smart sensors of a large smart building, and data acquisition in the complex production process in smart industry buildings. As mentioned above, data services are constantly updated and capable of integrating all smart sensor data fast and easily.

Data-collecting instruments are created for online data acquisition from a cyber-area such as web and application data logging, intelligent sensors, and intelligent mobile. All data is carried in a string of binary arrangements perceived as a message. This technology has been devised to be extensible and secure. It additionally utilizes data compression to minimize performances and bandwidth traffic, and cost reduction [6].

For data storage, SQL, no SQL, and New SQL databases toward Big Data accommodation are defined. Based on the current needs in smart buildings, information technology engineers determine a fit database management scheme for Big Data analytics in smart buildings (residential or industrial buildings).

In this state, real-time streaming data conveyed from intelligent sensors is stored in a row-based store, then earlier data is handled in a compressed columnar store (such as a matrix). Data searches are automatically done across the row and columnar data sets so that analytics can hold the renewed data; this is the best way to transfer data from intelligent sensors to ample data storage. Besides, data can be transformed toward JavaScript Object Notation (JSON) and placed into a cyber-area such as a software application based on web services (Hardtop platforms).

2.8 SMART SENSORS GENERATOR OF BIG DATA

In today's sophisticated world that utilizing intelligent sensors is a routine, systems are mainly dealing with Big Data that is possible to be digital in the first place or collected as analog signals, but eventually, need to be turned into the digital form to processing into microprocessors such as AVR and ARM or computers. Conventionally, Big Data was only used in web and social media in past years. Lately, IoT-based platforms deal with Big Data of the surrounding environment in a building captured by intelligent sensors. Therefore, many intelligent sensors in many buildings in a city or a country are becoming Big Data sources [22].

2.9 BIG DATA SOURCES

Initially represented as the digital format or collected in the analog form, information is given by intelligent sensors and controlled thanks to the microprocessors. Data is collected in predefined file formats: word, pdf, image, audio, and txt on personal computers. Advances in IoT devices and web technologies have enabled microprocessors and personal computers to be connected to other devices in any spot of the world. In today's applications, by using web 2.0 technologies, it is expected that data can be received from intelligent sensors and being processed as images, videos, and other formats. Additional Big Data sources comprise electronic mails, financial circulation on credit cards, and CCTVs.

2.10 SMART BUILDING APPLICATION

The smart building is state-of-the-art mutual communication in intelligent sensors, and intelligent electronic devices fasten on IoT-based platforms and, consequently, generate Big Data. Because of employing numerous sensors and devices, traditional control systems cannot act in low response time. For this reason, novel innovative and intelligent devices are required to integrate intelligent technologies to increase the quality of life.

According to the International Energy Agency-IEA, over 0.375 GJ/m2 electricity of the buildings is used by different energy consumer facilities inside buildings, essentially by air handling units. For this reason, in this chapter, HVAC system is highlighted. In Figure 2.2, energy consumption in different zones of smart buildings is shown [7]. In traditional buildings, due to the lack of intelligent sensors and intelligent electronic devices and actuators, the inefficient operation of existing lighting, space cooling, and space heating systems leads to energy losses and, finally, increases energy cost. On the other hand, an increase in energy consumption leads to increased emissions and greenhouse gases.

The necessity to reduce energy consumption and pollute gas emissions, smart building design using intelligent sensors and intelligent electronic devices has been a global concern. Building designers agree that smart buildings should be energy efficient and have the least amount of polluting gas emissions. For these reasons, architects and building engineers should consider the impact and outcome of traditional buildings compared to smart buildings' operations. The index of environmentally friendly laws and efficient energy consumption standards has been formed to predominate substantial challenges, including polluting gas emissions, low energy efficiency, air quality, and control remotely [8].

The fact that joint optimization of power consumption and energy efficiency, air quality, smart building, and lifecycle maintenance must be respected in the early design phase of smart buildings is accepted by most smart building users and building designers. A plausible approach is using intelligent sensors and intelligent IoT-based electronic devices.

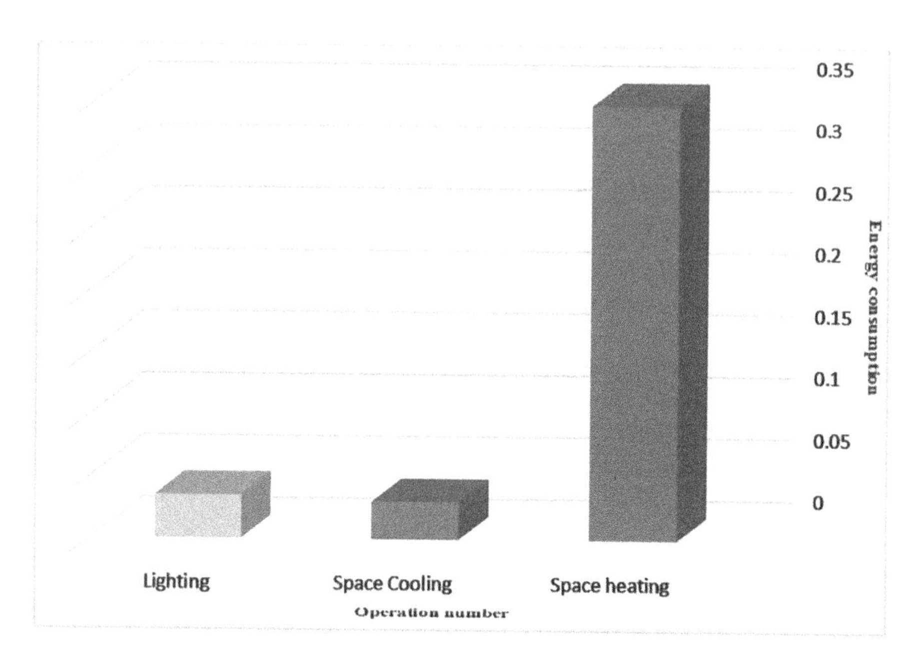

FIGURE 2.2 Energy consumption in the smart building per GJ/m2 (Computer Science Review 2021).

Lately, the fast-growing benefits of intelligent sensors and electronic intelligent devices industry and data systems (such as fog and cloud computing in Big Data) made it possible that various novel developments have been recommended for smart building purposes by utilizing intelligent sensors, which ended up to introduce the idea of "regarding smart sensors for smart buildings."

Smart building goals include the following :

- Improving the comfort of dwelling in a building
- Efficient energy consumption and decrease in the cost of energy
- Remote and central intelligent control in buildings to better control of the electronic devices
- Increasing the worthiness of the building
- Detecting the challenges in buildings management
- Accessibility to controlling required data (or Big Data)
- Independent controlling of different areas in buildings

One of the most important controllable sections in smart buildings is HVAC equipment. These systems are controllable by three methods, including local or remote monitoring:

- Heater/cooler on/off switch
- HVAC on/off switching
- Sauna and Jacuzzi on/off switch

Smart buildings are expected to use intelligent sensors and innovative electronic devices and adjust their performance to occupants' satisfaction. For example, the exterior condition monitoring involving air temperature and humidity would result in dealing with Big Data collected through wireless sensors linked by a distributed network. In the case of studying human health monitoring, accessing such data is of great importance. Intelligent sensors and required networks are implemented in various thermal regions of a building though they cover the whole parts.

The air conditioning facilities for each room or the heat region send directions to operators provided the temperature, humidity, and air quality states of every part are re-stored and controlled by intelligent sensors and smart grids in predetermined parameters. Today, the dimensions of an intelligent/wireless sensor are less than a centimeter, and it is effortless to install in the areas/sections of smart buildings. As a result, the distribution of hundreds or thousands of innovative devices and creating intelligent nodes does not create much complexity for users or smart building operators.

2.11 HVAC OPERATION MANAGEMENT IN A SMART BUILDING

Cooling and heating actions for the whole buildings are dependent on a central HVAC facility in today's modernized buildings. This central HVAC facility is not essentially considered in the same spot for all buildings, but it can be located on top of the roof, on any floor, in the basement, or even more than one central HVAC system might be a safe bet for some high-rise building. Organizational structures also take advantage of some central units for warming and cooling the buildings. In the early times of utilizing these kinds of operations, such methods were integrated after holding approaches based on automating.

Increasing the efficiency in a system is plausible by designing an automated system for a building regarding certain factors, namely, variables associated with the micro-level, demand factors, and weather conditioning.

Energy management plans and HVAC units are taking advantage of BAS the most. The automation of the building can be interpreted as a plan to managing energy based on advanced control firms to make building owners capable of efficiently control the air conditioning and heating devices. BAS is used when the systems and electrical equipment are connected through a network and interactions among them are accessible. To control the facilities in a local network, the automation program of such a building can act independently or take advantage of an Internet connection to implement the desired controlling outcomes.

2.12 DEVELOPED TENANT COMFORT AIR QUALITY CONDITION

In the most detailed descriptions, it is accepted that air conditioning implies applying a system that regulates temperature, humidity, and air quality. The comfort of building dwellers is possible due to the reduction of the density of the condensation, especially for specific spots such as pools. Conditioning the atmosphere of a region comprises extensive handling of the moisture in the air and controlling the temperature. In this context, the following terms are also discussed:

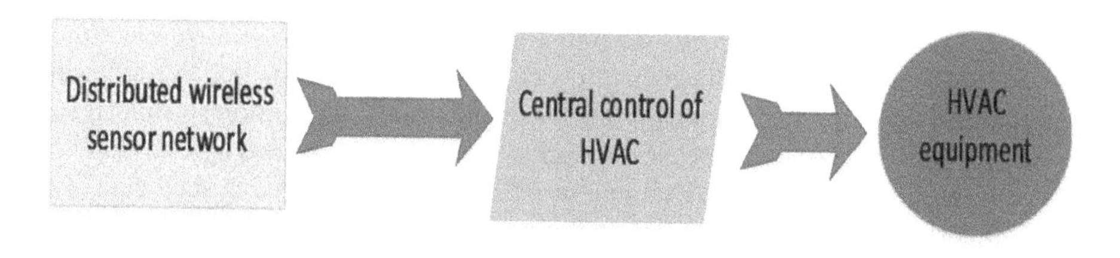

FIGURE 2.3 A HVAC operation in smart building management by using smart sensors.

- Tenant states must be observed in a real-time manner
- More comprehensive load-based control paradigms
- Developing fault detection must be considered, along with enhancing trend data performance
- Air quality management (CO_2)
- Alarm notifications of faults reduce downtime
- Automated changeover of failed equipment

Energy Management and Reduction of Operational Costs associated with HVAC systems are the most extensive consumer-consuming equipment and require efficient performance. HVAC and air conditioning generally are responsible for a significant portion of the total energy consumption in a building.

A conventional system accounts for roughly 70% of base building and 40% of cumulative building usage. The following strategies must be considered to overcome the mass-energy consumption by HVAC systems:

- The plant must take advantage of an optimized start/stop procedure
- Warm-up and cool-down sequences of the building
- Night-mode clarification
- Choosing automated seasonal plant cycles
- Settling seasonal heat modifications
- Control strategies according to the current load
- Economy cycle management involving the control of CO_2
- Observing duty cycles, also equipment runtime
- Control of occupancy along with handling the setback

As mentioned above, one of the main interests in smart buildings that are equipped with intelligent sensors and innovative devices is HVAC effectiveness. As it is given in Figure 2.3, a rational HVAC model includes considering intelligent sensors and innovative electrical devices through a network, which measures or identifies variable parameters and compares them according to predefined parameters and setpoints for temperature, humidity, and illumination to improve living conditions.

2.13 SECURE SMART ACCESS CONTROL FOR BUILDING ACCESS

Secure access control can be defined as a system capable of identifying those who have the authority to set controlling parameters for each zone.

2.13.1 Index for Access Control

Access control is a part of physical security services. In terms of access control, market segmentation is defined. Access control takes a wide range of solutions with a variety of factors that can be divided into three categories as follows:

- Smart electronic keys
- Entry phones
- Keypads

Fingerprint or different types of bio-smart sensors such as eye and face recognition sensors are known as solutions at additional security, price, and electric energy consumption levels.

2.13.2 Mobile Technologies for Greater Security

Since smartphones have been pandemic today, industries are aware of replacing their PIN systems, cards, and current keys because smartphones are the futuristic means of control. The inclusion of NFC technology and Bluetooth on smartphones provides a standard in the industry to exchange access control data to provide access to a remote reader. Smartphones can eliminate challenges and responsibilities associated with losing or eliminating a PIN code, card, or key. Using a personal case – lending it to others – is difficult for other people; especially, a mobile device for safe access can add more security than cards that can be easily shared. Users always bring them and probably do not leave them behind. Thanks to the biometric authentication of cell phones or PIN keys needed to open the device, additional security layers are beneficial.

2.13.3 Smart Access Control in Smart Building

Intelligent access control in smart buildings using intelligent sensors and intelligent electronic devices generally cover the following terms: a manual control system is meant to classify access in diverse locations. The objective of the classification is to schedule time, place, and people. The access control system does not have a limitation to the type of location, but the closed-to-location system can be employed in any building spot and provides the proper solution controlling the variables according to the desired parameters in each space. The intelligent access control is done as follows:

- Control by keyboard or fingerprint sensor
- The possibility of control and reporting of all control points by the central telephone system
- Control by cards that can be controlled with/without contact
- The use of peripheral protection systems to control the access control system
- Independent control of the inputs from each other
- Network control of all the inputs
- Use of innovative electronic locks on the inputs

2.13.4 Security Control System

An intelligent security control system is implemented by employing specific sensors such as motion sensors, magnetic sensors, and vibration sensors (glass break sensors). The advantages are the applicability of reporting, reporting each window and door position at each time, sending SMS messages to managers and owners, the ability to connect to the audio and lighting system in case an intruder enters. Other notable benefits of this system expressed are as follows:

- Asset protection
- Prevention of illegal entries
- Enhancement of personal safety
- Reduction of security costs
- Facilities management
- Inexpensive to maintain
- Difficult to duplicate
- Validate and invalidate a user in seconds
- Identify who, where, and when
- Readily adaptable to changing security needs

It adapts its intelligent access to a user to day life; this is suitable for smart buildings applying intelligent sensors and innovative electronics tools to identify the possible position of occupants. This information is especially beneficial for developing services based on the location of the control parameters, namely, health monitoring, internal navigation, procurement tracking, car smart parking, and activating access control. Figure 2.4 illustrates possible parking, restaurant, and coffee shop positions in a smart building with intelligent sensors and intelligent electronic devices. When a visitor begins the journey of walking in such an intelligent place, the program can suggest the most optimized roots toward a restaurant or a desired destination by an IoT connection. When a person approaches, the smart building recognizes the individual's position and provides safe access management. While the visitor lingers in a particular store (or any other spots), his/her tendencies are followed, and the innovative program gives suggestions according to the prior shopping records using smart shopping lists to maximize the market-based advertising.

Therefore, shopping assistance based on localization in such innovative structures is inspected as a reasonable strategy for learning the decision-making process and the shopping preferences. Indoor-localization intelligent applications are also beneficial to users in malls, museums, airports, and other significant massive structures.

2.14 SAFETY OR SECURITY APPLICATIONS IN SMART SENSORS AND BIG DATA

Buildings with an industrial purpose, like long-span bridges, dams, big fuel tanks, and skyscrapers, are vital elements of the economic foundation. In Figure 2.5, a bridge is monitored based on intelligent sensors for long-term monitoring. Accordingly, it is

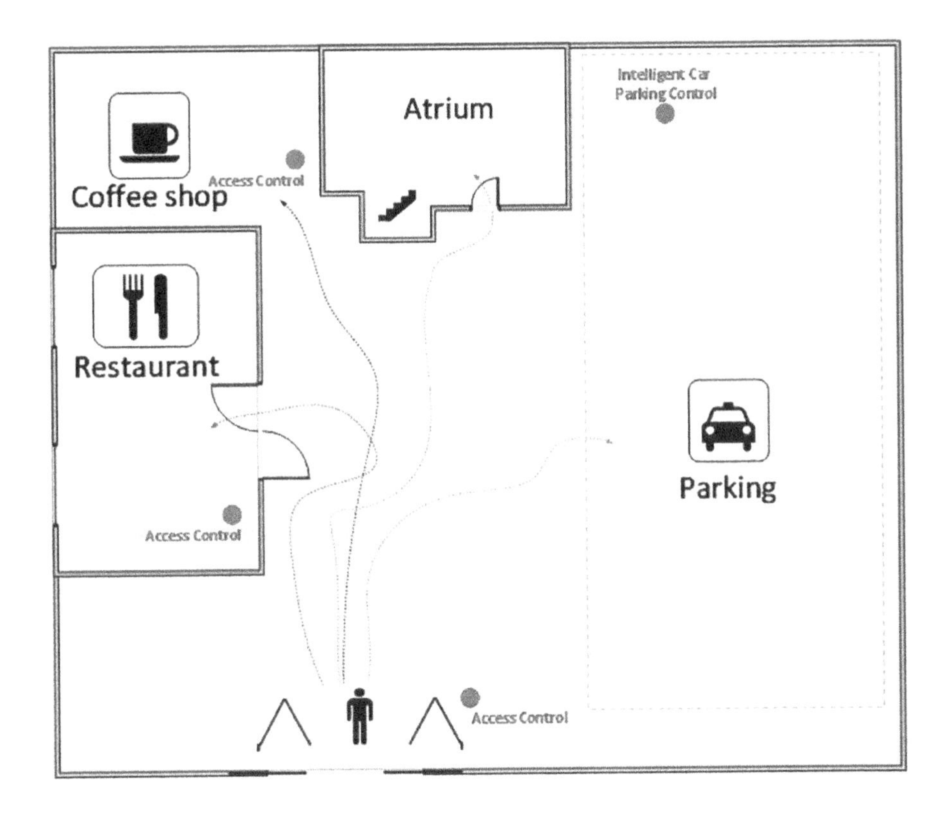

FIGURE 2.4 Smart access control in a smart building.

fundamental to observe their integrity and detect/pinpoint any possible damage or it approaches a risky situation; this is the purpose regarding SHMs.

Conventional SHM arrangements were based on wiring and consequently needed to be concentrated. On the other hand, a novel intelligent SHM operation and intelligent sensors – like accelerometers or strain gauges – are utilized in industrial or civil construction based on the control algorithms. These intelligent sensor nodes collect the mechanical parameters, namely, strain and vibration associated with the construction following distinct positions, carrying the data (Big Data) in a wire-based method or via a wireless network to the central monitoring service. Regarding the information generated by intelligent sensors and dealing with current Big Data, structural health monitoring can detect the damages in such structure to determine how critical the condition is; when the decision-making process will be accomplished, or only an alert will be sent to operators about the civil or industrial structure condition. Considering this decision, short-term and long-term monitoring is the primary structural health monitoring system [9].

SHM is accepted toward sensitive phenomena such as earthquakes, deluge or revers overflow, overloads or collisions in the bridge, and water leakage on the dam wall with a short-term perspective. Such arrangements are regularly applied in industrial constructions for a short period of about 1 hour to gather Big Data toward

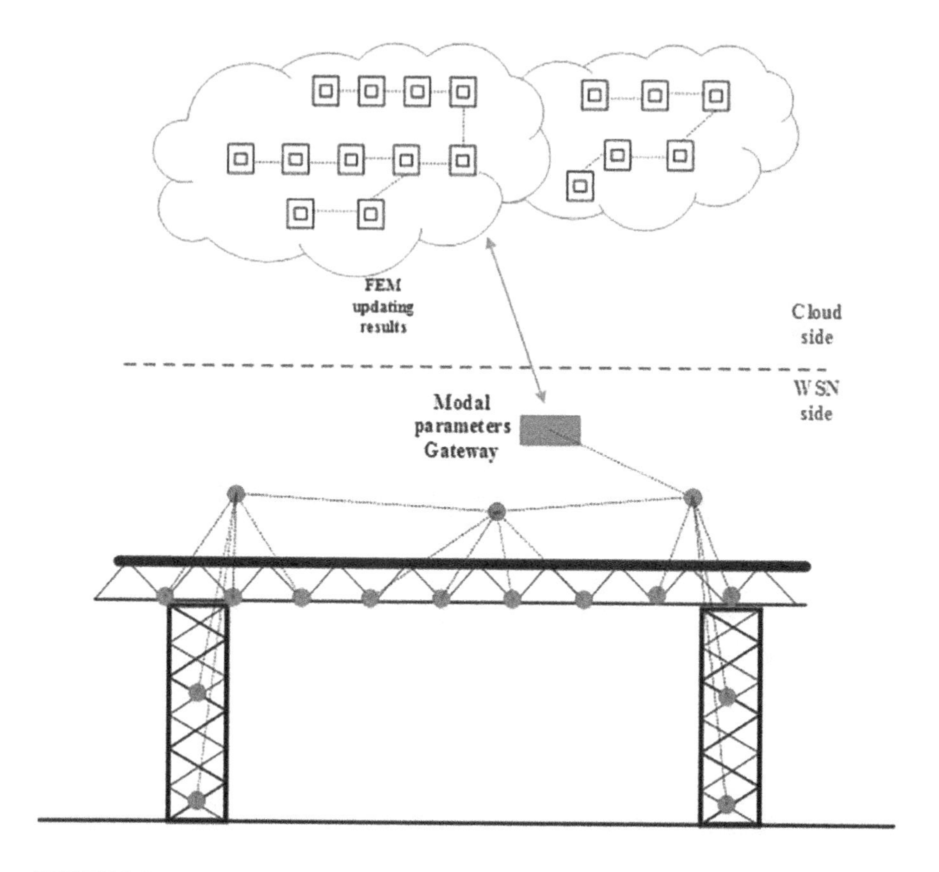

FIGURE 2.5 A wired-based structural health monitoring system in bridge.

offline diagnosis. Then, the other class of SHM is utilized for long-term applications of monitoring. Nodes of intelligent sensors are employed on such smart structures within months to tens of years; monitoring and controlling the structures' health condition is running according to the feedback data generated by installed smart sensors [3,18]. Monitoring operations with a short-term perspective needs to analyze data by engineers, but reporting the state of such innovative structures is available in real time. In traditional manners, systems are based on high-cost wire networks connected to the centralized data acquisition station, including extended cable networks, sensors, and in-field servers. For these reasons, wireless networks are considered in monitoring problems applying intelligent sensors to reduce the cost of networks in innovative civil or industrial structures (smart buildings).

2.15 CONCLUSION

In recent years, excellent development toward WSSNs and growing attention in applying WSSNs for SHM is witnessed. Wireless communication abolishes the necessity of wiring-related efforts and costs and denotes a remarkable drop in implementation expenses plus ease in extension, which contrasts sharply with traditional

TABLE 2.1
Difference among SHM and Monitoring of Environmental Parameters

	Structural Health Monitoring	Environment Monitoring
The kind and function of sensor	Accelerometers Strain gauges	Temperature Light Humidity
Pattern of sampling	Synchronous	Not necessarily synchronized
Frequency of sampling	00-000/second	per second, minute
Required algorithms for processing	On a bunch of data (>0000) centralized, intensive computational	Easy to distribute, simplified

SHM strategies. Table 2.1 overviews the fundamental contrasts between structural health monitoring and the regular employment of WSNs in environmental monitoring. A structural health monitoring system based on WSN will conceivably boost the precision and trustworthiness of the operation. Nevertheless, SHM is distinctive toward various perspectives of the current demands of networks comprising wireless sensors.

REFERENCES

[1] Vlachokostas, C. "Smart buildings need smart consumers: the meet-in-the middle approach towards sustainable management of energy sources." *International Journal of Sustainable Energy* 39, 7, 2020: 648–658.

[2] Jia, M., et al., "Adopting internet of things for the development of smart buildings: a review of enabling technologies and applications." *Automation in Construction* 101, 2019: 111–126.

[3] Zand, M., Nasab, M. A., Neghabi, O., Khalili, M., and Goli, A. "Fault locating transmission lines with thyristor-controlled series capacitors by fuzzy logic method," 2020 14th IPAPS, 2019, pp. 62–70, doi: 10.1109/IPAPS49326.2019.9069389.

[4] Ain, Q., et al., "IoT operating system based fuzzy inference system for home energy management system in smart buildings." *Sensors* 18, 9, 2018: 2802.

[5] Farzaneh, H., et al., "Artificial intelligence evolution in smart buildings for energy efficiency." *Applied Sciences* 11, 2, 2021: 763.

[6] Burgas, L., et al., "Integrated unfold-PCA monitoring application for smart buildings: an AHU application example." *Energies* 14, 1, 2021: 235.

[7] Hajjaji, Y., et al., "Big data and IoT -based applications in smart environments: a systematic review." *Computer Science Review* 39, 2021: 100318.

[8] Wang, P., and Luo, M. "A digital twin-based big data virtual and real fusion learning reference framework supported by industrial internet towards smart manufacturing." *Journal of Manufacturing Systems* 58, 2021: 16–32.

[9] Ahmad, I., et al., "Gray-box soft sensors in process industry: current practice, and future prospects in era of big data." *Processes* 8, 2, 2020: 243.

[10] Zand, M., Nasab, M. A., Hatami, A., Kargar, M., and Chamorro, H. R. "Using adaptive fuzzy logic for intelligent energy management in hybrid vehicles," 2020 28th ICEE, 2020, pp. 1–7, doi: 10.1109/ICEE50131.2020.9260941.

[11] Hamed, A.-N., et al., "Multi-objective optimization based robust scheduling of electric vehicles aggregator." *Sustainable Cities and Society* 47, 2019: 101494.

[12] Zand, M., Nasab, M. A., Sanjeevikumar, P., Maroti, P. K., and Holm-Nielsen, J. B. "Energy management strategy for solid-state transformer-based solar charging station for electric vehicles in smart grids," IET Renewable Power Generation 2020, doi: 10.1049/iet-rpg.2020.0399.
[13] Ghasemi, M., et al., "An efficient modified HPSO-TVAC-based dynamic economic dispatch of generating units," *Electric Power Components and Systems* 2020, doi: 10.1080/15325008.2020.1731876.
[14] Nasri, S., et al., Maximum Power Point Tracking of Photovoltaic Renewable Energy System Using a New Method Based on Turbulent Flow of Water-based Optimization (TFWO) Under Partial Shading Conditions. 978-981-336-456-1.
[15] Liu, X., and Cao, J. "Smart sensor networks for building safety." In *Big Data Analytics for Sensor-Network Collected Intelligence*. Academic Press, 2017, pp. 241–255.
[16] Zand, Z., Hayati, M., and Karimi, G. "Short-channel effects improvement of carbon nanotube field effect transistors," 2020 28th Iranian Conference on Electrical Engineering (ICEE), Tabriz, Iran, 2020, pp. 1–6, doi: 10.1109/ICEE50131.2020.9260850.
[17] Tightiz, L., Nasab, M. A., Yang, H., and Addeh, A. "An intelligent system based on optimized ANFIS and association rules for power transformer fault diagnosis," *ISA Transactions*, 103, 2020, 63–74, ISSN 0019-0578, doi: 10.1016/j.isatra.2020.03.022.
[18] Zand, M., et al., "A Hybrid Scheme for Fault Locating in Transmission Lines Compensated by the TCSC," 2020 15th International Conference on Protection and Automation of Power Systems (IPAPS), Shiraz, Iran, 2020, pp. 130–135, doi: 10.1109/IPAPS52181.2020.9375626.
[19] Zand, M., et al., "Robust speed control for induction motor drives using STSM control", 12th Annual power Electronic Drive Systems, & Technologies Conference (PEDSTC2021), IEEE, Index.
[20] Wu, X., et al., "Data mining with big data." *IEEE Transactions on Knowledge and Data Engineering* 26, 1, 2013: 97–107.
[21] Hajjaji, Y., et al., "Big data and IoT -based applications in smart environments: a systematic review." *Computer Science Review* 39, 2021: 100318.
[22] El-Hasnony, I. M., et al., "Improved feature selection model for big data analytics." *IEEE Access* 8, 2020: 66989–67004.
[23] Hajjaji, Y., et al., "Big data and IOT -based applications in smart environments: a systematic review." *Computer Science Review* 39, 2021: 100318.
[24] Molina-Cabrera, A., et al., "Latencies in power systems: a database-based time-delay compensation for memory controllers." *Electronics* 10, 2, 2021: 208.
[25] Rahimian, F. P. "Data-Driven Modelling of Non-Domestic Buildings Energy Performance."
[26] Rajaoarisoa, L. "Large-scale building thermal modeling based on artificial neural networks: application to smart energy management." In *Artificial Intelligence Techniques for a Scalable Energy Transition*. Springer, Cham, 2020, pp. 15–44.
[27] Rohani A, et al., "Three-phase amplitude adaptive notch filter control design of DSTATCOM under unbalanced/distorted utility voltage conditions," *Journal of Intelligent & Fuzzy Systems*, 2020, doi: 10.3233/JIFS-201667.
[28] Broujeny, R. S., et al., "A multi-layer system for smart-buildings' functional and energy-efficiency awareness: implementation on a real five-floors building." 2017 IEEE 8th International Conference on Awareness Science and Technology (iCAST). IEEE, 2017.

3 IoT-Based Condition Monitoring and Automatic Control of Rotating Machines

Rubia Ramesh Kumar, Saloni Sharma, Priyank Mehra, V. Berlin Hency, and O.V. Gnana Swathika
Vellore Institute of Technology

CONTENTS

3.1 INTRODUCTION

Over the recent years, the interest in utilizing Internet of things (IoT) to help connect us to our surroundings has peaked. This not only provides a way to communicate but also becomes a very handy tool when it comes to monitoring inaccessible regions constantly. Industrial IoT setups maintain connectivity throughout the workstation, especially for remote, rural, or offshore industries.

The model proposed gives an analysis of the motor in question in real time, which can be checked against set norms for optimum functioning. This is where control parameters are introduced as a measure to stabilize the motor unit in case the optimal working norms are exceeded. Condition monitoring system is set up in such industrial work zones, for example, in small-scale paper manufacturing industries, where there is a lack of full-time man-run monitoring system to rely on, satisfying the need for cautious surveying and checking.

Our goal is to develop a condition monitoring system, which can be set up in industrial workspace like paper manufacturing industry, which heavily relies on motors to facilitate the entire process from raw material to rolls of sheets utilized for various purposes. Here, each motor works in tandem with the other in order to

DOI: 10.1201/9781003201069-3

achieve required specifications for the end product. This greatly depends on smooth functioning of each motor and here is where we identify the possibility of motor malfunctioning due to several internal or external factors. The industries mainly run on squirrel cage induction motors or synchronous motors [1].

This provides us a solution to allow monitoring and routine maintenance, which in turn creates a non-disruptive manufacturing process. Table 3.1 discusses related tools and technologies in the field of IoT and automation, which gives us insight into the existing infrastructure developed to better the surveillance, administer remedies, and collect data, which are transmitted over the Internet facility.

TABLE 3.1
Overview of Related Tools and Technologies in the Field of IoT and Automation

Technology	Main Features	Remarks	References
Provides digital algorithm for speed control block of the motor.	Algorithm would be helpful as speed is an important parameter. This takes the technology to a digital platform.	Speed is only measured and not controlled, and it focuses on only one parameter, which is a demerit.	[2]
IoT platform is used for real-time condition monitoring of IoT-based vibration analysis instead of using myRIO.	It proposes real-time condition monitoring for electrical machines where challenges of data storage and scalability are ruled out.	Using cloud platform service provision entails the requirement of ensuring secure data storage facility.	[3]
Data acquisition at different nodes using sensors and then analysis using neural network.	It accommodates various parameters to identify the fault and makes the process smarter by using a self-learning tool, i.e., neural networks that identify the faults based on its past readings and results.	Using neural networks' platform requires intensive training to make the process fail-safe and a secure fault diagnosis method.	[4]
Establishes a software developed tool where a window of safe frequency for vibration and temperature is set, which should be matched with the operating frequencies to detect the fault.	More than one parameter is taken care of, which helps in more precise monitoring.	It is not a self-learning tool; a window has to be set by the user, which can be considered as a demerit.	[5]
Uses wireless sensors even in harsh environmental conditions such as in turbines, and data collected are sent to the user for analysis through a gateway using Ethernet.	It has made monitoring easy even in harsh environmental conditions. Ethernet usage is one of its merits.	Connection issues may arise leading to issues in analysis.	[6]

(Continued)

TABLE 3.1 (*Continued*)
Overview of Related Tools and Technologies in the Field of IoT and Automation

Technology	Main Features	Remarks	References
Uses wireless sensor network for monitoring for online and remote motor energy monitoring and fault diagnosis.	Wireless sensor networks are better than traditional sensors as the network can manage different nodes at a time.	Considering only few parameters can be considered as a demerit.	[7]
Spectrum synch (SS) technique is used, which enables timely defect detection in induction motors using electrical current signals.	No additional sensors are required so no complications in wiring and mounting. It detects flaws in bearings and rotor bars of induction motors.	Implementation of SS technique needs electric current datasets, which are acquired via the current sensors. This step has to be carried out flawlessly in order to enable accuracy in end result.	[8]
Motor temperature is studied for the usage in pulp and paper mill applications.	It studies the motor temperature and its impact on various components of the motor.	This study remains specific to Totally Enclosed, Fan Cooled (TEFC) motors only. The same findings and conclusions will not apply to other motor types within the industry.	[9]
It uses the parameters related to the winding resistance of the stator instead of sensors to monitor the temperature.	No additional mounting and arrangements required. Also, it accounts for the internal change in the temperature.	Sensor monitoring is an accurate and cost-effective method.	[10]
The **three** major predictive maintenance methods studied are sensors-based method, test sensor-based method, and test signal-based method.	Acquisition of data through sensors is more accurate and cost-effective.	Internet connectivity could be an issue as it includes online monitoring.	[11]
Laser mouse sensor measures revolutions per **minute** of a rotating shaft at different setups.	Different experimental setups are used, which provide precise results. Being contactless, it does not affect the working of the machine.	The LMS requires an enclosed space, which is dust-, oil-, and light-free in order to provide reliability.	[12]
Implementation of industrial automation using IoT with Raspberry Pi	The Raspberry Pi is one of the most compatible controllers as it has its own Wi-fi module and other services required.	It might impose some difficulties in interfacing sensors as it has only digital pins; hence, analog raw values cannot be obtained directly.	[13]

(*Continued*)

TABLE 3.1 (*Continued*)
Overview of Related Tools and Technologies in the Field of IoT and Automation

Technology	Main Features	Remarks	References
Feed cutting force estimated with help of current sensor installed on the AC servomotor of a computerized numerical control turning center.	Many parameters are estimated using only one sensor. It is used to monitor tool wear condition.	Need to follow many further calculations and procedures due to the usage of only one sensor.	[14]

The proceeding sections of the paper enlist in detail the preferred sensors for the main setup of the on-site framework and software components following the related work in industrial automation and IoT. Next, we identify the merits and challenges for this model proposed. The entire system is summarized including a block diagram to depict the proposed framework. Finally, the conclusion for the paper is given.

3.2 RELATED WORK

Table 3.1 provides an overview of related tools and technologies in the field of IoT and automation after analysis of documented work. It highlights the technology, main features of the developed model, and inferences with identified merits or demerits.

3.3 PROPOSED SYSTEM

The following section elucidates the components utilized to develop the proposed model.

The chosen controller, Raspberry Pi, runs on a 64-bit quad-core processor, which has a RAM of 1 GB and has a power consumption of 10 W. This makes it appropriate to use for IoT applications as it has a better power consumption rate compared to other processors. It is programmed to accumulate the sensor readings and communicate acquired data to remote user.

The main sensors opted to fit the data procurement model include the following in the proposed model. The LM35 is a device specifically designed to measure an object's hotness or coldness. LM35 is an accurate IC temperature sensor where the output is directly proportional to the temperature (in °C). It provides more precise results than a thermistor.

The HC-SRO4 ultrasonic sensor transmits an ultrasonic wave that gets received after it bounces off any object. It has an operative voltage of +5 V with distance measurement covering 2–450 cm. It has operating frequency of 40 Hz.

The SW-420 vibration sensor comes with a breakout board that includes the LM393 comparator and the adjustable onboard potentiometer for the selection of the sensitivity threshold and the LED signal indication.

The IR sensor emits infrared rays for sensing the surroundings. This uses IR LED for emitting and receiving rays. It has an operating range of 5 V with a power consumption of 3–5 mA.

Figure 3.1 depicts the block diagram for the IoT-based condition monitoring and automatic control of rotating machines. The flowchart in Figure 3.2 summarizes the entire working of the algorithm implemented.

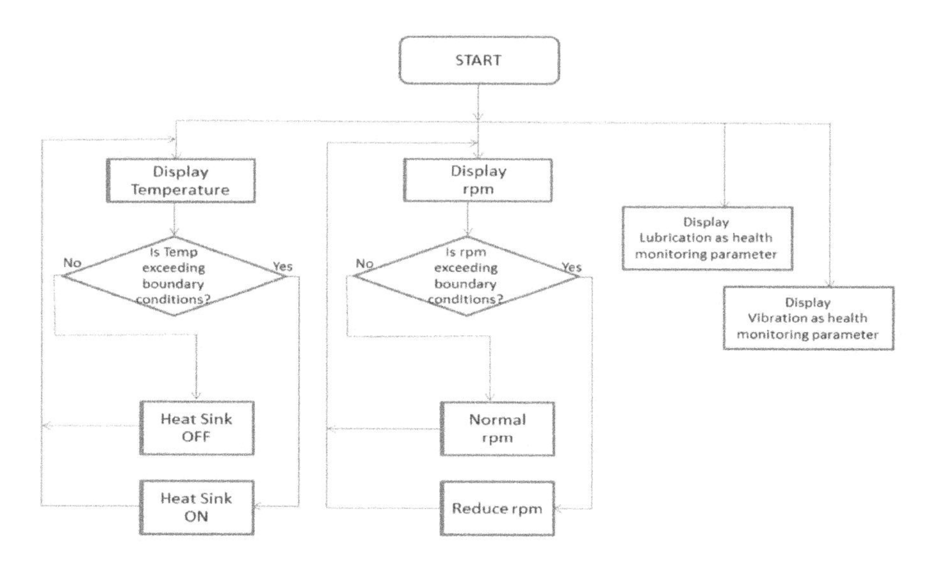

FIGURE 3.1 Block diagram of design approach.

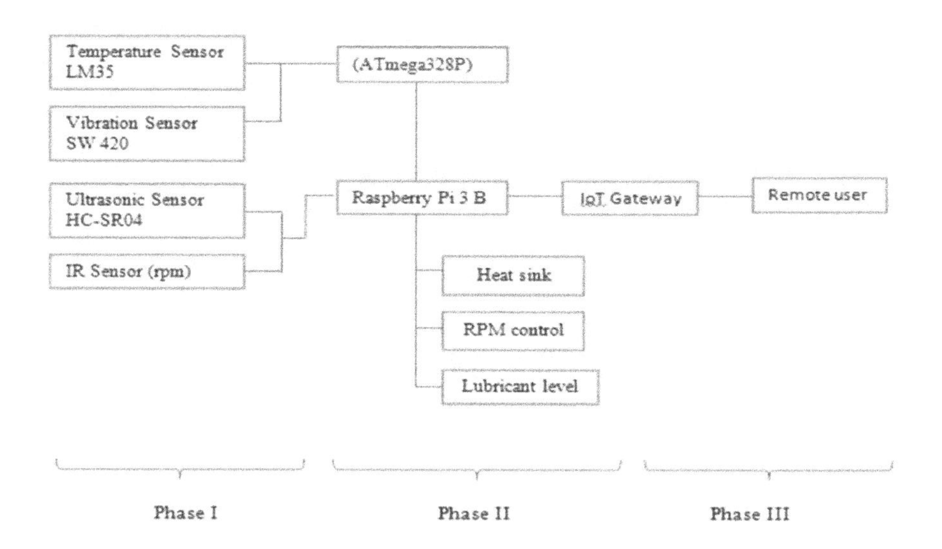

FIGURE 3.2 IoT-based condition monitoring and control system flow diagram.

It is depicted that the program executes sensor initiation for data collection from the sensors for collecting temperature, lubrication level, rpm, and vibration readings. The end product has IoT-based surveillance technique for the condition monitoring system.

By logging into the system from the online website for ThingSpeak, it allows us to access the specific channel for which we have set up the operation or sensor in multiple fields. Here, we have the ability to post or get data from ThingSpeak via this channel from website, device, or yet another channel. We will be utilizing this facility to connect with our sensors via the Raspberry Pi controller. The data from each sensor can be tracked onto the Web portal in real time. This accomplishes the end goal of the setup.

Using the ThingSpeak IoT platform, we can make the instruments, sensors, or websites to transmit data or information onto the cloud where it can be stored in channels. There are two sorts of channels, which are public channel and private channel.

The private channel stores the data by default, and the public channel can share these data with other members. After the data are successfully on a ThingSpeak channel, we can analyze, visualize, or calculate any other parameters needed as well.

The sensing elements have a control loop inherently implemented to automate the remedial measures in case the motor condition falls out of normal stable working conditions. Temperature and rpm monitoring gives us the chance to enable a window of optimum operation.

Remedial steps are instantly executed if the boundary conditions are exceeded according to the system boundaries set, which will depend on the motor. Now, the program will continue to check in a loop if the health of the motor is declining. Via the online portal, the remote user will constantly monitor this overall process.

When any of the parameters fall out of normal operation window, an email notification alerts the remote user of any changes in the health of the motor system. Also, when any control is evoked, then the user will come to know about this via an email message.

This notification will be useful even if the remote user is not logged into the Web portal at the moment. Hence, if the condition persists even after any control mechanism is initiated from the controller, then warning notification gets issued and further attention to the problem needs to be taken as soon as possible.

3.4 RESULTS AND DISCUSSION

The sensor data are displayed in the surveillance setup, which is depicted in Figure 3.3 for the remote user in the following manner. For each sensor, visual representation of the data uploaded onto the Internet is available once the user logs in using his credentials. Once the algorithm detects abnormalities in the data, a notification is sent via email to the concerned user about the risen issue.

Figures 3.4–3.6 show the IoT application Web portal displaying the sensor data uploaded to the remote user. The example of notification via email is depicted in Figures 3.7–3.9.

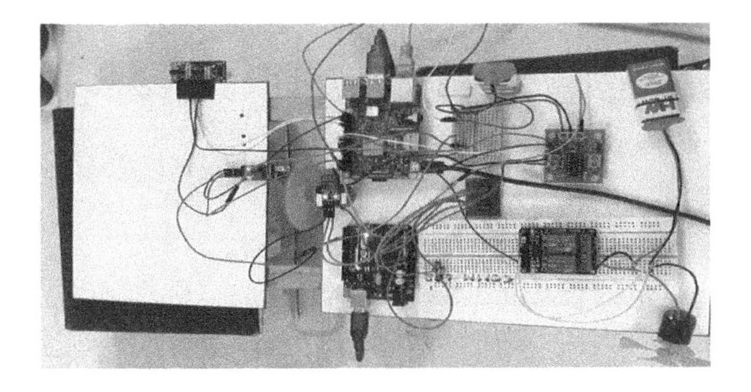

FIGURE 3.3 Raspberry Pi and ATmega328p test setup with sensors.

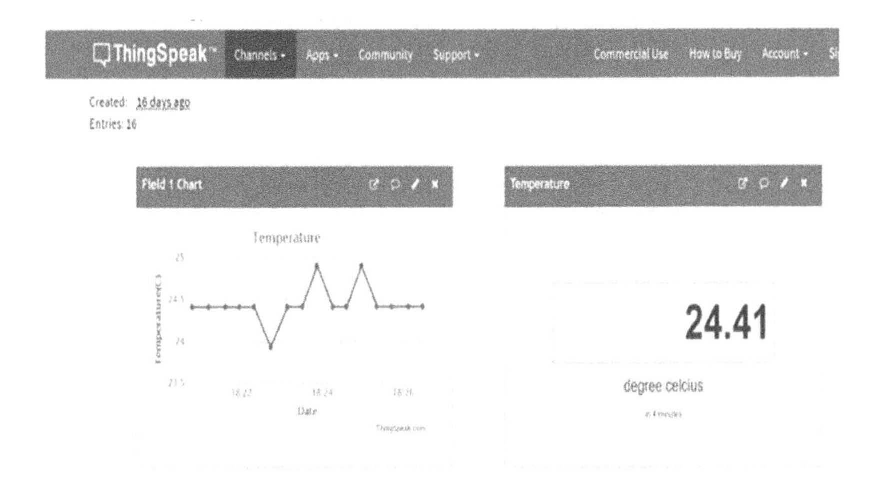

FIGURE 3.4 Web portal displaying temperature data.

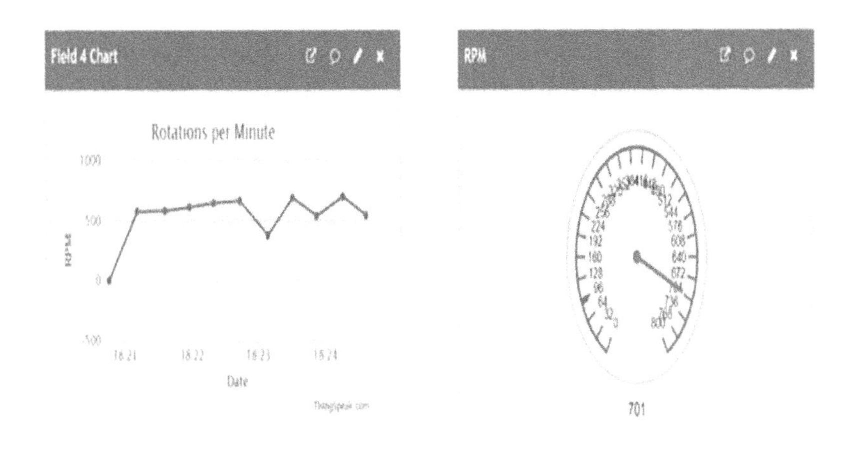

FIGURE 3.5 Graphical representation of rpm measurement with gauge.

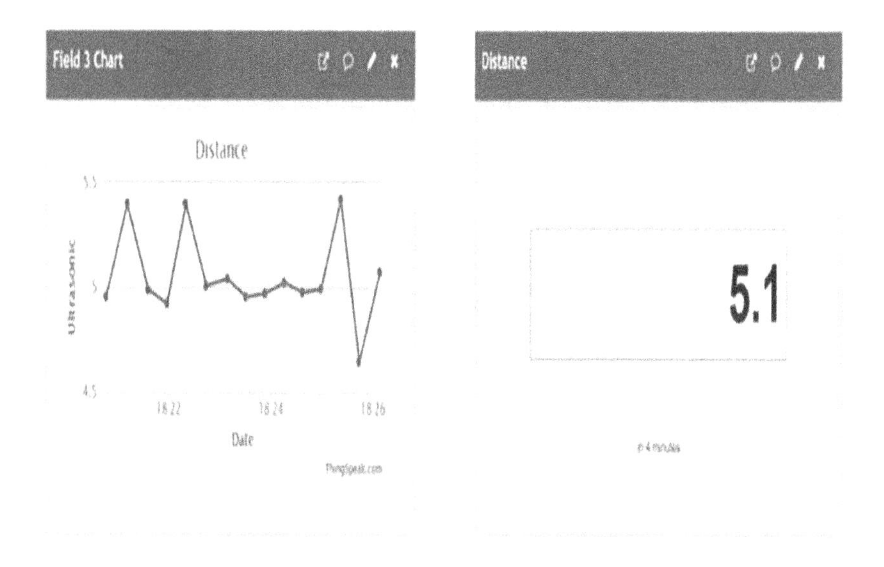

FIGURE 3.6 Level indication of lubrication tank.

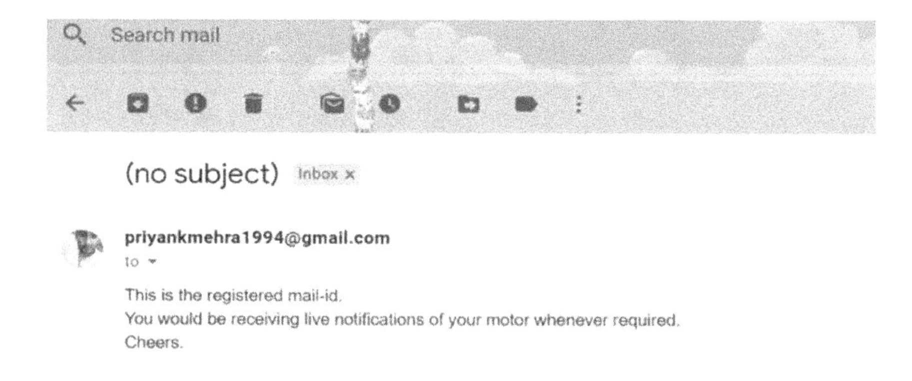

FIGURE 3.7 Email notification via IoT setup.

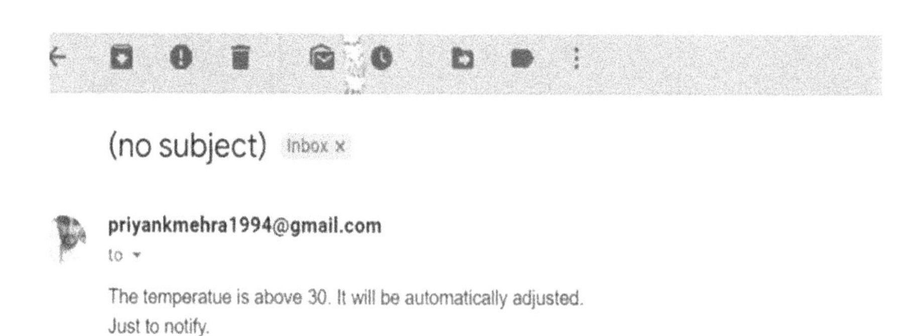

FIGURE 3.8 Email notification via IoT setup indicating temperature abnormality.

FIGURE 3.9 Email notifications to notify stability of the system.

3.5 CONCLUSION AND FUTURE SCOPE

In this paper, a method to measure and control the various parameters for condition monitoring and control of rotating machines with IoT is demonstrated. The existing technological solutions for the same are studied for enhancing the design from references [15–17]. The models from reference papers [18–21] gives us in-depth understanding of the various requirements faced in an industrial environment and the monitoring techniques applied which facilitates on-site data capturing and predictive analysis which is vital to build a sophisticated system.

The main idea in this chapter centers on providing remote access to the working conditions of motors in industrial work environment by using sensors to constantly read the environmental changes. Now, these changes can be continuously streamed onto the Internet, which would expand the reach to the information from far-off locations as well.

Thus, by deploying a sensor-based data acquisition system and combining it with a powerful communication tool such as IoT, we create a functional and efficient condition monitoring tool, which is equipped with data checking and communication capability in order to maintain constant surveillance and control mechanism on-site.

There is immense scope for additional technical upgrades, which can be integrated with this proposed model of IoT-based condition monitoring and automatic control of rotating machines. This system is developed in three main phases, and in each phase, technological modifications can be made to provide superior condition monitoring and control facilities.

The model is built relying on the data communicated by ultrasonic sensor, temperature sensor, rpm sensor, and vibration sensor. Additional sensors can be installed and coded to give better analysis of the motor performance.

The control implementation on the temperature stability and vibration fluctuations can be further aided by different stabilization methods based on not just the indication of fluctuations but also the severity of the issue. This will help increase the stability further.

The IoT implementation can also be upgraded by using analysis tool to produce statistical report for long-term study of the machines' health and perform comparative analysis. The data collected can be fed into a neural net to obtain highly accurate predictions of failure or to determine the reason for malfunction more precisely if training is provided for enough time. This would alleviate the longevity of the health of the machinery under observance.

The focus still primarily remains on providing the user with advanced surveillance of the industrial motors in a user-friendly and cost-effective way. This explains how there is room for flexibility and growth of the product in different aspects.

REFERENCES

[1] www.abb.com/pulpandpaper, ABB in Pulp and Paper.

[2] Baszynski, M., & Pirog, S. "A novel speed measurement method for a high speed BLDC motor based on the signals from the rotor position sensor", *IEEE Transactions on Industrial Informatics* 10, 1, 2013, 84–91.

[3] Ganga, D., & Ramachandran, V. "IoT based vibration analytics of electrical machines", *IEEE Internet of Things Journal* 5, 6, 2018, 4538–4549.

[4] Hou, L., & Bergmann, N. W. "Novel industrial wireless sensor networks for machine condition monitoring and fault diagnosis", *IEEE Transactions on Instrumentation and Measurement* 61, 10, 2012, 2787–2798.

[5] Ilonen, J., Kamarainen, J.-K., Lindh, T., Ahola, J., Kalviainen, H., & Partanen, J. "Diagnosis tool for motor condition monitoring", *IEEE Transactions on Industry Applications* 41, 4, 2005, 963–971.

[6] Peng, Y., Qiao, W., Qu, L., & Wang, J. "Sensor fault detection and isolation for a wireless sensor network-based remote wind turbine condition monitoring system", *IEEE Industry Applications Society Annual Meeting* 54, 2, 2017, 1072–1079.

[7] Bin, L., & Gungor, V. C. "Online and remote motor energy monitoring and fault diagnostics using wireless sensor networks", *IEEE Transactions on Industrial Electronics* 56, 11, 2009, 4651–4659.

[8] Li, D. Z., Wang, W., & Fathy, I. "A spectrum synch technique for induction motor health condition monitoring", *IEEE Transaction on Energy Conversion* 30, 4, 2015, 1348–1355.

[9] Ambers, T., & Bonnett, A. H. "Motor temperature considerations for pulp and paper mill applications", IEEE Transactions, IEEE 2002, pp. 115–128.

[10] Sonnaillon, M. O., Bisheimer, G., De Angelo, C., & Garcıa, G. O. "Online sensorless induction motor temperature monitoring", *IEEE Transaction on Energy Conversion* 25, 2, 2010, 273–280.

[11] Hashemian, H. M., & Bean, W. C. "State-of-the-art predictive maintenance techniques", *IEEE Transactions and Measurement* 60, 1, 2010, 226–236.

[12] Cheng, P., Mustafa, M. S. M., & Oelmann, B. "Contactless rotor RPM measurement using laser mouse sensors", *IEEE Transactions on Instrumentation and Measurement* 61, 3, 2012, 740–748.

[13] Mercant, H. K., & Ahire, D. D. "Implementation of industrial automation using IoT with raspberry Pi", *International Journal of Innovative Research in Science, Engineering and Technology* 168, 1, 2017, 44–46.

[14] Li, X., Djordjevich, A., & Venuvinod, P. K. "Current-sensor-based feed cutting force intelligent estimation and tool wear condition monitoring", *IEEE Transactions on Industrial Electronics* 47, 3, 2000, 697–702.

[15] Beguenane, R., & El HachemiBenbouzid, M. (n.d.), "Induction motors thermal monitoring by means of rotor resistance identification", *IEEE International Electric Machines and Drives Conference Record* 14, 3, 1999, 566–570.

[16] Yang, T., Pen, H., Wang, Z., & Chang, C. S. "Feature knowledge based fault detection of induction motors through the analysis of stator current data", *IEEE Transactions on Instrumentation and Measurement* 65, 3, 2016, 549–558.
[17] Ostojic, P., Banerjee, A., Patel, D. C., Basu, W., & Ali, S. "Advanced motor monitoring and diagnostics", IEEE Transactions on Industry Applications 2014.
[18] Kim, Y.-H., Youn, Y.-W., Hwang, D.-H., Sun, J.-H., & Kang, D.-S. "High-resolution parameter estimation method to identify broken rotor bar faults in induction motors", *IEEE Transaction on Industrial Electronics* 60, 9, 2013, 4103–4117.
[19] Shin, S. M., Choi, B. H., & Kang, H. G. "Motor health monitoring at standstill through impedance analysis", *IEEE Transaction of Industrial Electronics* 63, 7, 2015, 4422–4431.
[20] Bonnett, A. H. "Operating temperature considerations and performance characteristics for IEEE 841 motors", IEEE Transactions on Industry Applications, IEEE 2000, pp. 77–89.
[21] Brown, D. N., Jensen, T., & Kjaer, B. "The use of spectrum comparison for bearing fault detection", In *A Case Study from Alma Paper Mill*, Quebec, Canada.

4 Design of CNTFET-Based Ternary Processor for IoT Devices

Vidhi Choudhary and Reena Monica P
Vellore Institute of Technology

CONTENTS

4.1 INTRODUCTION

Building automation systems nowadays use Internet of things (IoT) to control operations and reduce cost. With the increase in the use of IoT devices, power efficiency becomes a vital factor of the VLSI (Very Large Scale Integration) industry. To design a successful IoT device, low power and minimized area are the primary requirements. As to cope with Moore's law, the feature size of CMOS (Complementary Metal Oxide Semiconductor) has to be scaled down; due to that, some challenges arise such as short-channel effects and increase in subthreshold current. So, CMOS-based devices are not suitable for portable and power-efficient electronic systems. Among numerous other replacements, carbon nanotube field-effect transistor (CNTFET) is the finest option present to substitute CMOS-based devices due to its complementary advantages like decreased leakage power, better control over channel formation, high current density, high mobility, ballistic transport mechanism, and no short-channel effects. CNTFET has the best device current carrying ability experimentally demonstrated to date [1]. Another merit of CNTFET is that its threshold voltage depends on the diameter of carbon nanotubes (CNTs). This leads to the designing of multi-valued logic (MVL) circuits. MVL offers advantages like reduction in overall chip area, speed improvement, and more information is processed. Among various MVL circuits, ternary logic is one of the best ones [2]. Ternary logic is way more advantageous than binary logic in terms of area and power efficiency. In ternary logic, the

DOI: 10.1201/9781003201069-4

usage of three logic levels instead of two results in high processing speed, a smaller number of gates, fewer signal lines, and number of computations that are reduced in signal processing and mathematical applications [3]. The proposed ternary processor has less area, reduced transistor count, reduced power, and less delay. The implementation is done using the Stanford University 32 nm CNTFET model [4].

4.2 CARBON NANOTUBE FET

A CNTFET transistor is made up of a single CNT or more number of CNTs in a form of array, as the channel replaces the existing silicon material channel [1]. The angle at which these nanotubes are folded plays a very important role in determining their electrical properties. If $n = m$, the CNT will be metallic; otherwise, it will be semiconducting. If n and m values of CNTs are varied, then the band diagram of the CNTs is obtained. By changing the diameter of the CNT, its threshold voltage can be varied accordingly. The mathematical expression for CNT's diameter is as follows, Equation (4.1):

$$D_{\text{CNT}} = \frac{\sqrt{3}a_0}{\pi}\sqrt{n^2 + m^2 + nm} \tag{4.1}$$

where $a_0 = 0.142\,\text{nm}$ is the distance present between two atoms of carbon and this pair (m, n) pictures the chirality vector.

The mathematical expression for threshold voltage of a CNTFET is as follows, Equation (4.2):

$$V_{\text{th}} \approx \frac{Eg}{2e} = \frac{\sqrt{3}}{3}\frac{aV\pi}{eD_{\text{CNT}}} \tag{4.2}$$

where $a = 2.49\,\text{Å}$ is the distance between two carbon atoms and $V = 3.033\,\text{eV}$ is the energy of bond between carbon-carbon atom. There are many similarities between structure of CNTFET and silicon transistor, like both have four terminals. For source and drain, CNTs that are heavily doped are selected. For channel, CNTs that are not doped are selected. The mechanical and thermal stability of CNTFET is much higher comparatively. There are few more advantages of CNTFET over silicon transistors like large current carrying capacity and high thermal conductivity [1].

The power–delay product (PDP) of the CNTFET-based logic gates, which are used to design the ternary processor, is being compared with traditional silicon-based logic gates [5]. After comparison, it clearly shows that CNTs-based logic circuits have high speed and consumption of their power is also very less in comparison with silicon-based logic circuits [5].

4.3 TERNARY CONTROL UNIT

The control unit is used to direct the operation of processor [6]. It controls memory, logical unit, and arithmetic unit of processor and instructs them how to respond to a given input. This ternary control unit is comprised of decoders, multiplexers, and binary buffers.

a. Ternary Decoder: Ternary decoder consists of negative ternary inverter (NTI) and standard ternary NOR (STNOR) [7]. The ternary decoder is one-input and three-output combinational circuit. Its circuit diagram is shown in Figure 4.1.

The output for ternary decoder for input x is given as in Equation (4.3):

$$X_k = \begin{cases} 2, & \text{if } x = k \\ 0, & \text{if } x \neq k \end{cases} \tag{4.3}$$

For $k = 0$, output (X_0) is high only when input signal is low, i.e., $x = 0$. For $k = 1$, output (X_1) is high only when input signal is $x = 1$. For $k = 2$, output (X_2) is high only when input signal is $x = 2$ [7].

b. Ternary Multiplexer: Multiplexer circuitry consists of ternary decoder, transmission gates, and binary inverters [8]. It is a 3 × 1 MUX with three inputs, one select line, and one output. Its circuit diagram is shown in Figure 4.2. The output waveform of this transmission gates-based [8] ternary multiplexer is shown in Figure 4.3. Its truth table is given in Table 4.1.

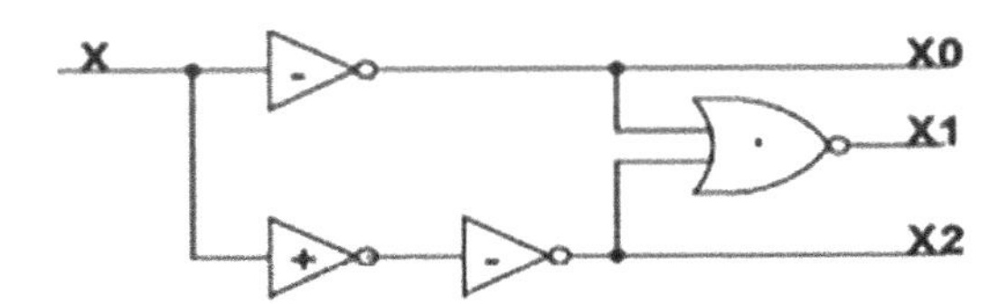

FIGURE 4.1 Ternary decoder circuit.

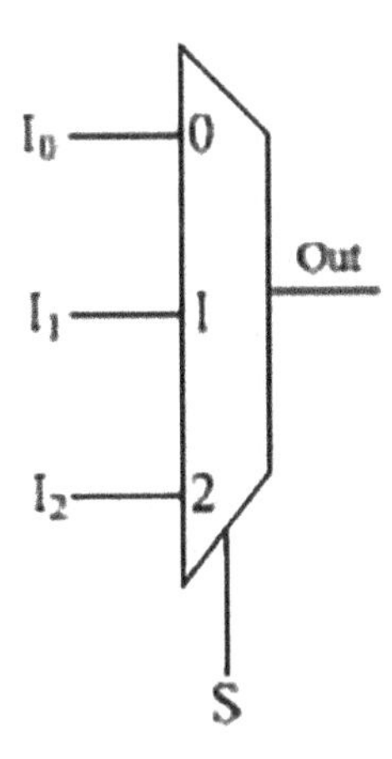

FIGURE 4.2 Ternary multiplexer circuit.

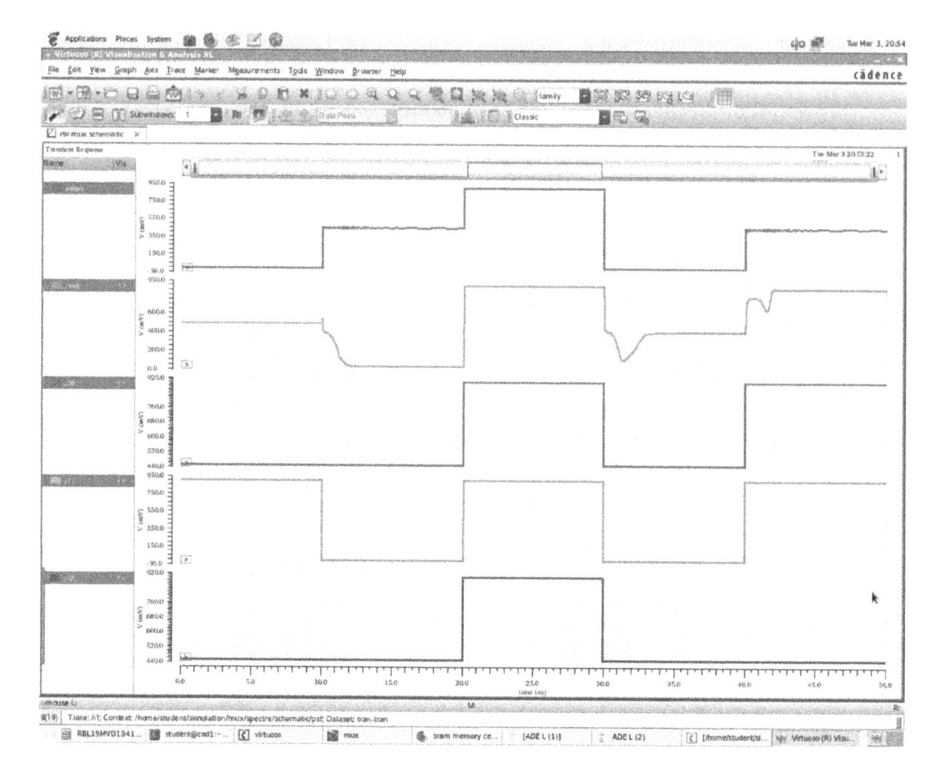

FIGURE 4.3 Output waveform of ternary multiplexer.

TABLE 4.1
Truth Table of Ternary Multiplexer

Select Line (S)	Output (out)
0	I_0
1	I_1
2	I_2

4.4 TERNARY ALU

ALU is the fundamental building block of processor. The ternary ALU consists of two units: ternary arithmetic unit and ternary logical unit.

a. *Ternary Logical unit*: Ternary logic unit consists of operations like AND, NAND, OR, NOR, NOT, and BUFFER [9]. The proposed ternary logic unit architecture is shown in Figure 4.4.

   When $S_0 = 0$, BUFFER + INVERTER circuit works as BUFFER, and if $S_1 = 1$, it works as INVERTER. When $S_0 = 0$, AND + NAND circuit works

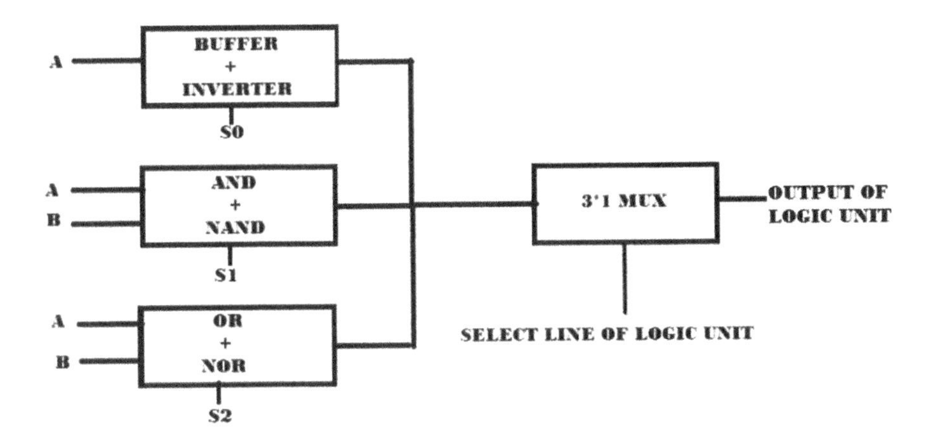

FIGURE 4.4 Block diagram of the ternary logic unit.

TABLE 4.2
Truth Table of Ternary Logic Unit

Select Line of Logic Unit	Output of Logic Unit
0	BUFFER + INVERTER
1	AND + NAND
2	OR + NOR

as AND, and if $S_1 = 1$, it works as NAND. When $S_0 = 0$, OR + NOR circuit works as OR, and if $S_1 = 1$, it works as NOR [9].

Select line of logic unit decides which unit will work and its truth table is given in Table 4.2.

Its output waveform is shown in Figure 4.5.

b. *Ternary Full Adder*: Input to full adder and carry circuit is given by successor and predecessor circuits' output [10]. In the successor part, when input is reaching low voltage, then right nFET is getting ON and half of V_{dd} is reaching the terminal of output. Similarly, when input is high, in that case, both left nFETs are getting ON and output terminal voltage is falling down to 0 V. In the other case, the output will be depending on pFET. The working of the predecessor unit is a reflection to the working of the successor unit.

In Figures 4.6 and 4.7, the proposed architecture is presented.

There are three input terminals A, B, and C_{in}, and sum and carry are the two output terminals. A two-level multiplexer architecture is presented, to get the output sum. The multiplexer present on the right is a ternary multiplexer and its select line is B input terminal. In Figure 4.8, its circuit diagram is presented. The multiplexer present on the left is a binary multiplexer

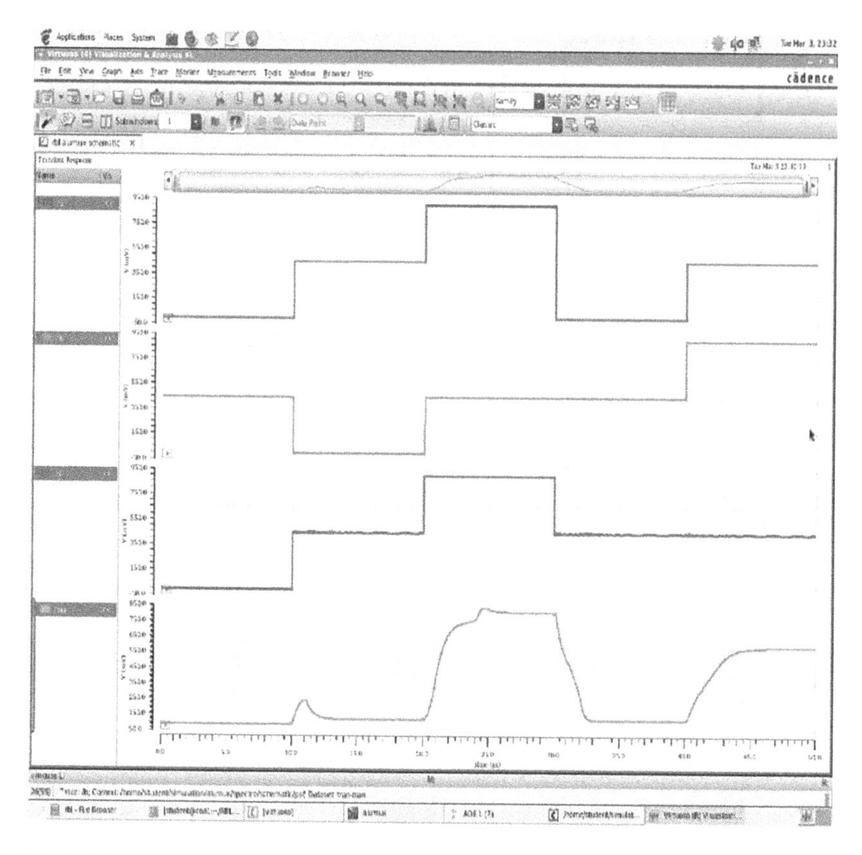

FIGURE 4.5 Output waveform of ternary logical unit.

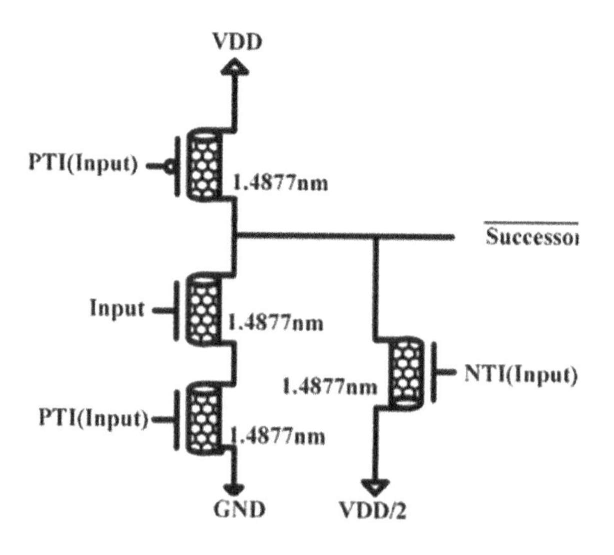

FIGURE 4.6 Successor circuit.

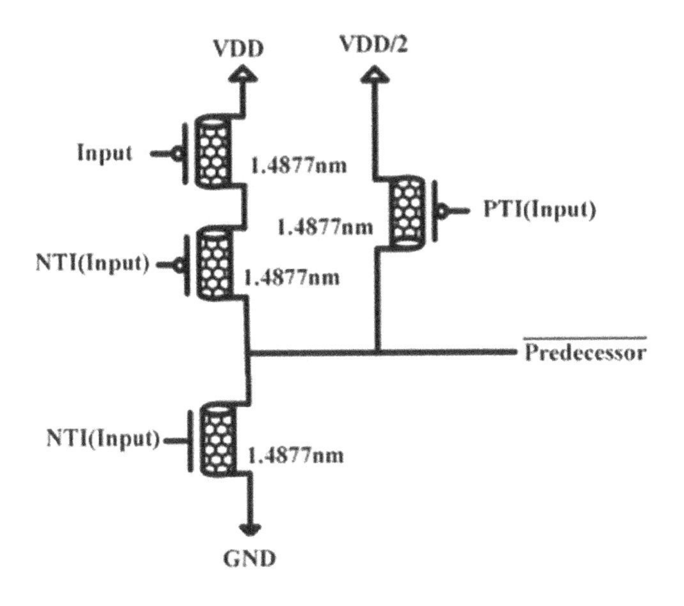

FIGURE 4.7 Predecessor circuit.

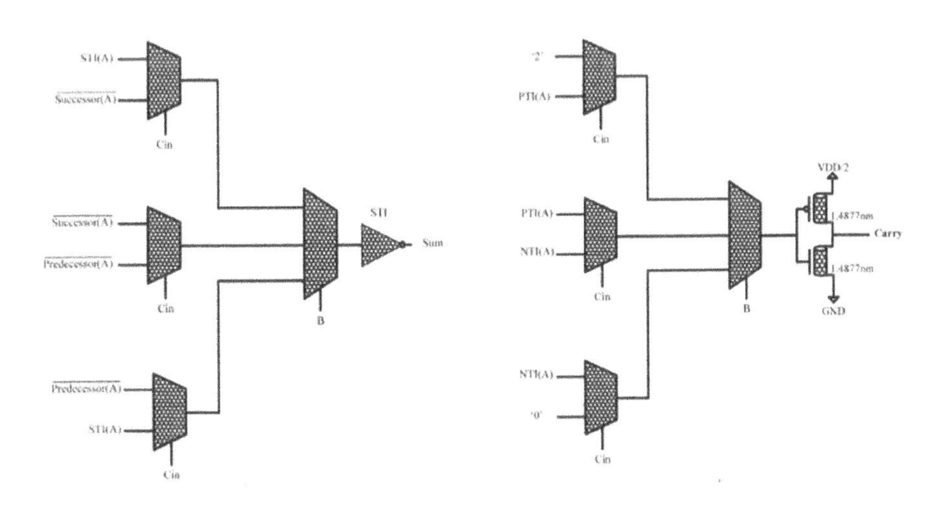

FIGURE 4.8 Ternary full adder.

and its select line is C_{in} input terminal. If $C_{in} = 0$ and $B = 0$, then the first terminal of MUX is selected and output is A. If $C_{in} = 0$ and $B = 1$, then the output of the sum terminal will be successor of A. In Figure 4.9, its output waveform is presented. For other combinations also, any one of the inputs is selected, and output is determined. Carry out circuit also works the same way: One of the inputs is selected, and the respective output is generated [10]. Its truth table is given in Table 4.3.

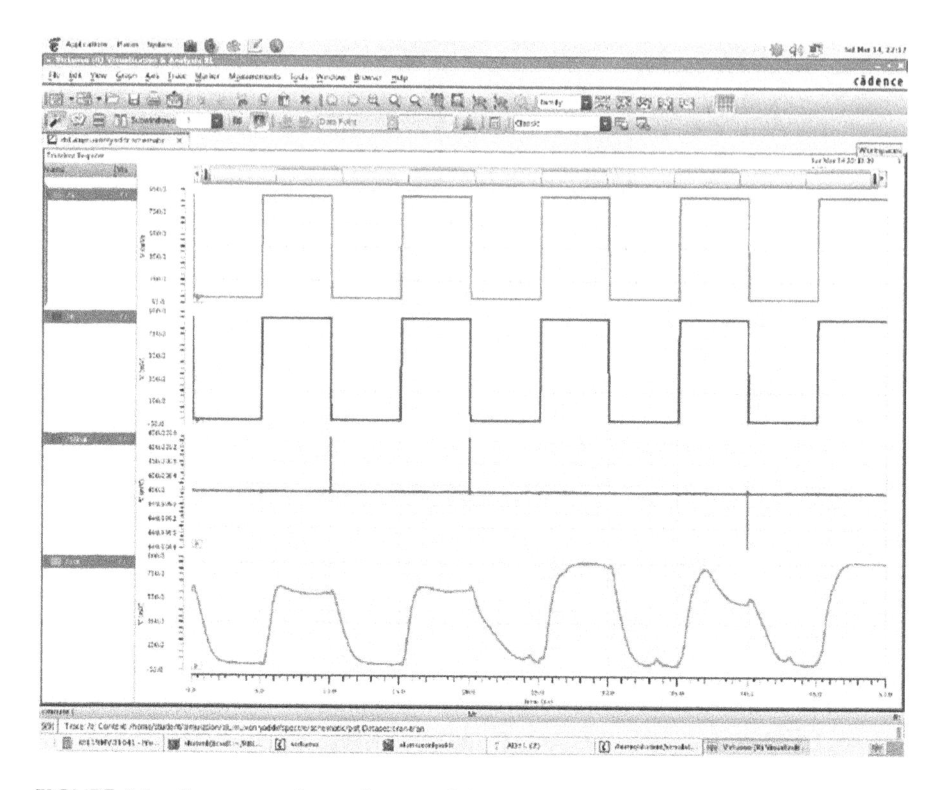

FIGURE 4.9 Output waveform of ternary full adder.

TABLE 4.3
Truth Table of Ternary Full Adder

$A + B + C_{in}$	SUM	C_{out}
0	0	0
1	1	0
2	2	0
3	0	1
4	1	1
5	2	1
6	0	2

c. *Ternary Multiplier*: The proposed multiplier is designed by multiplexer; one input B is given to select line of multiplexer [5]. Inputs of the multiplexer are 0, A, and $\bar{A}^2$. Its circuit diagram is shown in Figure 4.10. The equation of product is as given in Equation (4.4).

Product $= B_1\,(A) + B_2\,(\bar{A}^2)$, Equation (4.4)

In Figure 4.11, the presented multiplier's output waveform is shown. When $B = 0$, then input 0 is selected and output is zero. When $B = 1$, then

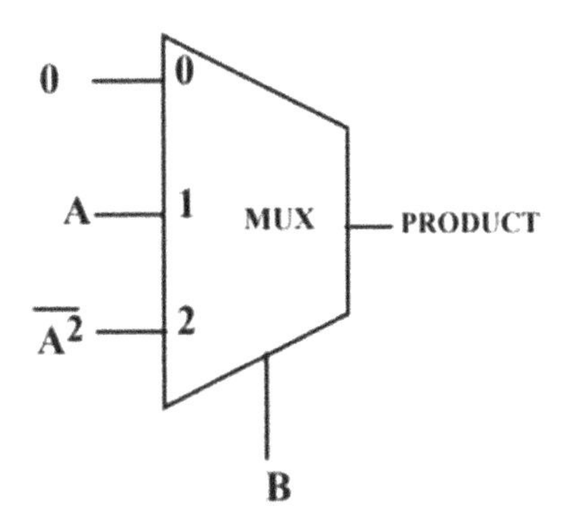

FIGURE 4.10 Ternary multiplier circuit.

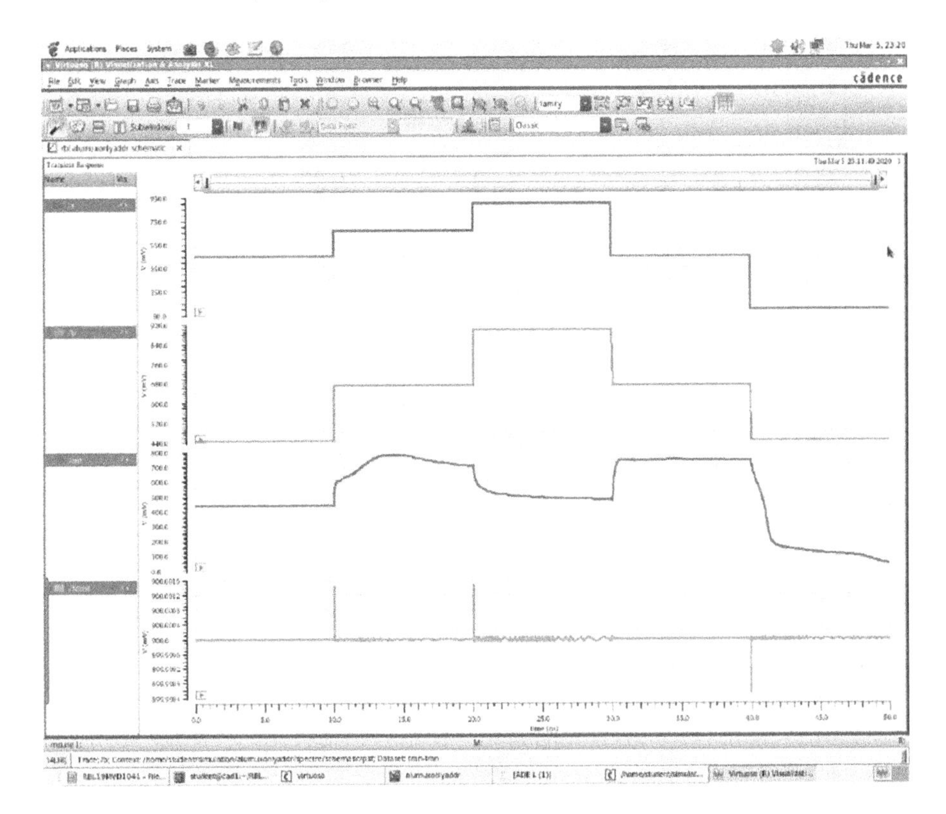

FIGURE 4.11 Output waveform of ternary multiplier.

input is selected as A and output is A. When $B = 2$, then input is selected as $\bar{A}^2$ and output is 0 if $A = 0$, output is 2 if $A = 1$, and output is 1 if $A = 2$ [5]. Its truth table is given in Table 4.4.

d. *Ternary ALU*: Its circuit diagram is shown in Figure 4.12. Ternary ALU consists of logic unit and arithmetic unit. Arithmetic unit consists of ternary full adder and ternary multiplier. Two 3×1 multiplexers are used as control

TABLE 4.4
Truth Table of Ternary Multiplier

A	B	Product
0	0	0
0	1	0
0	2	0
1	0	0
1	1	1
1	2	2
2	0	0
2	1	2
2	2	1

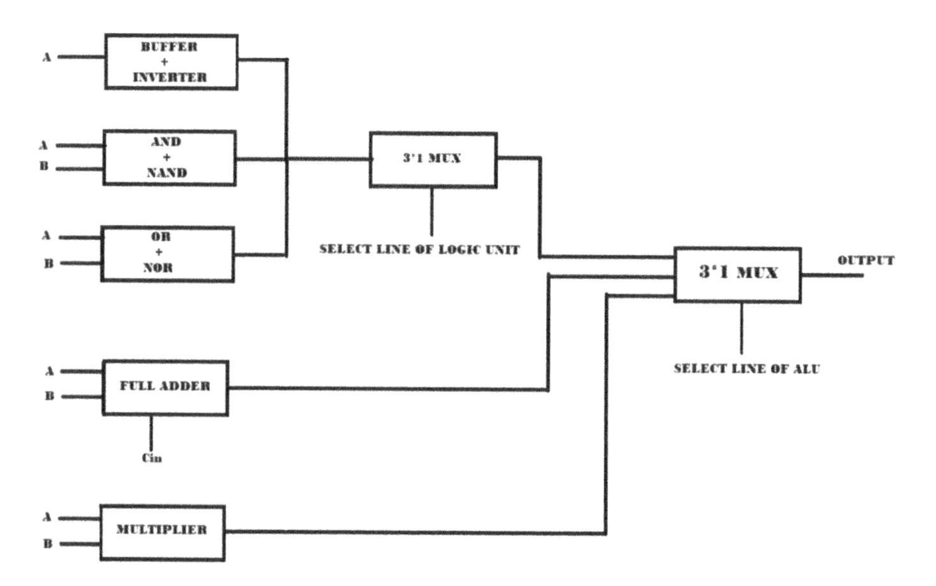

FIGURE 4.12 Circuit diagram of the ternary ALU.

unit. In Figure 4.13, the presented ALU's output waveform is shown. Select line of ALU decides which unit will get activated. Its truth table is given in Table 4.5.

4.5 TERNARY MEMORY UNIT

The implemented SRAM can perform read and write simultaneously, due to the presence of transmission gate-based memory unit. The memory unit includes standard ternary inverter (STI) and binary buffer [11]. The required threshold voltages for each transistor in each gate have been calculated and set individually. The write action and read action are executed in Cadence Virtuoso. Its circuit diagram is shown in Figure 4.14.

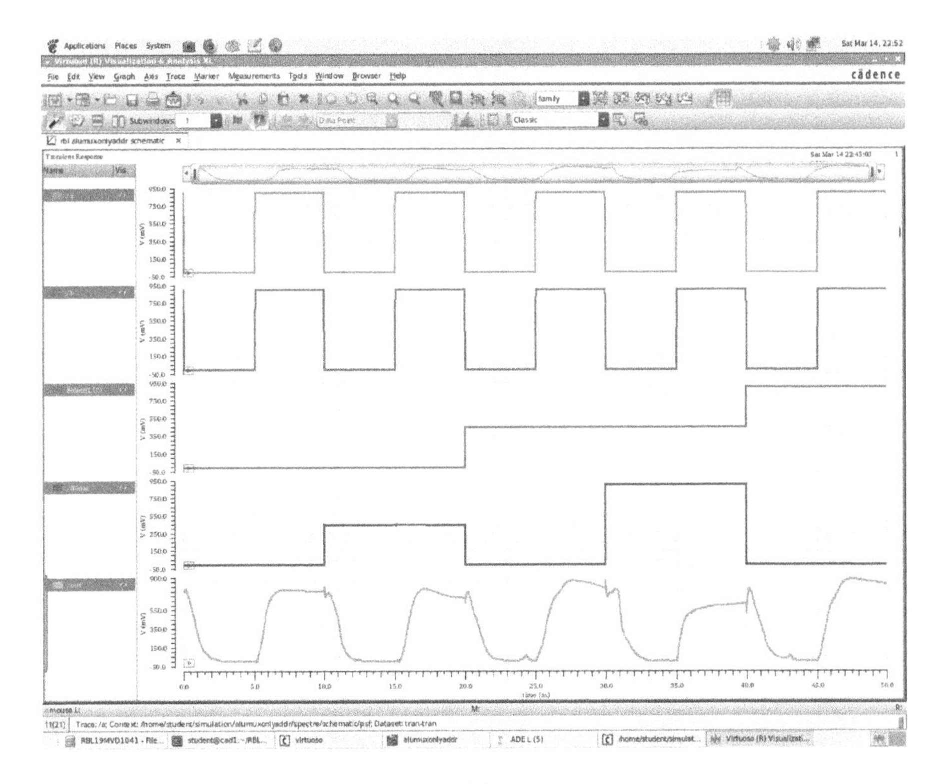

FIGURE 4.13 Output waveform of ternary ALU.

TABLE 4.5
Truth Table of Ternary ALU

Select Line of ALU Unit	Output of ALU
0	Logic unit
1	Full adder
2	Multiplier

The working of read action is as follows: In the beginning, the rbl terminal is already charged to half of the highest voltage level [12]. The three most basic logic levels of voltage, i.e., "0," "1," and "1/2," are fed to q and qb lines as input for read operation The given input levels are recognized by memory cell and read only when rwl terminal is at high level and rwlb terminal is at low level. The input given at q line is reflected as it is at output terminal, i.e., at rbl line whenever rwl line is high [12].

The working of write action is as follows: The transmission gate that is assigned to do write operation will send the correct data to storage unit. Whenever the terminal wwl is high and the terminal wwlb is low, the input is going to be stored in

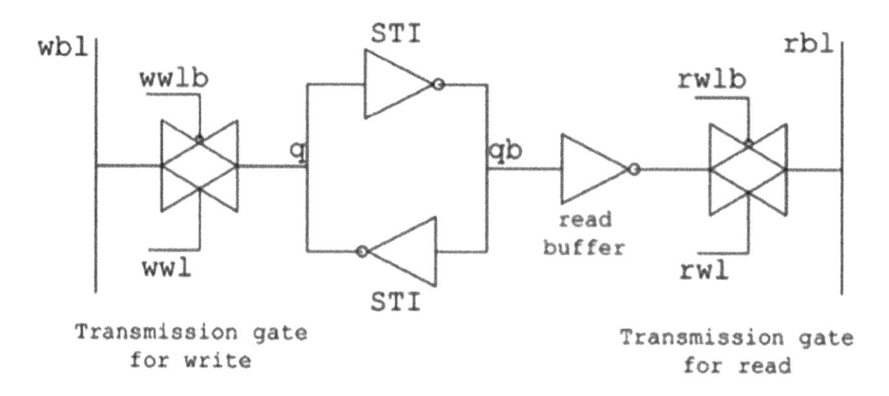

FIGURE 4.14 Circuit diagram of the ternary SRAM cell.

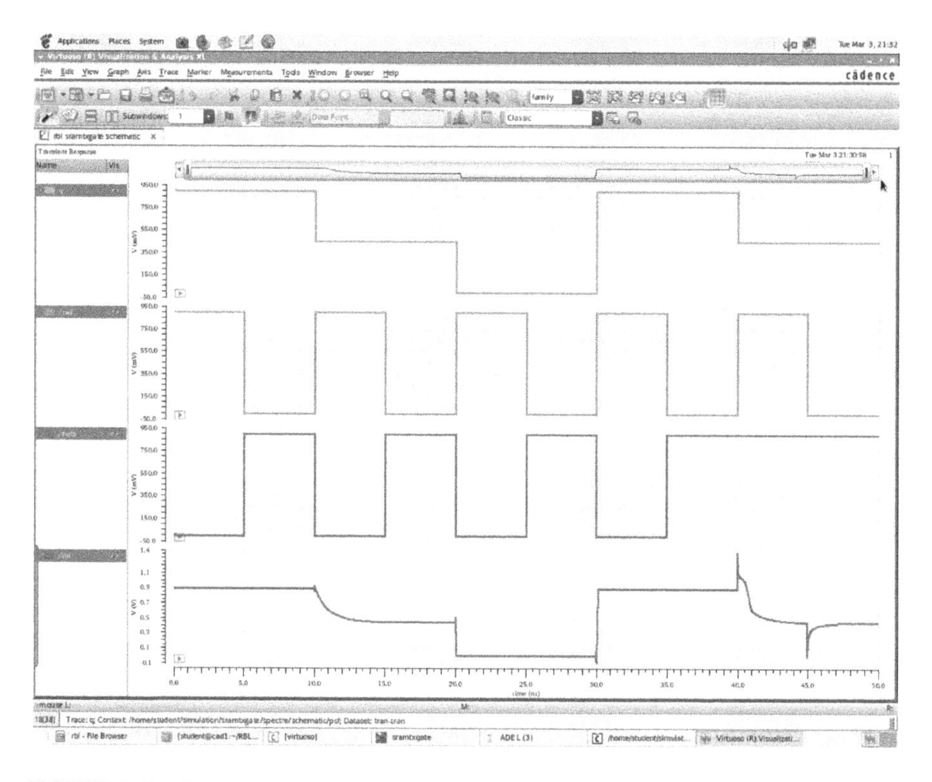

FIGURE 4.15 Output waveform for read operation.

memory unit and will be procured at q terminal [12]. Whenever input is "0" or "1," the transmission gate assigned for read action reads "0" and "1," but whenever input is "1/2," the gate is going to be OFF [12]. The output waveform for read operation is shown in Figure 4.15. The output waveform for write operation is shown in Figure 4.16.

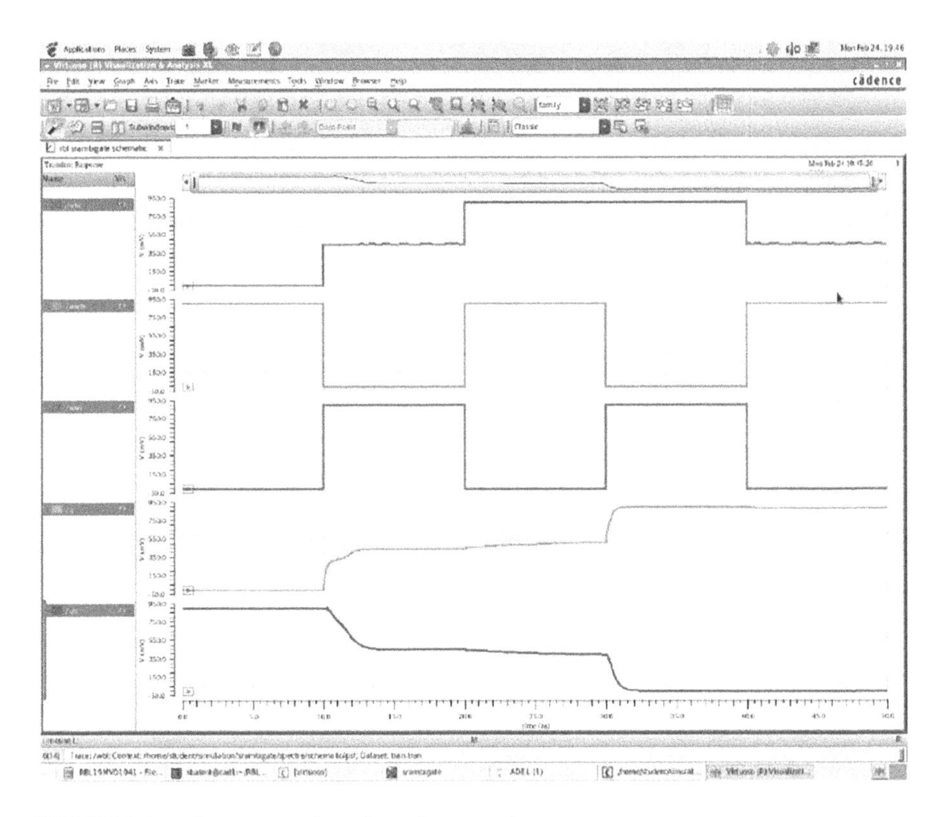

FIGURE 4.16 Output waveform for write operation.

4.6 TERNARY PROCESSOR

Its circuit diagram is shown in Figure 4.17. An array of SRAM memory cells has been created and connected to input terminals of ALU. Memory cell has been kept in read operation mode, and inputs are given to the input port of memory cell. These inputs are further sent to ALU and control unit for processing. In Figure 4.18, the output waveform is shown. According to select lines of control unit, input data are processed by ALU and further sent to output port of ternary processor. The simulation results obtained from Cadence Virtuoso are given in Tables 4.6 and 4.7.

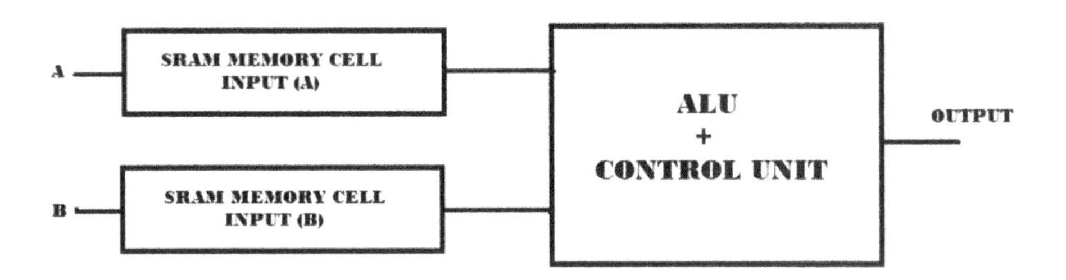

FIGURE 4.17 Circuit diagram of the ternary processor.

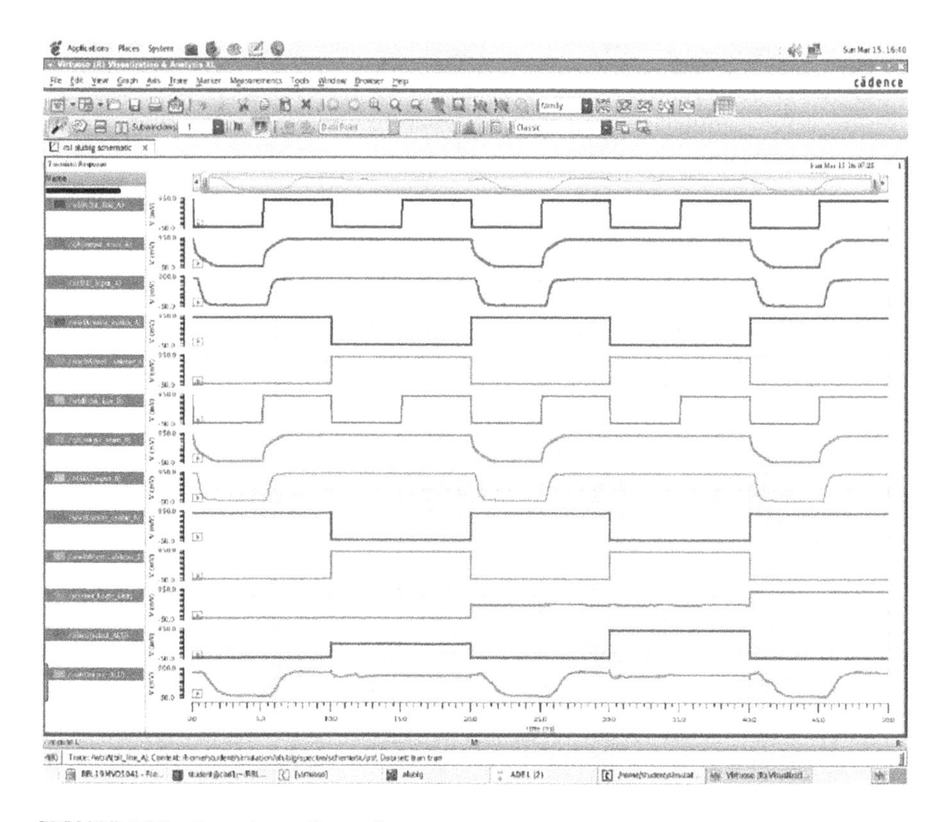

FIGURE 4.18 Output waveform of ternary processor.

TABLE 4.6
Table of Power and Delay for Each Unit

Design	Power (10^{-6} W)	Delay (10^{-11} seconds)
SRAM memory	0.529	3.01
Control unit	1.061	4.791
ALU	11.0485	8.157
Processor	12.6385	15.958

TABLE 4.7
Table of Power–Delay Product (PDP)

Design	PDP (10^{-17})
SRAM memory	1.592
Control unit	5.083
ALU	90.122
Processor	96.797

4.7 CONCLUSION

A compact, energy-efficient CNTFET-based ternary processor for IoT devices is proposed in this work. For ALU, two units, arithmetic unit and logic unit, have been proposed. A power-optimized full adder is used. To reduce area, the functionality of two gates is combined and then implemented, which also leads to minimized delay. Control unit is designed ternary multiplexer instead of basic transmission gates, and hence, area and delay are reduced. SRAM memory cell has been designed for both reading and writing in a single cell, which leads to reduction in power and area consumed by the cell. The power and delay of each unit are observed. Experimental results of the proposed processor show a significant reduction in power and delay in comparison with traditional CMOS-based designs. The PDP of novel ternary processor is calculated, and there is improvement of at least 70% in comparison with traditional processor. Hence, high-performance CNTFET-based ternary processor is proposed for the design of IoT devices.

REFERENCES

[1] Monica, P. R., and Sreedevi, V. T. "A low power and area efficient CNTFET based GDI cell for logic circuits", *ARPN Journal of Engineering and Applied Sciences*, 9, 12, 2014.
[2] Lin, S., Kim, Y.-B., and Lombardi, F. "A novel CNTFET- based ternary logic gate design", Circuits and Systems, MWSCAS'09. 52nd IEEE International Midwest Symposium, IEEE 2009.
[3] Dhande, A., Ingole, V., and Ghiye, V. *Ternary Digital System: Concepts and Applications*, SM Online Publishers LLC, 2014.
[4] Stanford University Nanoelectronics Group. Stanford University CNTFET Model. Retrieved from http://nano.stanford.edu/model.php?id=23.
[5] Sasi, S. K., and Reena Monica, P. "Ternary logic implementation and its application using CNTFET", Advanced Electronic Systems (ICAES). International Conference on IEEE, 2013.
[6] Nagata, Y., Miller, D. M., and Mukaidono, M. "Logic synthesis of controllers for B-ternary asynchronous systems." Multiple-Valued Logic, (ISMVL 2000) Proceedings 30th IEEE International Symposium on IEEE, 2000.
[7] Mukaidono, M. "Regular ternary logic functions—ternary logic functions suitable for treating ambiguity," *IEEE Trans. Comput.*, C-35, 2, 179–183, 1986.
[8] Vudadha, C., Sreehari, V., and Srinivas, M. B., "Multiplexer based design for ternary logic circuits", 2012 8th Conference on Ph.D. Research in Microelectronics and Electronics (PRIME), pp. 1–4, 2012.
[9] Dhande, A. P., and Ingole, V. T. "Design & implementation of 2-bit ternary ALU slice," Proc. Int. Conf. IEEE-Sci. Electron., Technol. Inf. Telecommun., pp. 17–21, 2005.
[10] Tabrizchi, S., Panahi, A., Sharifi, F., Navi, K., and Bagherzadeh, N. "A novel method for designing ternary adder cell based on CNFETs," *IET Circuits Devices Syst.*, 11, 5, 465–470, 2017.
[11] Shreya, S., and Sourav, S. "Design, analysis and comparison between CNTFET based ternary SRAM cell and PCRAM cell." Communication, Control and Intelligent Systems (CCIS), IEEE, 2015.
[12] Karthikeyan, S., Reddy, M. C. K., and Reena Monica, P. "Design of CNTFET-based ternary control unit and memory for a ternary processor," 2017 International Conference on Microelectronic Devices, Circuits and Systems (ICMDCS), 2017.

5 IoT-Based Smart Buildings

Swetha KK, Karthik G, V. Berlin Hency, and O.V. Gnana Swathika
Vellore Institute of Technology

CONTENTS

5.1 INTRODUCTION

In today's generation, technology plays a major role. We even tend to forget our meal schedule. There are also mobile applications that get access to our mobile's time and remind us to drink water accordingly. In this modern world situation, it is almost impossible to take care of ourselves. Due to immense stress put in the corporate world, adults and even youngsters are experiencing anxiety and panic attacks.

All these can be overcome by continuous and uninterrupted monitoring of the vitals of people living in smart buildings. In the current technological growth, this is possible to achieve by using communication technologies like Bluetooth, Zigbee, RF transceiver, global system for mobile communication (GSM), and Wi-fi. But these facilities face many drawbacks in bandwidth, cost, complex structure, and accuracy prediction. The aim of this paper is to overcome the above drawbacks and to enable monitoring of the vitals of people living in smart buildings.

5.2 LITERATURE REVIEW

Accuracy and rigidity are the two most important virtues expected from any life-saving technology. Table 5.1 shows the prevailing technologies for the transmission

DOI: 10.1201/9781003201069-5

TABLE 5.1
Technologies for Transmission and Processing of Data and Their Suitability for the Field

Technology for Transmission	Technology for Processing	Field Usage
Zigbee	LPC2138 microcontroller	No
Geographical positioning system	ARM7TDMI processor	Yes
Zigbee-enabled wireless sensor	MSP430	No
Web-based monitoring	Atmel AVR ATmega microcontroller and Nordic RF2401 transceiver	No
IoT	Raspberry Pi board	No
IoT	Arduino board	Yes

and processing of data and their suitability for the field. Node-based human vital monitoring system and geographical location positioning using Google Maps exist along with wearable, portable sensors for real-time health monitoring of soldiers. ARM processor-based mechanism has been proposed for the safety of soldiers on the battlefield. Arduino board is connected with various vitals monitoring sensor and with GPS-enabled real-time monitoring and tracking of soldiers on the battlefield as given in Table 5.1 [1]. A state of the art of existing systems for explosive detection is discussed and the future challenges for such a surveillance system is also discussed [2]. A mobile health monitoring system enables real-time monitoring of human body vitals without the presence of a medical supervisor. This system demands a microcontroller and radio frequency transceiver and receiver. Internet of things (IoT)-based local monitoring system of vitals of patients has thus been proposed [3]. Remote monitoring can be even more enhanced by using a camera. It can be placed on the robot. The programming language used for the robot is LINUX interfaced with Raspberry Pi. Passive infrared sensor and smoke sensor can be included to add more features to the system [4]. The real-time human vitals monitoring system can be done by using Raspberry Pi 3 board, which has built-in Wi-fi and Bluetooth modules. It is used to collect the human vital parameters like temperature, blood pressure, pulse rate, and saturated oxygen level. The vitals collected through sensors can be added to the cloud-based website. It is seen that not many efforts were shown toward the soldier's body vitals and location tracking while on the battlefield [5]. Further, there are so many obstacles like increased cost, high time delay, reduced throughput, and heavy in nature. All these drawbacks can be overcome by using a remote wireless real-time system [6]. There are various sensors that will also provide real-time data of soldier's health and trace geographical position and send it to the control room through IoT. This feature will help to reduce the problem of number of go missing during every unhealthy border situation [7]. Secure data transmission using lightweight secure IoT-assisted ECG [8]. Transport layer security maintains end-to-end security scheme and thereby saves communication bandwidth. Publish–Subscribe model enables the client to exchange messages through a broker. Fog node when used as an intermediate broker provides lightweight solution by off-loading computation and storage for security parameters [9]. Critical visual information can be collected by high-processing IoT-enabled sensors. This enables the relevant data to be sent to the authority and also to predict the abnormal activity intelligently and report in real time. Histogram clustering method has been used to retrieve keyframes through video surveillance [10]. The main task of IoT and Wireless Sensor Network (WSN) is to sense the data and send it to the base station. Encryption algorithms of asymmetric type consist of River Shamir Adelman (RSA) and Elliptic Curve Cryptography (ECC) algorithms, which provide high level of security but require high memory and storage. Symmetric type consists of DES and AES algorithms, which do not require huge memory and storage, so it can be preferred [11]. The continuous real-time data collection brings big data to light. Five V's (Volume, Variety, Value, Velocity, and Veracity) are still in working progress [12]. Wearable sensors are another major trend. Improved Bayesian convolution network allows data to be downloaded through traditional radio frequency [13]. Biosensing mask uses facial expressions as input to monitor the pain withstanding capability of the soldiers at the time of hardship [14]. Analysis of heartbeat using QRS wave enables the quick handling of depolarization [15]. Wireless body area network (WBAN) has 6° of freedom, three-dimensional position, and three-dimensional orientation. All these result in increased accuracy, precision, and robustness [16–18]. Device-to-device and device-to-machine communication is essential for military operations. The impact of mountains on the IoT devices plays a crucial role. Mountains act as reflectors and can reflect echo at 900 MHz. This can be overcome by two-sample t-tests [19,20]. HBC interfaced with WBAN is a recent trend. Human body itself is a transmission channel without being wired. Human body when given impulse signal powered by a battery enables the measurement of 52 signals from various points in the body from head to ankle [21].

5.3 THE PROPOSED SYSTEM

The aim of the proposed system is to track the geographical location of the sensor and also to continuously monitor the vitals. The sensor consists of two units, namely person's hub and nearby health unit. The person's hub is shown in Figure 5.1, the health unit is shown in Figure 5.2, and the combined block diagram is shown in Figure 5.3.

The person's hub consists of HBC-HMI node; it collects all the data from the sensors and decides the condition of the person. The node is connected to various sensors like temperature sensor, oxygen level detector, pulse sensor, and panic buzzer. Temperature sensor detects the temperature and determines whether it is normal. Oxygen level detector checks the oxygen level in soldier's blood. Pulse sensor checks for normality in person's pulse. Panic buzzer is a two-way switch. It can be operated by the individual, or when the vitals are abnormal, information will be passed on to the health unit also. Whenever the vitals are deviated from the preset healthy stable value, the system gets an alert signal and the corresponding data will be sent to the health supervisor in the health unit with an alert sound. All the vitals are interconnected to the HBC-HMI node, which sends the data to the ThingSpeak cloud. The data are accessed by the health center via ThingSpeak cloud to monitor the people's health continuously.

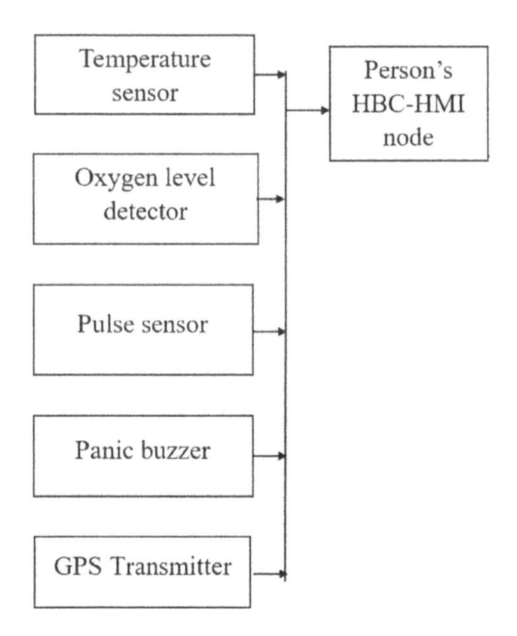

FIGURE 5.1 Integration of sensors.

FIGURE 5.2 Integration of cloud with the unit.

FIGURE 5.3 Integration of entire system with cloud.

5.4 IMPLEMENTATION

5.4.1 Process Flow

The working flow of the proposed system is described in Flowchart 5.1.

1. When all the sensors are ON, the GPS receiver tracks the location in the form of latitude, altitude, and longitude and sends it to the control room. The collected sensor values are checked if they are normal or abnormal and the GPS

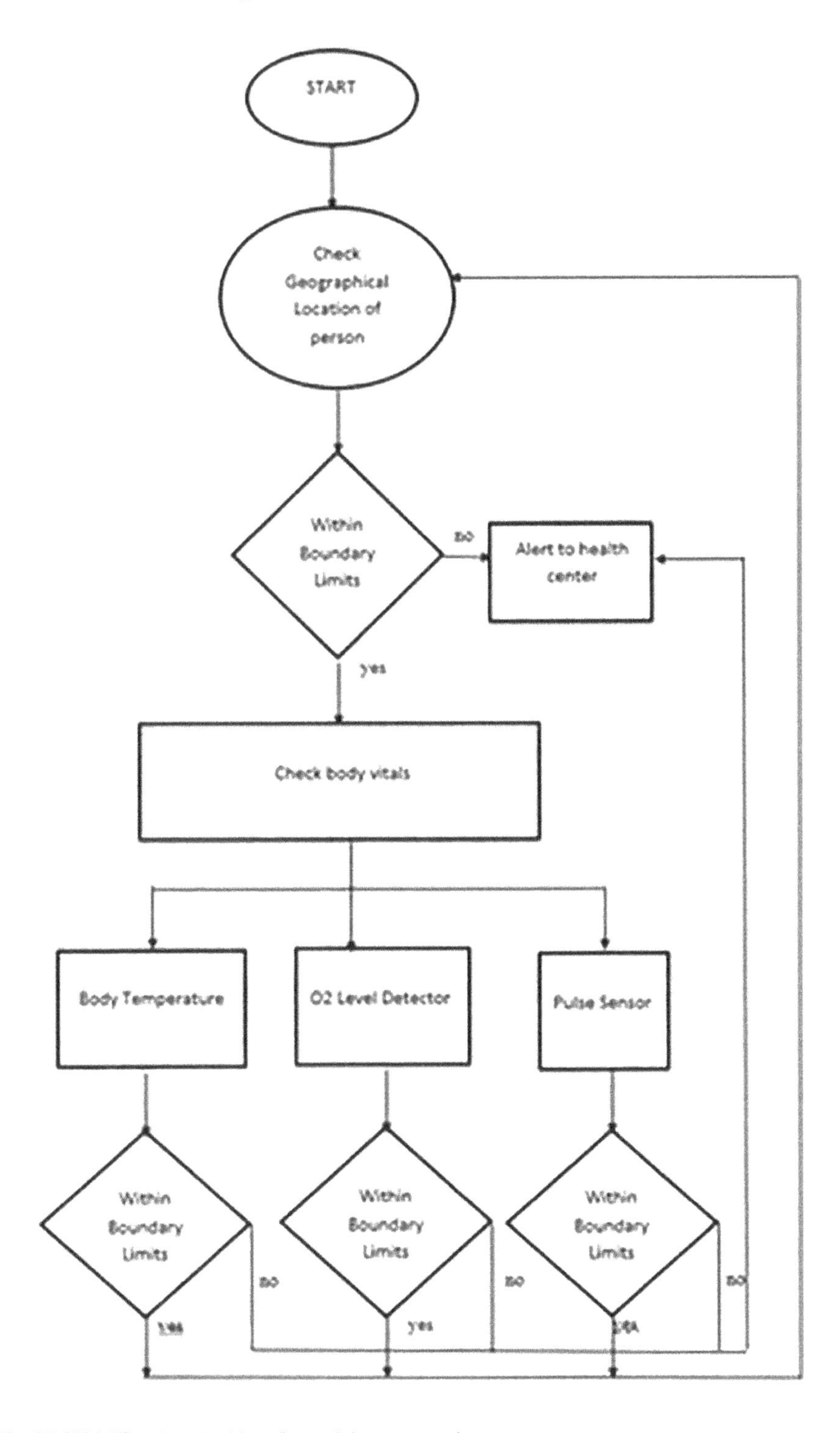

FLOWCHART 5.1 Working flow of the proposed system.

data are checked if the soldier lies within the nation's boundary. By sensing these two parameters, alert message is sent accordingly. The person will also be alerted through panic buzzer, since panic buzzer is a two-way switch.
2. LM35 temperature sensor is used to measure the body temperature of a person. Here, a temperature threshold level is set between 97°F and 99°F. Whenever the body temperature of the person increases beyond or decreases below this level, the alert sound (buzzer sound) will be sent to the control room.
3. Person's heartbeat is continuously monitored by V1.1 pulse rate sensor. The normal heart rate for a person is between 50 and 100 bits per minute (BPM). If the heartbeat lies above or below this range, alert sound will be transmitted to the medical supervisor in the control room.
4. The saturated oxygen level is measured with the help of pulse oximeter placed on soldier's chest. Whenever any abnormality is detected, a sensor-generated alert signal will be transmitted to the control unit.

The person's hub consists of HBC-HMI node; it collects all the data from the sensors and decides the condition of the individuals. The node is connected to various sensors like temperature sensor, oxygen level detector, pulse sensor, and panic buzzer. Temperature sensor detects the temperature and determines whether it is normal. Oxygen level detector checks the oxygen level in soldier's blood. Pulse sensor checks for normality in soldier's pulse. Panic buzzer is a two-way switch. Whenever the vitals are deviated from the preset healthy stable value, the system gets an alert signal and the corresponding data will be sent to the health supervisor in the health unit with an alert sound. Also, the geographical location of the person is also sent to the control room. All the vitals are interconnected to the HBC-HMI node, which sends the data to the ThingSpeak cloud. The data are accessed by the control room via ThingSpeak cloud to monitor the person's health continuously.

5.5 SOFTWARE SIMULATION

LabVIEW is compiler-based simulation software, which enables the real-time working of the proposed system. The real-time testing of the proposed system is done using LabVIEW. The simulation for oxygen level detection is shown in Figures 5.4 and 5.5. The simulation for temperature detection is shown in Figures 5.6 and 5.7. The simulation for pulse rate detection is shown in Figures 5.8 and 5.9.

In Figure 5.5, the oxygen level is simulated and the value is displayed in the panel as shown in Figure 5.4. The simulated value goes to the cloud for storage. The stored data can be accessed through the ThingSpeak cloud.

In Figure 5.7, the human body temperature is simulated and the value is displayed in the panel in Figure 5.6. Here, whether the temperature is normal or abnormal will be predicted in the simulation. The simulated value goes to the cloud for storage. The stored data can be accessed through the ThingSpeak cloud.

In Figure 5.9, the pulse rate is simulated and the value is displayed in the panel in Figure 5.8. The simulated value goes to the cloud for storage. The stored data can be accessed through the ThingSpeak cloud.

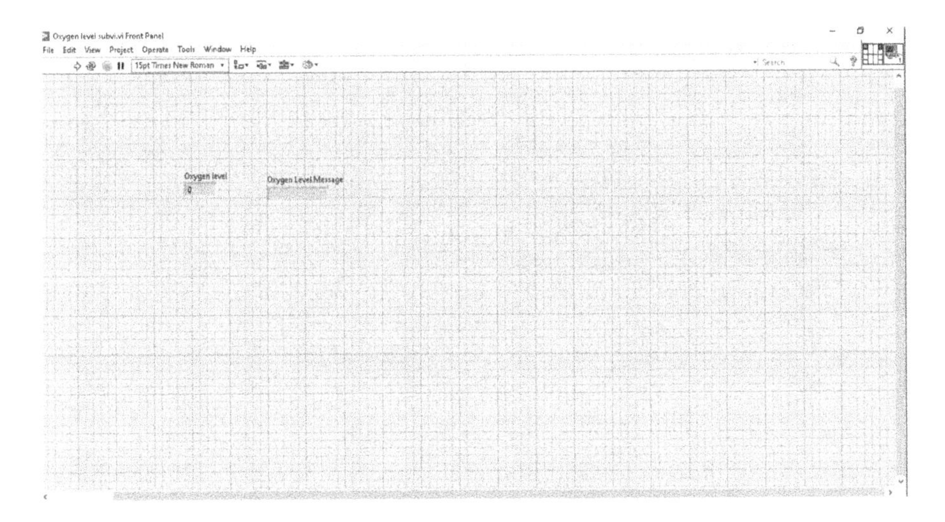

FIGURE 5.4 Simulation for oxygen level detection and display.

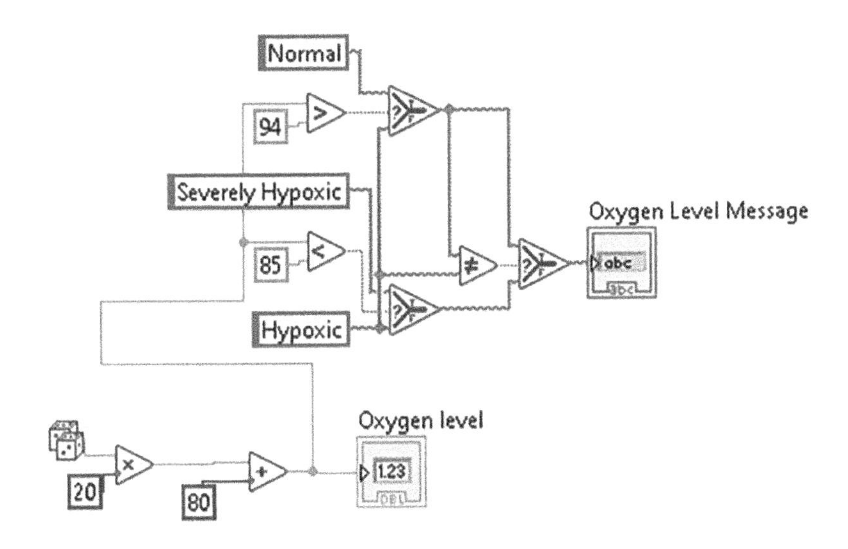

FIGURE 5.5 Simulation for oxygen level detection.

5.6 HARDWARE IMPLEMENTATION

The various hardware components required are given in Table 5.2. The processor chosen here is Raspberry Pi. It enables the integration with various sensors and detection of vitals. The various sensors, their input requirement, detection range, and the output nature are discussed.

The images of each component used and their description are as follows. MPC3008 ADC shown in Figure 5.10 is used for analog-to-digital conversion.

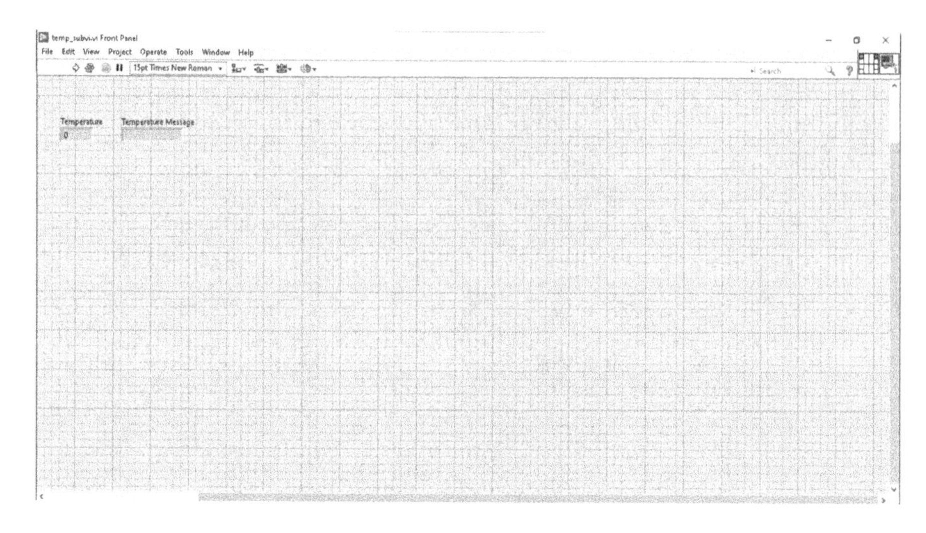

FIGURE 5.6 Simulation for temperature detection and display.

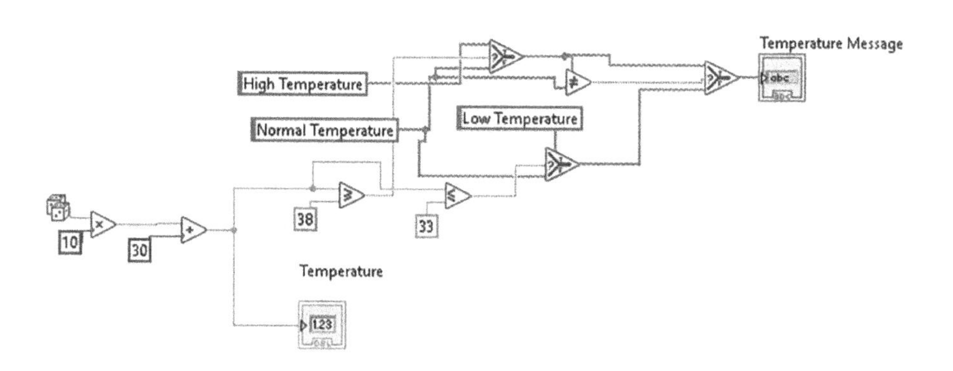

FIGURE 5.7 Simulation for temperature detection.

It has eight channels and supports ten-bit ADC conversion. Pulse oximeter is shown in Figure 5.11. It measures the heart rate and saturated oxygen level. The real-time working of pulse oximeter is shown in Figure 5.12. It shows digital display of heartbeat and saturated oxygen level. In the above figure, 99% is the saturated oxygen level and 79 BPM is the heartbeat pulse rate measured. Raspberry Pi 3 is shown in Figure 5.13, which has built-in Wi-fi and Bluetooth modules. It has a memory of 1 GB and 10/100 Mbps Ethernet. It has four ports and also enables video output. Figure 5.14 shows the LM35 temperature sensor. Its detection range is from −55°C to 150°C. The overall hardware integrated using breadboard connection is shown in Figure 5.15.

The measured temperature is sent to ThingSpeak cloud. The data appear as shown in Figure 5.16 for the control room. The measured saturated oxygen level is sent to

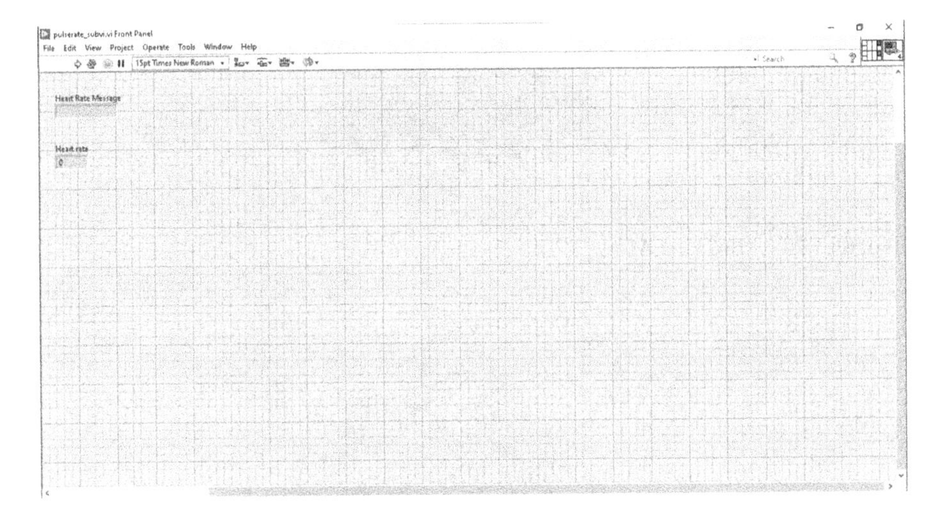

FIGURE 5.8 Simulation for pulse rate detection and display.

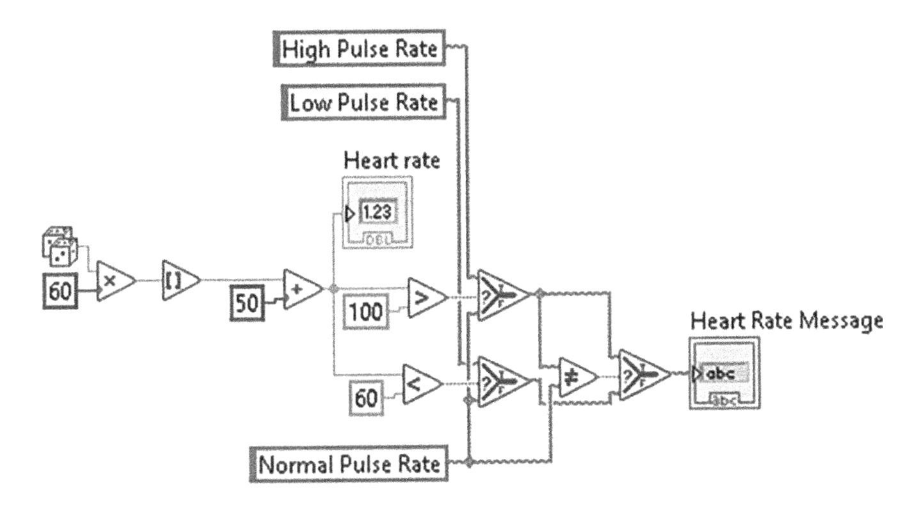

FIGURE 5.9 Simulation for pulse rate detection.

TABLE 5.2
Hardware Components Required

Sensor	Input	Range	Output
Temperature sensor (LM35)	5 V	−55C to 150C	−1–6 V
Pulse oximeter (MAX30100)	3 V	0%–100%	0%–100%
Panic buzzer (FBX521A)	12 V DC supply	100–150 m	Alarm
Gas sensor (MQ2)	5 V	300–10,000 PPM	Digital output of high and low

FIGURE 5.10 MPC3008 ADC.

FIGURE 5.11 Pulse oximeter.

ThingSpeak cloud. The data appear as shown in Figure 5.17 for the control room. The measured heart rate is sent to ThingSpeak cloud. The data appear as shown in Figure 5.18 for the control room. The real-time data of soldiers collected through ThingSpeak cloud are analyzed to know the number of persons under normal and abnormal vital conditions.

5.7 THE ANALYSIS

Decision tree algorithm of machine learning is used for the analysis. The advantage of using decision tree algorithm is that it splits the data at the points of major changes and groups the data with minor changes as the same. Decision tree algorithm consists of a root node, more than one internal node, and many leaf nodes. The root node acts as the main cause for split. The internal nodes are the results of the split. The leaf nodes are the final conclusion, which explains the effectiveness of the split. The algorithm works as shown in Flowchart 5.2.

RStudio is an integrated development environment, which supports R, a programming language for statistical computing and analysis. The people are further classified on the basis of the vital parameters as class 1, class 2, and class 3 as shown in Figure 5.19.

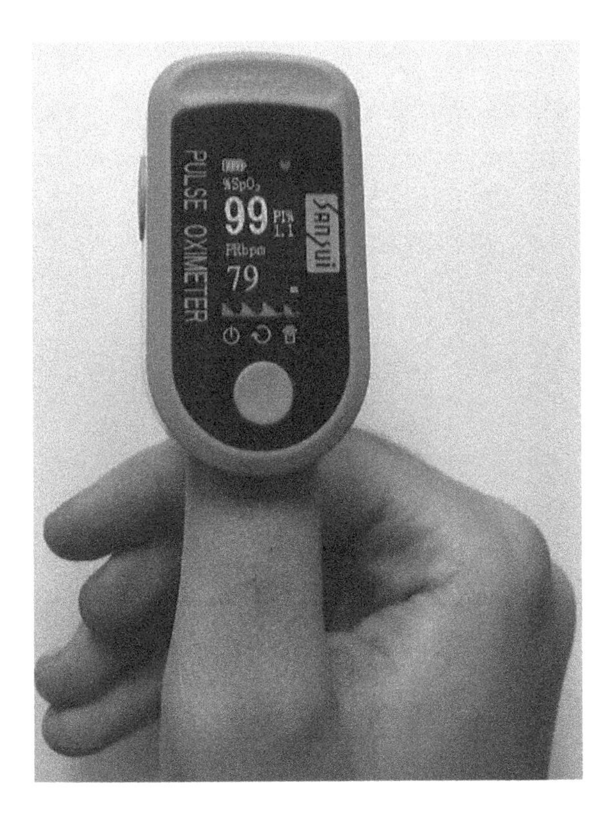

FIGURE 5.12 Real-time working of pulse oximeter.

FIGURE 5.13 Raspberry Pi 3.

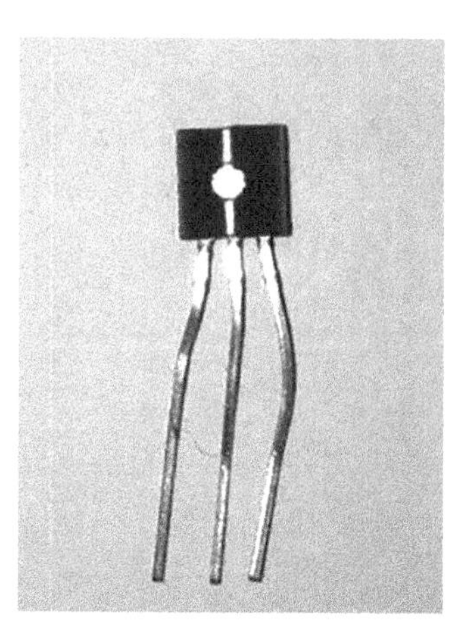

FIGURE 5.14 LM35 temperature sensor.

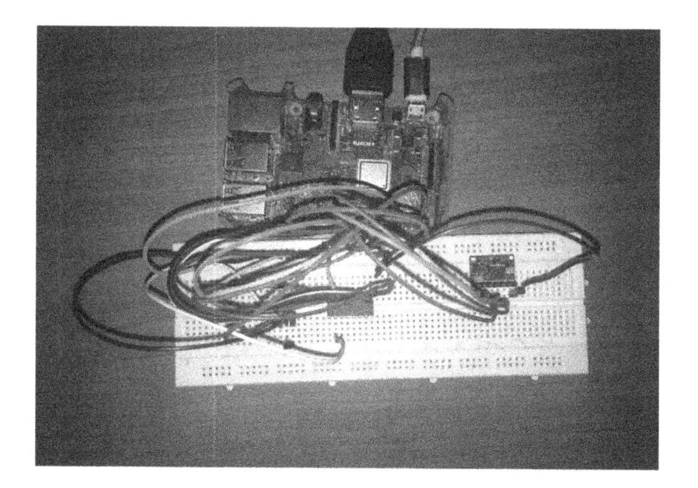

FIGURE 5.15 Overall hardware integrated using breadboard connection.

Class 1 shows that the people are under normal conditions. Class 2 shows that the people are under moderate health conditions. Class 3 shows that the people are under severe abnormal conditions. The people are classified on the basis of their temperature. This will enable the nearby health center to know the people under normal and abnormal health conditions. The people are classified on the basis of their oxygen level. This will enable the nearby health center to know the people under normal and abnormal health conditions. The people are classified on the basis of their blood pressure. This will enable the nearby health center to know the people under normal and abnormal health conditions. The people are classified on the basis of their pulse rate. This will enable the nearby health center to know the people under normal and abnormal health conditions.

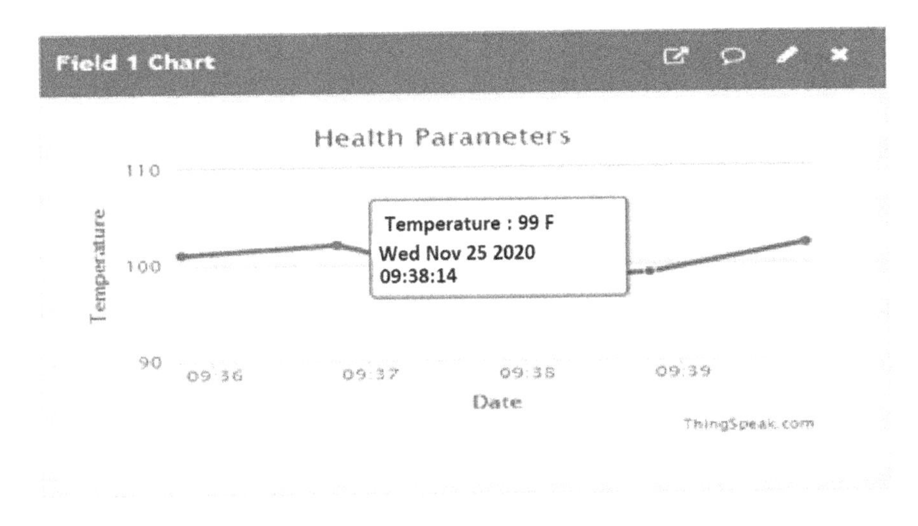

FIGURE 5.16 Measured temperature data.

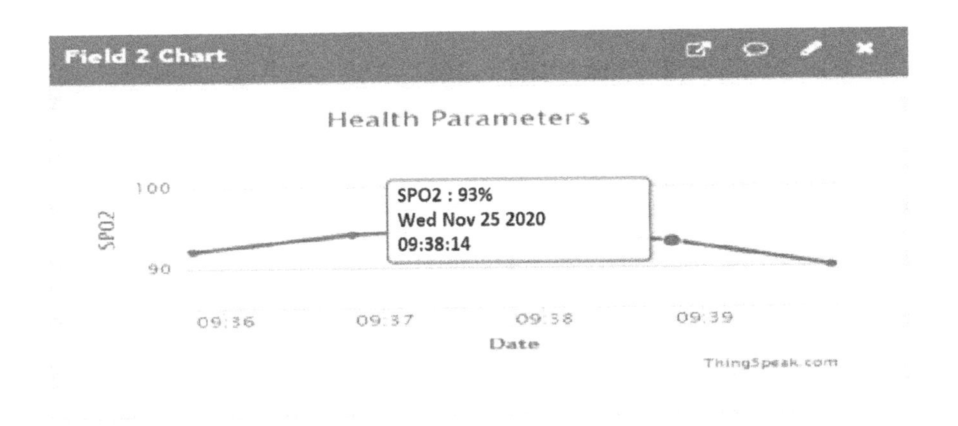

FIGURE 5.17 Measured oxygen level data.

The classification of people living in smart buildings based on their temperature, oxygen level, blood pressure, and pulse rate is shown in Figures 5.20–5.23, respectively. Through this, the nearby health unit personnel can monitor the person's vitals. The physical fitness of the people is also made available through this analysis. The number of people with normal and abnormal vitals can be observed.

5.8 RESULTS

In this paper, wearable sensors for continuous and real-time monitoring of people's vitals living in smart buildings along with the geographical position tracking are enabled using IoT. ThingSpeak cloud enables the data access for the control room. The analysis made using machine learning algorithm enables the nearby health unit to classify the number of people under abnormal vital conditions and healthy conditions.

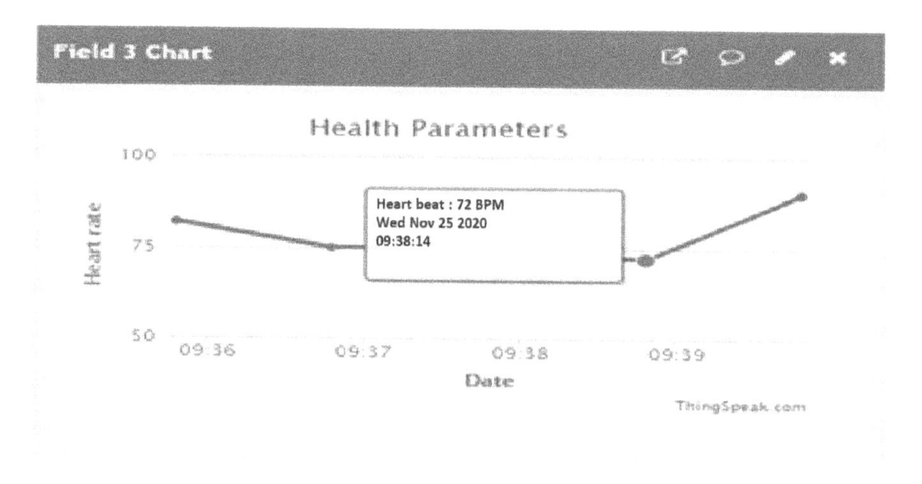

FIGURE 5.18 Measured heart rate data.

5.9 COMPARATIVE ANALYSIS

The existing system and the proposed system are compared to show the advantage of the proposed system and the novelty of the proposed design. The conclusions are given in Table 5.3. The above table shows the improved structure of the proposed system when compared to the existing system.

5.10 CONCLUSION AND FUTURE WORK

A revolutionary IoT interfaced with various sensors is introduced for the long-term, people's health monitoring based on human body vitals remote monitoring. The usage of various wearable sensors of various vitals monitoring for uncertainty prediction has been proposed in this project. The device includes various sensors and machine learning technology to provide information about monitored vitals to deduct abnormal health conditions. The system architecture includes Wi-fi and cloud onboard applications so the network can continuously be upgraded for the control room use. Real-time audio and video transmission acts as the future scope of this project. The need for more storage for audio and video signals demands payable clouds like Amazon AWS. It facilitates the storage minimum of 500 GB or even more.

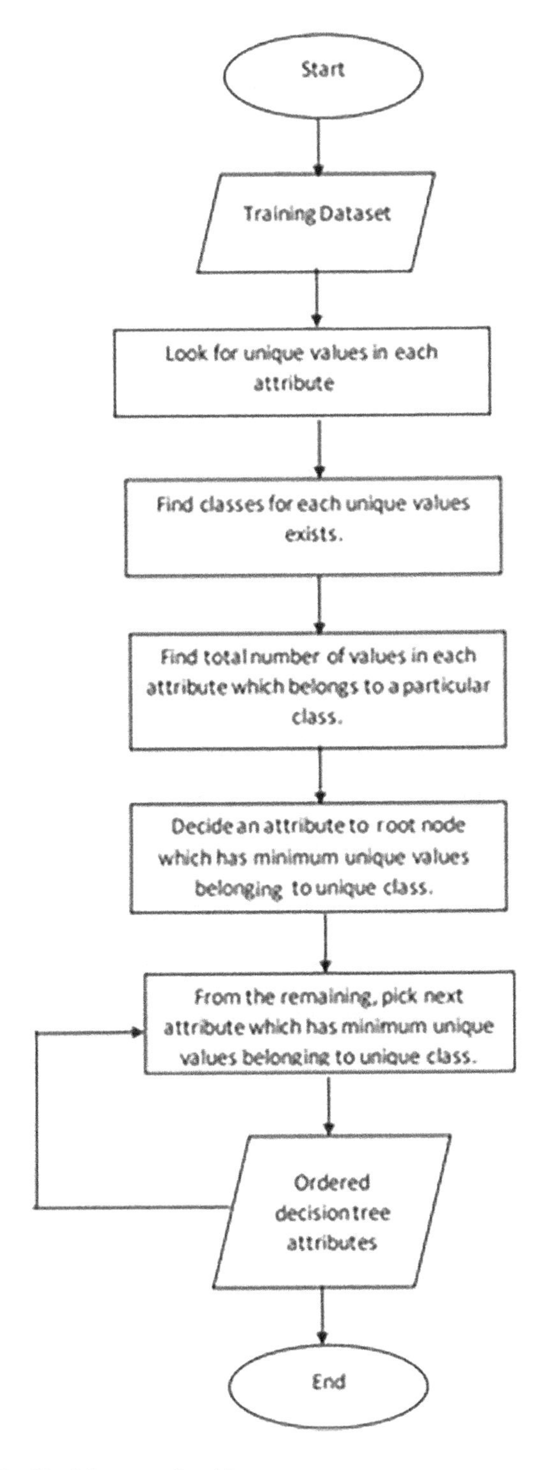

FLOWCHART 5.2 Decision tree algorithm.

```
(400, 3) (400,)
(134, 3) (134,)
Model Accuracy:  0.43283582089552236
[0.36448598 0.41121495 0.31775701 0.35514019 0.4245283 ]
|--- SPO2 <= 89.50
|   |--- Temperature <= 100.50
|   |   |--- SPO2 <= 87.50
|   |   |   |--- class: 3
|   |   |--- SPO2 >  87.50
|   |   |   |--- class: 1
|   |--- Temperature >  100.50
|   |   |--- Heart_Rate <= 90.50
|   |   |   |--- class: 3
|   |   |--- Heart_Rate >  90.50
|   |   |   |--- class: 3
|--- SPO2 >  89.50
|   |--- Temperature <= 101.50
|   |   |--- Heart_Rate <= 88.50
|   |   |   |--- class: 1
|   |   |--- Heart_Rate >  88.50
|   |   |   |--- class: 3
|   |--- Temperature >  101.50
|   |   |--- Heart_Rate <= 94.50
|   |   |   |--- class: 2
|   |   |--- Heart_Rate >  94.50
|   |   |   |--- class: 1

<Figure size 432x288 with 0 Axes>
```

FIGURE 5.19 RStudio code.

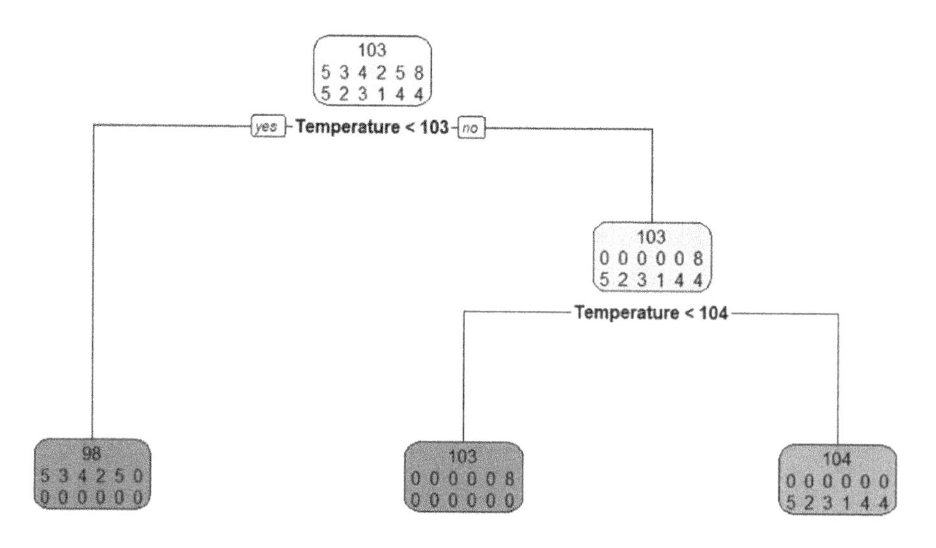

FIGURE 5.20 Classification on the basis of their temperature.

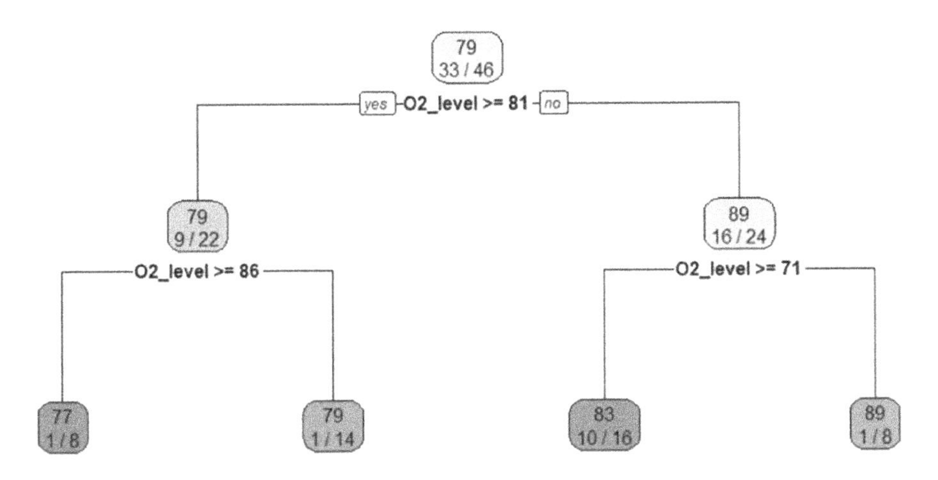

FIGURE 5.21 Classification on the basis of their oxygen level.

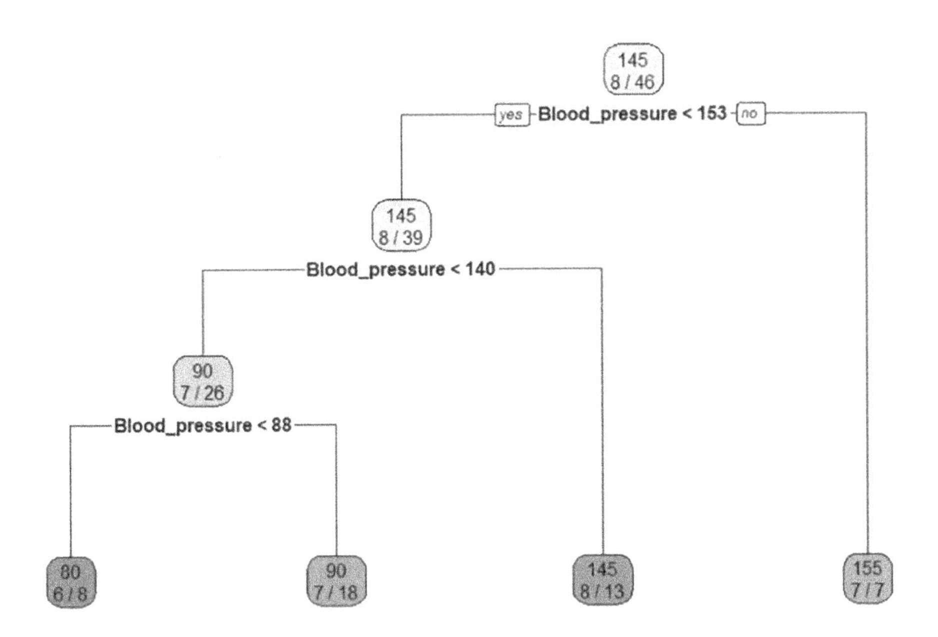

FIGURE 5.22 Classification on the basis of their blood pressure level.

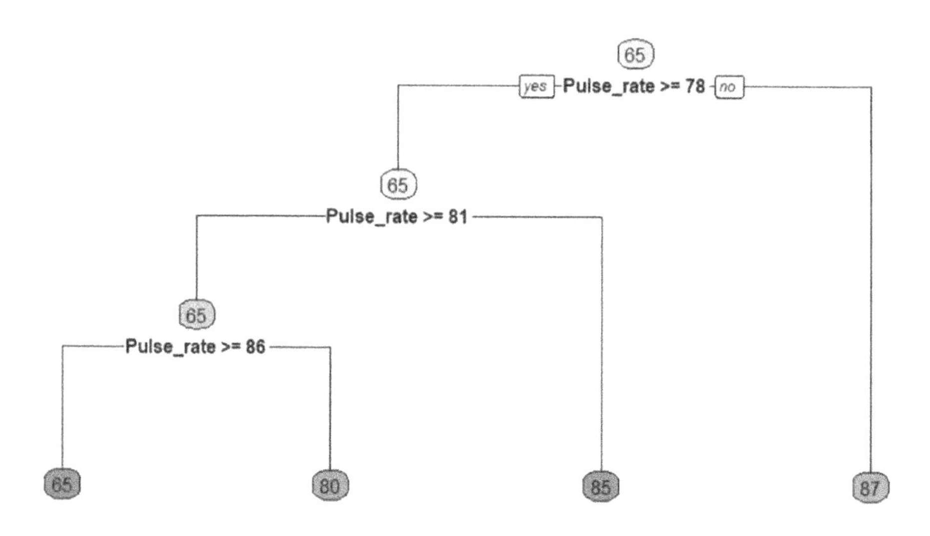

FIGURE 5.23 Classification on the basis of their pulse rate.

TABLE 5.3
Comparative Analysis

Parameters	Existing System	Proposed System
Sensors	Complex integration and high-level interface requirement [1,4–6].	Simple integration.
Network and storage	High-level networking needs to enable real-time monitoring of data [12,13,19].	Easy and free storage through ThingSpeak cloud.
Delay	Maximum of few minutes delay was unavoidable.	Maximum of few seconds delay was observed.
Throughput	The observed delay in reception has led to reduced throughput.	Reception rate of data is high, thereby increased throughput.
Cost	Complex integration and long-distance data transmission with less advanced wireless communication demanded increased cost for implementation [1,4–6].	Overall reduced cost.

REFERENCES

1 B. Iyer, and N. Patil (2018) Iot enabled tracking and monitoring sensor for military applications. *International Journal of system Assurance and Engineering Management.* 9(6):1294–1301.

2 A. Koz (2019) Ground-based hyperspectral image surveillance systems for explosive detection: Part I- State of the art and challenges. *IEEE Journal of Selected Topics in Applied Earth Observations and Remote Sensing.* 12(12):4746–4753.

3 A. Koz (2019) Ground-based hyperspectral image surveillance systems for explosive detection: Part II- Radiance to reflectance conversions. *IEEE Journal of Selected Topics in Applied Earth Observations and Remote Sensing*. 12(12):4754–4765.
4 M. Vanitha, M. Selvalakshmi, and R. Selvarasu (2016) Monitoring and controlling of mobile robot via internet through raspberry PI board. *2016 Second International Conference on Science Technology Engineering and Management (ICONSTEM)*, IEEE, pp. 462–466.
5 P. Raja, and S. Bagwari (2018) Iot based military assistance and surveillance. *2018 International Conference on Intelligent Circuits and Systems.*
6 G. Xu (2017) IoT-assisted ECG monitoring framework with secure data transmission for health care applications. *IEEE Access*. 8:74586–74594.
7 A. Diro, H. Reda, N. Chilamkurti, A. Mahmood, N. Zaman, and Y. Nam (2020) "Light weight authenticated-encryption scheme for IoT based on publish-subscribe communication". *IEEE Access*, 8.
8 J. Khan, J. Ping, B. Ahamad, S. Parveen, A. U. Haq, G. A. Khan, and A. K. Sangaiah (2019) Secure surveillance mechanism on smart healthcare IoT with probabilistic image encryption. *2019 Special Selection on Deep Learning Algorithms for Internet of Medical Things.*
9 A. Aziz, and K. Singh (2018) Light weight security scheme for internet of things. *Wireless Personal Communications.*
10 H. Lin, Z. Yan, Y. Chen, and L. Zhang (2018) A survey on network security related data collection technologies. *Special Selection of Internet of Things Big Data Trust Management* 6: 18345–18365.
11 Z. Zhou, H. Yu, and H. Shi (2020) Human activity recognition based on improved bayesian convolution network to analyse health care data using wearable IoT device. *IEEE Access* 8:86411–86418.
12 G. Yang, M. Jiang, W. Ouyang, G. Ji, H. Xie, A. M. Rahmani, P. Liljeberg, and H. Tenhunen (2017) IoT-based remote pain monitoring system: from device to cloud platform. *IEEE Access* 8.
13 J. Li, A. Ashraf, B. Cardiff, R. C. Panicker, Y. Lian, and D. John (2020). Low power optimisations for IoT wearable sensors based on evaluation of nine QRS detection algorithms. *IEEE Open Journal of Circuits and Systems* 1:115–123.
14 N. A. M. Alduais (2019) RDCM: an efficient real-time data collection model for IoT/ WSN edge with multivariate sensors. *IEEE Access* 7: 89063–89082.
15 R. K. Pathinarupothi, P. Durga, and E. S. Rangan (2018) IoT based smart edge for global health: remote monitoring with severity detection and alerts transmission. *IEEE Internet of Things Journal* 6(2):2449–2462.
16 D. Laurijssen, W. Saeys, S. Truijen, W. Daems, and J. Steckel (2019). Synchronous wireless body sensor network enabling human body pose estimation. *IEEE Access* 7:49341–49351.
17 Y.-W. Kuo, C.-L. Li, J.-H. Jhang, and S. Lin (2018). Design of a wireless sensor network based IoT platform for wide area and heterogeneous applications. *IEEE Access* 8.
18 P. Mehrotra, S. Maity, and S. Sen (2019). *An Improved Update Rate CDR for Interference Robust Broadband Human Body Communication Receiver.* School of Electrical and Computer Engineering, Purdue University.
19 T. O. Olasupo (2019) Wireless communication modelling for the deployment of tiny IoT devices in rocky and mountainous environments. *IEEE Sensors Letters* 3(7):1–4.
20 T. Kang, S. Kim, K.-I. Oh, J.-H. Hwang, J. Lee, H. Park, K. Byun, and W. Lee (2019) Evaluation of human body characteristic for electric signal transmission on measured body impulse response. *IEEE Transactions on Instrumentation and Measurement* 69(9):6399–6411.
21 S. Maity, and K. Mojabe (2018) Characterization of human body forward path loss and variablity effects in voltage-mode HBC. *IEEE Journal of Selected Topics in Health care and Remote Sensing* 12(12).

6 Benefits of Smart Buildings

Prasanna Venkatesh S, R. Ramesh, and C.T. Chidambaram
L&T Construction

CONTENTS

6.1 WHAT ARE SMART BUILDINGS?

Sensors, controllers, and software's online connectivity are used to monitor and control the various services equipment in the buildings and their performance and characteristics. Data are collected from the equipment on a timely basis in order to optimize the building environment and operations. Smarter technology gives us a greater comfort and reduces the consumptions based on the advance command and control mechanism (Table 6.1).

Figure 6.1 shows a simple scheme of the smart building technology. One of the examples of real time smart buildings is The 42 – in Kolkata.

DOI: 10.1201/9781003201069-6

TABLE 6.1
Shows Examples Comparing to the Traditional BMS System in Order to Get the Clear View about What Is Smart Building Technology

Traditional BMS System	Smart Building System
• Heating, ventilation and air-condition system is controlled and monitored through BMS based on the temperature using the programs which we create.	• Heating, ventilation and air-condition system is controlled and monitored through sensors which take the indoor and outdoor temperature data and automatically on/off the system using the programs, which increase the comfort level to the occupant.

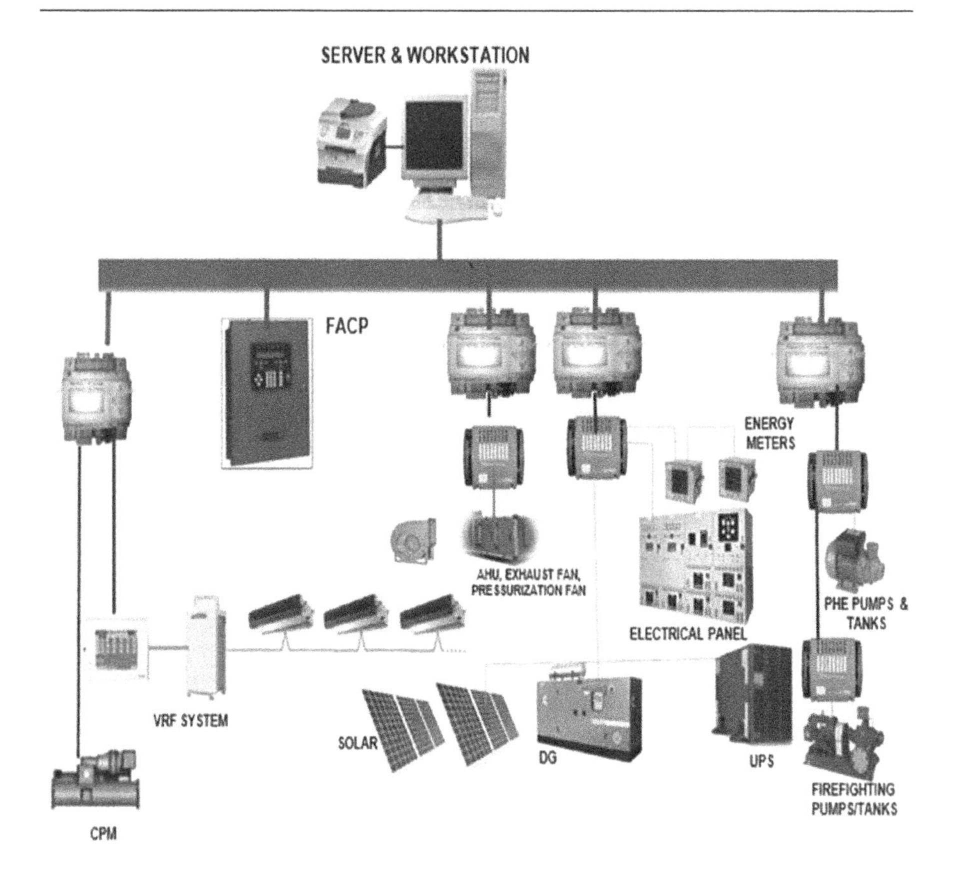

FIGURE 6.1 Simple scheme of the smart building technology.

6.2 WHAT ARE THE KEY COMPONENTS OF THE SMART BUILDING?

- **Sensors** – It is used to measure the parameters like temperature, occupancy, light, etc.
- **Controllers** – It is used to give directions to the system based on the collected data.

- **Output devices –** They command the equipment based on the command received from the controller. A simple example of devices is dampers.
- **Communications protocols –** It is used to communicate the different system based on the human command and also from the controller.
- **Dashboard or user interface –** It is the place where all the system and the equipment are displayed along with their parameters; it's a user friendly and interactive type platform for human machine interfaces with collection of data.

6.3 HOW BUILDINGS BECOME SMARTER?

We can use different types of smart technologies to make the building smarter, e.g., for office building, we have to give the comfort level to the working area in order to increase staff productivity. This can be achieved by varying the air-condition level and lighting system. Similarly, in residential areas, we can optimize the power usage based on the room occupancy, etc.

Few of the systems and their technology which is normally used in smart buildings are listed below.

- **Fire safety systems** can be used for detection of smoke during the fire and escape the people very safely by switching on the accessible doors using the cameras. Public Addressing (PA) systems which are integrated with the system help to communicate to them during the critical time. A simple scheme is shown in Figures 6.2 and 6.3.
- **Water supply systems** – It can be automated by integrating with motorized valves, water level sensors, water consumption monitoring, etc., so the usage of the water level on the ideal condition is controlled.

  A simple example is the water level sensor integrated with an overhead tank motor so that whenever the water level increases beyond the tank level, the pump is switched off automatically.
- **Chiller plants and air conditioning and heating systems** – It can be optimized based on the external air condition and weather data to reduce the energy. Also, based on the occupancy level, it can increase the cooling to provide comfort to the residents. A simple scheme is shown in Figure 6.4.
- **Building electrical loads** – The electrical distribution system can be designed in a way to segregate the system like critical and noncritical loads, which helps us to optimize the loads based on the category and usage. A sample dashboard which shows the electrical data consumed by smart buildings is as in Figure 6.5.
- **Multiple internal systems** like lighting, air conditioning, water, and ventilation can be connected to see how they affect each other throughout the day and optimize for efficiency.
- **Structural integrity** – It can be done by monitoring the vibration of the structural systems.

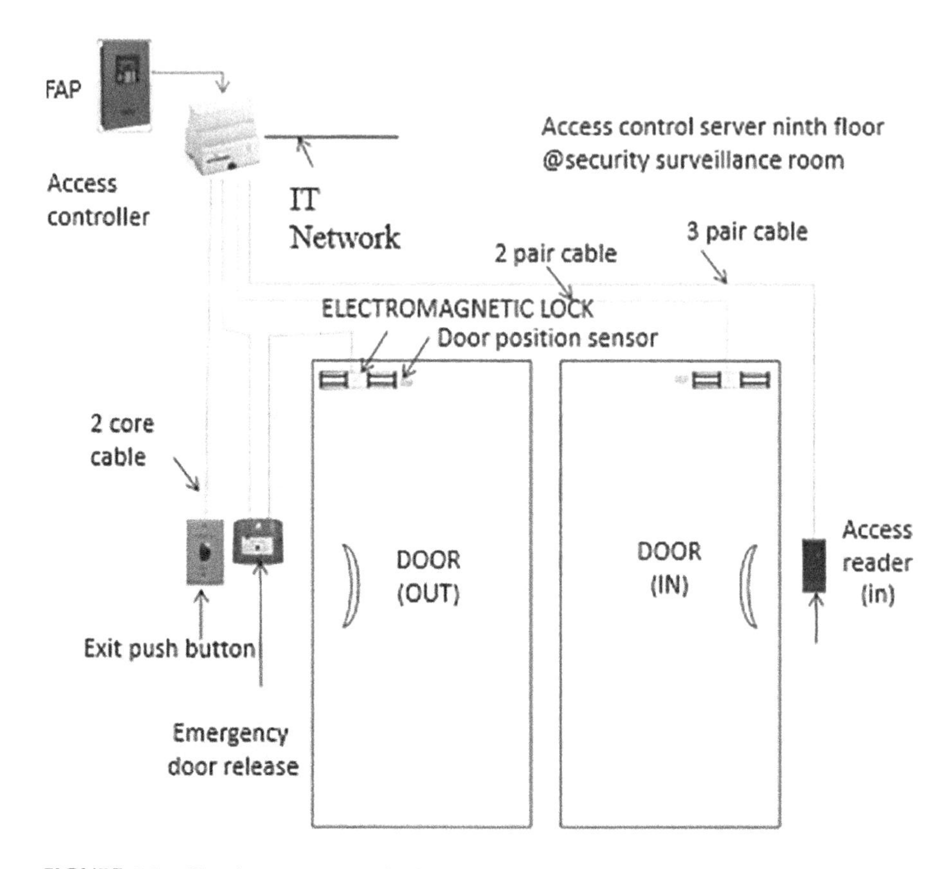

FIGURE 6.2 Simple access control scheme integrated to fire alarm panel (FAP).

- **Data collection** – It is used to analyze and reduce the consumption of energy, water, waste, etc.
- **Remote control over systems** – The IoT technology and cloud system helps the building manager to view and operate at any place, and it can be integrated to any number of buildings through internet.

There are wide ranges of services that can be integrated nowadays in order to make the building smarter; few system concepts are explained below.

6.4 WHAT ARE THE MAJOR BENEFITS OF SMART BUILDINGS?

6.4.1 Predictive Maintenance

The maintenance of the system can be planned easily with the help of the collected data from the server based on the operation of the equipment. This helps the building managers to plan the maintenance.

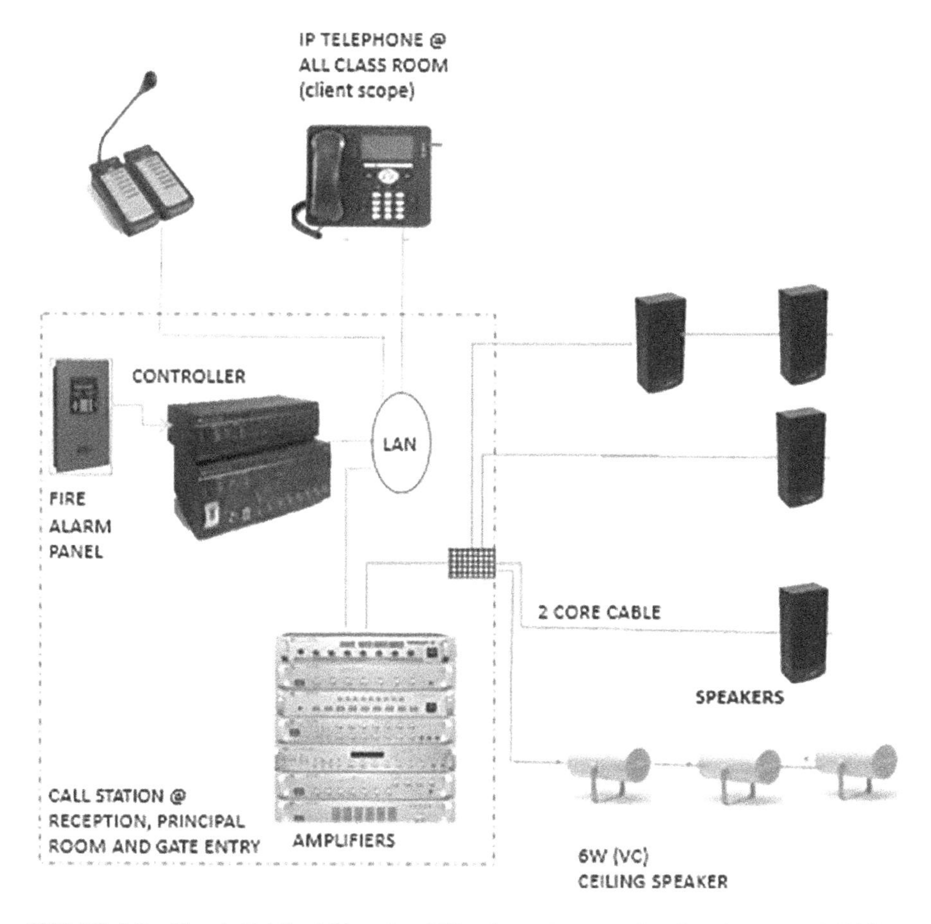

FIGURE 6.3 Simple Public Addressing (PA) scheme integrated to fire alarm panel (FAP).

6.5 MORE OCCUPANT PRODUCTIVITY

Smart technologies improvise the air quality, physical comfort, lighting, sanitation, energy, and ambient condition which enable the occupant to be more productive.

6.6 EFFICIENT CONSUMPTION OF ENERGY

Smart buildings are designed in such a way that the energy gets utilized efficiently irrespective of the internal and external conditions.

6.7 SMART BUILDINGS RESULT IN INCREASING THE ASSET VALUE

When smart applications become a part of the building, the asset value is bound to increase. Smart energy efficiency measures ensure that the building is well maintained and hence doesn't depreciate over a period of time. Instead, these smart applications add to the asset value of the structure, making it a preferred option to go for.

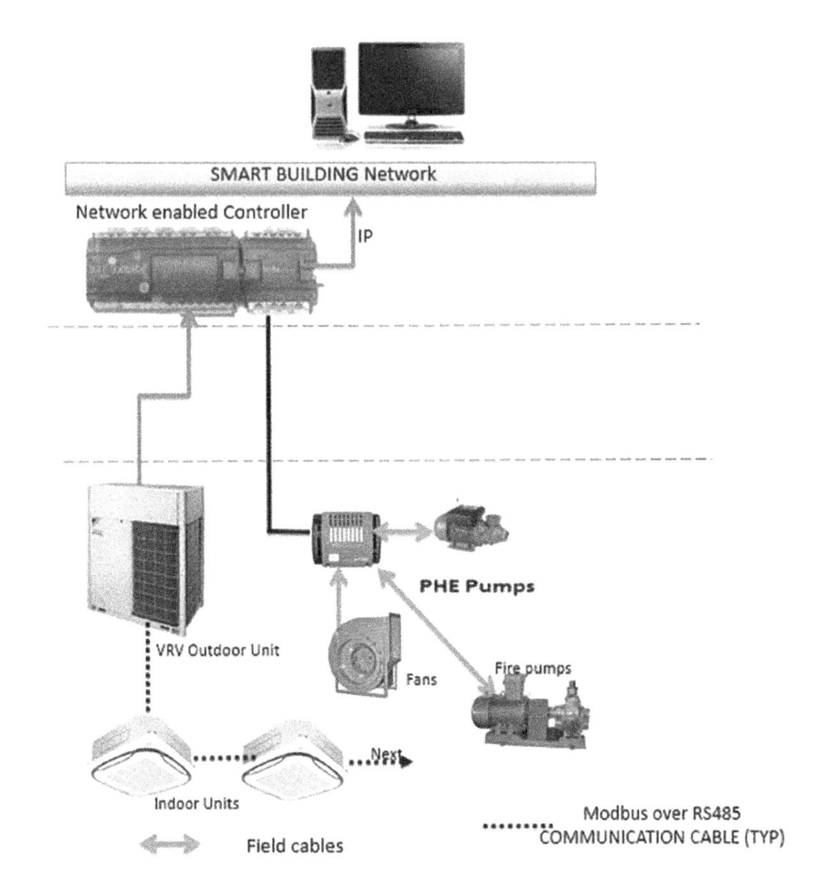

FIGURE 6.4 Simple scheme of Heating, Ventilation, and Control (HVAC) system.

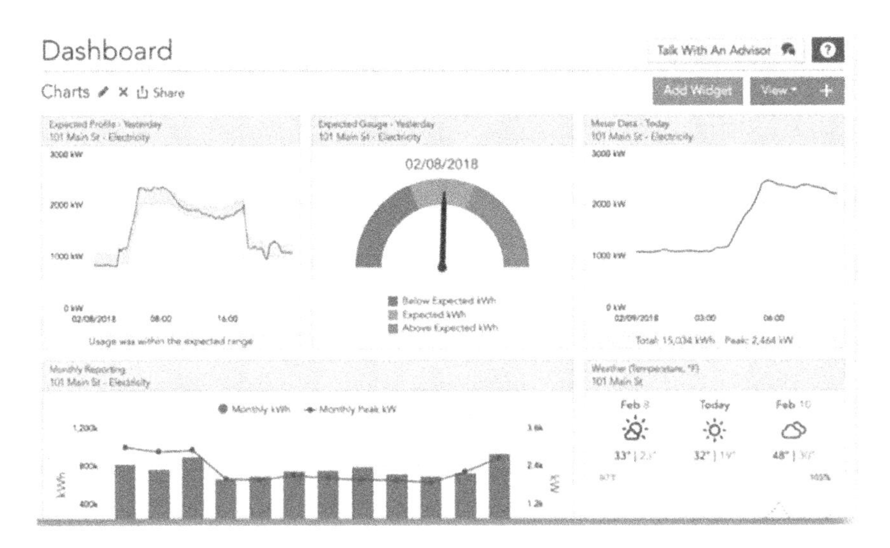

FIGURE 6.5 Dashboard.

6.8 REAL-TIME ACTION BECOMES EASIER WITH THE USE OF SMART TECHNOLOGY

With data flowing in, one has access to the energy numbers in the real time. This analysis of data helps in the control and monitoring systems that are placed in the building. The real-time action helps to plan and act well in advance. Preparing for any adversity well in advance makes the smart building concept a big hit these days.

6.9 SMART BUILDINGS ANTICIPATE WELL IN ADVANCE

Malfunctioning is well taken care of with the help of sensors placed in these smart buildings. An alert gets triggered as and when there is an issue with any part of a system within the smart building. All this helps in predictive maintenance of the facility, saving both costs as well as time.

The key benefits of smart buildings are listed below on the three major category.

6.9.1 Improved Reliability

Utility	Consumer	Society
Reduced operational cost	Improved level of service with fewer inconveniences	Reduction in the cost of products
Increased employee safety	Reduce the cost	Eliminates power blackouts
Increased revenue		Boost economy by improving infrastructure
High customer satisfaction		
Reduced capital cost		

6.9.2 Improve Economics

Utility	Consumer	Society
Creating a new market by leverages its resources.	Reduce the energy process and consumer bills.	Integration on different generation system in a single grid.
Reduce the electricity theft which increases the revenues	It increases the opportunity to optimize the consumptions	Improved operating and market efficiencies reduces the prices.
Improve faster billing system.	Integration of home area network by using smart meter for electricity interactions	Increase the investment of new energy system.
Reduce the operation and maintenance cost.	Reduction in transportation cost by using alternate fuel/electricity.	
	Creates an opportunity for consumer to sell unused electricity to grid.	

6.9.3 Improve Efficiency

Utility	Consumer	Society
Increase asset utilization	Increased capability, opportunity on consumption end of the value chain	Increase the accuracy of forecast through the combined efforts of consumers and delivery companies
Transmission and distribution losses will be reduced	Electricity market value will be increased.	Reduced consumption of power through conservation, demand response which result in reduction on T and D losses

6.9.4 Improved Environment

Utility	Consumer	Society
Increased capability to integrate intermittent renewable resources	Increase our opportunity to go for alternate energy source vehicles.	Reduced CO_2 emissions
Reducing the losses and energy conservations.	Improve opportunity to optimize energy-consumption behavior resulting in a positive environmental impact	Improves public health
	Creates an opportunity for clean energy generation which helps us to go green economy.	

6.10 CONCLUSION

Smart buildings provide us the comfort, safety, protection, and luxury by using the technology to the fullest benefits to improve our lifestyle. In future, more technological advancements will come up that may make our buildings even more “smarter.”

7 An Approach to Realize Luxury Transit Residential Tower Aided with State-of-the-Art Automation Technologies

O.V. Gnana Swathika
Vellore Institute of Technology

K. Karthikeyan
Larsen & Toubro Pvt. Ltd.

Vaishnavi Chirravuri
Vellore Institute of Technology

K.T.M.U. Hemapala
University of Moratuwa

CONTENTS

DOI: 10.1201/9781003201069-7

7.1 INTRODUCTION

In today's era, life has become so busy and hectic that attending to our daily chores is really difficult. Gone are those days when machines were designed to cut off the labor; these days, appliances are designed such that they reduce the involvement of humans to improve their comfort and finish all the tasks alone. That's the reason why automation has become an integral part of all aspects of our lives. Starting from simple washing machines to self-driven cars, automation has greatly influenced our lifestyles. With artificial intelligence, big data, machine learning, the Internet of Things, and chatbots around, they boost up the growth and development of automation. Specifically digging into automation, we find that smart homes/buildings are one of the greatest concepts. The idea of being able to control lights, fans, temperature, etc., by just using a smart phone or by giving commands using the voice assistants is really interesting. This technology enables users to monitor and control appliances from anywhere and at any time. With the growing attention toward home automation, a lot of research is being done on the technologies and protocols involved in it. Regardless of the amount of attention that has been drawn, it is still not being implemented in many developing countries. This is because of the basic yet important concerns of a home that are not totally met while designing a home automation model. These include safety, security, efficiency, lower energy and power consumption, simple architecture, and economic viability. Since kids and elderly people constitute a sizeable part of the population, it is thus very important to design a model that can be operated by anyone. A house with all these basic concerns is what is considered to be a luxurious home. When a home automation model is designed such that all the mentioned challenges are resolved, that model would create a huge demand for itself in the market. This chapter discusses elaborately the approaches to realize a real-time case study of luxury transit residential towers equipped with state-of-the-art automation technology.

7.2 LITERATURE REVIEW

When a model is designed, it must be affordable and user friendly because these two elements will inspire and make people confident to use the available models. Hence, these factors are very crucial in designing any automation model. Considering this, [1] proposed a model that can be controlled from anywhere. The Bluetooth technology present in this model takes voice commands, and another added advantage to this model is that unlike the conventional models, the use of wires is also reduced. Often, these models face limitations like a limited number of ports, low speed, and fixed architecture. [2] proposed a model where a Z-board is used instead of a microcontroller where each FPGA port represents a room. This proposed prototype consumes less power and is fast, user friendly, and affordable. Voice assistants like Siri, Alexa, Cortana, or Google Assistant are now very common in every household. They are very easy to use because all we have to do is give a voice command. Home automation models based on voice assistants are discussed in [3–5]. These assistants take our inputs in the form of voice commands and perform the tasks like switching the lights, fans, and a lot more. [5] Also introduced a feature where the Google Assistant not only performs the given tasks but also is interactive. All these models promote affordability and user-friendly architecture for drawing more people to use these models.

The sense of being safe and secure has never been totally achieved. Our homes/buildings must be safe and secure. But, as much as the security systems have been getting better, the thefts have also increased at the same rate. Apart from this, damage from fire or gas leakage has never stopped. Many home automation models provide safety and security from various threats like these. [6] presented a system such that the gas leakage system and fire detection systems are integrated and centralized into an M2M network which when deployed with machine learning and data mining is used to sense the abnormalities in the hidden patterns for early detection of fire or gas leakage which turns out to be a secured system. A little different from this concept, [7] proposed a prototype that is based on passwords and fingerprint system which recognized 95 out of 97 tested devices with an efficiency of 97.93%. The two-stage verification system in this model has improved the total safety of the system. Similarly, a Raspberry Pi–based home automation model that has a combination of RFID and GSM technologies was put forward in [8]. The RFID technology deployed in this system helps in enhancing security whereas the GSM technology transfers messages in the system. This same GSM technology is used to alert the owners through messages in case of any threats in [9]. A better model of a secured home was then found in [10], where PIR and vibration sensors were used to detect the motion in case of any thefts, and an HD security camera is installed which records everything to make the system more reliable. Zigbee technology is a relatively newer and affordable option for local personal networks. [11] discussed a model where the Zigbee protocol is used to build a two-tiered network that is connected to nodes that transfer messages with the real-time constraints of home automation environment eliminating the problem of limited transmission.

In recent times, the crisis of sustainability has been the need of the hour. Many measures are being taken by the people as well as the organizations to lead a sustainable life. One such thing that could be done in a home automation model is to use renewable energy sources for generating power and also lower the consumption levels. By implementing this, smart homes will also become efficient ones. [12] proposed a model that uses a web application to monitor the metering of the appliances and can be controlled accordingly. This system helped in preventing the power distribution anomalies and had an online billing method which made the entire system efficient. Another interesting model has been discussed in [13], which adapts to the environment and modifies temperature, lighting settings according to the environment enhancing the efficiency of the system. Generally, in home automation models, there is latency in the data transmission between the devices to local networks which reduces the speed of operation and increases energy consumption. In [14], a model is presented that uses a Li-Fi network which improves the speed of data transmission which indeed increases the energy efficiency and the speed of the model. There is another interesting model that controls the ventilation of a building intending to improve efficiency. In [15], a model is designed which has two controller operations: schedule based and event based, where the input parameters are directly fed into a programming control where output conditions are like full ventilation, partial mechanical ventilation, and natural ventilation. This model alone has seen a saving of 372,577.55 INR. Solar energy is one of the abundant renewable sources available. [16] presented a building automation model that uses a fuzzy logic approach to optimize the energy use by using the solar energy available. This model turns out to consume little energy without actually compromising on the need of the operator making it very efficient. With the same objective of improving energy efficiency, a model is explained in [17] that discusses an automation system with open protocol communication and intelligent electronic devices. Along with the 8-bit microcontrollers, the module TCP protocol is employed in it which uses a master-slave method that reduces the energy consumption of the entire system. In [18], a model based on the SMS technology and voice recognition were introduced. This design has a fault identification feature that shows the status of the loads, by improving the accuracy of the system by 90%, which in turn increases the efficiency.

There are so many technologies, protocols, and devices that can be used to make a better version of a smart home. In the vast field of home automation, there is so much that can be improved upon. [19] provided an interesting insight into how automation has taken shape over the years by discussing the past, present, and future of it. Similarly, [20,21] discuss the emerging technologies and techniques that can be deployed in the existing home automation models to make them better. Now that voice assistant–based home automation models are also largely built, [22] discusses all the aspects of a voice assistant like the features, cost, privacy, and security issues and compare the results.

7.3 HVAC PROJECT DESIGN

A localized variable refrigerant flow (VRF) or variable refrigerant volume (VRV) system is provided for each apartment unit. Multiple indoor ceiling recessed fan coils or ceiling suspended fan coils with two (2) numbers of outdoor condensing units are provided for 2-, 3-, 4-, and 5-bedroom apartment unit types. Multiple indoor ceiling recessed fan coils are provided for the penthouse and master penthouse unit type. Based on these proposed provisions, if one (1) number of the outdoor condensing unit is not in working condition, the occupier(s) will not have great discomfort in their sleep as the other condensing unit(s) is able to serve the other area of the apartment unit.

7.3.1 VRF Systems

All residential apartments (2/3/4 BHK/penthouse) will have dedicated VRF systems, and the system diagram as in Figure 7.1.

Indoor units will be "furred" in fan coils or a ductable type. Only grilles will be visible as in Figure 7.2.

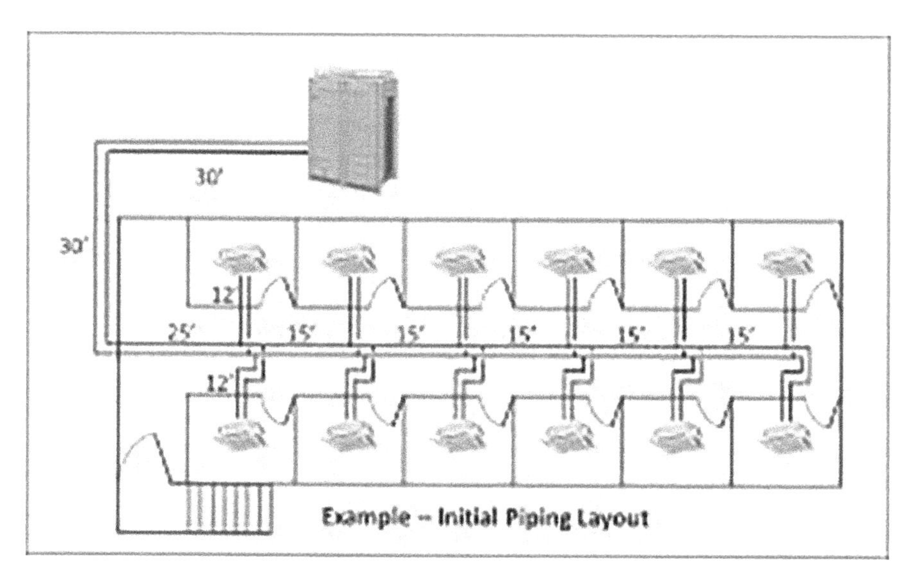

FIGURE 7.1 VRF system diagram.

FIGURE 7.2 Indoor units.

FIGURE 7.3 High wall/cassette units.

7.3.2 High Wall/Cassette Units

Some areas of the apartment, such as the maid's room and other small rooms, will have decorative type (high wall/cassette) units as shown in Figure 7.3. This is due to the technical requirements, since the dehumidified air quantity required in such rooms is very low and are to be operated at unscheduled times.

7.3.3 Energy Recovery Ventilators

Energy recovery ventilators are proposed for air ventilation as in Figure 7.4.

7.3.4 Condensing Unit

Condensing units (single/multiple: based on cooling load) will be located in the balcony within the space carved out from the dwelling units and finally concealed with louvered cupboards as shown in Figure 7.5. The condensing units will be with anti-corrosive treatment, to take into account, coastal application. Minimum 2nos. condensing units shall be provided in each apartment.

7.3.5 Toilet Ventilation

Toilet ventilation will be horizontal, terminated at the balcony level, and concealed as per architectural intent.

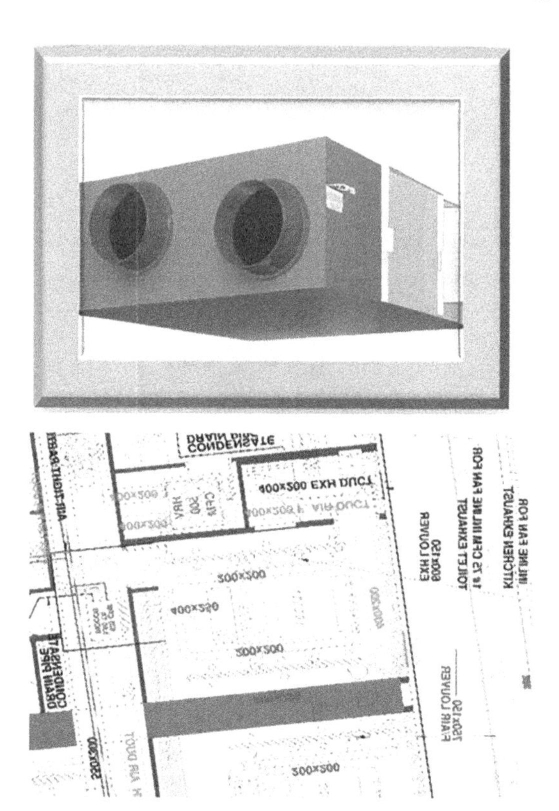

FIGURE 7.4 Energy recovery ventilators.

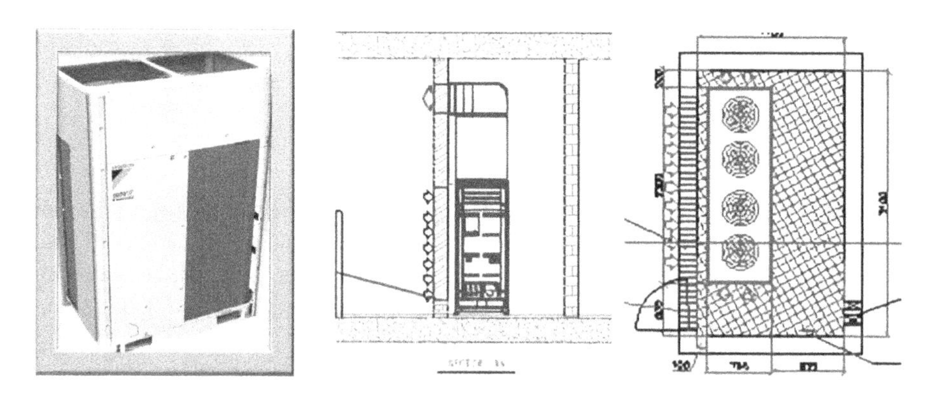

FIGURE 7.5 Condensing unit.

7.3.6 Kitchen Ventilation

Kitchen ventilation will also be horizontal, and termination of the exhaust duct will be at the balcony level and concealed as per architectural intent.

7.3.7 VRF Control Units

Controls of the VRF units will comprise the Intelligent touchpad controller not envisaged as in Figure 7.6.

7.3.8 Common Areas of the Apartment Tower

Entrance lobby, internal corridors of the apartment tower, is centrally air-conditioned. Each floor has a chilled water AHU (on the floor, for the floor), which is ducted and provides air-conditioning to the corridors. Fresh air from the common areas is blended in the return air. A central chilled water plant for the apartment is located in the basement of the residential tower.

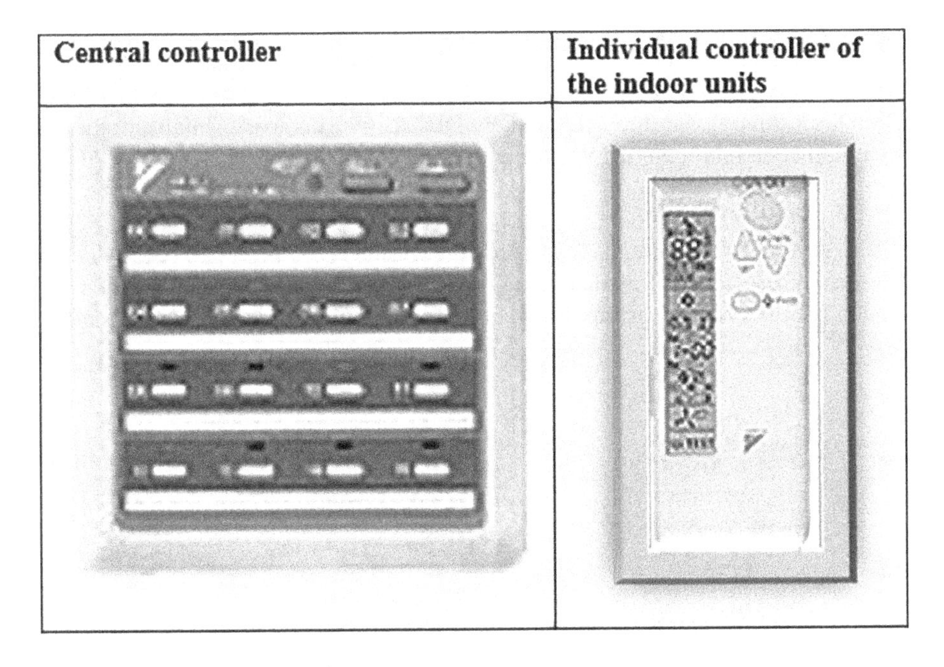

FIGURE 7.6 VRF control units.

7.3.9 Electric Metering and Billing Systems for HVAC System

The central chilled water system will be fed from the main LT panel and shall be metered. The cost on account will be proportioned to all the apartment owners for billing purposes.

Apartment VRF will be fed from the apartment kWh meter; thus, the cost of air-conditioning will be captured there.

7.4 BHK: HVAC SYSTEM PROPOSAL

7.4.1 Electrical Services

The electrical services for 4BHK residential apartment are presented in Figure 7.7.

7.4.1.1 Source of Power

Single source 3 phase 415 V AC power supply to each residential apartment shall be fed from the metering panel located in the building core area up to the subdistribution board located within each apartment through XLPE insulated copper/aluminum conductor armored cable.

7.4.1.2 Subdistribution of Power

Subdistribution of power shall be addressed from the subdistribution board to address power requirements in various areas. All circuits shall be protected with ELCBs (30 mA sensitivity). All three phase SDBs/DBs shall be compartmentalized; the wet area shall be fed through SELV transformer and control supply shall be 55 V AC.

7.4.1.3 Standby Power

LT DG sets for 100% power backup of complete residential tower shall be provided in the second basement. Infrastructure and space of UPS for critical lighting and automation with 10-minute backup time requirements within apartments for hassle-free

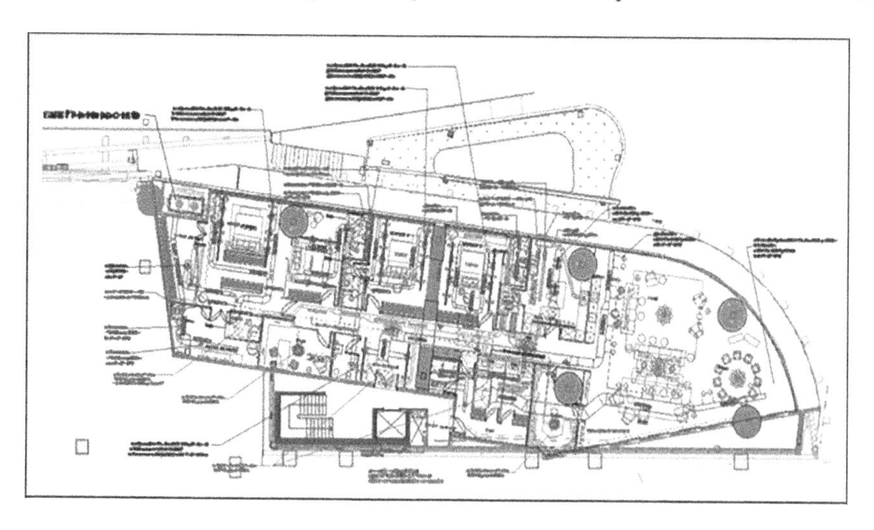

FIGURE 7.7 Electrical services for 4BHK residential apartment.

operations provisioned in each apartment (UPS supply and installation by the apartment owner).

7.4.1.4 Metering with Communication

A dual source energy meter in the floor metering panel for each apartment; dual source energy metering for common area services.

7.4.1.5 Cable and Wires

Cables shall be with copper conductors up to 25 mm^2 size and with aluminum conductors for higher sizes; Fire-resistant low smoke wires shall be used for final wiring from distribution boards

7.4.1.6 Cable Trays and Raceways

Hot dip/pregalvanized perforated cable trays and raceways shall be used for cable containment.

7.4.1.7 Conduits

GI conduits shall be used for all surface mounting application in ceiling/wall for all types of wiring.

7.4.1.8 Wiring Devices

All switches and small power wiring accessories shall be polycarbonate body; weatherproof accessories to be provided for external services in balconies and wet areas; USB chargers shall also be provided in each room.

Switching of lighting shall be through low-voltage switches while power sockets shall be through conventional switches.

7.4.1.9 Light Fixtures

All light fixtures in the common area shall be of the LED Type. Light fixture selection for the entrance lobby and all internal areas shall be as per lighting designer's requirements. Motion sensors are to be used in the apartment dressing room.

7.4.1.10 Home Automation System

Smart living:

- Smartphone and tablet control (I-pad included)

Comfort living:

- Lighting/dimming control
- Climate controls
- Curtain control

Safe living:

- Main entrance/servant maid entrance – Video door phone
- Automatic door lock with access control

- Fire alarm integration
- Gas leak detection
- Panic alarm

Joyful living:

- Audio/video system

Eco living:

- Energy saving

7.4.1.11 Surge Protection System

Surge protection shall be provided in incoming power supply to the apartment.

7.4.1.12 Earthing

The TNS earthing system shall be used for earthing of all electrical equipment.

7.4.2 Fire Alarm and Public Evacuation System

1. Smoke/multicriteria detector with a sounder base shall be provided for all bedrooms; smoke/multicriteria detectors shall be provided for other enclosed area of apartments; heat detectors shall be provided for kitchen/pantry areas.
2. Speakers shall be provided in all areas for evacuation purposes.
3. Hooters, manual call points, and directional sounders shall be provided in common area exit paths outside apartments.
4. The PE system shall take precedence over any piped music system in the common area.
5. Fire alarm devices shall be wired with circuit integrity cables.

7.4.3 Lighting System for the Apartments

For the lighting design, the intent was to provide sufficient comfort for the residents and to create a different ambience at different times of the day and to provide adequate lighting to carry out every day's task. We took our cues from the interior designers and provided a combination of decorative fixtures like pendants, chandeliers, table lamps, floor lamps etc., and accent lights for the focal artwork and accessories, bookshelves, art niches at indoor plans. Where necessary, we had supplemented with general lighting to provide proper illumination levels at each part of the apartment.

The light fixtures that we had used are highly efficient LED lamps with good glare controls and warmer color temperature to enhance the interior ambiance. These are imported light fixtures predominantly from different parts of Europe.

For the predominant residences, there will be dramatic lighting, emphasizing the interiors, furniture, and selected artworks; we had made sure that there is enough task lighting available in places like kitchen, worktables, and by the bedside for reading purposes. We also made sure that there is not only horizontal lighting but also vertical lighting so that there is appropriate lighting for the grooming purposes in the washrooms.

All the architectural ceiling downlights will be provided by the client to the customer.

The client will provide only the infrastructure provisions for all the other light fixtures such as decorative fixtures including pendants, wall-mounted fixtures, table lamps, floor lamps etc. and the light fixtures that come in the millworks and ceiling cove lights, curtain lights, planter uplights.

7.4.4 Lighting System for the Public Areas

There are enough decorative fixtures to provide the grandeur of the public areas, accent lighting to accent the selected Interiors furniture, artworks, interior planting, etc., we also provided enough lighting in places like gym, meeting rooms, reading rooms, lounges, and play areas, so that they create high energy and enough comfort for both business and casual meetings and entertaining. We had created moodier and low-level lighting for the screening rooms where the residents can enjoy watching the movies with their families and friends.

Once again, all these areas are fitted with highly efficient glare-free and warmer color temperature light fixtures to provide the proper mood and ambiance, and they are controlled by preset dimming control systems.

The light fixtures that we had used are highly efficient LED lamps with good glare controls and warmer color temperature to enhance the interior ambiance.

These light fixtures are controlled by 4scene preset dimming automation systems to provide different moods and ambiance according to the time of the day.

Similar to the high-quality interiors, the lighting design intent is to pamper the residents with the appropriate high-quality lighting. What is emphasizing is not the quantity of light but the quality of light.

7.4.5 Plumbing System

The services are engineered to meet aspects of performance, reliability, high user satisfaction and toward sustainable aspect to meet the best of the industry benchmark.

- The sanitary fixtures and fitting are modern, state of the art, ease of user operation, and significantly water efficient to meet the world-class benchmark on the water-saving requirements.
- The apartments are planned with reliable treated water supply toward normal and hot water supply. The quality of water meets WHO guidelines toward the water for domestic use. The back-end water supply piping is suited for domestic water supply and completely noncorrosive.
- The hot water supply is through a centralized high-capacity, energy-efficient heat pump unit adequate to cater for hot water requirement for all

the bathrooms and for kitchen. The storage and supply would cater for peak and long hot water demand at the bathrooms for showers and bathtub at the master bathroom. The hot water is also planned with minimal dead water piping length enabling a short-time period toward hot water supply delay.

- The water supply pressure is within the acceptable minimum and maximum supply pressure as per US/EN standards.
- The water storage in the centralized plant room is for over 2 days, and therefore, there is all-time ensured water supply at the apartment.
- The drainage system is highly dependable with engineered soil, waste, and vent system. All traps are with a 50-mm water seal to ensure no compromise on the vent system and no foul air entering the occupant space.
- The stormwater drainage at the balcony is well engineered to ensure no flooding in these areas.
- The plumbing installation is provided with ease of access for maintenance.

7.4.6 Fire Protection System

- The apartment is provided with an engineering and reliable sprinkler system in all areas. It is imperative to note the system is highly reliable, and there is no nuisance of operations under normal/regular conditions. It is well established in the historic installation that the probability of sprinkler operation under "No Adverse Condition" is 1 in 16 million.
- The sprinkler system is provided with reliable water supply and will have all regular testing and maintenance to meet the functional requirement.
- The entire system is monitored at the fire control and command control. Any untoward situation shall be attended to and respondent by the fire commandants.

7.5 INFORMATION AND COMMUNICATION TECHNOLOGY INFRASTRUCTURE SERVICES

7.5.1 Introduction

Information and communication technology (ICT) is now an integral part of social, economic, and political issues of the world. Networks of the future will be digital and intelligent and will offer high transmission capacity and flexible bandwidth; in addition, they will be easily accessed and connected while their services will be personal and tailored to individual needs.

These will allow us to interact in ways previously not possible – available at any time and any place. In addition to providing entertainment and business services, networks of the future will provide education, health, and other public services.

ITC One Colombo One Residence is well placed to meet these challenges ahead and meet the varied needs of its local and international customers and pave the way for the region's new dynamism in the ICT industry well into the new knowledge decade.

As the technology and mode of transport are changing fast, a broad approach to suit all future types of services will have to be borne in mind, while designing the infrastructures for buildings.

A properly designed building with a clear access path supports the "triple play" services, viz telephony, data, and video services. Also, supports future advanced services, warranting higher speeds and higher bandwidth, planned to be available in near future, for faster provision of services.

7.5.2 Services Offered

The short rejoinder provides guidelines and general insight for customers with the details on the ICT facilities designed and offered as in building services at this real-time network.

A single-mode 6-core fiber optic back bone cable provided from the main service provider room to each apartment consolidation panel. Communication back bone includes data and Wi-Fi system for each apartment.

7.5.3 Apartment Consolidation Panel

The apartment consolidation cabinet is a space to house the service provider network termination equipment, Telecom Module, and satellite master antenna television (SMATV) Splitter. It also serves as the distribution point for 2/3/4/5BHK/penthouse/ master penthouse.

The apartment owner would be responsible for the purchase and installation of all active components such as the Wi-Fi router, access point, telephone, set-top box, network switches, and their related connectors and adaptors. The typical cable connectivity within the consolidated panel is shown in Figure 7.8.

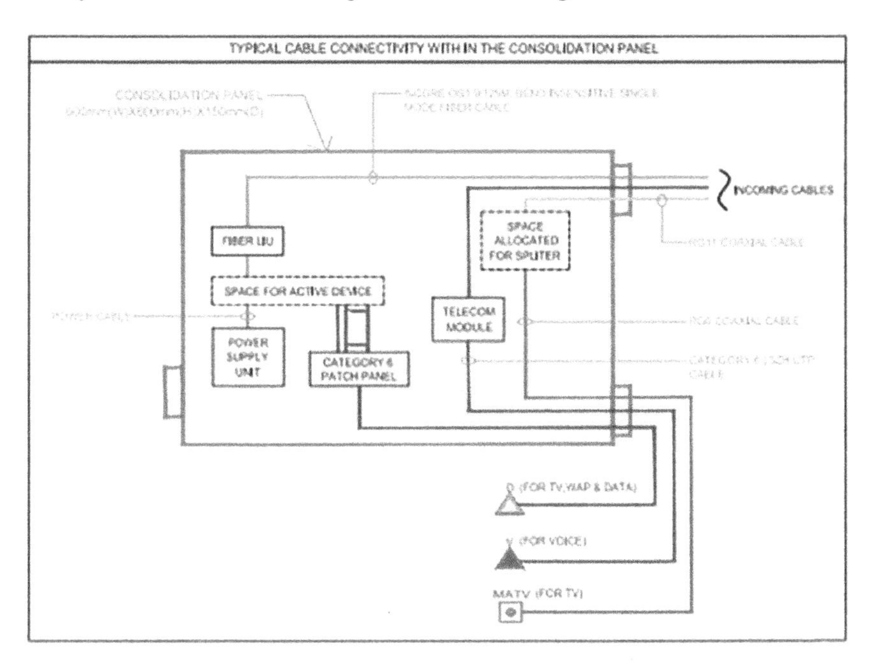

FIGURE 7.8 Typical cable connectivity within the consolidated panel.

7.5.3.1 Internet

Category 6 high-speed internet cable provision for each study table at all apartments.

7.5.3.2 Wireless Access Point (WAP)

High-speed WAP (Wi-Fi) provision for all bed rooms and living areas, lift lobby, and corridors.

Wi-Fi provisions designed are supported by many applications and devices including video game consoles, home networks, mobile phones, major operating systems, and other types of consumer electronics.

7.5.3.3 Telephone

Telephone point provision for all bedrooms, study table, WC, kitchen, living areas, and lift lobby.

7.5.3.4 SMATV

RG6 socket and Category 6 Information Outlet TV provision at all bedrooms and living room. The SMATV channels are to be used both free to air and pay TV shall be available from the Dish Farm infrastructure.

IP based backup connectivity from SMATV head-end and Dish Farm located at the top of the tower to the hotel server room.

7.6 SECURITY

An independent security network is installed, meaning that dedicated switches, routers, and other networking appliances are used exclusively by the security systems.

7.6.1 Standards

The standards and concepts below have been applied for creation of the security concept:

- ISO 31000 – Risk management.
- ISO 27001 – Information security management.
- IWA 14/2013 – Impact test specifications for vehicle security barriers.
- BS EN 62676-4:2015- Video surveillance systems.
- BS EN 50133 – Alarm systems. Access control systems.
- IS 11064 – Ergonomic design of control centres

7.6.2 Surveillance

Video surveillance systems are installed to provide comprehensive coverage of the whole complex. Cameras will be monitored by a dedicated onsite security force manning a CCTV room.

The residential areas to be monitored under CCTV coverage include:

- Entry points to the building at the ground level and basements
- Lift lobbies at the ground level
- Inside all lift cars

- Exit points onto the terrace
- Engineering areas
- Common areas:
  - Level 04 – Amenities, residential pool deck, garden
  - Level 05 – Transfer floor level
  - Level 06 – Amenities area
  - All refuge areas at various levels
  - Levels 19, 20 and 21 – Sky bridge connections
  - Level 50 – Roof top

No cameras will be placed in areas where there is a reasonable expectation of personal privacy.

7.6.3 Lighting

Security lighting will provide illumination for residents as well as to aid natural surveillance by the CCTV system of areas such as pathways, building entrances, and vehicle parking areas.

Internal hard-wired communications are provided between all of the guard houses, in addition to security personnel carrying walkie-talkie sets. A hotline is also installed between the security control rooms and the engineering control rooms.

7.6.4 Access

Dedicated security guard posts adjoin all the vehicle inspection holding areas, in which controls for the road blockers are located, as listed below:

- Residencies entry/exit gate
- Service gate (common for hotel and residences)

License plate readers will be deployed at all vehicular entries and exits, combined with a driver image capture facility.

The provision for pedestrian screening areas covers all pedestrian entries to the buildings, as listed below (no equipment):

- Residences ground floor screening area.
- Residence basements screening areas.
- Residences service screening area.

The residential lifts will be installed with electronic access control to restrict unwarranted access to the apartment floors. Additionally, in the reception area, there is a manned desk at which visitors will be required to register.

7.6.5 Safety Features Provided in the Case Study

Table 7.1 discusses about the safety features incorporated in this case study.

TABLE 7.1
Proposed Safety Features

	Safety Features
1	Structure is 2 hours fire rated
2	All staircases, lift lobbies, and resident corridors are provided with pressurization
3	All stairways are separated from the remainder of the building by 1 hour fire resisting construction and 30 minutes fire doors form a stairway enclosure
4	The refuse areas are provided inside the building in case of emergency. The refuge area provided on the periphery of the floor at least on one side protected with suitable railings.
5	Fire doors shall be fitted with self-closing devices to ensure the positive latching of the door
6	Separate fire pump room provided in building including diesel-operated fire engine with 2 hours water storage capacity
7	Fire hydrant system is provided throughout the building
8	The building is protected with approved automatic fire sprinkler system
9	Portable fire extinguishers are provided throughout the building
10	Protected fire fighters lobby as per local requirement
11	Deluge valve fire-fighting system is provided for LPG bank
12	Gas suppression system provided for server room and electronic private automatic branch exchange (EPABX) room
13	Fire lift has been provided in the building
14	Fire command center is provided at ground level
15	Addressable smoke detectors are provided throughout the building
16	Fire alarm call points, public address, and fire fighters talk back system provided in building
17	LPG leak detectors for individual apartment
18	UPS backup for emergency lightings
19	Emergency lighting at common areas.
20	Directional illuminated exit signs with battery backup
21	Smoke extraction system provided for all basements

7.7 VERTICAL TRANSPORTATION IN ITC ONE COLOMBO ONE RESIDENTIAL TOWER

- Four (4) high-rise passenger elevators of 1350 kg capacity (18 pax) running in a 4-car group for maximum efficiency at 4.0 m/seconds with wide shaped cars serving from B3 through to ground, to Level 49
- An average interval wait time around 40–45 seconds – good rating by international standards during peak hours for the high-speed passenger lifts in a high-rise luxury residential tower.
- Handling capacity, 7%–8%, of building population during a 5-minute peak interval which is also a very good rating indicating there are enough passenger lifts in the tower which is also borne out by the good waiting intervals, i.e., a well- elevatored building.
- Passenger lifts have large capacity wide-shaped cars with tall entrances and ceiling height, giving a feeling of spaciousness and luxury. Passengers can travel in comfort as the car loadings are expected to be low, and car carrying capacity is large.

- Provision made in cars for silent and smooth ride comfort, good ventilation and information displays and connection to ITC *WelcomAssist* for assistance at any time during a journey.
- Two (2) high-speed service lifts of 1350kg capacity, (18 pax) running in a 2-car duplex group operation for peak efficiency with deep-shaped cars running at 3.5 m/seconds serving from B3 through to ground, to Level 49. This indicates there are sufficient lifts available for BoH operations to provide quick and responsive services to apartment occupants.
- Service cars are deep shaped which can comfortably accommodate a stretcher so that any medical emergency can be handled easily. These are also the building fire lifts; higher lift speed also means quicker BoH services will be available to residents.
- All lifts conform to EN81-1 European lift code and other required safety norms.

Note:

- Please add your own comments about passenger lifts interior finishes.
- You may also like to name the successful vendor who will be providing the lifts in this tower.

7.8 PROPOSED REMOTE CONTROL UNIT LOGIC FOR USE CASES/SETTINGS

7.8.1 First Guest Arrival (The Guest Has Arrived to the Room after Check-in)

The lock senses the first arrival and passes the information to RCU over contact closure. As soon as the guest card is inserted into the card holder, the RCU sets the room to the welcome scene. (There should be an option to bypass TV power socket from key tag)

Following are welcome scene settings:

If the arrival time is between 6 a.m. and 6 p.m.: (This may change)

Lights: All lights on except balcony lights
Temp: 22°C
Fan speed: High
TV: On

If the arrival time is between 6 p.m. and 6 a.m.: Turn down mood (this may change)

Lights: Both the bedside lamps on,
Vestibule and bathroom vanity counter lights on
Rest all lights off
Temp: 22°C
Fan speed: High
TV: On

7.8.2 Guest Card Removal (When the Guest Leaves the Room)

The RCU allows a waiting period of 30 seconds and then sets the following: (This may change)

Lights: All off
Temp: 22°C
Fan speed: Low
TV: Off/standby

Do not disturb (DND)/make my room (MMR) settings are retained as was set before the removal of the card.

(The last known state of lights and temp is stored in the RCU's memory. This is referred as "Guest Setting")

7.8.3 Subsequent Guest Arrival

The lock senses the subsequent arrival and passes the information to RCU over contact closure.

As soon as the guest card is inserted into the card holder, the RCU sets the room to "Guest Setting."

7.8.4 Privacy Setting (DND)

The guest can turn on the DND from the service panel. When the privacy is set, the indicator (red color) in service panel indicates that it is set.

The corridor panel also indicates that the privacy has been set on.

The RCU passes the DND set information to the lock via contact closure. The lock is also set into the privacy mode. When the lock is set into the privacy mode – the unlocking is denied for maid card (housekeeping staff). It can still be opened by the guest card/admin card.

The privacy setting is retained even after the guest card is removed from the key card holder.

In the DND mode, bell should not function.

7.8.5 MMR

The guest can turn on the MMR from the service panel. When the MMR is set, the indicator (blue color) in the service panel indicates that it is set on.

The corridor panel also indicates that the MMR has been set on.

7.8.6 Housekeeping Arrival

When the housekeeper arrives to the room and uses the key to open the room, if the lock is set to the DND mode, then the lock denies the card.

In other situations, the lock will open and pass the information to RCU that the door has been opened using the maid card. In this situation

- If the guest is inside the room (the guest card is placed into the card holder), then no changes happen to light/AC settings
- If the room is unoccupied, then the RCU sets the room to "Housekeeping Scene" (irrespective of the time of the day) the details of which are as follows:

(This may change)

Lights: All lights On
Temp: 24°C
Fan speed: Low

7.8.7 Evening Turn Down

The housekeeper performs the evening turn down service. Before leaving the room, the room is set to "Evening Turn down" scene. The settings for this scene are as follows:

Lights: Both the bedside lamps on, vestibule and bathroom vanity counter lights on.
Rest all lights off
Temp: 22°C
Fan speed: High

7.8.8 Bedside Master Switch

When the master switch is activated
No change:
TV
Reading lights (left and right)
Writing table lamp
One light in toiler/shower
Door bell
AC set temp
AC fan speed
Power sockets
Action: (This may change)
Rest all lights Off
Antistumble light power socket should be activated
Motion sensor (with predefined timer) for bathroom lights should get activated.
When the master switch is deactivated
No change:
TV
Reading lights (left and right)
Writing table lamp
One light in toiler/shower
Door bell
AC set temp
AC fan speed

Power sockets
Action: Turn down mood (This may change)
Both the bedside lamps on
Vestibule on
Bathroom vanity counter lights on
Antistumble light power socket should be deactivated
Motion sensor (with predefined timer) for bathroom lights should get deactivated.

7.8.9 Good Night Switch

When good night switch is activated
No change:
AC set temp
AC fan speed
Power sockets
Action: (This may change)
All lights off
TV Off/standby
DND set (doorbell deactivated)
Night lamp on
Antistumble light power socket should be activated (if not already done so by MASTER)
Motion sensor (with predefined timer) for bathroom lights should get activated (if not already done so by MASTER)
When good night switch is deactivated
No change:
AC set temp
AC fan speed
Power sockets
Action: Turn down mood (this may change)
Both the bedside lamps on
Vestibule on
Bathroom vanity counter lights on
Antistumble light power socket should be deactivated.
Motion sensor (with predefined timer) for bathroom lights should get deactivated.

7.8.10 Valet Service Function – Laundry Service

Hardware support:
Valet request switch with multicolor LED indication (VRS) - generally at bed side/vestibule.
Valet delivery switch with multicolor LED indication (VDS) - inside laundry compartment.
Corridor panel with valet request unique indication.
Door contact at door which opens inside the guest room.
Door contact at door which opens outside of the guest room for laundry pickup and delivery.

Operation: (LED color may change)

1. Guest presses VRS. LED glows pink in VRS/VDS/corridor panel.
2. Guest places laundry inside laundry compartment.
3. Butler notices LED indication on corridor panel for value request.
4. Butler opens laundry compartment door from outside so door contact is triggered and LED indication in VRS/VDS changes to blue color indicating laundry is picked up. LED indication in corridor panel goes off.
5. When Butler delivers laundry back in laundry compartment, Butler presses VDS and LED indication changes to green in VRS/VDS.
6. Guest opens laundry compartment door from inside to pick up laundry. Door contact is activated and LED indication in VRS/VDS goes off indication cycle is completed.

7.8.11 Movement Sensor

Timer based movement sensor (at least two numbers) – Low voltage/high voltage.

Bathroom and vestibule lights to be controller (this may change).

Move sensors to be activated/deactivated for master/good night switch.

7.9 BYPASSED CIRCUITS

Following circuits are not operated by GRMS controls (But still direct power should feed from same GRMS with MCB protection)

Minibar.

Mobile/Laptop charger points.

Other live sockets.

iPad docket charging socket.

Option to bypass TV socket.

UPS power (emergency power backup)

- Light circuit is the vestibule is powered by the UPS line.

7.9.1 Corridor Panel

- It should have indication for DND (red), MUR (green), guest occupancy (orange), valet (pink) (where applicable) – LED color may change.
- It should also have "Please wait/Come later" indication. This is helpful when the guest wants the service staff to visit at a later point in time. This will also need an additional button in bathroom and/or bedroom. This is an optional but preferred feature. ITC may decide to remove.

7.9.2 Door Strike Operation

The hotel has electric door strike for iPad-controlled door look release.

The strike is connected to RCU and it needs 12 VDC for its operations.

In addition, one more such circuit (12 VDC) is required for buzzer operation for this feature.

Both these circuits need to be operated with the timer. The strike circuit operates for 15 seconds (configurable) and then closes automatically. The buzzer circuit operates for 5 seconds (configurable) and closes automatically.

7.9.3 Other Specifications

- 0–10 V DC modulated valve control.
- Power supply for valve 24 VAC for valve (amperage to be specified).
- Separate/independent temperature sensor (accuracy to be mentioned).
- 12 V DC supply for door strike and door buzzer.
  - RMS should maintain its status of lights/AC/DND/MUR etc. during power recycle.
- Each/group of light circuit should have individual power inputs. This means some circuit may be powered by 230 mains, some by 230 UPS, some by 48 VDC, and some by 12 VDC.
- ELV doorbell power supply should be provided in RCU.
- Heating pad should have separate relay or not depends on the bathroom layout.
- Communication port: The system must have a communication port to integrate with iPad-based room control. This should support two-way communication. The same needs to be tested in conjunction with the supplier of iPad solution.

7.9.4 Laptop Software Utility for Trouble-shooting to Work with the Same Communication Port and Same Communication Protocol, Provided for iPad Solution

- Automatic syntax check for each category of commands, i.e., on/off, dimmer, HVAC, Service panel (DND/MUR etc.), etc.
- Automatic CRC calculation, if any, for entered command.
- Window displaying actual command sent to RMS.
- Window displaying actual response received from RMS, after each command sent and executed.
- Visual status after each command executed.
- Any other testing parameter for effective trouble-shooting at site.

7.10 PROPOSED REMOTE CONTROL UNIT LOGIC FOR TV MUTE SYSTEM-USE CASES/SETTINGS

7.10.1 Single TV Room: Main Room TV On – Bedside/Bathroom Phone Ring

- TV can be muted (if not already muted) on incoming rings for better attention OR phone pick up (configurable).
- During the “Mute” period, it is continuously monitored if the guest unmutes main room TV using the remote controller.
- On phone hang up event, TV will be unmuted (if not already unmuted).

- If the hotel decides to mute main room TV on incoming rings and phone is picked up from bathroom, main room TV will be unmuted as soon as bathroom phone is picked up.
- If the hotel decides to mute main room TV on incoming rings and the guest does not pick up phone, main room TV will be unmuted after certain number of rings OR on phone stops ringing (configurable).

7.10.2 Multiple TV Room: Bedroom TV On, Living Room TV On – All Phones Ring

- Both bedroom/living room TVs can be muted (if not already muted) on incoming rings for better attention if opted so, by hotel. After this, if the bedroom phone is picked up, living room TV will be unmuted immediately else if living room phone is picked up, bedroom TV will be unmuted immediately else if bathroom phone is picked up, both bedroom/living room TVs will be unmuted immediately.
- Alternatively, specific area TV will be muted if the phone is picked up from that area. If the phone is picked up from the bathroom, neither TV will be muted.
- During the "Mute" period, it is continuously monitored if the guest unmutes main room TV using the remote controller.
- On phone hang up event, TV will be unmuted (if not already unmuted).
- If the hotel decides to mute main room TV on incoming rings and the guest does not pick up phone, all TVs will be unmuted after certain number of rings OR on phone stops ringing (configurable).

7.10.3 Communication with TV for Mute/Unmute Command/Status

This is done through two-way communication using RS232 port (data port) of TV and not through one communication like IR.

7.11 CONCLUSION

In this paper, we have presented a prototype of a luxurious residential tower that is aided with state-of-the-art automation technologies. With this model, we tried to emphasize the fact that this infrastructure with all the latest and efficient technologies can be achieved with very little power consumption without actually compromising on the quality of outputs. The proposed prototype is sustainable, safe, secure, and lavishly attractive. All the various aspects of home automation have been discussed taking care of all the required parameters. This prototype is definitely much safer, efficient, and smarter than most of the existing models. This model is flexible according to the user's choice and is unique in its own way.

REFERENCES

[1] Kannapiran S and Chakrapani A, 2017. A novel home automation system using Bluetooth and Arduino. *International Journal of Advances in Computer and Electronics Engineering* 2(2), 41–44.

[2] Swathika OVG and Hemapala KTMU, 2019. IoT based energy management system for standalone PV systems. *Journal of Electrical Engineering & Technology* 14(5), 1811–1821.
[3] Sen S, Chakrabarty S, Toshniwal R, and Bhaumik A, 2015. Design of an intelligent voice controlled home automation system. *International Journal of Computer Applications* 121(15).
[4] Soj RP, Soudeep S, and Gnana Swathika OV. 2019. IoT-based energy management system with data logging capability. *Proceedings of International Conference on Sustainable Computing in Science, Technology and Management (SUSCOM), Amity University Rajasthan*, Jaipur-India.
[5] Srinath MS, Kishore MN, and Praveena MA. 2018. Interactive home automation system with google assistant. *International Journal of Pure and Applied Mathematics* 119(12), 14083–14086.
[6] Gupta Y, et al., 2017. IoT based energy management system with load sharing and source management features. *2017 4th IEEE Uttar Pradesh Section International Conference on Electrical, Computer and Electronics (UPCON)*. IEEE.
[7] Jose AC, Malekian R, and Ye N, 2016. Improving home automation security; integrating device fingerprinting into smart home. *IEEE Access* 4, 5776–5787, doi: 10.1109/ACCESS.2016.2606478.
[8] Ananthakrishanan V, et al., 2018. GSM based energy management system. *International Journal of Pure and Applied Mathematics* 118(24).
[9] Singh A, Pal A, and Rai B, 2015. GSM based home automation, safety and security system using android mobile phone. *International Journal of Engineering Research & Technology (IJERT)* 4(05).
[10] Swathika OVG, et al., 2021. IoT-based energy management system with data logging capability. In *Advances in Smart Grid Technology*. Springer, Singapore, pp. 547–555.
[11] Baviskar J, Mulla A, Baviskar A, and Desai J, 2015. Implementation of 802.15. 4 wireless sensor network in real-time monitoring and control system for greenhouse. *Asia-Pacific Journal of Multimedia Services Convergent with Art, Humanities, and Sociology* 5(5), 87–105.
[12] Majee A and Swathika OVG. 2017. IoT based reconfiguration of microgrids through an automated central protection centre. *2017 International Conference on Power and Embedded Drive Control (ICPEDC)*. IEEE.
[13] Suneetha K and Sreekanth M, 2020. Smart home monitoring and automation energy efficient system using IoT devices. In *Emerging Research in Data Engineering Systems and Computer Communications*. Springer, Singapore, pp. 627–637.
[14] Singh A, et al., 2018. Arduino based home automation control powered by photovoltaic cells. *2018 Second International Conference on Computing Methodologies and Communication (ICCMC)*. IEEE.
[15] Martinez DW and Chua AY, 2017. New design and automation concept of an energy-efficient, tertiary building for mixed-mode ventilation system. *International Journal of Automation and Smart Technology* 7(4), 163–178.
[16] Martirano L, Parise G, Parise L, and Manganelli M, 2016. A fuzzy-based building automation control system: optimizing the level of energy performance and comfort in an office space by taking advantage of building automation systems and solar energy. *IEEE Industry Applications Magazine* 22(2), 10–17, doi: 10.1109/MIAS.2015.2459097.
[17] Suhanto S, Faizah F, and Kustori K, 2019. Designing a building automation system with open protocol communication and intelligent electronic devices. *Journal of Physics: Conference Series* 1381(1), 012006. IOP Publishing.
[18] Majee A, Madhav B, and Swathika OVG, 2018. IoT based microgrid automation for optimizing energy usage and controllability. *2018 Second International Conference on Electronics, Communication and Aerospace Technology (ICECA)*. IEEE.

[19] Katre SR and Rojatkar DV, 2017. Home automation: past, present and future. *International Research Journal of Engineering and Technology* 4(10), 343–346.
[20] Swathika OVG and Hemapala KTMU, 2019. IOT-based adaptive protection of microgrid. *International Conference on Artificial Intelligence, Smart Grid and Smart City Applications*. Springer, Cham.
[21] Tatyasaheb MP and Shinde MB, 2016. A review on home automation system using different techniques. *International Research Journal of Engineering and Technology (IRJET)* 3(06), 2996–3000.
[22] Hoy MB and Alexa S, 2018. Cortana, and more: an introduction to voice assistants. *Medical Reference Services Quarterly* 37(1), 81–88.

8 ANN-Based Overcurrent Relay Using the Levenberg–Marquardt Algorithm for Smart Cities

Aayush Sharma, O.V. Gnana Swathika, and V. Berlin Hency
Vellore Institute of Technology

CONTENTS

8.1 INTRODUCTION: BACKGROUND AND DRIVING FORCES

A relay is an integral part of the power system network. It has an ability to isolate the fault from the power system network [1]. Various electromagnetic or electromechanical relays are widely used in order to preserve power system equipment. But due to their physical nature, these conventional relays encounter functional limitations. Due to the presence of the magnetic coil in its physical structure, it comes across mechanical losses due to the high magnitude of current during fault, affecting the operational time and thus the performance of a relay [2–5]. When the network current surpasses the threshold or operating current of the system, it is categorized under overcurrent fault. Being renowned of its inverse time characteristic which means fast operation at a high value of fault and slow operation at a low value, the overcurrent relay is largely used in the power system network. Due to the excessive use of electricity, the cases of short circuit are quite frequent, resulting in the operational failure of the overcurrent relay inducing intolerable amount of current in the network, causing system procrastination leading to unnecessary electromagnetic heating and then wearing off

DOI: 10.1201/9781003201069-8

of the other power system equipment [6–8]. It is evident from the literature that these characteristics of the overcurrent relay may be replicated using a microcontroller and suitable programming techniques as reported in [9–16]. Microcontrollers based on different algorithms are used to model relay characteristics [16–21]. Overall, these digitally designed relays prove to be an asset in terms of electric network safety by overcoming physical limitation of the conventional overcurrent relays. Recent studies on the area of implementation of the conventional relay on the digital platform using the artificial neural network (ANN) have caught the sight of many researchers. With ANN's high computation strength, it is easy to deploy any mathematical nonlinear equation solving algorithm and also to provide better insight by contemplating the data received from observations including their graphical analysis facilitating a real-time watch over the operational status of the relay as represented in [22–30]. Use of electronic devices and programmed ICs reduces the physical bulkiness and the functional limitations of the conventional overcurrent relay and provides better calculation of the restoration time. A lot of research is observed in the implementation of the overcurrent protective relay using microprocessors and microcontrollers as reported in [31–37]. Overcurrent relay like definite time and inverse time are realized on the digital and electronic platform running on various algorithms as indicated in [38–42]. Since it is programmed, it provides better accuracy, sensitivity, and reliability. Better approximation of the restoration time is also achieved using fuzzy logic or the ANN. Use of electronic devices minimizes the overall physical weight of an electric network along with quick restoring facilities for minor faults. The radial distribution network is prone to frequent overcurrent faults and demands the extensive use of the overcurrent relay for fault detection, fault clearance, and system restoration. Several studies and research are reported in this field [4]. This paper demonstrates the digital design of the IDMT relay using a Levenberg–Marquardt method–based ANN working on MATLAB to compute the nonlinear current values. The ANN is chosen for its better accuracy when it comes to data analysis or predicting any mathematical entity close to perfection by applying several mathematical series. The designed algorithm allows the reconfiguration feature, categorization of current, and a liberty to add any feature to enhance the functionality of the proposed ANN-based overcurrent relay. The real-time monitoring of the network and data logging feature are available which helps in categorizing the type of fault. The performance of the relay is tested for different fault current values, and its restoration time is also analyzed. Section 8.2 discusses the design requirements of the proposed relay. Section 8.3 explains the Levenberg–Marquardt algorithm. Section 8.4 proposes the algorithm that replicates the IDMT characteristics with some additional features. Section 8.5 elaborates the results and discussion which is a collection of test cases subjected to the ANN-based IDMT relay with suitable results. Section 8.6 summarizes the overall results of the proposed algorithm.

8.2 DESIGN

Levenberg–Marquardt method–based ANN based IDMT characteristic of the relay is realized using MATLAB. MATLAB acts as a master controller where techniques like inverse differential-based restoration time and overcurrent fault

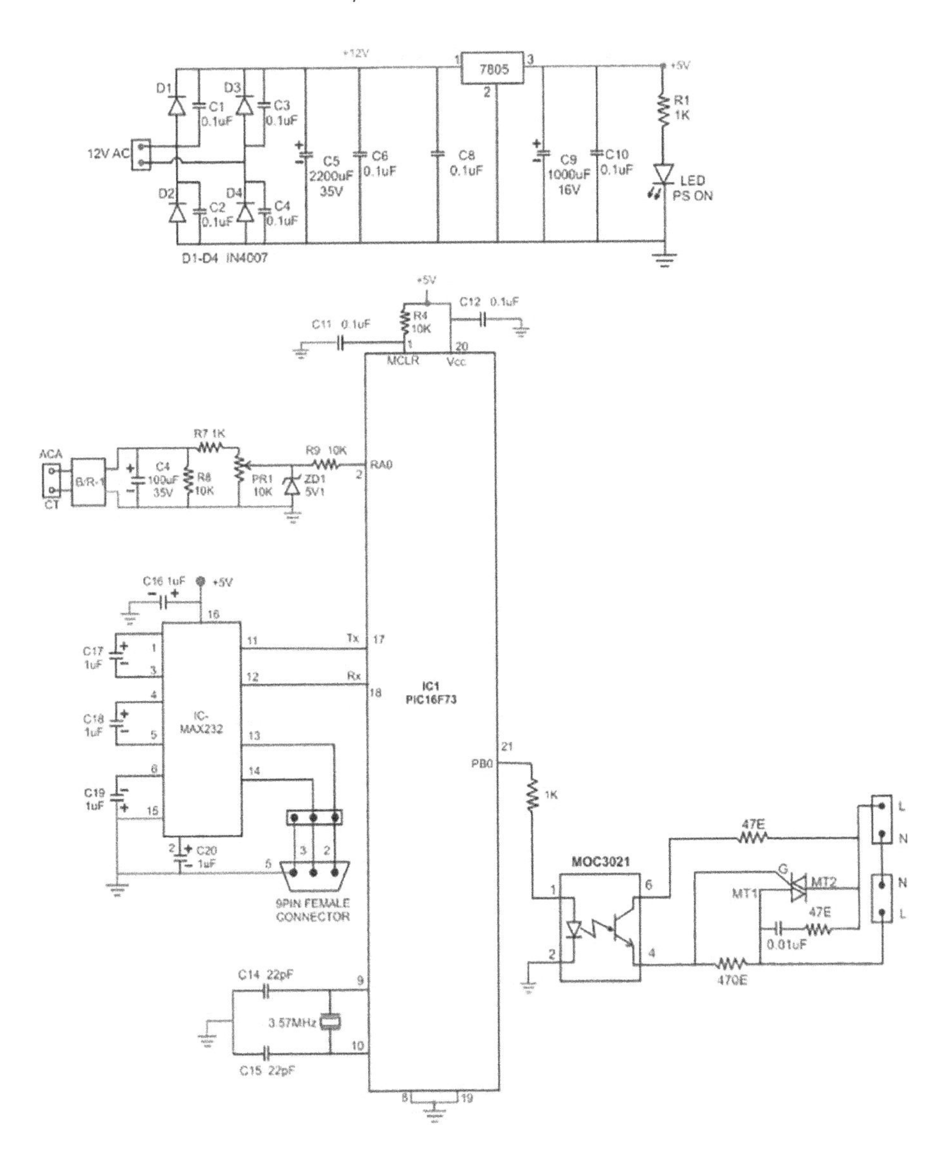

FIGURE 8.1 Circuit diagram.

categorization with time limit are implemented in MATLAB software. The PIC 16F73 microcontroller is used in conjunction with the MATLAB interface to enable the data acquisition of current and to trigger the relay functioning according to the user profile. MAX 232 IC is used to facilitate serial port communication between the MATLAB and microcontroller. Use of a solid-state relay (MOC3021) controller by a microcontroller allows for modulation of control times in relay switching, subsecond relay switching. To examine the system shown in Figure 8.1, four parallel loads of 50A (current on the scale of 100) are used in this design of an overcurrent relay.

8.3 OVERVIEW OF LEVENBERG–MARQUARDT ALGORITHM

It is a standard mathematical algorithm used for solving nonlinear equations. Under this method, a function is minimized, i.e., the sum of squares represented as in equation (8.1):

$$\min_{x} f(x) = \|F(x)\|_2^2 = \sum_i F_i^2(x) \tag{8.1}$$

Vector representation of the function $F(x)$ is given in equation (8.2):

$$\min_{x \in \kappa^{\eta}} f(x) = \sum_{i=1}^{m} \left(\bar{y}(x, t_i) - \bar{\varphi}(t_i)\right)^2 \tag{8.2}$$

where,

$y(x,t)$ and $\varphi(t)$ are scalar quantity.

```
net.inputs{1}.processFcns = {'removeconstantrows','mapminmax'};
net.outputs{2}.processFcns = {'removeconstantrows','mapminmax'};


net.divideFcn = 'dividerand';
net.divideMode = 'sample';
net.divideParam.trainRatio = 70/100;
net.divideParam.valRatio = 15/100;
net.divideParam.testRatio = 15/100;


net.trainFcn = 'trainlm';  % Levenberg-Marquardt


net.performFcn = 'mse';  % Mean squared error

net.plotFcns = {'plotperform','plottrainstate','ploterrhist', ...
  'plotregression', 'plotfit'};



[net,tr] = train(net,inputs,targets);


outputs = net(inputs);
errors = gsubtract(targets,outputs);
performance = perform(net,targets,outputs);
```

FIGURE 8.2 Pseudo code.

After discretizing this function, we receive an integral as in equation (8.3):

$$\min_{x \in \kappa^{\eta}} f(x) = \sum_{i=1}^{m} \left(\bar{y}(x,t_i) - \bar{\varphi}(t_i)\right)^2 \tag{8.3}$$

Now the vector *F*(*x*)[42] is given as in equation (8.4):

$$F(x) = \begin{bmatrix} \bar{y}(x,t_1) - \bar{\varphi}(t_1) \\ \bar{y}(x,t_2) - \bar{\varphi}(t_2) \\ \cdots \\ \bar{y}(x,t_m) - \bar{\varphi}(t_m) \end{bmatrix} \tag{8.4}$$

The MATLAB toolbox of the LVM algorithm is used by an ANN in minimizing the function, *F*(*x*). Figure 8.2 depicts the implementation of an ANN that computes the minimum restoration time required for this digital relay to restore the resumed condition. The output obtained is hence plotted as a graph.

8.4 ALGORITHM DEVELOPED

The proposed algorithm is depicted in Figure 8.3 and is elaborated in the following steps:

1. Start
2. Read real time current signal from serial port.

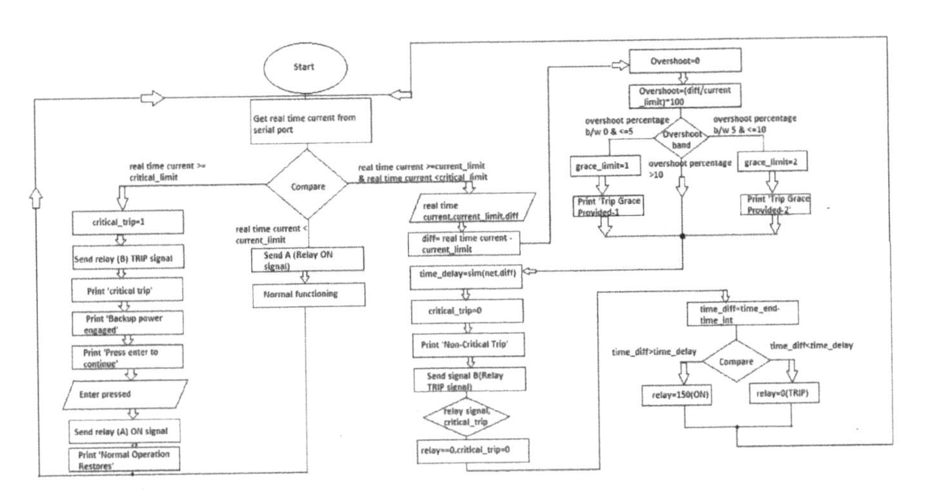

FIGURE 8.3 Proposed algorithm flowchart.

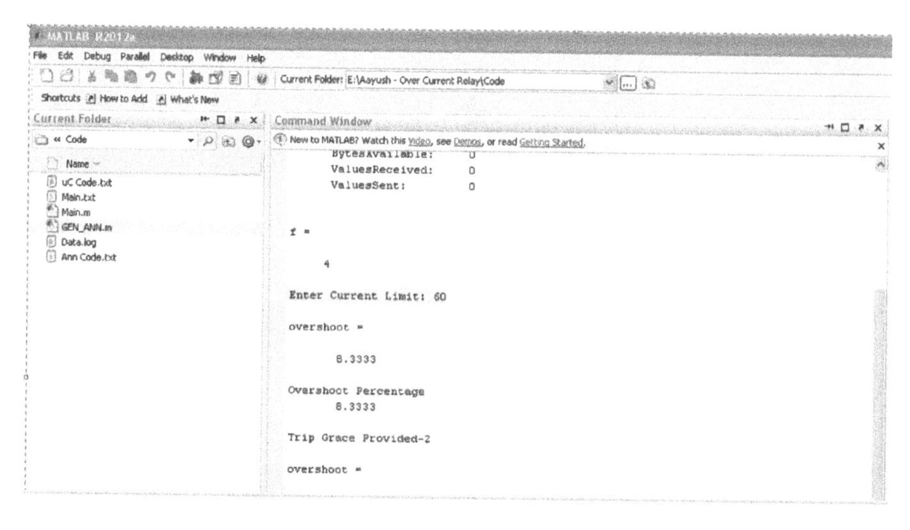

FIGURE 8.4 Current limit setting.

3. Enter current_limit
4. Cases:
   i. real time current >=critical_ limit
   ii. real time current < current_limit
   iii. real time current >=current_limit & real time -current <critical_limit
      critical_limit = 2*current_limit
      current_limit = Enter by user

The algorithm allows user to set the current_limit as shown in Figure 8.4 according to demand of an electrical network.

Case i.

1. real time current >=critical_limit
2. critical_trip=1
3. send TRIP signal(B) to relay
4. Display "Critical trip"
5. Display "Back-up power engaged" as shown in Figure 8.5
6. Display "Press enter to continue"
7. Press Enter
8. Send ON signal(A) to relay
9. Display "Normal Operation Restores"

Case ii.

1. Real time current <current_limit
2. Send ON signal to relay; relay = 150
3. Normal functioning of relay

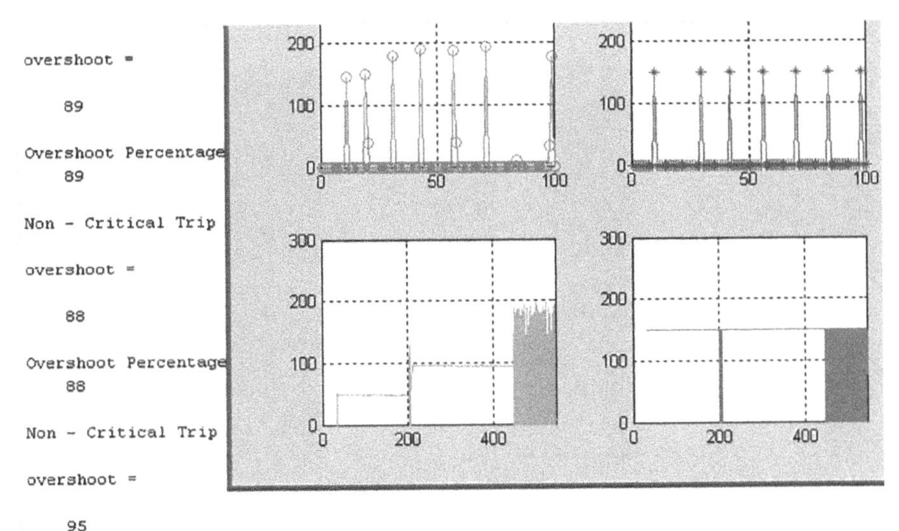

FIGURE 8.5 Console display.

Case iii.

1. real time current >=current_limit & real time current <critical_limit
2. Compute variable diff; diff =real time current-current_limit
3. Compute overshoot; overshoot=(diff/current_limit)*100

    a. Overshoot b/w 0 and <=5,grace_limit=1,Display "Trip Grace Provided_1
    b. Overshoot b/w 5 and <=10,grace_limit=2,Display "Trip Grace Provided_2

4. Compute time_delay using the ANN.
5. time_delay=sim (net, diff): MATLAB function of ANN.
6. critical_trip=0,Display "Non critical trip"
7. Send TRIP signal (B) to relay; relay=0.
8. If relay==0 & critical_trip=0,Calculate time_diff=time_end-time_int

    a. time_diff>time_delay, send ON signal to relay; relay=150
    b. time_diff<time_delay, send TRIP signal to relay; relay=0.

9. Move to Start Command.

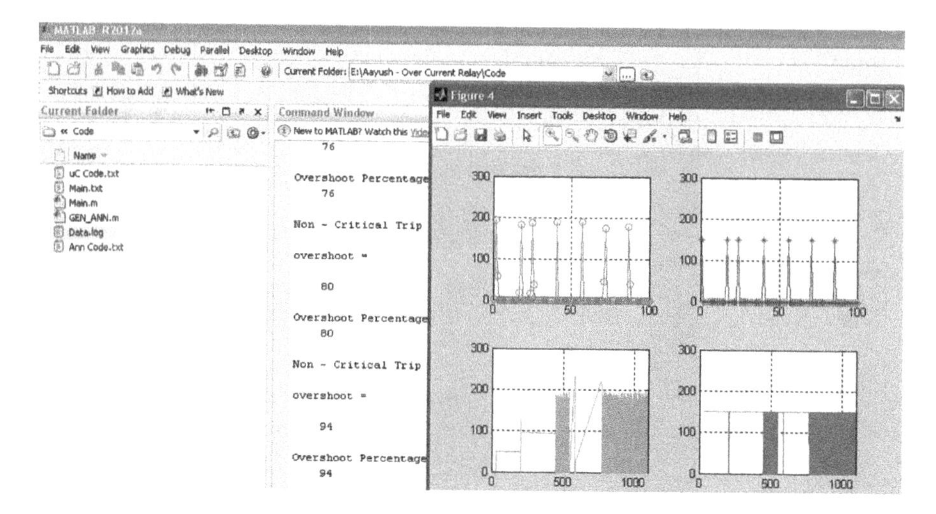

FIGURE 8.6 Console screen with real-time data and MATLAB screen with an overshoot value.

```
while(1)
{
        if(Usart_Data_Ready())
        {
                                ch=Usart_Read();

                                if(ch=='A' || ch=='a')
                                {
                                        PORTB.bit0=1;
                                }

                                if(ch=='B' || ch=='b')
                                {
                                        PORTB.bit0=0;
                                }

        }

        value=value+adc_read(0);

        if(count>99)
        {
                temp=value/100;

                digit3=temp%10;

                temp=temp/10;
                digit2=temp%10;
```

FIGURE 8.7 Relay tripping code.

The proposed algorithm absolutely imitates the inverse time features of the Inverse Definite Mean Time (IDMT) overcurrent relay using a MATLAB-controlled solid-state relay having ANN for computing minimum restoration time by working out the Levenberg–Marquardt algorithm function. The designed relay also showcases additional features as shown in Figure 8.6.

a. Overshoot percentage calculation providing grace time for a specific range of overshoot.
b. Critical trip when the real-time value exceeds the threshold value, i.e., critical limit =2*current_limit.
c. The design has a scope for reprogrammability according to user demands.
d. A trained ANN is engaged to compute minimum restoration time using MATLAB methods for nonlinear least-squares problems.
e. MATLAB is used for real-time plotting and analysis of current and switching waveform simultaneously in a single console.
f. MATLAB also provides a feature for real-time data logging of important fault parameter such as fault time and date, fault magnitude, and fault restoration state.

The pseudo code shown in Figure 8.7 is used for the tripping of the relay.

8.5 RESULTS AND DISCUSSION

The designed digital relay is examined under several conditions. Out of those, few test cases are discussed below: Case i: current_limit=60 is shown in Figure 8.8. The current value here is taken on a scale of 100. A – ON mode of the relay; B – TRIP mode of the relay. It is evident from the observation Table 8.1 that for values less than 60, the relay operates normally.

Once the current value runs beyond the current limit, i.e., real time current>current_limit, then the relay trips down for the amount of time, computed by the ANN. This case represents noncritical trip (critical_trip=0) scenario. Once the nature of fault (critical/noncritical) is identified, the MATLAB works accordingly to the logic. It is observed from the Table 8.1 that for current value > current_limit but less than critical_limit (noncritical trip), a time delay is evaluated by the ANN which is nothing but the trip time length of the designed relay. No grace time is provided in this case. Let us assume a 0%–10% overshoots. But this may be provided for multiple bands of the overshoot percentage. The grace limit is one of the characteristics of this designed relay which gives an extra delay for low magnitude faults. The overshoot calculated in this case is 76.66667%. Furthermore, when the real-time current value exceeds the threshold value, i.e., 2*current_limit, the nature of fault shows that it is a critical trip, i.e., critical_trip=1, the relay would get engaged quickly in order to save electrical network from this high fault magnitude. The algorithm is designed to act quickly and engage backup power supply at the time of critical trip. The relay switching and real-time current value are being displayed on single console as shown in Figure 8.9 which graphically shows the real-time data, entire operating status of the relay, and real-time current status throughout the entire event.

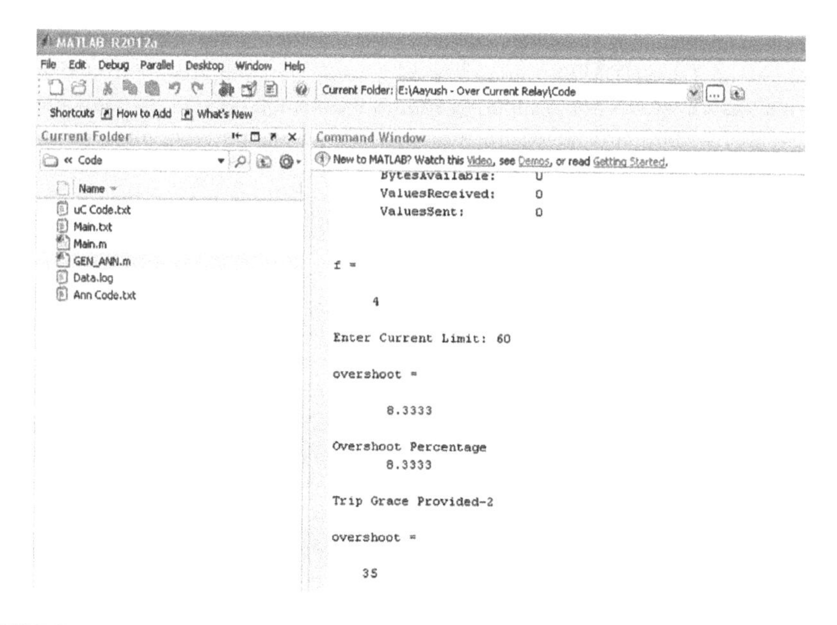

FIGURE 8.8 MATLAB screen with current limit 60.

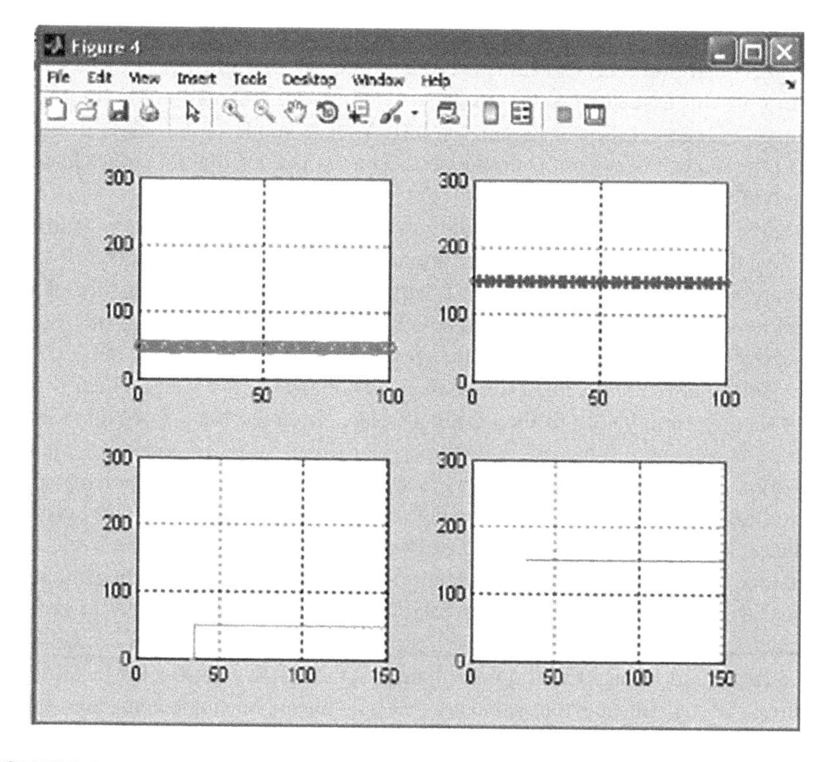

FIGURE 8.9 Console screen. 2D display with current (Amps) on y-axis, time (sec) on x-axis.

TABLE 8.1
Overshoot Values

Real-time Current	Current Difference	Time_delay ANN Computated	Relay Signal (A/B)	Grace Provided	Overshoot%
Below 60	NA	NA	A	NA	NA
106.000000	46.000000	1.375377	B	0	76.666667
130.000000	70.000000	NA	B	NA	NA

TABLE 8.2
Overshoot Value

Real-time Current	Current Difference	Time_delay ANN Computated	Relay Signal (A/B)	Grace Provided	Overshoot%
Below 80	NA	NA	A	0	NA
110.000000	30.000000	1.135773	B	0	37.500000
116.000000	36.000000	1.336847	B	0	45.000000
119.000000	39.000000	1.428926	B	0	48.750000
126.000000	46.000000	1.564223	B	0	57.500000

Case ii. current_limit=80

For the current value less than 80, the relay works on the ON mode as shown in Table 8.2. Once the value goes beyond the current limit, then the relay trips for time evaluated by the ANN. This is observed in Table 8.2.

Case iii. Current_limit=100 is shown in Figure 8.10

It is observed from Table 8.3 that for a current value less than 100, the relay operates at the ON mode. As the real-time value gets high and marginally (110) above the limit value (100), it receives grace value = 1, and the relay functions under the noncritical and TRIP mode. As fault current goes beyond the critical value (100*2), i.e., the last row of Table 8.3, then the critical_trip=1, and the relay trips and backup power gets engaged in order to safeguard the electrical distribution network. The data gets stored at data logs as shown in Figure 8.11. The switching of the relay is visible on the console as indicated in Figure 8.12. The red line represents a real-time current value. Similarly, the blue line represents live restoring time data or real-time switching waveform of the designed relay. The green waveform represents real-time data logging of current, correspondingly, the pink-colored waveform represents real-time data logging of the real-time status as shown in Figure 8.12.

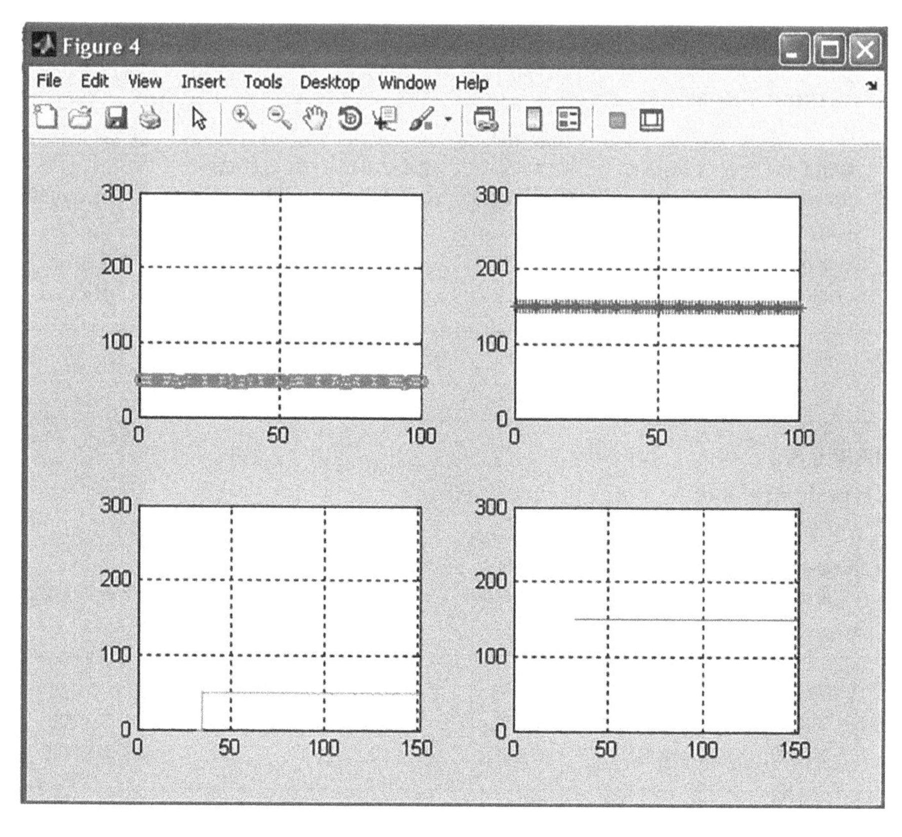

FIGURE 8.10 Console screen. 2D display with current (Amps) on y-axis, time (sec) on x-axis.

TABLE 8.3
Overshoot Values

Real-time Current	Current Difference	Time_delay ANN Computated	Relay Signal (A/B)	Grace Provided	Overshoot%
49.000000	NA	NA	A	0	NA
96.000000	NA	NA	A	0	NA
110.000000	10.000000	1.368550	B	1	10.000000
129.000000	29.000000	1.413558	B	0	29.000000
146.000000	46.000000	1.375377	B	0	46.000000
188.000000	88.000000	1.785433	B	0	88.000000
200.000000	100.000000	1.676870	B	0	100.000000
233.000000	133.000000	NA	B	0	133.000000

```
8456  2/4/2017 18:45:34.468 Current Limit: 100.000000  Real Time Current: 0.000000
8457  2/4/2017 18:45:34.578 Current Limit: 100.000000  Real Time Current: 0.000000
8458  2/4/2017 18:45:34.718 Current Limit: 100.000000  Real Time Current: 0.000000
8459  2/4/2017 18:45:34.812 Current Limit: 100.000000  Real Time Current: 0.000000
8460  2/4/2017 18:45:34.953 Current Limit: 100.000000  Real Time Current: 0.000000
8461  2/4/2017 18:45:35.046 Current Limit: 100.000000  Real Time Current: 0.000000
8462  2/4/2017 18:45:35.187 Current Limit: 100.000000  Real Time Current: 0.000000
8463  2/4/2017 18:45:35.296 Current Limit: 100.000000  Real Time Current: 0.000000
8464  2/4/2017 18:45:35.421 Current Limit: 100.000000  Real Time Current: 31.000000
8465  2/4/2017 18:45:35.546 Current Limit: 100.000000  Real Time Current: 180.000000  Current Difference: 80.000000  Overshoot Percentage: 80.000000  Time D
8466  2/4/2017 18:45:35.734 Current Limit: 100.000000  Real Time Current: 0.000000
8467  2/4/2017 18:45:35.906 Current Limit: 100.000000  Real Time Current: 0.000000
8468  2/4/2017 18:45:36.031 Current Limit: 100.000000  Real Time Current: 0.000000
8469  2/4/2017 18:45:36.156 Current Limit: 100.000000  Real Time Current: 0.000000
8470  2/4/2017 18:45:36.25 Current Limit: 100.000000  Real Time Current: 0.000000
8471  2/4/2017 18:45:36.39 Current Limit: 100.000000  Real Time Current: 0.000000
8472  2/4/2017 18:45:36.5 Current Limit: 100.000000  Real Time Current: 0.000000
8473  2/4/2017 18:45:36.64 Current Limit: 100.000000  Real Time Current: 0.000000
8474  2/4/2017 18:45:36.734 Current Limit: 100.000000  Real Time Current: 0.000000
8475  2/4/2017 18:45:36.875 Current Limit: 100.000000  Real Time Current: 0.000000
8476  2/4/2017 18:45:36.984 Current Limit: 100.000000  Real Time Current: 0.000000
8477  2/4/2017 18:45:37.109 Current Limit: 100.000000  Real Time Current: 0.000000
8478  2/4/2017 18:45:37.234 Current Limit: 100.000000  Real Time Current: 0.000000
8479  2/4/2017 18:45:37.359 Current Limit: 100.000000  Real Time Current: 0.000000
8480  2/4/2017 18:45:37.453 Current Limit: 100.000000  Real Time Current: 61.000000
8481  2/4/2017 18:45:37.609 Current Limit: 100.000000  Real Time Current: 169.000000  Current Difference: 69.000000  Overshoot Percentage: 69.000000  Time D
8482  2/4/2017 18:45:37.734 Current Limit: 100.000000  Real Time Current: 40.000000
8483  2/4/2017 18:45:37.828 Current Limit: 100.000000  Real Time Current: 0.000000
8484  2/4/2017 18:45:37.953 Current Limit: 100.000000  Real Time Current: 0.000000
8485  2/4/2017 18:45:38.078 Current Limit: 100.000000  Real Time Current: 0.000000
```

FIGURE 8.11 Real-time data logging.

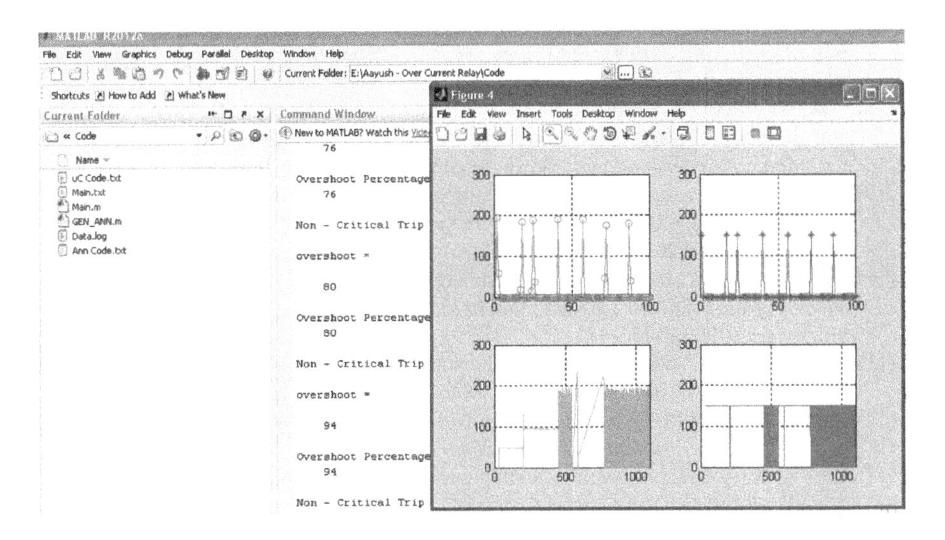

FIGURE 8.12 Switching, current data at a current limit value of 100.

8.6 CONCLUSION

The designed relay completely follows the inverse differential characteristic of the IDMT relay. Use of the ANN helps to evaluate minimum restoration time using the Levenberg–Marquardt algorithm. The proposed design and system implementation allows data collection in the MATLAB interface which may be extended to be connected with Supervisory Control and Data Acquisition System (SCADA) or online monitoring and control system. They have huge applications in the smart city, where it is important to provide state-of-the-art protection to the distribution network. Thus, the ANN-based IDMT relay is designed, tested, and validated successfully for a small network. It may also be extended to a larger network as well.

REFERENCES

[1] A Conde, E Vazquez, "Application of a proposed overcurrent relay in radial distribution networks", *Electric Power Systems Research* 81, 2, 2011, 570–579.

[2] MM Eissa, OP Malik, "A new digital directional transverse differential current protection technique", *IEEE Transactions on Power Delivery* 11, 3, 1996, 1285–1291.

[3] AG Jongepier, L van der Sluis, *IEEE Transactions on Power Delivery* 9, 3, 1994, 1289–1297.

[4] E Koley, R Kumar, S Ghosh, "Low cost microcontroller based fault detector, classifier, zone identifier and locator for transmission lines using wavelet transform and artificial neural network: a hardware co-simulation approach", *International Journal of Electrical Power & Energy Systems* 81, 2016, 346–360.

[5] TK Isaac, and OVG Swathika, "Optimum coordination of using overcurrent relay using firefly and ant colony optimization algorithm", *2017 International Conference on Computing Methodologies and Communication (ICCMC)*. IEEE, 2017.

[6] OVG Swathika, and KTMU Hemapala, "Optimized overcurrent relay coordination in a microgrid system", *Recent Advances in Computer Science and Communications* 12, 2020, 1.

[7] OVG Swathika, and S Hemamalini, "Prims-aided dijkstra algorithm for adaptive protection in microgrids", *IEEE Journal of Emerging and Selected Topics in Power Electronics* 4, 4, 2016, 1279–1286.

[8] OVG Swathika, K Karthikeyan, and S Hemamalini. "Multiple DG synchronization and de-synchronization in a microgrid using PLC", In *Advanced Computing and Communication Technologies*. Springer, Singapore, 2016, pp. 565–572.

[9] OVG Swathika, and S Hemamalini. "Graph theory and optimization algorithms aided adaptive protection in reconfigurable microgrid", *Journal of Electrical Engineering & Technology* 15, 1, 2020, 421–431.

[10] V Himanshu, et al., "Optimal coordination of overcurrent relays using simulated annealing and brute force algorithms", In *Intelligent Engineering Informatics*. Springer, Singapore, 2018, pp. 177–183.

[11] G Benmouyal, "Design of a digital multi-curve time-overcurrent relay", *IEEE Transactions on Power Delivery* 5, 4, 1990, 1725–1731.

[12] OVG Swathika, "LUT assisted adaptive overcurrent protection of reconfigurable microgrids", *International Journal of Smart Grid-ijSmartGrid* 2, 1, 2018, 13–26.

[13] YVVS Murty, WJ Smolinski, S Sivakumar, "Design of a digital protection scheme for power transformers using optimal state observers IEEE Proceedings C - Generation", *Transmission and Distribution* 35, 3, 1988, 224–230.

[14] GV Kshirsagar, GN Mulay, S Yeolekar, "TMS320F28335 based single phase overcurrent protection implementation using numerical relay", *2014 6th IEEE Power India International Conference (PIICON)*, 2014, pp. 1–5.

[15] I Ahamed, K Vydeeswaran, and OVG Swathika. "Microgrid fault clearance with linear programming algorithms", *2017 2nd International Conference on Communication and Electronics Systems (ICCES)*, IEEE, 2017.

[16] S Jasleen, et al., "Performance analysis of graph algorithms for microgrid protection", *Journal of Telecommunication, Electronic and Computer Engineering (JTEC)* 10, 1–8, 2018, 115–118.

[17] NH Hussin, MH Idris, M Amirruddin, MS Ahmad, MA Ismail, FS Abdullah, NM Mukhta, "Modeling and simulation of inverse time overcurrent relay using MATLAB/Simulink", *2016 IEEE International Conference on Automatic Control and Intelligent Systems (I2CACIS)*, 2016, pp. 40–44.

[18] HM Sharaf, HH Zeineldin, DK UIbrahim, EEDA El-Zahab, "Directional inverse time overcurrent relay for meshed distribution systems with distributed generation with additional continuous relay settings", *12th IET International Conference on Developments in Power System Protection (DPSP 2014)*, 2014, pp. 1–6.

[19] "IEEE standard inverse-time characteristic equations for over current relays", *IEEE Std C37.112-1996*, 1997, p. i.
[20] OVG Swathika, and KTMU Hemapala. "Optimized overcurrent relay coordination in a microgrid system", *Recent Advances in Computer Science and Communications* 12, 2020, 1.
[21] G Benmouyal, M Meisinger, J Burnworth, WA Elmore, K Freirich, PA Kotos, PR Leblanc, PJ Lerley, JE McConnell, J Mizener, J Pinto de Sa, R Ramaswami, MS Sachdev, WM Strang, JE Waldron, S Watansiriroch, SE Zocholl, "IEEE standard inverse-time characteristic equations for overcurrent relays", *IEEE Transactionson Power Delivery* 14, 3, 1999, 868–872.
[22] A Tjahjono, A Priyadi, M Pujiantara, MH Purnomo, T Taufik, A Shaban, X-H Yu, "Modeling characteristic curves of digital overcurrent relay (DOCR) for user-defined characteristic curve using artificial neural network", *2016 International Conference on Computational Science and Computational Intelligence (CSCI)*, 2016, pp. 478–483.
[23] DC Yu, JC Cummins, Z Wang, H-J Yoon, LA Kojovic, D Stone, "Neural network for current transformer saturation correction", 1999 *IEEE Transmission and Distribution Conference (Cat. No. 99CH36333)*, 1999, 1, pp. 441–446.
[24] DN Vishwakarma, Z Moravej, "ANN based directional overcurrent relay", *2001 IEEE/PES Transmission and Distribution Conference and Exposition. Developing New Perspectives (Cat. No.01CH37294)*, 2001, 1, pp. 59–64.
[25] R Venkatesan, B Balamurugan, "A realtime hardware fault detector using an artificial neural network for distance protection", *IEEE Transactions on Power Delivery* 16, 1, 2001, 75–82.
[26] A Tjahjono, A Priyadi, M Pujiantara, MH Purnomo, T Taufik, A Shaban, X-H Yu, "Modeling characteristic curves of digital overcurrent relay (DOCR) for user defined characteristic curve using artificial neural network", *2016 International Conference on Computational Science and Computational Intelligence (CSCI)*, 2016, pp. 478–483.
[27] MA Mohamad Idin, MK Osman, NA Mohd Napiah, Z Saad, KA Ahmad, S Omar, "Time-current characteristic measurement of overcurrent relay in power system using multilayer perceptron network", *2010 International Conference on Intelligent and Advanced Systems*, 2010, pp. 1–5.
[28] H Lin, JM Guerrero, C Jia, Z-H Tan, JC Vasquez, C Liu, "Adaptive overcurrent protection for microgrids in extensive distribution systems, *IECON 2016–42nd Annual Conference of the IEEE Industrial Electronics Society*, 2016, pp. 4042–4047.
[29] YG Mostafa, M Shafik Aly, "Neural network based overcurrent voltage controlled protection system in large electrical networks", *2009 IEEE Bucharest PowerTech* 2009, pp. 1–6.
[30] DS Kumar, BM Radhakrishnan, D Srinivasan, T Reindl, "An adaptive fuzzy based relay for protection of distribution networks", *2015 IEEE International Conference on Fuzzy Systems (FUZZ-IEEE)*, 2015, pp. 1–6.
[31] MA Ali, FM Bendary, "Design of prototype non directional overcurrent relay microcontroller-based", *22nd International Conference and Exhibition on Electricity Distribution (CIRED 2013)*, 2013, pp. 1–4.
[32] Q Yang, Z Zhang, X Zhao, J Cunningham, M McCleery, PA Crossley, "A multi-function protection and control relay designed using multiple micro-controllers", *1993 Fifth International Conference on Developments in Power System Protection*, 1993, pp. 99–102.
[33] T Bujanovic, P Ghosh, "Adaptive algorithm for microprocessor based distance relays in smart grid", *2016 IEEE Smart Energy Grid Engineering (SEGE)*, 2016, pp. 358–364.
[34] "Relay scheme design using microprocessor relays", *2015 68th Annual Conference for Protective Relay Engineers*, 2015, pp. 405–447.
[35] A Zamani, TS Sidhu, A Yazdani, "A protection strategy and microprocessor-based relay for low-voltage Microgrids", *IEEE Transactions on Power Delivery* 26, 3, 2011, 1873–1883.

[36] B Osorno, "Application of microprocessor based protective relays in power systems", *2009 IEEE Industry Applications Society Annual Meeting*, 2009, pp. 1–8.
[37] FMA Hussain, N Khan, N Mariun, S Mahmod, "Microprocessor-based distance relay", *Proceedings National Power Engineering Conference*, PECon, 2003, pp. 43–46.
[38] OG Swathika, and S Hemamalini. "Relay coordination in real-time microgrid for varying load demands", *ARPN Journal of Engineering and Applied Sciences* 11, 5, 2016, 3222–3227.
[39] D Uthitsunthorn, T Kulworawanichpong, "Optimal overcurrent relay coordination using genetic algorithms", *2010 International Conference on Advances in Energy Engineering* 2010, pp. 162–165.
[40] KM Silva, BF Kusel, "DFT based phasor estimation algorithm for numerical digital relaying", *Electronics Letters* 49, 6, 2013, 412–414.
[41] BY Vyas, B Das, RP Maheshwari, "Improved fault classification in series compensated transmission line: comparative evaluation of chebyshev neural network training algorithms", *IEEE Transactions on Neural Networks and Learning Systems* 27, 8, 2016, 1631–1642.
[42] G Dartmann, E Zandi, G Ascheid, "A modified Levenberg–Marquardt method for the bidirectional relay channel", *IEEE Transactions on Vehicular Technology* 63, 8, 2014, 4096–4101.

9 A Neural Network–Based Vector Control Scheme for Regenerative Converters to Use in Elevator Systems

K.T.M.U. Hemapala and
Suren Senadheera Wewalage
University of Moratuwa

O.V. Gnana Swathika
Vellore Institute of Technology

CONTENTS

DOI: 10.1201/9781003201069-9

9.1 INTRODUCTION: BACKGROUND AND DRIVING FORCES

Elevator units installed in multistory buildings provide the services for transporting people among different floors. Due to the space limitations in many cities and other areas, many of the existing and future buildings in the world are getting taller. Therefore, the elevator systems installed in these buildings are getting faster in their day-to-day operations [1–4]. These elevator systems have become an important part of the installation in high-rise buildings for vertical transportation [5].

Consumption of energy in these elevator systems has become common as of lighting system installations in the buildings [6]. However, when it compares with lighting systems, energy consumption of elevator systems is much higher than that [7–8]. The main reasons for this observation are the huge electrical traction machines and heavy loads incorporated in these elevator systems combined with continuous operation around the clock [9]. On behalf of addressing the green building concepts with these kinds of systems in todays world, extraction of regenerative energy from these systems in a more efficient and useful manner has become a more important consideration [10].

The common method of construction in regenerative drive systems is to replace the passive diode rectifier at the input side of the motor drive with a two-way active converter which can act as a rectifier in the normal input mode and an inverter in the regeneration mode [11–15]. The main switching element in active front end converters currently in use is the insulated gate bipolar transistor (IGBT). Generally, these types of IGBT switches are regulated with standard techniques in vector control methodology via proportional–integral (PI) controller–based techniques.

9.2 EXISTING ELEVATOR SYSTEMS

During the operation of elevator systems, the main traction motor of that elevator acts both in the motor mode and generator mode. When the elevator is going up with a heavy load or coming down with a light load in its cabin, the main traction motor operates in the motoring mode and absorbs power from the utility supply into the motor drive. When it is going up with a light load or coming down with a heavy load in its cabin, the main traction motor operates in the generating mode and releases power from the motor drive to the utility supply. This process is based on the four-quadrant operation of motor drives used in the motor. Figure 9.1 shows more details of four-quadrant operation for a motor drive.

As shown in the figure, when the torque applied by the motor is similar to its rotational direction (first and third quadrant operation), it operates in the motoring mode and absorbs power from the utility supply. When the torque applied by the motor is opposite to its rotational direction (second and fourth quadrant operation), it operates in the generating mode.

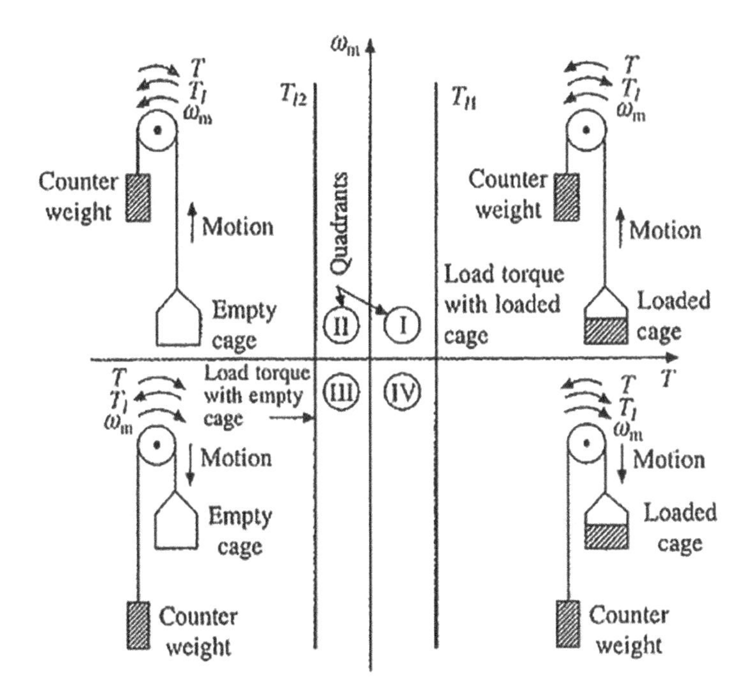

FIGURE 9.1 Four quadrant operation of a motor driving a hoist load.(https://www.eeeguide.com/four-quadrant-operation-of-motor-drive/).

9.3 CONVENTIONAL BRAKING RESISTORS

Before the extraction of elevator regenerative power comes into picture, braking resistors were used in elevator systems to dissipate the energy generated in the braking/regeneration process of elevator motors. Figure 9.2 shows the arrangement of braking resistors in a traditional elevator drive system.

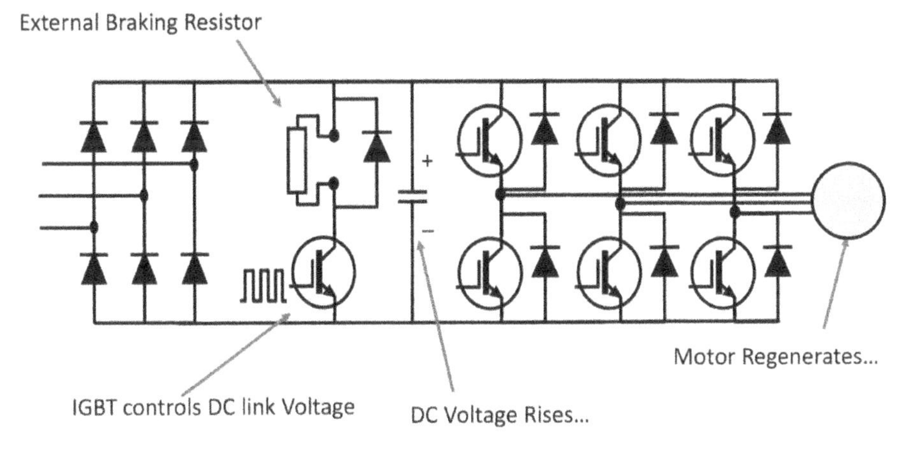

FIGURE 9.2 Application of breaking resistor in elevator drives. (https://www.invertek-drives.com/variable-frequency-drives/iknow/braking-and-regeneration-14).

As shown in the figure, when the motor operates in the generating mode, the inverter drive connected to the motor is giving power back to the DC link capacitor, and the DC voltage rises. When the DC voltage rise comes to a specific maximum safety voltage level, the IGBT unit connected parallel to the DC link operates the braking resistor and dissipates this extra energy as heat and controls the DC link voltage within safe limits.

9.4 NEW AC/DC BIDIRECTIONAL CONVERTER

When this braking resistor is replaced with a regenerative converter, the dissipated heat energy can be harvested in a useful manner. Figure 9.3 shows the application of the regenerative converter into the motor drive system by replacing the braking resistor.

When designing a switching control system that has some improved behavioral aspects when compared to the existing switching control systems, it is important to analyze the behavior of real-world elevator systems. This research contains the studies of several office and apartment building complexes that help in understanding

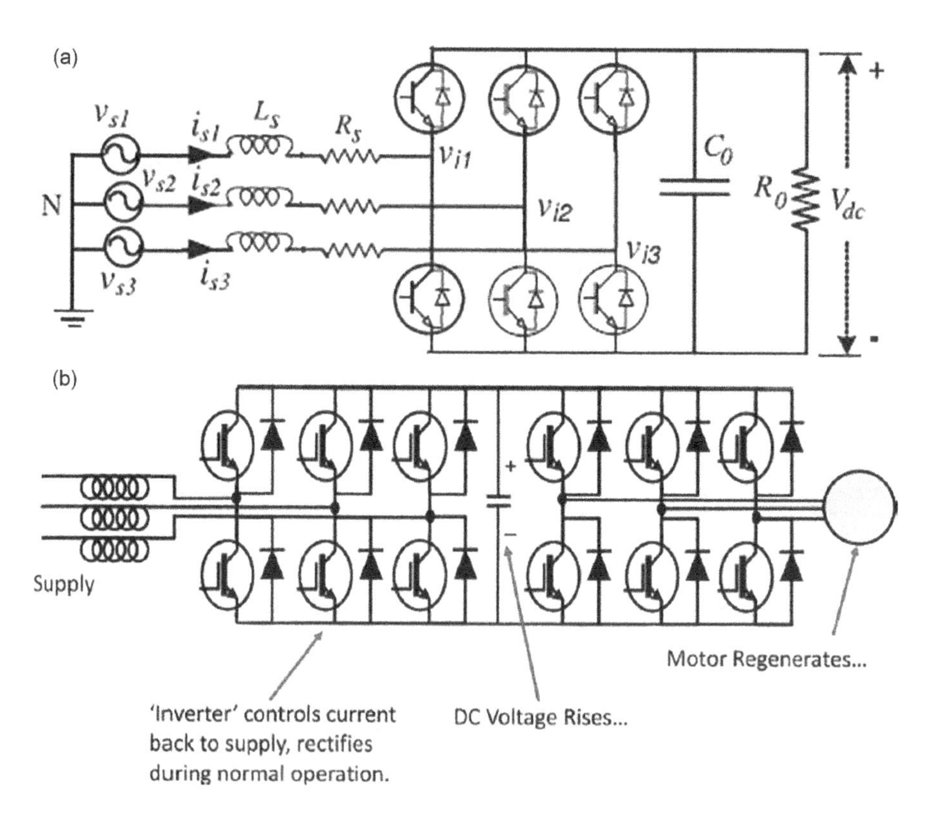

FIGURE 9.3 (a) Shows the detailed view of regenerative converter to be added to the motor drive. (b) Shows the total diagram of motor drive after adding regenerative converter to the motor drive. (https://www.invertekdrives.com/variable-frequency-drives/iknow/braking-and-regeneration-14).

different key factors that might be important to be incorporated into the system in obtaining a much more realistic elevator behavioral quality.

The flow of this process can be explained as follows: Initially, the site data are collected. These data will be converted into data types which can be processed with MATLAB simulation models. Here, mainly the elevator load data will be converted into motor torque values. After that, these data will be simulated in a standard PI model and proposed neural network (NN) model separately. Then, the output data will be recorded separately for comparison purposes. Finally, these results will be compared with each other, and the relevant performance will be reflected as the final assessment. A block diagram of the complete process is shown in Figure 9.4 for more clarity.

9.5 MEASUREMENT OF INPUT PARAMETERS IN THE SYSTEM

During the measurement of real-world elevator data, several parameters were measured as follows:

1. Utility side AC voltage (V)
2. Utility side AC current (A)
3. Utility side AC frequency (Hz)
4. Utility side energy (kWh)
5. Motor rotational speed (rpm)
6. Elevator load (kg)
7. Traveling direction (Up/Down)

9.5.1 Utility Side AC Voltage (V), Current (A), Frequency (Hz), and Energy (kWh)

A three-phase energy analyzer was used for the recording of above parameters from the elevator system. Sampling time of the energy logger was set to 1 s. Figure 9.5 shows an image of the energy logger.

9.5.2 Traction Motor Speed (rpm)

This was done by using a speed sensor module. A magnetic pointer was attached to the main traction wheel, and the speed sensor was aligned to that point to get the rotational speed [1]. An image of the speed sensor module is shown in Figure 9.6 for reference.

The output of this sensor is forwarded to record in the data logger. In addition to this, a noncontact RPM meter also was used to measure the rotational speed. The main purpose of using an RPM meter is to verify the accuracy of data recorded via the speed sensor/data logger. An image of the RPM meter is shown in Figure 9.7 for more details. During this comparison, it was noticed that both the readings were matching with each other.

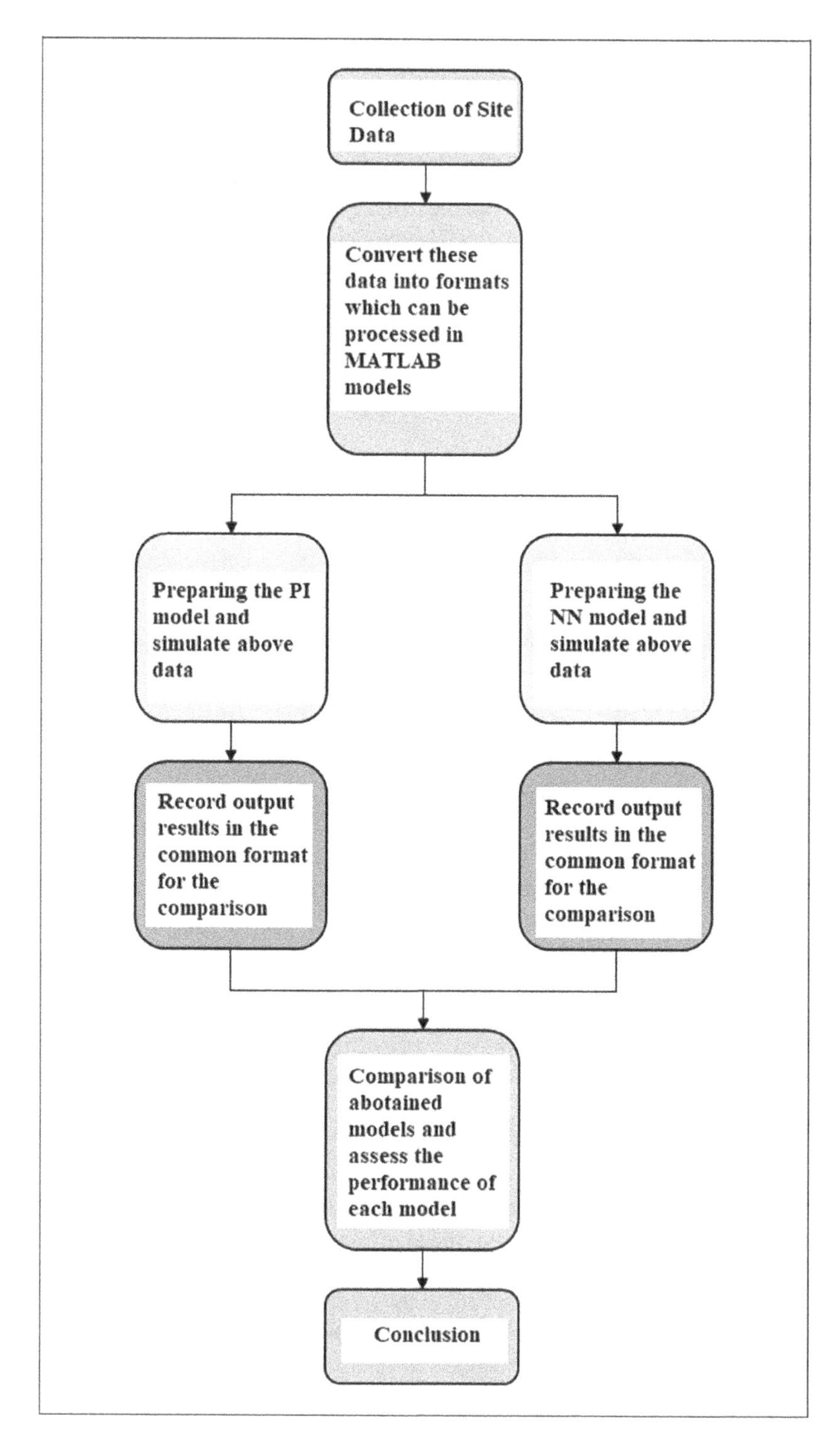

FIGURE 9.4 Simplified block diagram for the process.

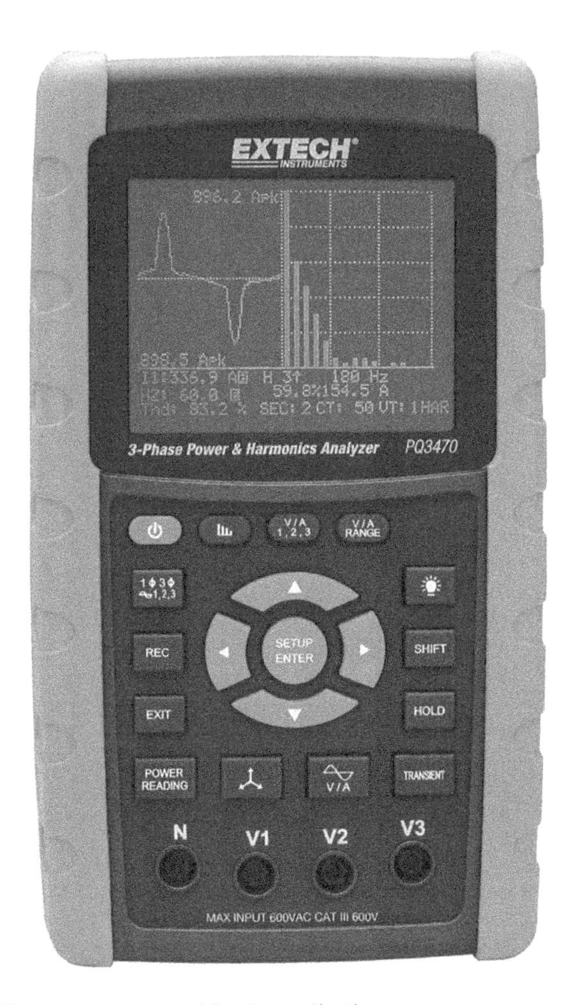

FIGURE 9.5 Energy analyzer used for the application.

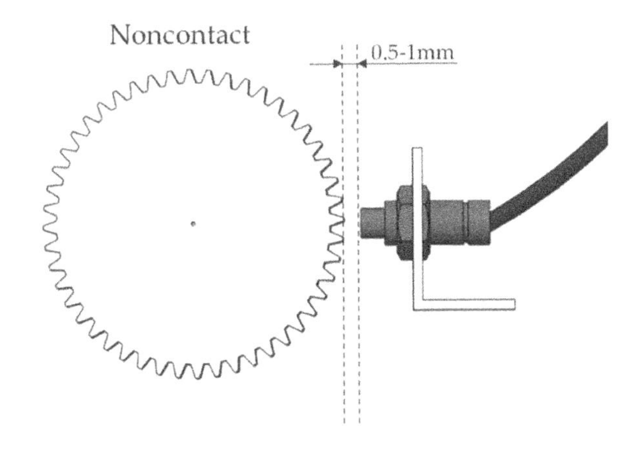

FIGURE 9.6 Separately installed speed sensor.

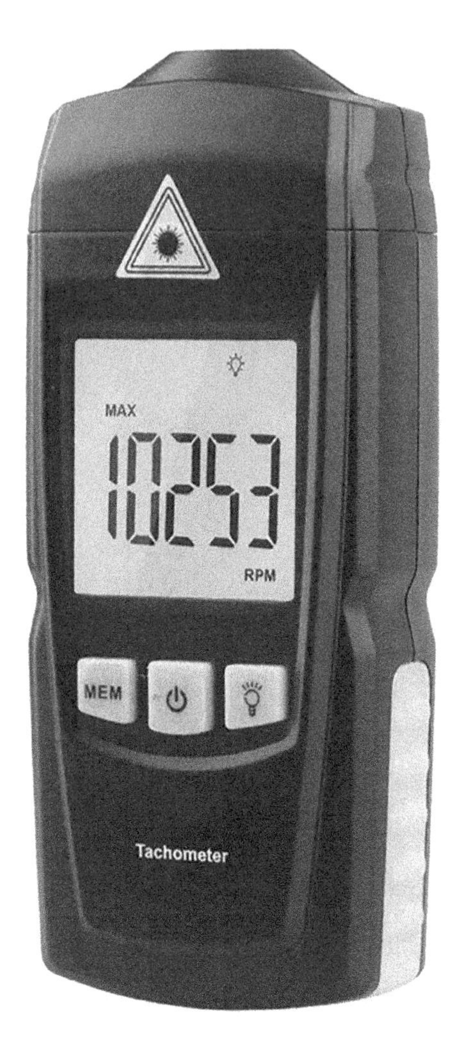

FIGURE 9.7 Noncontact revolutions per meter (RPM) meter.

9.5.3 Elevator Load (kg)

Elevator load measurement was done by using an elevator load sensor installed on elevator ropes fixed to the elevator frame. Figure 9.8 shows an image of the location where the load sensor was installed. The sensor location in 2:1 rope ratio diagram is shown in Figure 9.9. Figure 9.10 shows a clearer image of the load sensor installed on elevator ropes.

During the time of data recording, there was an unstable situation in the load sensor reading. This was mainly due to the dynamic behavior of passengers and the elevator system. Hence, the load sensor reading at the time of triggering the door closing motor which is mounted on the elevator cabin was recorded as the input load for the elevator system until the next stop.

FIGURE 9.8 Mounting location of elevator load sensor.

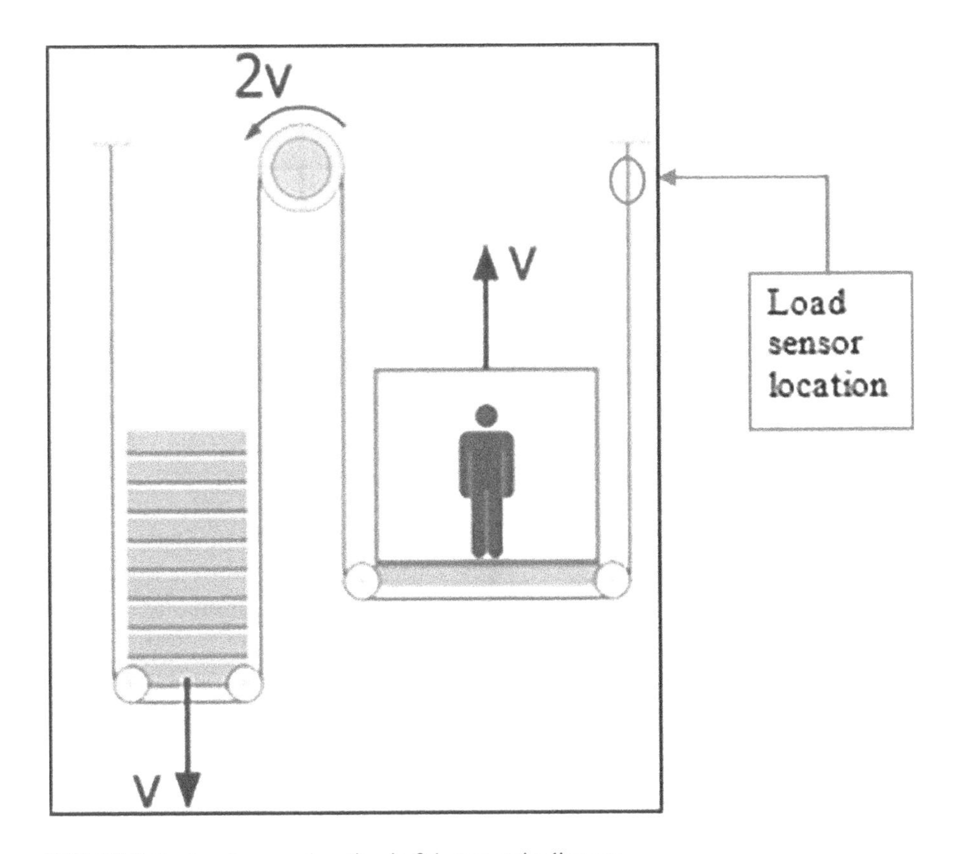

FIGURE 9.9 Load sensor location in 2:1 rope ratio diagram.

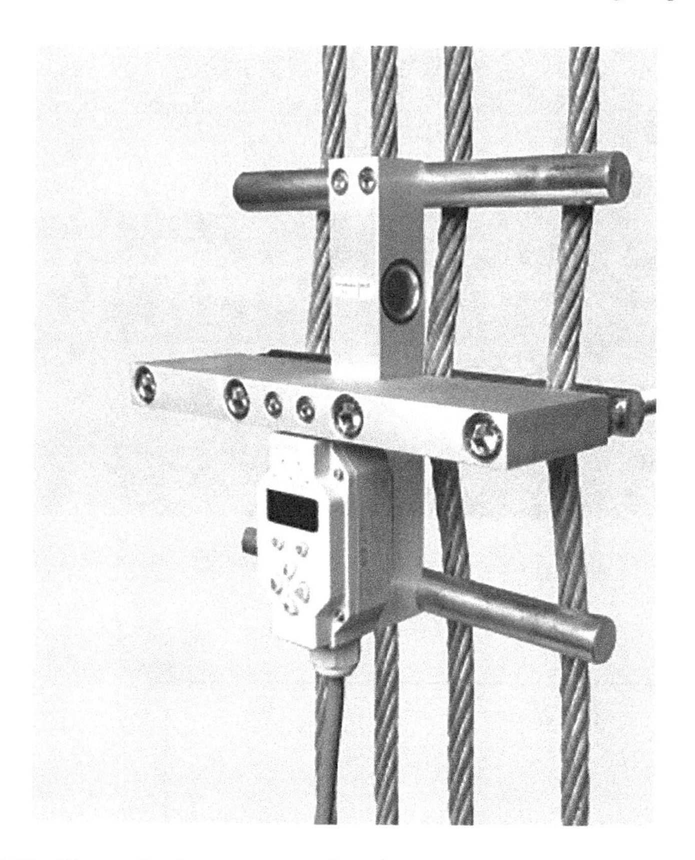

FIGURE 9.10 Elevator load sensor mounted on the ropes.

For more clarity, assume that the elevator is starting the nth term of its journey by closing the doors mounted on elevator cabin for the nth term. Then, the load sensor reading at that time is recorded as the input load of elevator for the nth term of its journey. Once the elevator was stopped at a certain destination floor by completing the nth term of its journey, it will open the doors to start the $(n+1)^{th}$ term. At the time of door closure to start the $(n+1)^{th}$ term of elevator's journey, available reading of the load sensor is recorded as the input load of the elevator system for the $(n+1)^{th}$ term of its journey. In this way, the issue of getting unstable readings from the load sensor could be avoided up to a satisfactory level. The output of these sensors was recorded in the data logger, as shown in Figure 9.11.

9.5.4 Elevator Travelling Direction (Up/Down)

This input was recorded by referring the travel direction signal output from the elevator controller. The input data from this unit were recorded in the data logger.

In this process, four multistory buildings were randomly selected for data collection, which are shown in Tables 9.1–9.4.

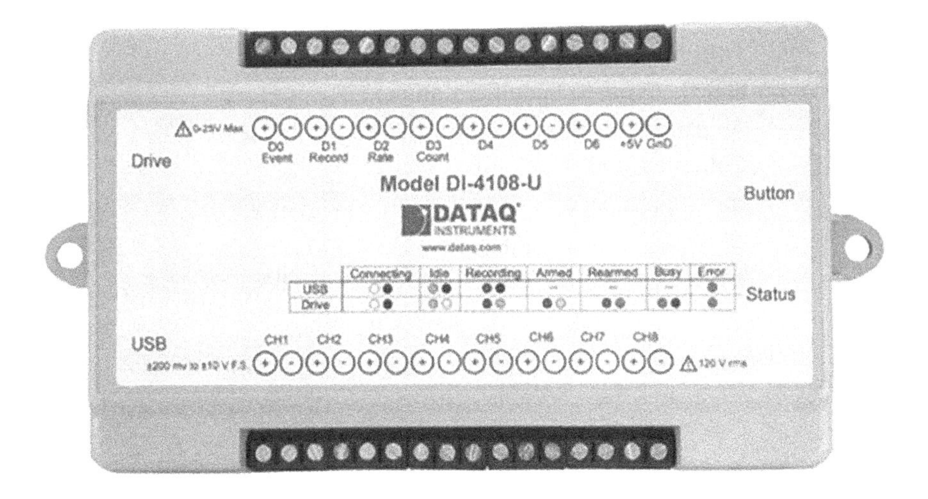

FIGURE 9.11 Data recording logger.

Results of the site collected data are arranged in tables accordingly. Then, these data were analyzed on MATLAB Simulink platform, and resulting data were tabulated. Figure 9.12 shows the MATLAB Simulink model used to simulate these data. Preparation of this model was mainly based on the details indicated in Figure 9.3b.

TABLE 9.1
Elevator System Specifications of Twenty-Story Office Building Complex at Narahenpita

No.	Description	Details
1	No. of elevators in the building	5 nos
2	Load capacity of each elevator	1050kg
3	Vertical speed of elevator	2.0m/s
4	Type of the traction motor	PM/Gearless
5	Maximum torque of traction motor	670 Nm
6	Rated speed of traction motor	190rpm
7	Traction sheave diameter	400mm
8	Counterweight	1650kg
9	Empty car weight	1200kg
10	Rope ratio	2:1

TABLE 9.2
Elevator System Specifications of Fifteen-Story Apartment Building Complex at Boswell Place, Colombo – 06

No.	Description	Details
1	No. of elevators in the building	1 no
2	Load capacity of each elevator	630 kg
3	Vertical speed of elevator	1.0 m/s
4	Type of the traction motor	PM/Gearless
5	Maximum torque of traction motor	110 Nm
6	Rated speed of traction motor	382 rpm
7	Traction sheave diameter	100 mm
8	Counterweight	1050 kg
9	Empty car weight	800 kg
10	Rope ratio	2:1

TABLE 9.3
Elevator System Specifications of Twelve-Story Apartment Building Complex at Moore's Road, Colombo – 06

No.	Description	Details
1	No. of elevators in the building	1 no
2	Load capacity of each elevator	630 kg
3	Vertical speed of elevator	1.0 m/s
4	Type of the traction motor	PM/Gearless
5	Maximum torque of traction motor	450 Nm
6	Rated speed of traction motor	95 rpm
7	Traction sheave diameter	400 mm
8	Counterweight	1050 kg
9	Empty car weight	800 kg
10	Rope ratio	2:1

TABLE 9.4
Elevator System Specifications of Eight-Story Apartment Building Complex at Frankfort Place, Colombo – 04

No.	Description	Details
1	No. of elevators in the building	1 no
2	Load capacity of each elevator	800 kg
3	Vertical speed of elevator	1.0 m/s
4	Type of the traction motor	PM/Gearless
5	Maximum torque of traction motor	570 Nm
6	Rated speed of traction motor	95 rpm
7	Traction sheave diameter	400 mm
8	Counterweight	1320 kg
9	Empty car weight	1000 kg
10	Rope ratio	2:1

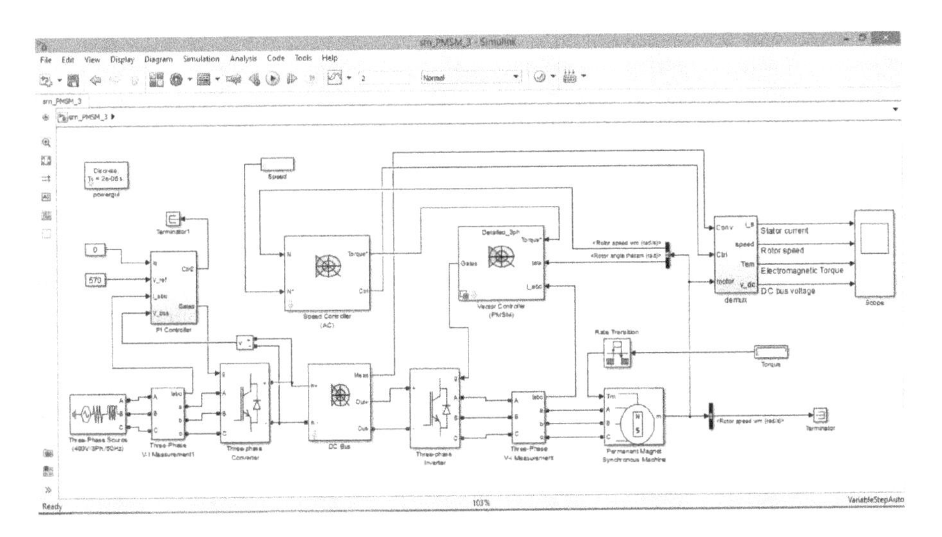

FIGURE 9.12 MATLAB Simulink model of the standard PI regulator-based switching controller of AC/DC bidirectional converter.

9.6 SYSTEM DATA INPUTS

Based on these collected data for each building, the torque and speed reference data were calculated for all the four buildings (office building complex at Narahenpita, apartment building complexes at Boswell Place, Moore's Road, and Frankfort Place). Then, these inputs were used in PI-based and NN-based MATLAB simulation models to compare the performance of each model with respect to each building.

By considering the office building complex at Narahenpita, a sample of calculation data for torque and speed can be detailed as follows:

Calculation for torque data:
Reference passenger load = 640 kg
Empty car weight = 1200 kg
Counterweight = 1620 kg

Load applied on the motor = Passenger load + Empty car weight – Counterweight

$$= 640 + 1200 - 1650\,\text{kg}$$
$$= 190\,\text{kg}$$

Traction sheave diameter = 400 mm
Elevator rope ratio = 2:1 (then, the torque will become a half)

Hence the generated torque in motor = $190 \times 9.8 \times (200/1000) \times 0.5$ **Nm**

$$= 186.2\ \text{Nm}$$

Calculation of speed data:
Vertical elevator speed = 2.0 m/s
Traction sheave diameter = 400 mm
Elevator rope ratio = 2:1 (then, the speed will become double)

Hence the motor speed = $(2.0\,\text{m/s}) \times 2/[(400\,\text{mm}) \times \pi/1000]$ **rev./s**

$$= 3.18\ \text{rev./s} \times 60\ \text{s/min.}$$
$$= 190\,\text{rpm}$$

Then, the site collected data were simulated with the above PI regulator model to convert them into the common platform to compare with the newly proposed neural network model. These resulting data were tabulated based on each building.

When these simulated output data from the PI model are compared with site collected data, it shows a slight improvement in the PI model simulated data. This is because of the losses and measurement errors of site collected data.

When these data were analyzed, it seems that the nature of power regeneration pattern from these elevator systems mainly depends on four parameters: elevator load, elevator speed, elevator travelling direction, and elevator travelling distance.

9.7 SUMMARY OF PI REGULATOR MODEL SIMULATED DATA

Data related to four elevator systems collected from randomly selected multistory buildings in Colombo area were presented in the above chapter. The results of these studies are used in designing a system that has the capability to function with more improvements compared to the PI regulator-based model. By improving a new system based on these types of practical performance levels, it is easier to achieve higher accuracy levels than those of the existing basic systems.

During this study, it could be noticed what are the main system parameters affecting the efficiency of power regeneration process in elevator systems. After that, it was further studied on how to improve the efficiency of the process by improving the efficiency of each parameter with different aspects. The effects that exert power regeneration according to the elevator load and elevator travelling distance were extensively studied, which will help to determine the controlled inputs of the proposed system.

9.8 PROPOSED SYSTEM OVERVIEW

The system contains four major modules. They are utility supply side voltage sensor, utility supply side frequency meter, motor drive side voltage sensor, and the main NN controller. The input from the utility supply side voltage sensor is considered to smooth the voltage waveform of the regenerated signal from the system. Frequency meter input is considered in maintaining the system output frequency within allowable limits of utility system supply. The motor drive side voltage sensor input is considered to smoothly maintain the DC link voltage levels within allowable limits of the system. The NN controller takes all these inputs and modifies the control signal sending to the space vector–pulse width modulation (SV-PWM) generator to control the on–off operation/frequency of IGBT switches in the converter.

9.9 PROPOSED SYSTEM BLOCK DIAGRAM

The block diagram of the proposed system is shown in Figure 9.13 for clear details. Initially, the three-phase reference signals are converted into two-phase stationary reference frame signals by the Clarke transform. Then, these signals are converted into two-phase signals in the rotating reference frame by the Park transformation. After that, these signals are input to the NN-based controller. Here, the neural network controller compares these signals with the reference input signals, and the rotating reference frame signals are forwarded as outputs of the system. These signal outputs are then inverse transformed by the Park transformation in the rotating reference frame. Then, these rotating reference fame signals are again converted into stationary reference frame signals through Clarke transformation. Then, these signals are forwarded to the SV-PWM generator to generate control signals of IGBT switching devices in the converter. Calculation block diagram of the system is shown in Figure 9.14.

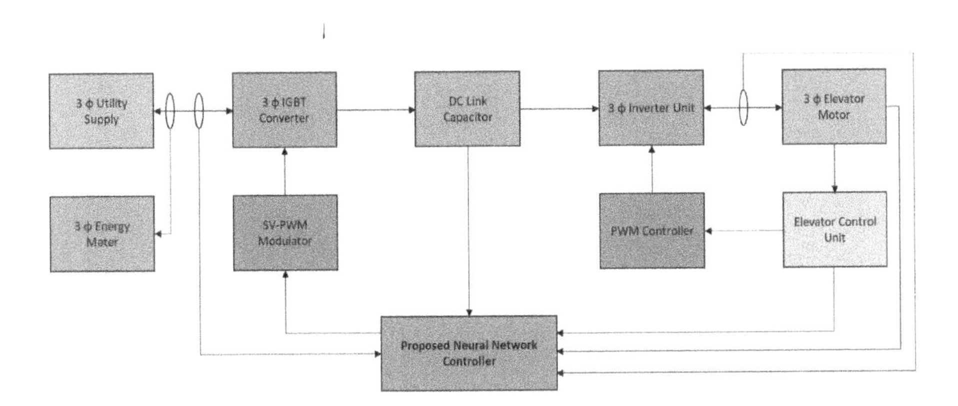

FIGURE 9.13 System block diagram of the proposed model.

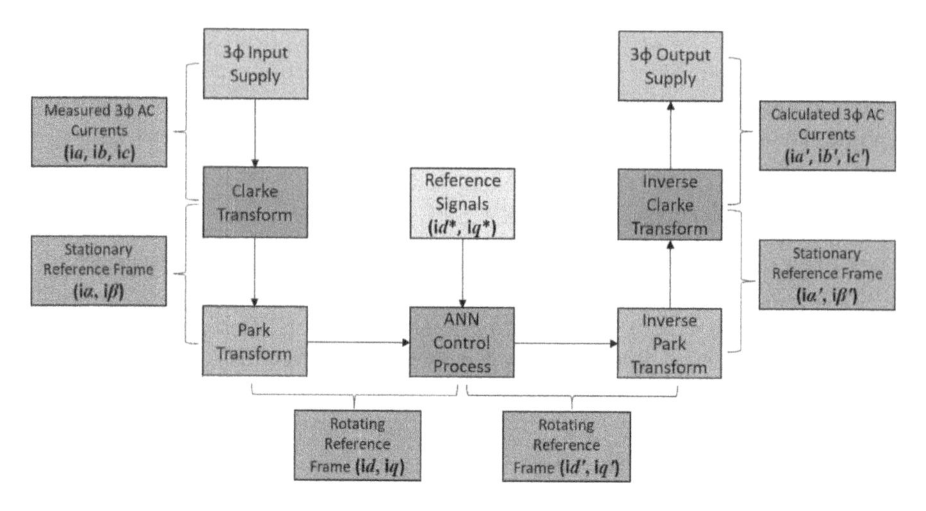

FIGURE 9.14 Calculation block diagram of the proposed model. (https://www.switchcraft.org/learning/2016/12/16).

9.10 SIMULINK MODEL OF NN-BASED CONTROL SYSTEM

The main part of this model is the NN-based model reference controller. As indicated in the above explanations, this system takes the inputs from the utility power supply and motor stator. Based on this information, the controller gives the output signal to the three-phase inverter [2–4].

Simulink model of the NN-based control system is shown in Figure 9.15. The detailed internal view of the controller model is shown in Figure 9.16 with internal NN components.

Initially, the NN model was trained using generated data sets based on randomly selected data from the original records from four buildings. Figure 9.17 shows the training process of NN model reference controller.

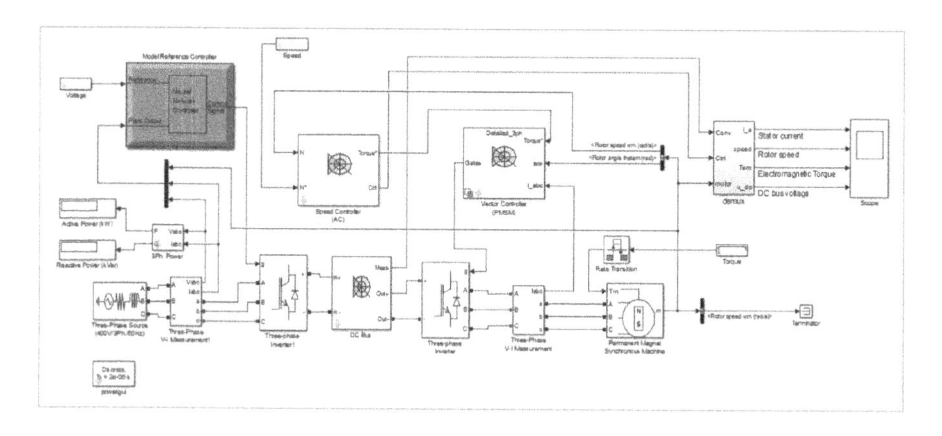

FIGURE 9.15 Simulink model of NN-based controller.

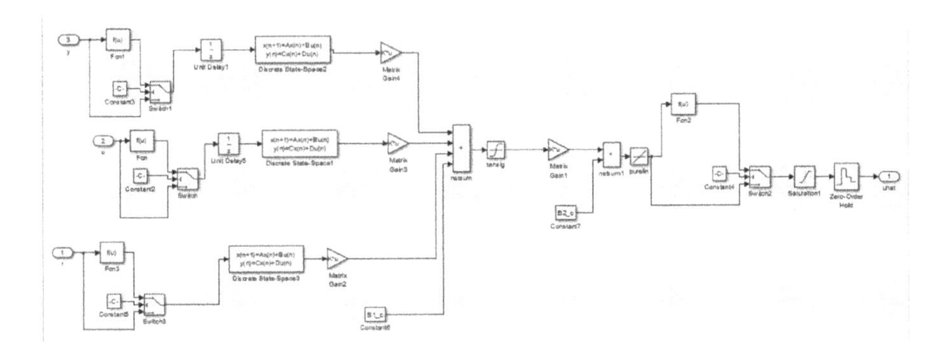

FIGURE 9.16 Internal NN components of NN-based controller.

There are six parameters which were applied to the NN-based model during its simulation.

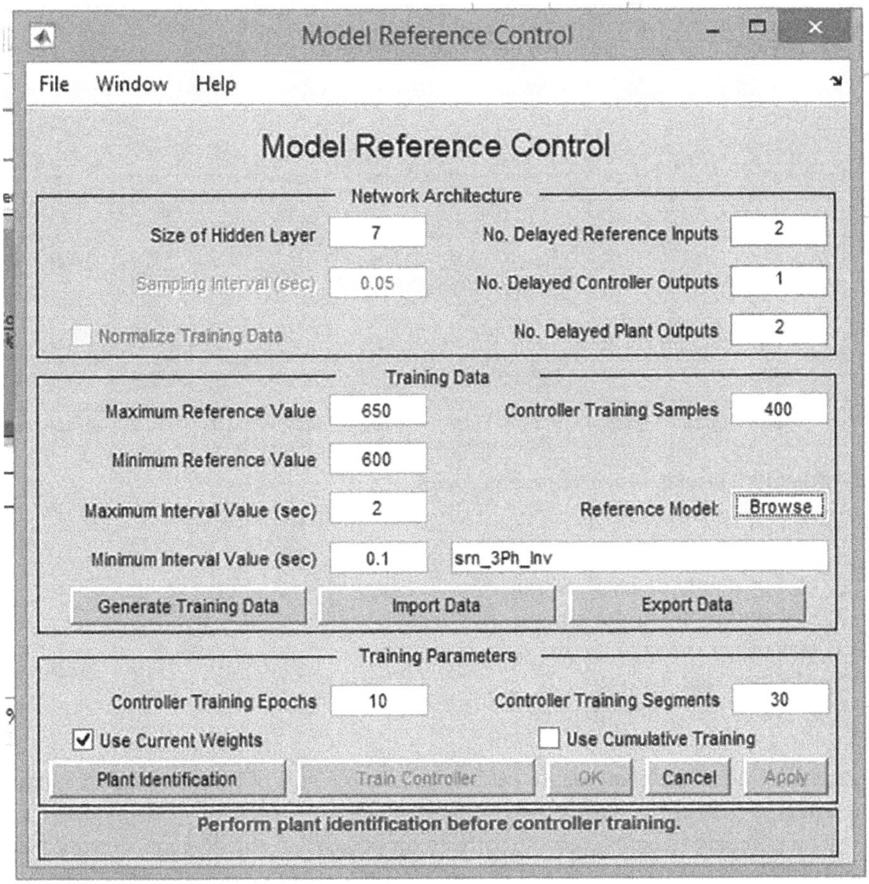

FIGURE 9.17 Plant model identification details.

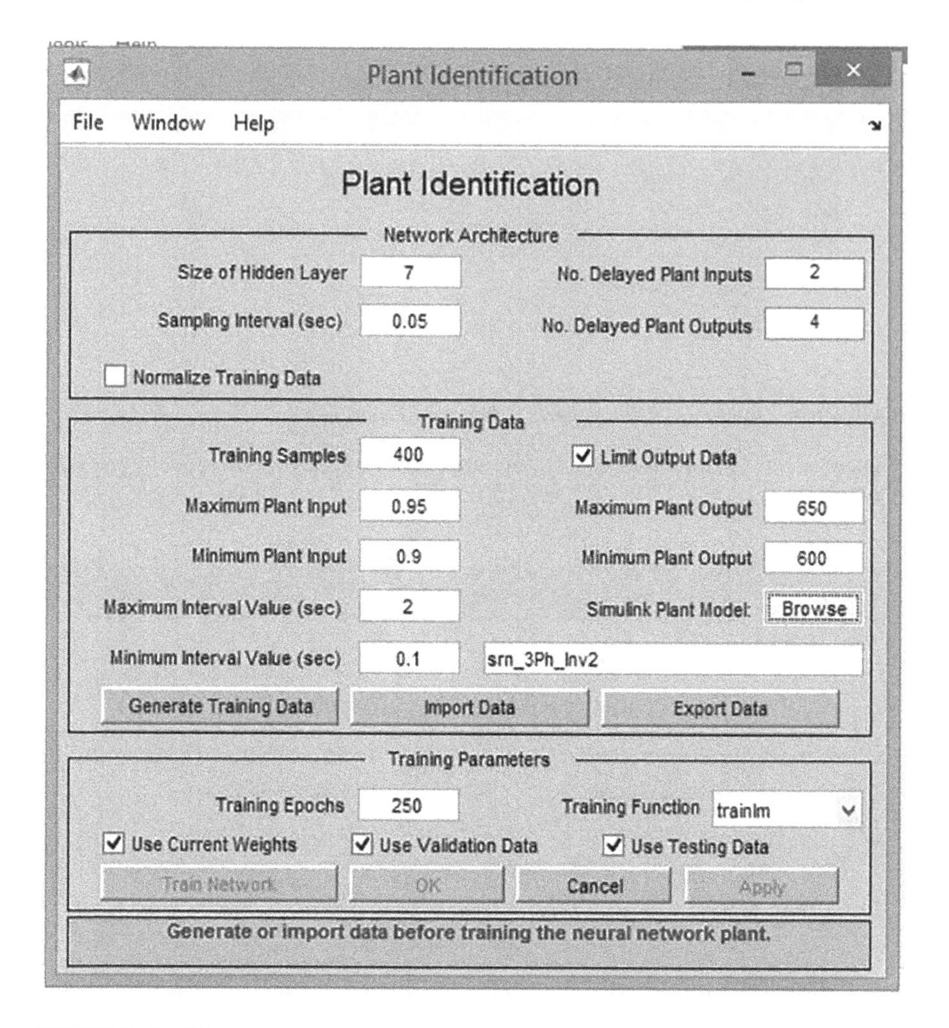

FIGURE 9.18 Plant model identification details.

1. Utility supply three-phase voltage
2. Utility supply three-phase currents
3. Utility side three-phase power frequency
4. Rotational speed of the main traction motor
5. Elevator load
6. Elevator travelling direction

Figure 9.18 shows the plant identification process as a part of training the NN model reference.

Some generated results during the training process of the NN model reference controller are shown in Figure 9.19.

Some of the training, validation, testing and performance data results randomly obtained during the training process of NN are shown in Figure 9.20–9.23, respectively.

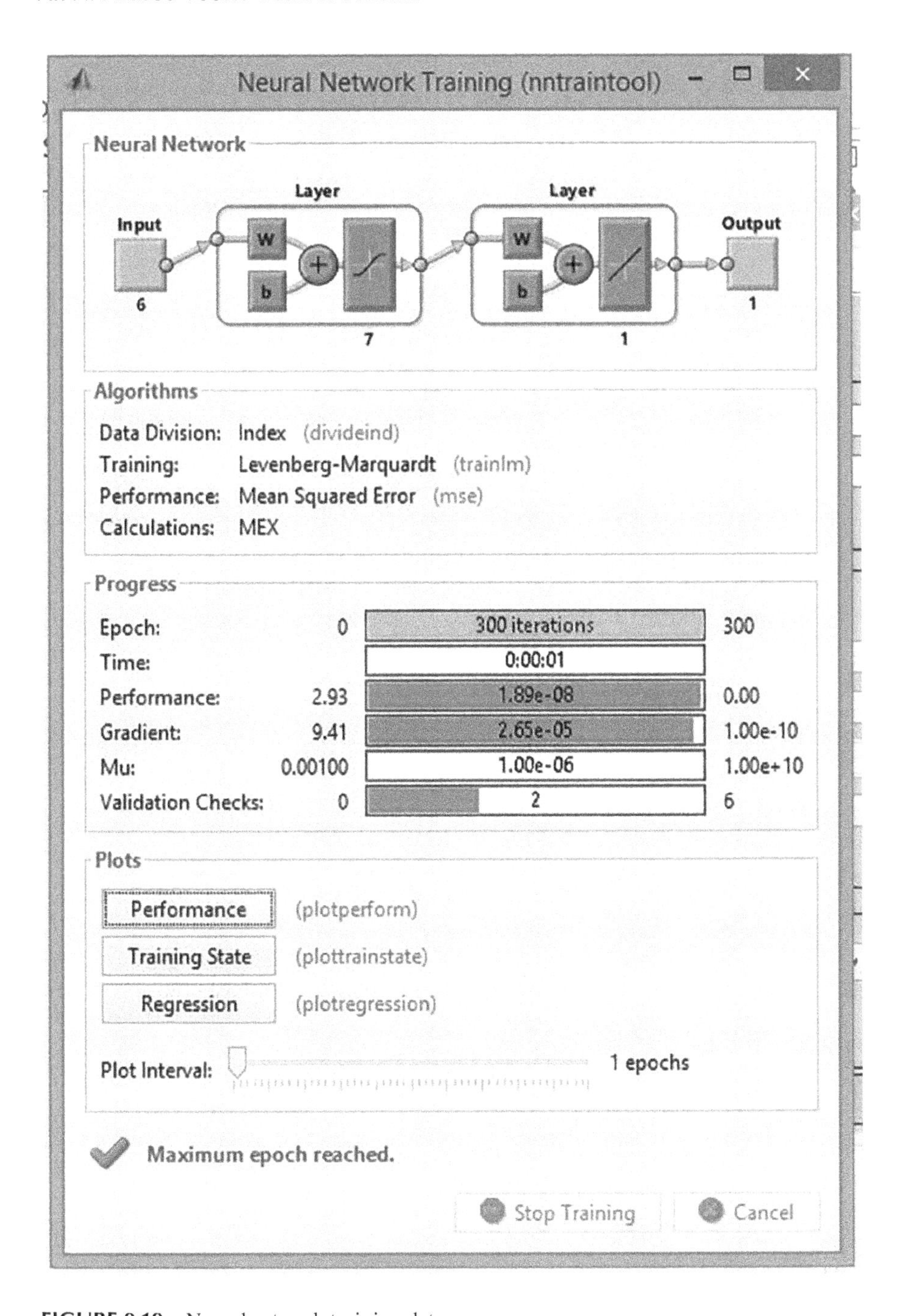

FIGURE 9.19 Neural network training data.

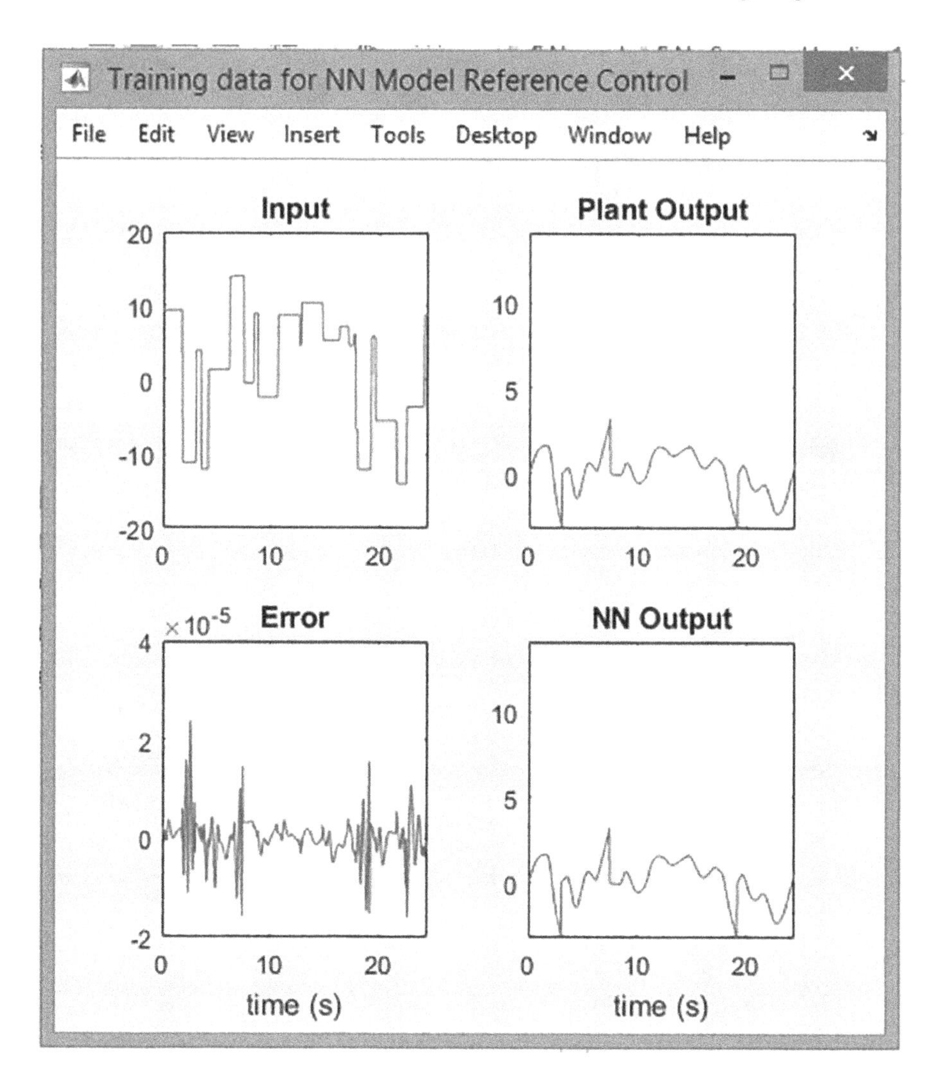

FIGURE 9.20 Random training results obtained during the training of NN model.

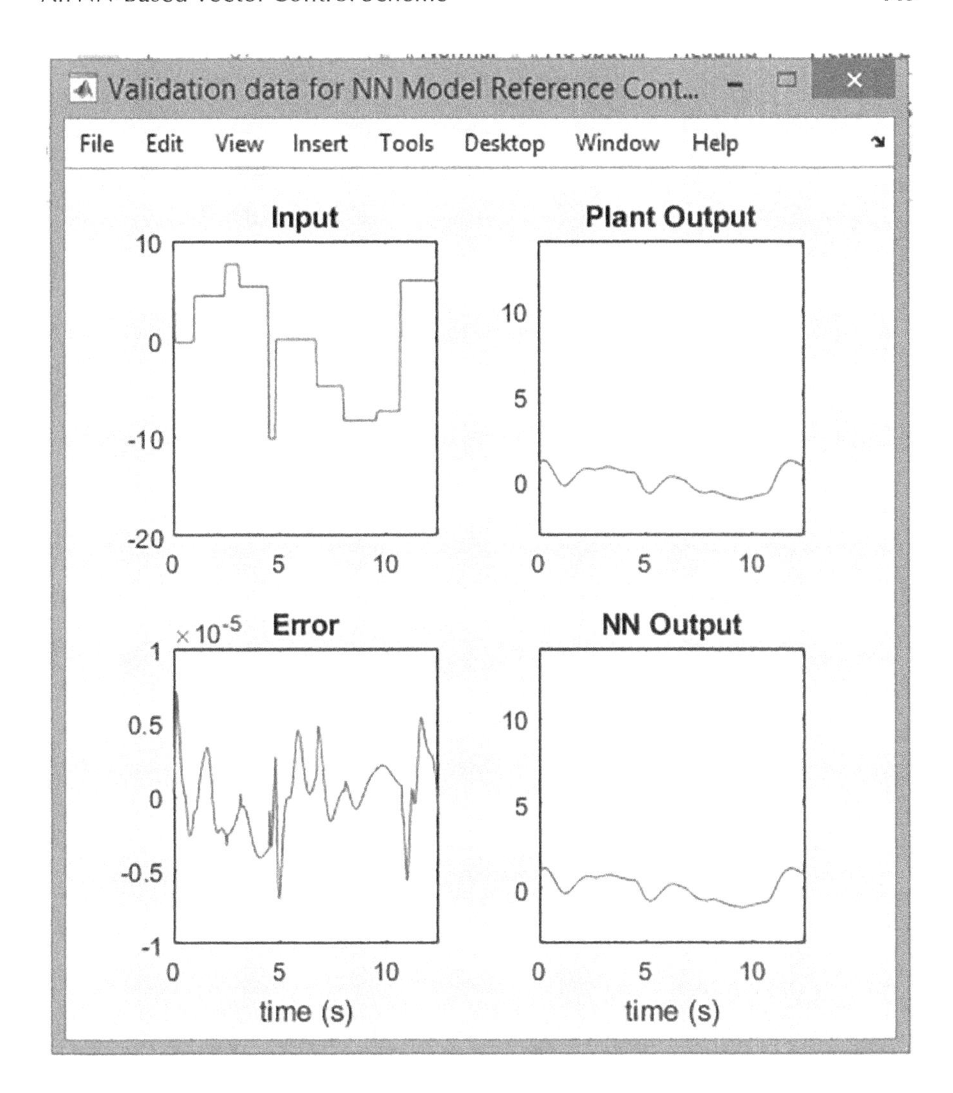

FIGURE 9.21 Random validation results obtained during the training of NN model.

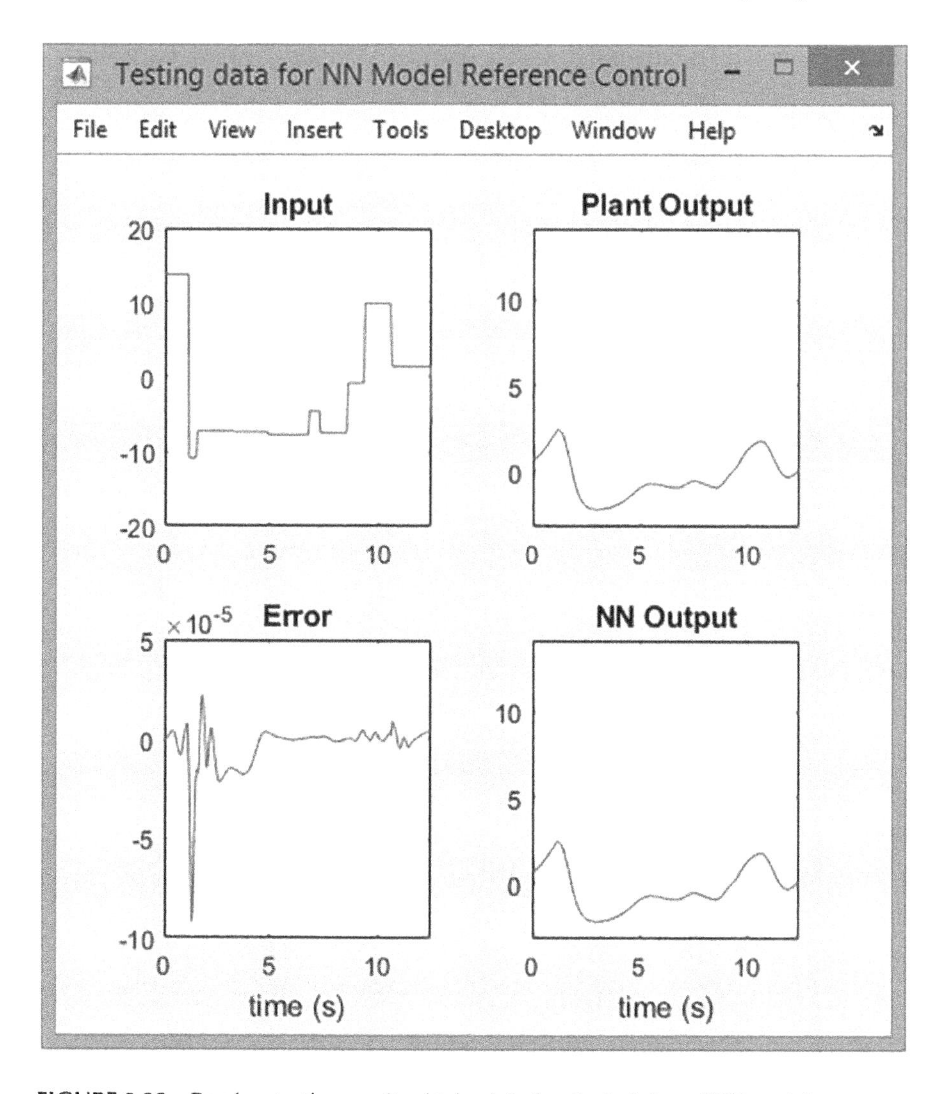

FIGURE 9.22 Random testing results obtained during the training of NN model.

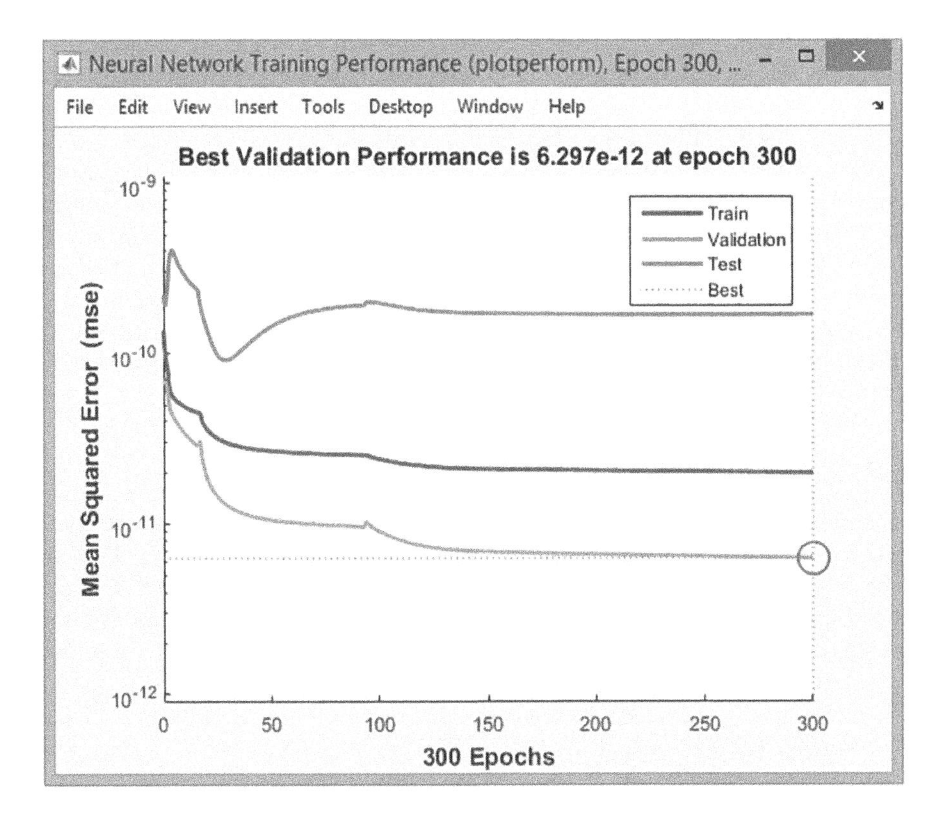

FIGURE 9.23 Random performance results obtained during the training of NN model.

9.11 SYSTEM OUTPUTS

Based on the block diagram shown in Figure 9.4, a combined Simulink model of an Active Front End (AFE) converter was established with power electronic modelling tools available in MATLAB Simulink library. This model was used to implement a system analysis with an NN-based vector control technique and to carry out a comparison study between the NN-based control method with the traditional vector control method. An AC/DC pulse width modulation converter was used as the front-end converter. A DC bus block was used as the DC link capacitor in the simulation model. Inside the process of converter simulation arrangement, a system evaluation procedure can be implemented much closer with actual elevator operational situations. This includes the collecting parameter values of direct and quadrature (dq) axis values, generating the dq axis voltage control signals and position of voltage space vector from real-time calculation.

With the digital signal processing execution of this NN-based regulator, the collected momentary values of the system current and voltage are sending across a zero-order hold (ZOH) block. This ZOH applies to the regulator output also before it is attached to pulse width modulation generating a component in the converter module.

The arbitrarily created current reference signal will be inside the adequate current limits for tracing confirmation of the NN regulator. Here, the initial states can be generated randomly. Rated current and pulse width modulator saturation limits of AFE module will not be used for the training purposes of the NN controller.

After starting of the system, this NN regulator rapidly adjusts the existing current levels of dq axes into their new values. When these dq currents change to new values, the NN regulator reinstates dq axes current values to their new reference input current levels instantly. In this way, the NN regulator is rapidly tuned to new reference current values whenever an adjustment occurred in the reference values within rated current levels of AFE switching module and pulse width modulator saturation limits. This demonstrates the robust and optimum regulating competency of the proposed NN regulator.

9.12 COMPARISON OF OUTPUT DATA

For comparison, the current loop PI controller is designed by using the conventional standard method as shown in Figure 9.12. The improvements of the discrete PI regulator were considered referring to the equivalent discrete system of the transfer function. With a sample time of $T_s = 1$ ms, there was no stable PI gains obtained for the conventional vector control method. However, the NN controller gives a higher stability level at this stage. When we consider a smaller sampling time such as $T_s = 0.1$ ms, the existent dq currents of the standard vector controller are oscillating at higher unacceptable levels when compared to the NN regulator, and hence, there are many distortions and unbalances in the three-phase utility system also [5].

Several more comparisons have been carried out with different dq reference input current levels. All those experiments indicate that this NN regulator's performance is better than the PI regulator–based standard vector controller mechanism. Generally, the NN based regulator is able to reach a reference value more rapidly and become

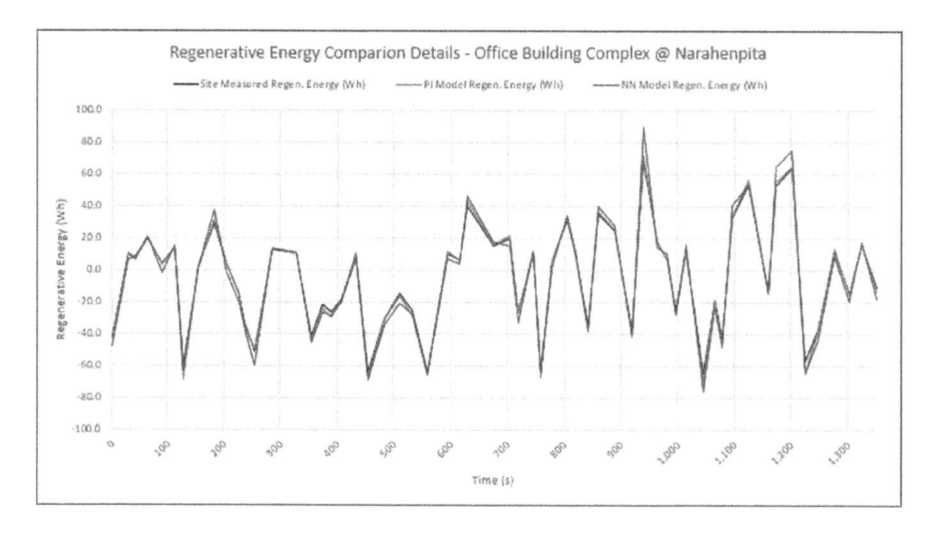

FIGURE 9.24 Regenerative energy comparison for the office complex at Narahenpita.

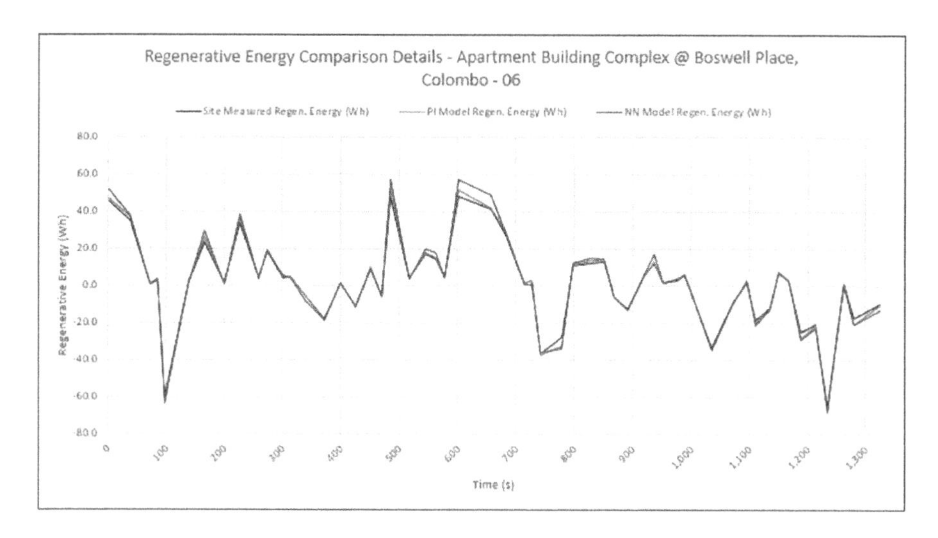

FIGURE 9.25 Regenerative energy comparison for apartment complex at Boswell Place.

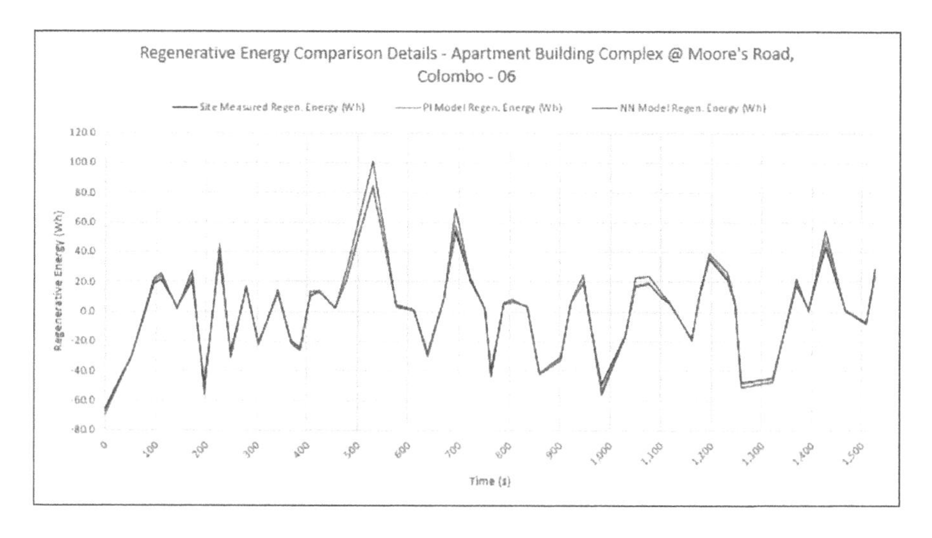

FIGURE 9.26 Regenerative energy comparison for apartment complex at Moore's Road.

stable nearby these reference values using considerably small oscillations. Since these output regenerative power from elevator systems are always having frequent fluctuations along with the system operation, the quick recovery behaviors in the NN-based controller systems can improve the system efficiency up to a satisfactory level.

Comparison of PI model output data and NN model output data were put on graphs separately based on each building. The sample of comparative graph for PI and NN energy regeneration of the office building complex at Narahenpita has been shown in Figure 9.24. The sample of regenerative energy comparison for the apartment building complex at Boswell Place has been shown in Figure 9.25. A sample PI

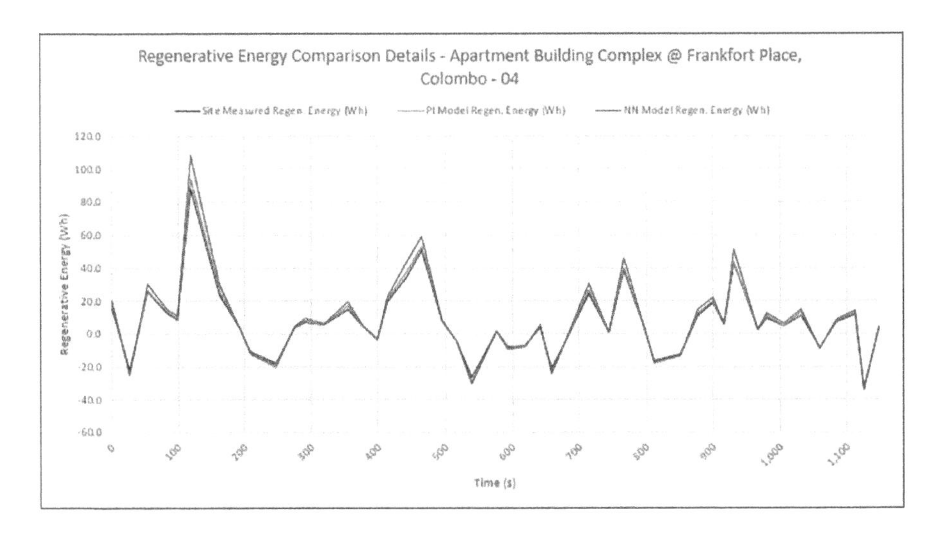

FIGURE 9.27 Regenerative energy comparison for apartment complex at Frankfort Place.

and NN model energy regenerating comparison is shown in Figure 9.26. A sample energy regeneration comparison of PI and NN model for the Apartment Building Complex at Frankfort Place is shown in Figure 9.27. The complete data set is available in Appendix 1.

9.13 ENERGY CALCULATION RESULTS

1. Energy regeneration details of the 20-story office building complex at Narahenpita. In this building, there were five nos. of elevators to serve the passenger demand of the building. All the five elevators seem to be matching with each other in operation and passenger traffic so that effects on site collected data will be negligible. Therefore, only one elevator reading could be considered and multiplied by five for further comparisons. However, at the end of the total calculation process, a tolerance will be added to compensate these kinds of site errors.

   By considering the total regenerative output energy from PI model data, total monthly energy regeneration of the existing elevator system is follows:

$$1.18 \frac{\text{kWh}}{\text{day}} \times 25 \frac{\text{day}}{\text{month}} = 29.5 \frac{\text{kWh}}{\text{month}} \tag{9.1}$$

   By considering the total regenerative output energy from NN model data, total monthly energy regeneration of the proposed NN based system is given as follows:

$$1.74 \frac{\text{kWh}}{\text{day}} \times 25 \frac{\text{day}}{\text{month}} = 43.5 \frac{\text{kWh}}{\text{month}} \tag{9.2}$$

Accordingly, the improvement in energy regeneration from the proposed NN-based system:

$$\frac{43.5-29.5}{29.5}\times 100\% = 47.46\% \tag{9.3}$$

2. Energy regeneration details of a 15-story apartment building complex at Boswell Place, Colombo-06.

   By considering the total regenerative output energy from PI model data, total monthly energy regeneration of the existing elevator system is given as follows:

$$1.83\frac{\text{kWh}}{\text{day}}\times 30\frac{\text{day}}{\text{month}} = 54.9\frac{\text{kWh}}{\text{month}} \tag{9.4}$$

By considering the total regenerative output energy from NN model data, total monthly energy regeneration of the proposed NN based system is as follows:

$$2.72\frac{\text{kWh}}{\text{day}}\times 30\frac{\text{day}}{\text{month}} = 81.6\frac{\text{kWh}}{\text{month}} \tag{9.5}$$

Accordingly, the improvement in energy regeneration from the proposed NN-based system is as follows:

$$\frac{81.6-54.9}{54.9}\times 100\% = 48.63\% \tag{9.6}$$

3. Energy regeneration details of a 12-story apartment building complex at Moore's Road, Colombo-06.

   By considering the total regenerative output energy from PI model data, total monthly energy regeneration of the existing system is as follows:

$$1.97\frac{\text{kWh}}{\text{day}}\times 30\frac{\text{day}}{\text{month}} = 59.1\frac{\text{kWh}}{\text{month}} \tag{9.7}$$

By considering the total regenerative output energy from NN model data, total monthly energy regeneration of the existing system is as follows:

$$2.76\frac{\text{kWh}}{\text{day}}\times 30\frac{\text{day}}{\text{month}} = 82.8\frac{\text{kWh}}{\text{month}} \tag{9.8}$$

Hence, the improvement in energy regeneration from the proposed NN-based system is given as follows:

$$\frac{82.8-59.1}{59.1}\times 100\% = 40.10\% \tag{9.9}$$

4. Energy regeneration details of an eight-story apartment building complex at Frankfort Place, Colombo-04.

   By considering the total regenerative output energy from PI model data, total monthly energy regeneration of the existing elevator system is given as follows:

$$2.91\frac{\text{kWh}}{\text{day}}\times 30\frac{\text{day}}{\text{month}}=87.3\frac{\text{kWh}}{\text{month}} \tag{9.10}$$

   By considering the total regenerative output energy from NN model data, total monthly energy regeneration of the proposed NN-based system is as follows:

$$3.77\frac{\text{kWh}}{\text{day}}\times 30\frac{\text{day}}{\text{month}}=113.1\frac{\text{kWh}}{\text{month}} \tag{9.11}$$

   Therefore, the improvement in energy regeneration from the proposed NN-based system:

$$\frac{113.1-87.3}{87.3}\times 100\%=29.55\% \tag{9.12}$$

9.14 AVERAGE ENERGY IMPROVEMENT

Accordingly, the average improvement of the proposed NN-based system compared to the existing system is given as follows:

$$\frac{47.46+48.63+40.10+29.55}{4}=41.44\% \tag{9.13}$$

If we allocate around 10% tolerance for possible calculation errors and other measurement errors in the site,

$$41.44\%\times 0.9=37.30\% \tag{9.14}$$

Hence, with the application of this method, it is possible to obtain a 37% of growth in energy regeneration process according to the above calculations.

9.15 IMPROVEMENTS IN INPUT SIGNAL QUALITY

During the performance comparison between the PI regulator-based converter and NN controller-based converter, another important point could be found. It was noticed that there is a considerable reduction in current waveform distortion in the proposed NN controller-based converter when compared to the PI regulator-based converter operation.

Figure 9.28 shows the input current waveform for the PI regulator-based converter for a specific motor operation period. Figure 9.29 shows the input current waveform

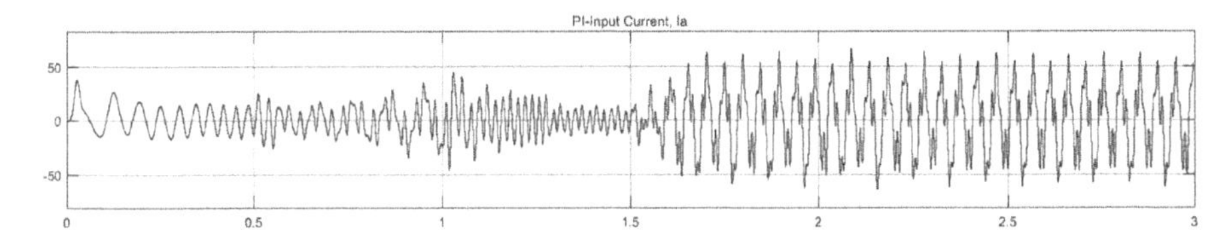

FIGURE 9.28 Phase-A current waveform of PI regulator-based converter.

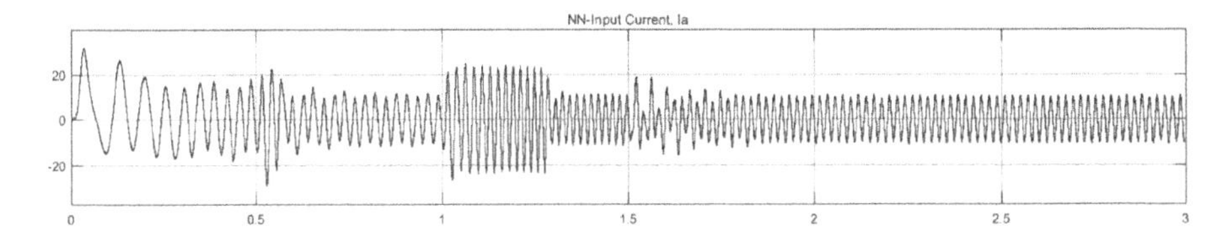

FIGURE 9.29 Phase-A current waveform of NN controller-based converter.

for the NN-based converter under same motor operation conditions as above for the comparison.

Accordingly, the reduction of waveform distortion in the NN-based converter can be clearly noticed here.

9.16 OVERALL SYSTEM IMPROVEMENTS

Therefore, the improvements obtained with the proposed NN controller can be summarized as follows:

1. Minimized current distortions and three-phase unbalances in the utility power system due to low output oscillations.
2. More reduced sampling and computing power requirement [12].
3. Quick responses in dynamic system behaviors [13].
4. Forecasting of energy regeneration behavior with real-time system dynamics.
5. With these improvements, around 37% of energy saving can be expected compared to existing regenerative converters.

9.17 SYSTEM LIMITATIONS

Here, the data processing and all the system performance comparison activities have been carried out using software simulation models and concepts. Nevertheless, the system modeling has been done so that it is satisfactorily matching with real world practical situations. With the help of site collected data through multiple repetitive and testing processes, it was possible to align these simulation model outputs with more practical scenarios in a reasonable way.

However, the optimization of implementing the proposed neural network system in industrial environments haven't perfectly covered under this document. For the future work, it is planned to continue the study of further developing this proposed neural network system to match with harder industrial situations [12–14].

REFERENCES

[1] L Chen, X Zhang, Z Yan, and R Zeng, "Matching model of dual mass flywheel and power transmission based on the structural sensitivity analysis method," *Symmetry* 11, 187, 2019.

[2] S Vinnakoti, and VR Kota, "ANN based control scheme for a three-level converter based unified power quality conditioner," *Journal of Electrical Systems and Information Technology* 5, 526–541, 2018.

[3] J Jayachandran, and R Murali Sachithanandam, "ANN based controller for three phase four leg shunt active filter for power quality improvement," *Ain Shams Engineering Journal* 7, 275–292, 2016.

[4] VR Kota, and S Vinnakoti, "An artificial neural network based controller for MLC-UPQC with power angle adjustment," in *IEEE Region 10 Conference (TENCON)*, Malaysia, 2017.

[5] S Li, M Fairbank, C Johnson, DC Wunsch, E Alonso, and JL Proano, "Artificial neural networks for control of a grid-connected rectifier/inverter under disturbance, dynamic and power converter switching conditions," in *IEEE Transactions on Neural Networks and Learning Systems*, 2013.

[6] E Figueres, G Garcera, J Sandia, F Gonzalez-Espin, and JC Rubio, "Sensitivity study of the dynamics of three-phase photovoltaic inverters with an LCL grid filter," *IEEE Transactions on Industrial Electronics* 56, 3, 706–717, 2009.

[7] M Nomura, H Ikejima, S Morita, and E Watanabe, "Regenerative power control for VVVF motor drive (critical braking method applied to the elevator)," IEEE, 1988.

[8] M Kandpal, V Patel, and K Lad, "Regenerative elevator with backup plan," *International Research Journal of Engineering and Technology (IRJET)* 04, 03, 2017.

[9] A Rufer and P Barrade, "A supercapacitor-based energy-storage system for elevators with soft commutated interface," *IEEE Transactions on Industry Applications* 38, 5, 2002.

[10] S Marsong and B Plangklang, "Implementation analysis of an elevator energy regenerative unit (EERU) for energy saving in a building," *2016 13th International Conference on Electrical Engineering/Electronics, Computer, Telecommunications and Information Technology (ECTI-CON)*, IEEE, 2016.

[11] G Aswathi, S Nalini, and R Sudeep Kumar, "Imulation of active front end converter based VFD for induction motors," *International Journal of Scientific & Engineering Research* 4, 6, 2013.

[12] G Wrona and K Malon, "Sensorless Operation of an Active Front End Converter with LCL filter," *IEEE*, 2014.

[13] F Huerta, S Stynski, S Cóbreces, M Malinowski, and FJ Rodríguez, "Novel control of three-phase active front-end converter with compensation of unknown grid-side inductance," in *IEEE Transactions on Industrial Electronics* 2011.

[14] M Parvez, S Mekhilef, NML Tan, and H Akagi, "An improved active-front-end rectifier using model predictive control," *IEEE* 2015.

[15] A Fekik, H Denoun, N Benamrouche, N Benyahia, and M Zaouia, "A fuzzy–logic based controller for three phase PWM rectifier with voltage oriented control strategy," *International Journal of Circuits, Systems and Signal Processing* 9, 2015.

10 Protection in Smart Building
Mini Review

P. Tejaswi and O.V. Gnana Swathika
Vellore Institute of Technology

CONTENTS

10.1 INTRODUCTION: SMART BUILDING

The key components in a smart microgrid are storage, distributed generation, and smart buildings [1–3]. A smart building automatically controls the building's operations such as heating, air conditioning, lighting, ventilation, and security. A smart building uses both technologies as well as processes to create a safe and comfortable environment for all [4–7]. It combines services of the building which include utilities and exchange digital, analog information with each other, potentially to a central control point for monitoring and action [8–10]. To collect data and manage the business functions and services, sensors, actuators, and microchips are used in smart buildings [11]. This infrastructure aids facility managers, owners, and operators to enhance asset reliability and performance. It minimizes energy use, assessing the impact of buildings environmentally, and optimizes usage of space [12].

A microgrid comprises low to medium voltage network with small load clusters, distributed generation sources, and storage units [13]. It includes the generation of electric power, transmission, distribution, and utilization. The individual plug loads, lighting subsystems, information technology (IT) equipment, and heating, ventilation, and air conditioning (HVAC)–related equipment are grouped as a majority of

DOI: 10.1201/9781003201069-10

electrical loads within smart buildings [14]. The protection and security issues of individual buildings are improved by the adaptive protection schemes and optimization of subsystems [15–16]. The challenges that are addressed in the protection of smart buildings are failure of conventional relays, settings of directional overcurrent relays, coordination of protective devices, and uncertainty in communication links. The security issues are addressed by employing a network of wireless sensor nodes extensively in the buildings, collecting the data from those sensors, and modeling control algorithms that evaluate this sensor data. This will activate the appropriate building subsystems optimally.

A microgrid central protection unit is employed for the dynamic structure of microgrids to overcome the drawbacks of current transformer mismatch, the need for an uninterrupted link, dependence on high communication performance, and synchronization in [17].

Protection issues of low-voltage (LV) microgrids are discussed in [18] for the future protection of LV microgrids to achieve high speed, reliable, and selective operation protection.

S-transform and Hilbert–Huang transform algorithm is employed in [19] to reduce the time synchronization problem and relay coordination. Hilbert–Huang transform algorithm works effectively for high impedance faults, and grid-connected and islanded mode.

Communication-assisted digital relays are used to detect and clear all faults including high impedance faults [13]. Reliability is improved with a communication-assisted central controller to various measurement units for a minimized cost. Communication-assisted digital relays avoid employing extra relays at each end of every line.

A new directional element is introduced in [12] to address the problems of incorrect fault direction identification, ruling out existing impedance relays as workable solutions for microgrid protection. For asymmetrical faults, the proposed directional element uses the superimposed negative sequence impedance magnitude and angle. In the case of symmetrical faults, the proposed directional element uses the superimposed positive sequence impedance magnitude in addition to the torque angle and positive sequence current.

Hybrid particle swarm optimization (PSO) algorithm and linear programming are used for optimal coordination of directional overcurrent relays in [20]. When a hybrid PSO algorithm is used in directional overcurrent relays, the entire time of operation of all relays is minimized.

Ref. [21] presents the overall review of protection techniques that are applied to address the issues of microgrid protection in both islanded and grid-connected mode. A comparative analysis is done to each technique in which the suggestions, advantages, and disadvantages are discussed for the micro grid's protection in the future.

The effects of operating conditions and protection system on the reliability indices of a microgrid using a short-term outage model are presented in [22].

Ref. [23] presents the solution for issues of protection such as sympathetic tripping, blinding, and coordination in the islanded and grid-connected mode of operations.

Ref. [24] presents a probabilistic model for carrying out predictive analysis of microgrid reliability to determine protective triggering probability actions operating under abnormal conditions.

Ref. [25] presents central protection system aided with fuzzy decision, and graph algorithms allows appropriate coordination of overcurrent relay to the microgrid which causes network disconnection to the minimum portion of the network.

10.2 ARCHITECTURE OF SMART BUILDINGS

The integration of connection of various devices and communicating on a general platform are termed as smart buildings. The architecture of smart buildings is shown in Figure 10.1 which includes three distinct levels like management level, automation level, and field device level in [2].

IT, communications network with operator units, monitoring, programming units, connected operator stations, and other computer peripheral devices connected to a server (data processing device) are included in the management level. A human system interface is enabled by a number of data and information processing packages. Software packages such as simple information processing systems control the entire complicated building services via the internet from a single room. It runs the building plant, security, equipment, energy management, lighting, and other services.

A dedicated communications network, control equipment, and connectivity device are included in the automation level. This level consists of operator units, control devices, operator panels, monitoring, as well as programming units connected to a server (data processing device). This level relates to controllers which serve boiler units, chillers, air handling units, primary plant, and other equipment in the plant.

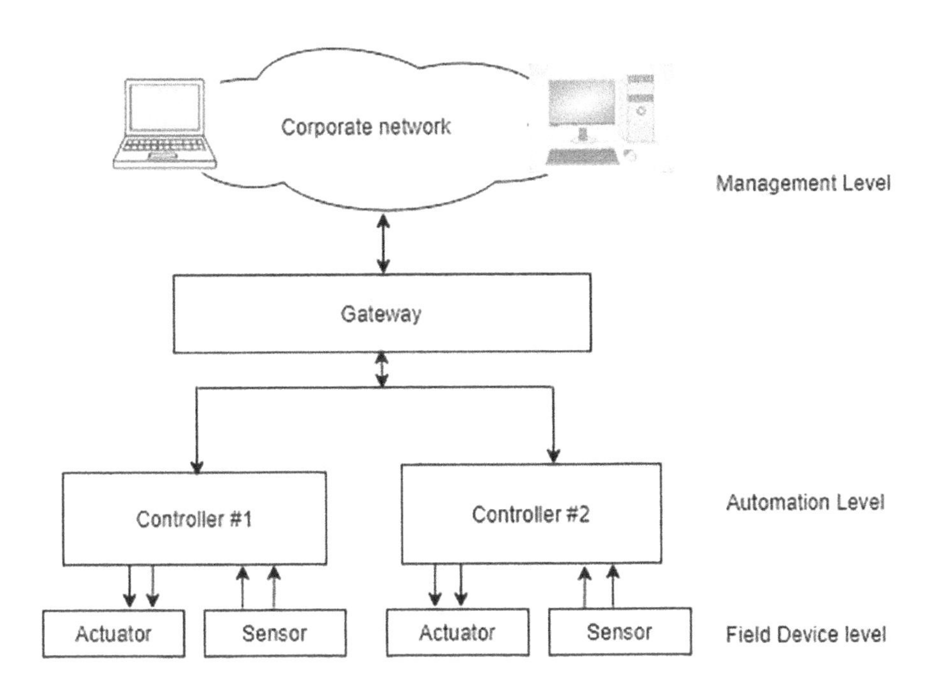

FIGURE 10.1 Architecture of smart buildings.

Sensors are the physical devices connected to particular equipment and plant in the field device level. Smart building is connected to its physical environment with the help of these devices. Examples of these level devices are temperature sensors, passive infrared (PIR) detectors, light switches, fans, and valves. The function of the smart building depends on the connection of common language. The function is attained with the help of standardized communication protocols provided at each or across its three levels of network architecture. The general protocols of the smart building include LonWorks, Hypertext Transfer Protocol (HTTP), Modbus, Konnex (KNX), and Internet Protocol.

10.3 NEED OF SMART BUILDINGS

A building is transformed into a smart building which is advantageous for both the organizations working within and the owner. These benefits include savings in energy to gains in productivity to sustainability. The strategies of smart building include minimizing energy costs, the productivity of the facility staff, enhance building operations, decision-making in the organization, and support efforts for sustainability. The use of optimal start/stop is one of the examples of energy efficiency. With the help of the optimal start/stop strategy, the building automation system is allowed to learn when it should bring the air conditioning system online for a specific zone in the building. Electrical loads are grouped into critical, high priority, and nonessential loads. When the load in the building is increasing and approaches the peak limit setting, the nonessential loads are switched off, followed by the high-priority loads.

The applications of smart building are directed by the accruing commercial need for smooth information flow and increasing performance across an organization. It minimizes the operating costs of enterprise and supplies a more time-responsive building [2]. The protection issues which are significant in a smart building are dynamics in fault current levels, blinding of protection, false tripping, and bidirectional fault currents. The security issues which are of significance in a smart building are confidentiality, a threat to the integrity, buildings, available information of organization, and other elements of the business. Protection mechanisms are employed to deal with overcurrent protection and security issues in a smart building (Tables 10.1 and 10.2).

10.4 PROTECTION ISSUES IN MICROGRID

The protection issues in microgrid are shown in Figure 10.2 and are explained below.

1. Dynamics in fault current levels: The level of fault current is altered by the penetration of distributed energy resources (DERs). The islanded and grid-connected modes of operation of the microgrid also affect the magnitude of fault current. The sensitivity of the protection devices is minimized.
2. Bidirectional fault current: The perforation of DERs affects the direction and fault current level. Therefore, the traditional unidirectional overcurrent relays fail to give protection for microgrids.

3. False tripping: This issue arises when a DER present in a healthy feeder contributes to a fault occurring on an adjacent feeder.
4. Blinding of protection: The fault current contributed by the utility grid is decreased due to contribution from distributed generation sources. Consequently, the feeder relay fails to detect the fault condition.

10.5 CHALLENGES AND SOLUTIONS FOR THE PROTECTION OF MICROGRID

TABLE 10.1
Challenges and Solutions for the Protection of Microgrid

Challenges	Solutions
The conventional relays fail to operate due to issues like a reconfiguration of network and variation in magnitude and direction of short-circuit current.	The feeder currents are continuously monitored by the central protection center online to identify the exact faulted feeder and overcurrent fault occurrence and provide appropriate relay settings to clear faults in the shortest possible path.
The presence of distributed generation units in the radial distribution line makes coordination of the recloser(s) with fuses on the laterals as a challenging task.	Instead of reclosers at the line, an effective protection scheme assisted by communication implements common directional overcurrent relays at the line. This protection scheme also assists the intertripping and blocking transfer functions.
The settings of directional overcurrent relay (DOCR) are affected since coordination between the DOCRs is lost and also due to the type and location of distributed energy sources present, various operating modes of microgrid, and penetration level.	Adaptive directional overcurrent relaying method related to the superimposed positive sequence and negative sequence currents is proposed.
The reliability of adaptive protection schemes includes uncertainty in communication links and protection systems.	The decision tree scheme permits the adaptive protection to implement the best scheme and take decisions globally to rectify faults relying on the uncertainties considered. It's not required to estimate the topologies of microgrid and store their corresponding protection coordination settings in this method.
The fault levels and configuration will alter depending on the system's operation between grid-connected and islanded modes.	Microgrids with customer-owned distributed generation sources are protected with the help of the communication-assisted digital relay technique. Digital relays consist of standard over/under voltage and overcurrent protection methods.

TABLE 10.2
Methods of Protection for Grid-Connected and Islanded Mode

S.no	Scheme of Protection	Applied Methods	Faults
1	Differential protection	OC relays and communication link	LG, LLL
2	Multiagent protection	IEDs, network zoning, wavelet coefficients of transient current for fault location, communication link.	LG, LLG-HIF
3	Current traveling waves based protection	Current traveling waves for fault location, busbar voltages for faults detection	-
4	Inverse-time admittance-based protection	Directional element, zoning, inverse time admittance relay	LG, LL, LLG, LLL
5	Adaptive directional overcurrent protection	Numerical directional overcurrent relays with the directional interlocking capability	LLL, LL, LG
6	Pattern recognition	Spectral energy contours, time–frequency transform (S-transform), calculation of differential energy	LG, LLG, LL, LLL LLLG HIF

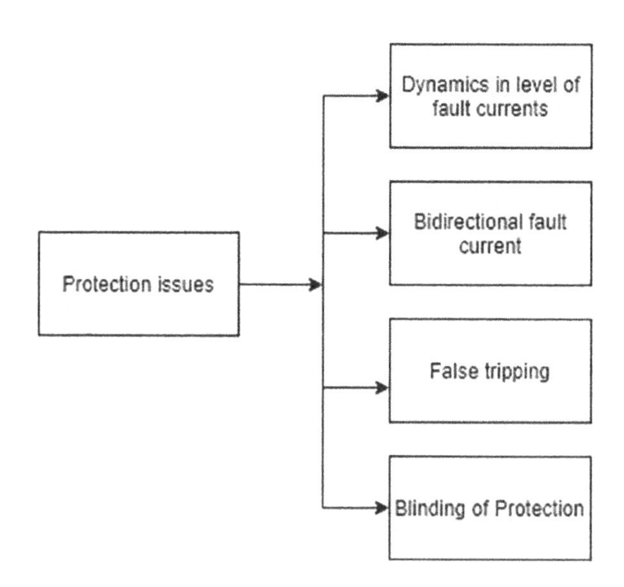

FIGURE 10.2 Protection issues in microgrid.

10.6 PROTECTION STRATEGIES OF SMART BUILDINGS IN MICROGRID

Microgrid operates during normal and island operation, and the protection during this condition is given by modern numerical relay with microgrid central control and monitoring unit. For microgrid protection, field-programmable gate array acts fastly, detects fault correctly, and also reduces fault detection time in [6].

The disadvantages of differential current protection are overcome with the help of central protection unit which is a communication-assisted protection scheme for microgrids. The overall microgrid has the ability to opt for various restraint current calculation algorithms and adjust the protection for multiterminal zone according to the topology variations. The suggested system is a more versatile backup protection scheme and is reliable which works under communication failures in [7].

Conventionally, the circuit breakers are responsible for clearing the fault at the two ends of the line with a fault. A novel decision tree method of protection coordination decides the arrangement of applying strategies optimally according to the microgrid topology. A decision tree scheme is an effective and robust tool for classification and making decisions for providing protection coordination in microgrids taking into account certain uncertainties [8]. To clear a fault in the microgrid, the decision tree scheme identifies the best sequence of strategies. In the decision tree method, it's not required to estimate the topologies of microgrid and store their appropriate settings of protection coordination. The optimal protection coordination in each microgrid topology is achieved by the protection system.

For an islanded microgrid dynamic security, integration of digital under/over frequency relay protection and load frequency control (LFC) is proposed in [9] for protecting the islanded microgrid and supporting the frequency stability against deviations of high frequency. The high penetration of renewable energy sources (RESs), system uncertainty, and random load variations warn the dynamic security of microgrid and cause under/over frequency relaying and disconnect some generations and loads, which may lead to system collapse and cascading failure. The LFC readjusts the deviations of frequency to its permissible limits under various load disturbances, transient conditions, and RES's penetration levels.

Conventional protection methods of distance and overcurrent have disadvantages when applied to microgrid components since the fault current variation in the circuit is very small and circuits are short. A new dynamic state estimation-based protection (EBP) algorithm is suggested to test the consistency of the protected zone between measurements and the dynamic model. The following observations are made based on the EBP method: (i) it is resistant to balanced or unbalanced conditions; (ii) it responds correctly to fault locations and types; (iii) it tolerates some loss of measurements (communications) in [10].

Wireless networks are broadcasting networks widely employed because security issues are increasing [3]. Anybody within the radio frequency range can interrupt the signal with the help of wireless networks. Anybody with a Wi-Fi capable device can read the transmission if the signal is not encrypted.

Security is one of the important components in smart buildings because the protection of sensitive information is essential. Security mechanisms such as user data privacy protection methods and usable authentication mechanisms are studied in [11].

10.7 CONCLUSION

The use of smart buildings is extensively directed by the collective commercial requirement for increased performance. In smart building protection, issues and security threats are prominent due to the manipulation of information or services that may lead to a loss in an organization and also to minimize operating costs and increase greater sustainability. This paper ensures an understanding of smart building protection and security issues to protect human life. The daily activities of a smart building are prominently affected by data-driven applications. If appropriate security mechanisms are not executed, the effect of data-driven applications may have a serious effect in terms of the privacy of the users.

REFERENCES

1. Tharakan, KI, and OVG Swathika, "Optimum coordination of using overcurrent relay using firefly and ant colony optimization algorithm," *2017 International Conference on Computing Methodologies and Communication (ICCMC)*, IEEE, 2017.
2. Swathika OVG, and KTMU Hemapala, "Optimized overcurrent relay coordination in a microgrid system," *Recent Advances in Computer Science and Communications* 12, 2020: 1–00.
3. Swathika OVG, and S Hemamalini, "Prims-aided dijkstra algorithm for adaptive protection in microgrids," *IEEE Journal of Emerging and Selected Topics in Power Electronics* 4, 4, 2016: 1279–1286.
4. Swathika, OVG, K Karthikeyan, and S Hemamalini, "Multiple DG synchronization and de-synchronization in a microgrid using PLC." In *Advanced Computing and Communication Technologies*, Springer, Singapore, 2016, pp. 565–572.
5. Swathika OVG, and S Hemamalini, "Graph theory and optimization algorithms aided adaptive protection in reconfigurable microgrid," *Journal of Electrical Engineering & Technology* 15, 1, 2020: 421–431.
6. Verma H, et al., "Optimal coordination of overcurrent relays using simulated annealing and brute force algorithms." In *Intelligent Engineering Informatics*, Springer, Singapore, 2018, pp. 177–183.
7. Swathika OVG, "LUT assisted adaptive overcurrent protection of reconfigurable microgrids," *International Journal of Smart Grid-ijSmartGrid* 2, 1, 2018: 13–26.
8. Ahamed I, K Vydeeswaran, and OVG Swathika, "Microgrid fault clearance with linear programming algorithms," *2017 2nd International Conference on Communication and Electronics Systems (ICCES)*, IEEE, 2017.
9. Saluja J, et al., "Performance analysis of graph algorithms for microgrid protection," *Journal of Telecommunication, Electronic and Computer Engineering (JTEC)* 10, 1–8, 2018: 115–118.
10. Swathika OVG, and KTMU Hemapala, "Optimized overcurrent relay coordination in a microgrid system," *Recent Advances in Computer Science and Communications* 12, 2020: 1–100.

11. Swathika OVG, and S Hemamalini, "Relay coordination in real-time microgrid for varying load demands," *ARPN Journal of Engineering and Applied Sciences* 11, 5, 2016: 3222–3227.
12. A Hooshyar, and R Iravani, "A new directional element for microgrid protection," *IEEE Transactions on Smart Grid* 9, 6, 2018.
13. E Sortomme, SS Venkata, and J Mitra, "Microgrid protection using communication-assisted digital relays" *IEEE Transactions on Power Delivery* 25, 4, 2010.
14. S Beheshtaein, M Savaghebi, JC Vasquez, JM Guerrero, "Protection of AC and DC microgrids: challenges, solutions and future trends," *IECON2015-Yokohama*, 2015.
15. H Muda, and P Jena, "Superimposed adaptive sequence current based microgrid protection: a new technique," *IEEE Transactions on Power Delivery* 2016.
16. NP Padhy, and P Jena, Nptel course on introduction to smart grid.
17. TS Ustun, C Ozansoy, and A Zayegh, "Differential protection of microgrids with central protection unit support," *IEEE 2013 Tencon – Spring.*
18. HJ Laaksonen, "Protection principles for future microgrids," *IEEE Transactions on Power Electronics* 25, 12, 2010.
19. A Gururani, SR Mohanty, and JC Mohanta, "Microgrid protection using Hilbert–Huang transform based-differential scheme," *IET Generation, Transmission & Distribution* 2016.
20. Y Damchi, HR Mashhadi, J Sadeh, and M Bashir, "Optimal coordination of directional overcurrent relays in a microgrid system using a hybrid particle swarm optimization", *International Conference on Advanced Power System Automation and Protection*, 2011.
21. S Mirsaeid, DM Said, MW Mustafa, MH Habibuddin, and K Ghaffari, "An analytical literature review of the available techniques for the protection of micro-grids," *International Journal of Electrical Power & Energy Systems* 58, 2014: 300–306.
22. X Xu, J Mitra, T Wang, and L Mu, "Evaluation of operational reliability of a microgrid using a short-term outage model," *IEEE Transactions on Power Systems* 29, 5, 2014.
23. K Vagicharla, and H Muda, *Evaluation of Technologies for Smart Microgrid Protection Schemes*, Springer, 2019.
24. X Xu, T Wang, L Mu, and J Mitra, "Predictive analysis of microgrid reliability using a probabilistic model of protection system operation," *IEEE Transactions on Power Systems* 32, 4, 2017.
25. OVG Swathika, S Angalaeswari, V Anantha Krishnan, K Jamuna, and JL Febin Daya, "Fuzzy decision and graph algorithms aided adaptive protection of microgrid," *Energy Procedia* 117, 2017: 1078–1084.

11 A Review of Bio-Inspired Computational Intelligence Algorithms in Electricity Load Forecasting

Siva Sankari Subbiah
Kingston Engineering College

Jayakumar Chinnappan
Sri Venkateswara College of Engineering

CONTENTS

DOI: 10.1201/9781003201069-11

11.1 INTRODUCTION

In the modern era, the rapid growth of the world population and the global energy consumption creates the necessity for the development of smart buildings. The smart buildings are the structure with automated processes for controlling the operations of the electrical equipment like fan, light, and air-conditioning using the intelligent concepts. It helps to reduce the energy consumption, yields remarkable financial savings, and enables the effective maintenance by activating the proper maintenance procedures at the right time [1]. As the population grows, the energy demand also grows. Most of the energy in the world is consumed by the buildings. The buildings in Europe consume 40% of the total energy [2].

As the population increases, there is no way for reducing the energy demand in the future, so the generation of the energy should be increased or the consumption of the energy should be reduced. The cost of generating the electricity is an expensive solution, so the reduction of energy consumption is the better solution [3]. The energy demand can be reduced by introducing the smart buildings and the accurate forecasting of the energy consumption. In order to minimize the power grid usage and maximize the efficiency of the services in the building, the energy consumption in the smart buildings should also be optimized [1]. In addition to that, the consumption of the energy should be adjusted based on the fluctuations in the electricity price [4], so the forecasting of the electricity helps to monetize the energy in smart buildings.

Artificial intelligence (AI) helps to build the machines with intelligence similar to humans. Nowadays, the concept of AI is utilized in most of the applications and replaces the humans for a variety of activities such as controlling the robots, medical diagnosis, forecasting, and remote sensing. The time series forecasting such as weather forecasting [5], stock prediction [6], load demand forecasting [7,8], energy consumption forecasting in smart buildings [9], wind power forecasting [9–11], rainfall prediction [12], pothole detection [13], and heart disease prediction [14] can be effectively done with AI. The AI is utilized in agriculture for improving the farming by effectively predicting the crop yields, soil monitoring, plant disease prediction, and agricultural robots [15].

The optimization techniques play a major role in reducing the complexity and improving the accuracy of developing efficient AI-based models. Another important field of AI is cybersecurity. In the modern digital world, AI models help to secure the sensitive data and to prevent the hacking. An effective usage of AI in the organizations and the businesses saves billions of dollars. The stock market also utilizes AI for predicting the trend of the price of the stock. The education institutions also utilize AI concepts to analyze the performance of teaching and learning. The AI technology is utilized in smart buildings for increasing adaptability of the building, maintaining user comfort, balancing energy consumption, and managing energy usage. The machine learning is one of the subfield of AI that makes the machines to learn from the input data and build the models for future utilization. It is the most important growing research topic in all fields.

The machine learning plays a key role in solving the complicated problems of nonlinear and uncertainty such as power system optimization [16], load forecasting [8], natural language processing [17], speech recognition [18], face recognition [19], cancer prediction [20], text mining [21] and drug discovery [22], and toxicity prediction [23]. It has an ability to handle the large volume of data with high dimensions. There are two major categories of machine learning techniques, namely supervised learning and unsupervised learning. The supervised learning performs the classifications and predictions by utilizing both the input and output data during training, so it makes the classification and prediction with the known input and output pair [24]. On the contrary, the unsupervised learning utilizes only the input data and finds the internal structures of the data.

Even though the machine learning works well in improving the performance of classification, prediction, and clustering, it has some limitations while processing a large volume of uncertain and nonlinear data [25]. In order to overcome these issues, the subfield of the machine learning called deep learning was introduced. It is a large artificial neural network (ANN) that stacks multiple hidden layers between input and output layers and analyzes the nonlinearity among the uncertain data [26]. The clustering concepts also can be employed with the neural network (NN) to enhance the performance [27]. The optimization algorithms along with the machine learning greatly improve the performance of the learning.

In recent years, the bio-inspired computing evolved with strength in optimizing the complex problems in mathematics, computer science, and biology effectively [28]. It provides a set of biologically inspired optimization methods that were developed based on the inspirations toward the biological evolutions in nature. In the field of computer science, the computation of AI is enhanced by introducing the bio-inspired computing. It follows the design principles of biological nature for solving the complex problems that cannot be handled by the traditional methods [29]. The load forecasting using machine learning can handle the nonlinear nature of the load data and forecast the future load with less error compared to traditional statistical methods. However, it guarantees the improved accuracy, it suffers from the longer training time and also less optimal convergence, so the load forecasting using machine learning with bio-inspired algorithms provides a better accuracy by overcoming these issues [30]. The utilization of bio-inspired algorithms to find the optimal solution in load forecasting increases in recent days. The researchers enhance the load forecasting performance using bio-inspired algorithms in different tasks like the hourly load forecasting, daily load forecasting, monthly load forecasting, yearly load forecasting, weekdays load forecasting, weekends load forecasting, and peak load forecasting. The nomenclature utilized in this chapter is shown in Table 11.1.

The rest of the chapter is organized as follows. Section 11.2 describes the importance of bio-inspired computing. Section 11.3 highlights the significance and working procedure of the evolution-based algorithms and Section 11.4 discusses the most popular swarm intelligence-based algorithms such as particle swarm optimization (PSO), ant colony optimization (ACO), bees colony optimization (BCO), firefly optimization (FFO), bat algorithm (BA), gray wolf (GW) algorithm, and cuckoo search (CS) algorithm. Section 11.5 presents the importance of neural system-based algorithms and Section 11.6 describes the role of AIS-based bio-inspired algorithms in improving the performance of forecasting. Section 11.7 reviews the role of bio-inspired computing in electricity load forecasting. Section 11.8 provides the conclusion.

11.2 BIO-INSPIRED COMPUTING

The bio-inspired computing is a subset of the natural computation that solves the complex problems by following the biological models [31]. It differs from the conventional AI in the way of approach it follows. The bio-inspired computing utilizes the evolutionary approach, whereas the conventional AI utilizes the creationist approach. It is used to solve the optimization problems in the machine learning. For every problem, there is a set of inputs and a set of outputs.

The optimization provides the best solution for the problems by finding the right input that helps for obtaining the best solution/outcome. It makes a variation in the input parameters to maximize or minimize the objective functions [32,33]. The general classification of the bio-inspired intelligence algorithms is shown in Figure 11.1. The following sections discuss the evolution-based algorithms, swarm intelligence-based algorithms, neural system-based algorithms, and AIS-based bio-inspired algorithms.

TABLE 11.1
Nomenclature

ACO	Ant Colony Optimization
AI	Artificial Intelligence
AIS	Artificial Immune System
ALO	Antlion Optimizer
ANN	Artificial Neural Network
BA	Bat Algorithm
BBO	Biogeography-based Optimization
BCO	Bees Colony Optimization
BPNN	Backpropagation Neural Network
CNN	Convolutional Neural Network
CS	Cuckoo Search
DE	Differential Evolution
EHO	Elephant Herding Optimization
ELM	Extreme Learning Machine
EMD	Empirical Mode Decomposition
EMD–GRA–MPSO–LSSVM	Empirical Mode Decomposition–Gray Relational Analysis–Modified Particle Swarm Optimization–Least Squares Support Vector Machine
EP	Evolutionary Programming
FFO	Firefly optimization
GA	Genetic Algorithm
GM	Gray Modeling
GRA	Gray Relational Analysis
GRNN	Generalized Regression Neural Network
GRU	Gated Recurrent Unit
GW	Gray Wolf
LSSVM	Least Squares Support Vector Machine

(Continued)

TABLE 11.1 (*Continued*)
Nomenclature

LSTM	Long-/Short-term Memory
mEDE	Modified version of Enhanced Differential Evolution
MFO	Moth–Flame Optimization
MI	Mutual Information
MLP	Multilayer Perceptron
MPSO	Modified Particle Swarm Optimization
PSO	Particle Swarm Optimization
RBF	Radial Basis Function
RNN	Recurrent Neural Network
SSA	Singular Spectrum Analysis
STLF	Short-term Load Forecasting
ARIMA	Autoregressive Integrated Moving Average
SARIMA	Seasonal Autoregressive Integrated Moving Average
PE	Percentage Error
ME	Mean Error
MAE	Mean Absolute Error
MAPE	Mean Absolute Percentage Error
MSE	Mean Square Error
RMSE	Root Mean Square Error
TBATS	Trigonometric seasonality Box-Cox transformation ARIMA errors Trend Seasonal components

11.3 EVOLUTION-BASED OPTIMIZATION ALGORITHM

The evolution-based algorithms are designed based on the inspiration of the biological evolution such as selection, mutation, reproduction, and recombination for achieving the global optimization. The candidate solution and the fitness function play a major role in bio-inspired computational intelligence algorithms for providing the quality solution for the problem. It evolves over a period due to its dynamic nature. The important characteristics of the evolutionary algorithms are population-based algorithm, fitness-based algorithm, and variation-driven algorithm. It does not use any assumptions for the fitness, so it is suitable for all types of problems. It has the ability to find the solution for any hard problems. The widely utilized evolutionary algorithms are genetic algorithm (GA) and differential evolution (DE).

11.3.1 GENETIC ALGORITHM

Genetic algorithm is an optimization algorithm that follows the natural selection and genetics. It is suitable for the real-time problems that do not have any derivative information. It has a good parallel capability and works faster and more efficient compared to the conventional methods. It has the ability to optimize both discrete

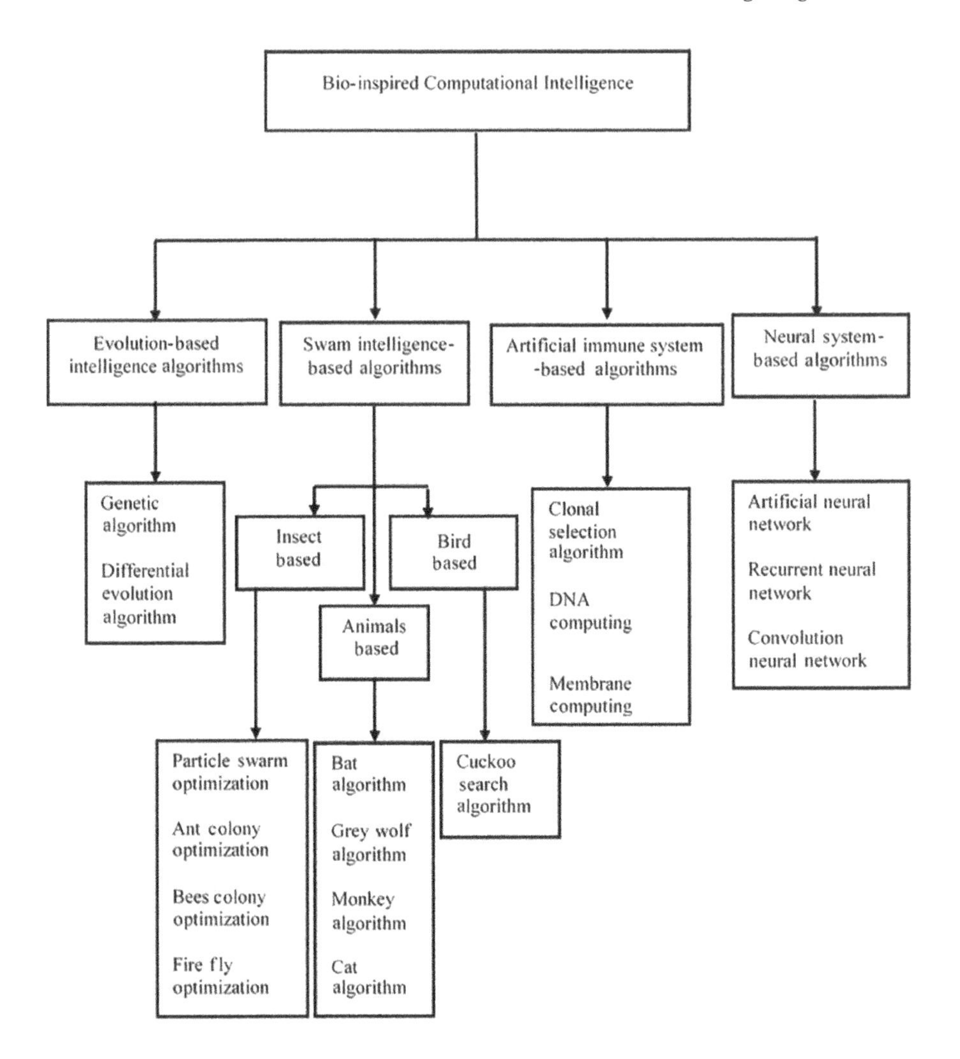

FIGURE 11.1 Classification of bio-inspired intelligence algorithms.

and continuous functions. Hence, it can optimize effectively the multiobjective problems. It is also suitable for the problems with large search space and large number of parameters [31].

The important terminologies utilized in the GA are population, gene, allele, chromosomes, phenotype, genotype, encoding, decoding, genetic operator, and fitness function. The population is the set of possible solutions to the given problem, the gene is one element of the chromosome, the chromosome is one solution to the problem, the allele is the value taken by the gene for the chromosome, the phenotype is the population in actual solution space, the genotype is the population in computational space, the encoding is the transformation from phenotype to genotype, the decoding is the transformation from genotype to phenotype, the genetic operators alter the genetic composition in offspring, and the fitness function is the function that takes solution as input and makes the input for that solution [34]. The procedural steps of the GA are as follows:

Step 1: First, the construction of the initial population randomly or from other heuristics.
Step 2: Selection of the parents for mating from the constructed population.
Step 3: Generation of offspring by applying the crossover and mutation on the selected parents.
Step 4: Replacement of the existing individual from the constructed population by the generated offspring.
Step 5: Repeating these steps until the termination condition encounters.

In order to avoid the occurrence of the convergence toward the local optima, the care should be taken while defining the fitness function. For some problems, the calculation of fitness value is time-consuming. The GA has limitations in handling the dynamic data and the simple problem that has a derivative function [35].

11.3.2 Differential Evolution Algorithm

The DE is the heuristic optimization algorithm that focuses on the population approach for solving the nonlinearity issues in the problem. Storn and Prince introduced the DE algorithm in 1996. It has the stochastic nature same as that of GA. It utilizes the individual population for finding the optimal solution. It differs from the GA in performing the mutation. The GA performs the mutation by making some perturbations to the genes, but the DE performs the mutation by creating the arithmetic combinations of the individuals [36]. As the DE is the population-based algorithm, it follows the global search strategy and one-to-one competition strategy. Hence, it adjusts the search strategy by tracking the current search with the global convergence dynamically [37]. The procedural steps followed by the DE are as follows:

Step 1: Initialize the number of population, scaling factor, crossfactor, and a maximum number of evolution.
Step 2: Perform the fitness evaluation.
Step 3: Produce the new generation of individual by performing the mutation, crossover, and selection operations.
Step 4: Repeat step 3 until the termination condition encounters.

11.4 SWARM INTELLIGENCE-BASED OPTIMIZATION ALGORITHM

The swarm intelligence algorithms are developed based on the behavior of the biological swarms such as insects like bees, ants, and fireflies; animals like lions, monkeys, fish and cats; and birds like cuckoos in their colonies [38]. These insects, animals, and birds live in a group as a colony and the interaction among them in the colony is established directly or by stimulating the biological behaviors [39,40]. It considers many individuals of homogeneous topology. It utilizes five important principles. They are proximity, diversity, adaptability, quality, and stability principles. The proximity principle represents the ability of the swarm to carry the simple computation and space. The diverse principle represents the ability of the swarm to carry the activities among broader multiple channels. The adaptability principle represents the ability of the swarm in changing the behavior for the computationally worthy mode. The quality principle represents the ability of the swarm in making the response for the quality factors from the environment. The stability principle represents the ability of the swarm in maintaining the same stable-state behavior for the dynamic environment [30]. The following section discusses the popular swarm intelligence optimization algorithms such as PSO, ACO, BCO, FFO, BA, GW algorithm, and CS algorithm.

11.4.1 Particle Swarm Optimization

The PSO is an excellent optimization method that is utilized by many real-time applications. It was developed based on the behavior of animals in finding food sources when they do not have any captain in their swarm. The animals work as follows in finding food.

- The members in this group randomly find food by following any one of the members who are near to the food sources. Simultaneously, the flocks will find the food through communication with other members who are in a better situation.
- Once the animals find out the better situation, they inform this to their flocks. Immediately the members also move to that place to get the food.
- The process is repeated until the food sources is discovered.

The animals can find the best optimum food sources by using two capabilities, namely local best (*lb*) and global best (*gb*). The *lb* is the capability of finding the best food position by their own memory and the *gb* is the capabilities of finding the best position by getting the knowledge from their neighbor. The particles can move from one position to another by the velocity. Let the particle "*i*, " time "*t*, " local best "*lb*," global best "*gb*," and the particle "*i*" at time "*t*" in the search space is $P_i(t)$. The particle can change its present position by adding the velocity to it.

$$P_i(t+1) = P_i(t) + V_i(t+1) \tag{11.1}$$

where $P_i(t+1)$ represents the particle "*i*" at time "$t+1$" in the search space. The velocity of the particle "*i*" at time "$t+1$" is denoted as $V_i(t+1)$.

$$V_i(t) = V_i(t-1) + c_1 r_1 \left(lb(t) - P_i(t-1)\right) + c_2 r_2 \left(gb(t) - P_i(t-1)\right) \tag{11.2}$$

where "c_1" and "c_2" are the acceleration coefficients. The "r_1" and "r_2" are the random vectors (random numbers distributed in the interval 0 and 1).

The step-by-step procedure followed by the PSO is as follows:

Step 1: Set the size of the swarm to "*N*, " such that the value of "*N*" should not be too small or too large.

Step 2: Generate the population "P" with the range $P(B)$ and $P(A)$ by random order to get the particle P_1, P_2, P_3,..., P_n such that $P(B) \leq P < P(A)$ where $P(B)$ represents the lower limit and $P(A)$ represents the upper limit.

Step 3: Let initial particles are $P_1(0)$, $P_2(0)$, $P_3(0)$, ..., $P_n(0)$. The vector coordinates of the particles are represented as $P_j(0)$ where $j = 1,2,3,\ldots n$. The particle j at ith iteration is represented as $P_j(i)$. The velocity of jth particle at ith iteration is represented as $V_j(i)$. The objective function value of each particle is represented as $f[P_1(0)], f[P_2(0)], f[P_3(0)], \ldots, f[P_n(0)]$.

Step 4: Calculate the speed of all particles.

Step 5: Set iteration $i = 1$. First, find the $P_{\text{best}}(i)$ with a minimum value of objective function $f[P_j(i)]$ and G_{best} with a minimum value obtained from all the previous iterations. Then, find the velocity of the particle $V_j(i)$ and calculate positions or coordinates of particle "j" at the ith iteration using the Eq. (11.1).

Step 6: Check the position of all particles, whether the positions of all particles are equal or not. If the positions of the particles are not equal, then repeat step 5 by incrementing the "i" value by 1 ($i = i + 1$) and calculate new values for $P_{\text{best}}(j)$ and G_{best}. If the positions of the particles are equal, then stop the iteration that shows that the flocks reached the best optimal food position.

Step 7: Stop the iteration using stopping criterion or terminating criterion if the iteration continues with no convergence found. The terminating criterion may be the number of iterations. Obtain the expected solutions. If there is no improvement in the observed values over a number of iterations, the objective function slope is approximately zero and the normalized swarm radius is close to zero.

11.4.2 Ant Colony Optimization

The ACO is the swarm-based optimization algorithm that was designed based on the behavior of the ant in the wild. The foraging behavior of the ant plays a major role in the design of ACO [41]. The ants trace the pheromone trails for finding the best shortest path between ant's nest and the source of the food. And, it takes the decision based on the pheromone. When the pheromone is stronger, the ant takes a positive decision toward the path. The ants keep the pheromone while moving from one place to another, so the stronger pheromone represents many ants followed the path. Thus, the ants find the path by using this self-organizing process. The ACO performs three important functions, namely ant solution construction, pheromone update, and demon actions [35].

The ACO algorithm uses the computational agent like artificial ant for searching the optimal solution for the given problem. In ACO, the optimization problem finds the shortest path in the weighted graph. First, the artificial ants find the solution by tracing the edges in the graph. Then, it compares the different paths found by different ants. Finally, it updates the pheromone in each edge and repeats these processes in each iteration. The artificial ant selects the next edge from the graph by considering both current position and pheromone level. In general, the probability of the artificial ant movement from the state "a" to state "b" is as follows:

$$p_{ab}^{k} = \frac{\left(T_{ab}^{\alpha}\right)\left(\eta_{ab}^{\beta}\right)}{\sum_{c \in \text{allow}_a} \left(T_{ac}^{\alpha}\right)\left(\eta_{ac}^{\beta}\right)} \tag{11.3}$$

where p_{ab}^{k} represents the probability of transition from the state "a" to the state "b" by the ant "k, " "T_{ab}" represents the quantity of pheromone deposit in the path formed during the transition from the old state "a" to the new state "b," "η_{ab}" represents the desire of the state transition, "α" represents the controlling parameter of "T_{ab}" and "η_{ab}" and "β" represents the evaporation coefficient of pheromone. The pheromone update is performed as follows:

$$T_{ab} = (1 - p)T_{xy} + \sum_{k} \Delta T_{xy}^{k} \tag{11.4}$$

11.4.3 Bees Colony Optimization

The BCO is designed based on the generic behavior of the bees in nature. Several swarm intelligence algorithms emerged based on the mating and foraging behavior of the bees. The swarm algorithms which are based on the foraging behavior are artificial bees colony algorithm [42], BCO algorithm, virtual bees algorithm, beehive algorithm, bee swarm algorithm, and bees algorithm [43,44]. The main process of the algorithm depends on the foraging and the waggle dancing habits of honeybees [45]. In BCO, the artificial ants follow the principles followed by bees for their nectar collection. It forms a small number of individuals and searches for the best solutions by exchanging information with each of the autonomous artificial bees. Each bee in the collection should find one solution for the problem by performing the forward and backward passes. During the forward pass, each bee explores the neighboring bee toward the current solution; subsequently, it performs the constructive move and does the local search. During the backward pass, the bees share the objective value found in the forward pass. The BCO finds the optimal solution by setting the number of bees who must involve in the search and also the number of passes to be performed in each iteration [46]. The population-based BCO constructs the colonies of the multiagent system and achieves the stronger coordination with multitasking capability in the team.

11.4.4 Firefly Optimization

The FFO is the nonconventional swarm optimization algorithm that was inspired by the flashing behavior of the fireflies. The bioluminescent glow generated by the fireflies is identified as the main particle by the agents to communicate with each other efficiently. The search space is identified more efficiently by the partner fireflies with the glow generated by the brighter fireflies. The color of the glow may vary with the insect. It may be yellow, pale-red, or green. The real fireflies generate the luminescent light for attracting the mating partners for their communication, to communicate the warning message, and for attracting the potential prey. As the distance between the fireflies increases, the brightness of the light gets decreased. The FFO algorithm is inspired by these behaviors of the real fireflies for finding the optimal solution. The step-by-step procedure of the FFO is as follows:

Step 1: Initialization of the objective function.
Step 2: Generation of the initial population.
Step 3: Determination of the intensity of the light.
Step 4: Evaluation of the attractiveness of the fireflies.
Step 5: Movement of the fireflies from weaker glow to brighter glow.
Step 6: Update of the light intensities.
Step 7: Setting rank for the fireflies based on the light intensity.
Step 8: Determination of the solution from the ranked fireflies.

The FFO algorithm can deal with the nonlinear problems and also the multimodel optimization problems effectively by following the behavior of fireflies. It finds the globally optimized solution with the high speed of convergence.

11.4.5 Bat Algorithm

The BA is inspired by the echolocation and foraging behavior of the bats. The loudness and the variation in the pulse rates of emission play a major role. Some of the bats may have an extraordinary sense of hearing. When the bats move from one place to another, they generate sounds that bounce in the forward direction along the path and send back the echoes. The bats discover the size of the object and the distance of the object after receiving the echoes. It also determines the speed of their transition from the echo sound. They have the capability to detect the differences between the food and its barriers from the background. The bats fly randomly with the fixed frequency at some velocity by varying the wavelength and loudness for searching the food. They adjust the wavelength and the pulse rate emission automatically depends on the proximity of its target [47]. The BA follows the three assumptions for stimulating the foraging behavior.

1. All bats sense the distance by using the echolocation and differentiate the prey from the background barriers.
2. The bats fly with the velocity "v_i," fixed frequency "f_m," wavelength "w" at the position "X_i" with the loudness "A_0" for searching the prey. They automatically adjust the wavelength based on the target and continue the search.
3. The loudness varies from the large positive to the minimum value.

The BA strengthens the local search by generating the possible set of solutions and finding the optimal solution on the cyclic basis. Like this, it generates the local solution that is close to the optimal solution randomly. Finally, it finds the global optimum solution for the problem [48]. The BA focuses on these behaviors of bats and finds the optimal solution in many applications.

11.4.6 Gray Wolf Algorithm

The GW algorithm is a meta-heuristic algorithm that inspired by the leadership and hunting behavior of the GWs in nature. As the GWs are apex predators in nature, they are at the top position in the food chain. Generally, the wolves live as a group with an average number of members ranged from 5 to 12. Each member in the group has some dominant characteristics. Each of the groups has one leader wolf called alpha wolf which has the right to take a decision regarding hunting and selecting the sleeping place and the time to walk. All member wolves will respond by keeping their tails down. The beta wolves are subordinates to alpha wolves. They communicate the commands of alpha and send the feedback to the alpha wolf. The delta wolf is a subordinate wolf to alpha and beta. The last dominant wolves in the group are the omega. They are allowed to eat at the last. As the inspiration toward the GWs, the GW algorithm is designed by considering the first fitness solution like an alpha, the second fitness solution like a beta, and the third fitness solution like a delta. The mathematical model of hunting is guided by the alpha. The GW algorithm follows these procedures for finding the optimal solution.

The optimization process in GW algorithm is done by using the alpha, beta, and delta. Let *t*th iteration is represented by "*t*," the coefficient vectors are represented by $\vec{M}$ and $\vec{N}$, the wolf position is represented by $\vec{L}$, the coefficient $\vec{a}$, the random vectors [in the range between 0 and 1] are represented by $\vec{v_1}$ and $\vec{v_2}$, and the prey position is represented by $\overrightarrow{L_P}$. During the optimization, the position of the wolves is updated as follows:

$$\vec{G} = \left|\vec{N}.\overrightarrow{L_{P(t)}} - \vec{L}(t)\right| \tag{11.5}$$

$$\vec{L}(t+1) = \overrightarrow{L_P}(t) - \vec{M}.\vec{G} \tag{11.6}$$

where

$$\vec{M} = 2a.\vec{v_1} - \vec{a} \tag{11.7}$$

$$\vec{N} = 2.\vec{v_2} \tag{11.8}$$

During the iteration process, the first, second, and third best individuals are taken as the alpha, beta, and delta. The omega wolves adjust their locations based on the locations of the alpha, beta, and delta. The target solution produced by the GW algorithm reduces the possibility of trapping into the local extreme [49].

11.4.7 Cuckoo Search Algorithms

The CS algorithm is the latest meta-heuristic algorithm [21] that is inspired by the brood parasitism habit of the cuckoos. It follows the breeding and levy flight behavior of cuckoos in searching and finding the solution. Each cuckoo can lay only one egg at a time and randomly choose the other host bird nest for keeping the eggs. The cuckoo algorithm assumes there is a fixed number of host nests and utilizes both local and global random walk. Let the candidates are (*bi*, *ci*). The procedural steps followed by the CS algorithm is as follows:

Step 1: Generation of the population of "*n*" number of nests.
Step 2: Random selection of the nest "*r*."
Step 3: Laying the egg (*br*', *cr*') in the nest "*r*" where
$br' = br +$ Randomwalk (levy flight)br and
$cr' = cr +$ Randomwalk (levy flight)cr.
Step 4: Comparison of the fitness of the cuckoo egg with host egg.
Step 5: Replacing the host egg, if the cuckoo egg fits more than the host egg.
Step 6: Abandonment of the host nest by the host bird, when the host bird detected the replacement.
Step 7: Building the new nest if the probability of identifying the cuckoo egg is less than 0.25 ($p < 0.25$). It avoids the local optimization.
Step 8: Repeating the process until the terminating condition encountered.

11.5 ARTIFICIAL IMMUNE SYSTEM-BASED OPTIMIZATION ALGORITHM

The AIS is based on the structure and principles followed by the immune system of vertebrates like self-monitoring, error tolerance, distributed computation, diversity, and adaptation [50,51]. It includes the strengths such as immune memory, reinforcement learning, feature extraction, robustness, immune recognition, self-monitoring, error tolerance, distributed computation, diversity, and adaptation. The important efficiency-deciding factor of AIS is the mutation operator. It helps to achieve low complexity and better performance. The AIS-based optimization algorithms can be applied for a variety of applications like optimization, data analysis, network intrusion detection, and machine learning. The important AIS algorithms are clonal selection, DNA (deoxyribonucleic acid) computing, and membrane computing algorithm [35].

11.6 NEURAL SYSTEM-BASED ALGORITHM

The NN-based algorithms are inspired by the functioning of the human brain. The biological human brain has a number of neurons and each neuron has a local connection with each other. Similarly, the NN has a number of functional units and has a weighted connection with each other. There is no central control in making the decision. It processes the inputs received from the external world, makes adjustments in the weight assigned to each connection, and generates the output. The ANN consists of a number of layers. They are grouped into three layers, namely input, output, and hidden layers, based on the functionalities it performs. The input layer is receiving input from the external world; the output layer is the last layer in the ANN structure, which generates the final output; and the hidden layer is placed between input and output layers, generates the intermediate results, and updates the weight for minimizing the difference between actual and expected outcomes. There are several NN-based algorithms developed for finding the solution for all types of problems with linear, nonlinear, stationary, nonstationary, uncertain, and complex data.

Some of the popular NN algorithms are backpropagation neural network (BPNN), multilayer perceptron (MLP), radial basis function (RBF), recurrent neural network (RNN), long-/short-term memory (LSTM), convolution neural network (CNN), and gated recurrent unit (GRU).

11.7 ROLE OF BIO-INSPIRED COMPUTATIONAL INTELLIGENCE ALGORITHMS IN LOAD FORECASTING

The accurate load forecasting is very important for the energy-efficient economic operation of the power system. The bio-inspired algorithms play a major role in improving the accuracy of the load forecasting. The following section discusses the bio-inspired algorithms utilized by various researchers for enhancing the load forecasting performance. Adika et al. [52] presented a fuzzy inference model with PSO for forecasting the short-term load. The membership function and rule set utilized in the fuzzy logic is fixed. It possesses the complexity in forecasting the short-term load, so the author introduced the PSO to optimize the membership function. The results showed that the fuzzy inference with PSO produced better forecasting performance for both hourly based weekday and weekend load compared to the traditional fuzzy system.

Mishra et al. [30] introduced the short-term load forecasting (STLF) model in which the performance of the MLP was improved by using GA and PSO. Generally, the MLP network utilizes the backpropagation algorithm that may take a longer time and also not converge optimally, so the bio-inspired algorithms GA and PSO were utilized to converge optimally and to reduce the computation time. As a result, compared to GA, the MLP with PSO produced optimal load forecast with reduced time. Nguyen et al. [53] described the challenges of developing the smart energy management in smart grid, smart homes, and smart buildings. The solutions suggested by using the bio-inspired algorithms such as evolutionary-based algorithms and swarm-based algorithms by various researchers were discussed. Ozerdem et al. [54] introduced a model for predicting the short-term load using BPNN with PSO. The experiment was conducted using the energy demand data collected from the North Cyprus-based energy company. The BPNN with PSO is suitable for regression problems like energy demand and produced better results.

Reddy et al. [55] utilized a BA for improving the performance of BPNN in STLF. Sarhani et al. [56] introduced the hybrid forecasting model with feature selection and optimization techniques. The dimensionality of the dataset is reduced by selecting the relevant features for the forecasting process. Followed by the feature selection, the PSO was employed for tuning the parameters of support vector regression (SVR). Tian et al. [57] improved the performance of the STLF using the moth–flame optimization (MFO) along with the support vector machine (SVM). The ensemble empirical mode decomposition (EMD) was applied to decompose the input load series, and the parameters of the SVM are tuned by utilizing the MFO. Bento et al. [58] utilized the BA for tuning the parameters of the LSTM in forecasting the short-term load. The BA was utilized for selecting memory capacity, dropping frequency, learning rate, and dropping factor of the LSTM. The BA was evaluated for obtaining the suboptimal solution and also the global optima. The BA improves the network function of the LSTM and excels in producing the improved performance compared to traditional LSTM.

Wenbin Ma [59] enlightens the power of PSO in tuning the parameters of the SVM for the forecasting of power system short-term load. The performance of the SVM with the PSO is compared against RBF. As a result, SVM with PSO outperformed RBF.

Ghiasi et al. [60] designed a novel prediction model for the electricity load where the improved bees algorithm was utilized for increasing the local and also the global search abilities. The BPNN was utilized with feature weighting and BCO algorithm. This hybrid forecasting system improved the accuracy of forecasting. Zeng et al. [61] utilized the switched delay PSO along with the extreme learning machine (ELM) for STLF. Zhiping et al. [62] presented the new model for load forecasting where the ACO was introduced for enhancing the performance of the SVM. As a result, the ACO greatly improved the performance of the load forecasting. Ahmad et al. [63] developed a hybrid model for forecasting the day-ahead load using the combination of feature selection, NN, and optimization. The mutual information (MI) feature selection is utilized for removing the irrelevant and redundant features. The ANN is trained at high speed with a multivariate autoregressive algorithm, and the modified version of enhanced differential evolution algorithm (mEDE) was utilized to reduce the error. As a result, the ANN with MI and mEDE outgunned the ANN with MI and the bilevel forecasting models [36].

Alhmoud et al. [64] presented a STLF system with different optimization techniques in the NN. The authors demonstrated the NN-based forecasting model for the Jordan power system with evolutionary optimization techniques for the parameter tuning of the neural network. The optimization algorithms tested are PSO, GA, and elephant herding optimization (EHO). The performance of two-layer NN is compared against the single-layer NN with PSO, GA, and EHO. The two-layer and single-layer NNs with PSO achieve better results by producing the least errors compared to GA and EHO. Abeyrathna et al. [65] introduced the new hybrid model for STLF that combines the PSO algorithm and GA for solving the local minima issue of the ANN. The local minima and training error issues of the backpropagation training algorithm are solved effectively by utilizing the combination of both PSO and GA. When the PSO suffers from the local minima problem, the GA mutation and crossover functions are introduced. Al-Roomi et al. [66] introduced the model for load forecasting in which the configuration of the NN was set effectively by introducing the biogeography-based optimization (BBO). It helps to find the best combination of the transfer functions for the hidden layer and output layers. As a result, the ANN performance was improved by correctly finding and setting the configuration of the network with the help of BBO.

Fallah et al. [67] conducted a survey to discuss the role of computational intelligence approaches in load forecasting. The author discusses both the heuristic and meta-heuristic methods for improving the performance of load forecasting for an efficient energy management. The review concludes that the ANN performance can be improved by correctly finding and setting the configuration of the network with the help of optimization algorithms. The review also states and compares the pros and cons of the single method and hybrid methods (combination of ANN with optimization algorithm) for load forecasting. The result showed that the hybrid methods guarantee an improved accuracy than the single methods. Niu et al. [68] introduced the hybrid system for improving the forecasting accuracy of short-term load. The combination of the denoising methods

TABLE 11.2
Summary of the Related Research Works

No.	Authors	Title/ Forecasting Type	Dataset	Methodology	Comparison Methodology	Performance Measures	Remarks
1	Ahmad et al. [36]	Short-term load forecast of microgrids by a new bilevel prediction strategy/ day-ahead load	DAYTOWN (Ohio, USA) and EKPC (Kentucky, USA) collected from PJM electricity market	Mutual information with a modified version of enhanced differential evolution algorithm	MI+ANN Bilevel forecasting	Mean Absolute Percentage Error (MAPE), variance	Guarantees improved accuracy, reduction of the execution time, and improvement in the scalability
2	Olagoke et al. [71]	Short-term electric load forecasting using neural network and genetic algorithm/ day-ahead load	Daily load data collected from the Transmission Company of Nigeria, National Control Centre, Osogbo, Osun State, Nigeria Temperature was collected from the Internet	ANN–GA	ANN	Mean absolute percentage error (MAPE)	Produces better forecasting results than simple ANN ANN with the bio-inspired GA tunes the parameters and the design of neural network well and reduces the error
3	Abeyrathna et al. [65]	Hybrid particle swarm optimization with genetic algorithm to train artificial neural networks for short-term load forecasting/ monthly load	Electricity Generating Authority of Thailand	ANN–PSO–GA	ANN, ANN–GA, ANN–PSO	Mean absolute percentage error (MAPE)	PSO–GA handles effectively the local minima and training error issue of BPNN

(Continued)

TABLE 11.2 (*Continued*)
Summary of the Related Research Works

No.	Authors	Title/ Forecasting Type	Dataset	Methodology	Comparison Methodology	Performance Measures	Remarks
4	Niu et al. [68]	A short-term load forecasting model with a modified particle swarm optimization algorithm and least squares support vector machine based on the denoising method of empirical mode decomposition and gray relational analysis/daily load	Jibei area of north of Hebei Province, China	EMD–GRA–MPSO–LSSVM	BPNN, SVM, LSSVM, PSO–LSSVM, MPSO–LSSVM	Mean absolute percentage error (MAPE), Root mean square error (RMSE), mean absolute error (MAE), R^2	Improves the generalization ability and the robustness Achieves high forecasting accuracy
5	Saber et al. [69]	IoT-based online load forecasting/ hourly load	Load and weather data	NN + PSO	NN	Mean absolute percentage error (MAPE)	NN+PSO achieves promising forecasting results compared to neural network
6	Al-Roomi et al. [66]	Optimizing load forecasting configurations of computational neural networks/ hourly load	Halifax Dockyard Weather Station, Nova Scotia, Canada	Multilayer feed-forward ANN with BBO		Mean square error (MSE)	Suitable for solving complex problems at high speed Provides solutions for local optima issue of BPNN and improves the learning capacity

(*Continued*)

TABLE 11.2 (*Continued*)
Summary of the Related Research Works

No.	Authors	Title/ Forecasting Type	Dataset	Methodology	Comparison Methodology	Performance Measures	Remarks
					-		Easy to configure the network by finding the input variables, number of layers, type of transfer function, and training algorithms
7	Wang et al. [73]	Swarm intelligence-based hybrid models for short-term power load prediction/ day-ahead load	New South Wales in Australia	Cuckoo search-Singular spectrum analysis-Seasonal autoregressive integrated moving average CS–SSA–SARIMA, CS–SSA–SVR	SVR, SSA–SVR, PSO–SSA–SVR, SARIMA, SSA–SARIMA, PSO–SSA–SARIMA	Mean absolute error (MAE), Mean absolute percentage error (MAPE)	Adds strong robustness and universal forecasting capacities to the forecasting models CS–SSA with SARIMA and SVR produces impressive results
8	Alhmoud et al. [64]	Short-term load forecasting for Jordan's power system using neural network based different	NEPCO temperature, calendar, and load data	NN–PSO	NN–GA and NN–EHO	Percentage error (PE), Mean square error (MSE), Root mean square error (RMSE), Mean error (ME)	Better performance with two-layer NN Single-layer NN–PSO outperforms NN–GA and NN–EHO

(*Continued*)

TABLE 11.2 (*Continued*)
Summary of the Related Research Works

No.	Authors	Title/ Forecasting Type	Dataset	Methodology	Comparison Methodology	Performance Measures	Remarks
9	Zhao et al. [70]	An optimized gray model for annual power load forecasting/ yearly load	China and Shanghai city annual electricity consumption	Rolling–ALO–GM (GM optimized by ALO with rolling mechanism)	GM, PSO–GM, ALO–GM, GRNN, rolling–GM, rolling–PSO–GM	Mean absolute Percentage error (MAPE), Root mean square error (RMSE)	The hybrid gray model optimized by nature-inspired meta-heuristic ALO algorithm improves the accuracy of the annual load forecasting
10	Alduailij et al. [74]	Forecasting peak energy demand for smart buildings/ day-ahead load	Energy meter data of five large government buildings in Cardiff, UK	Autoregressive integrated moving average (ARIMA) and Trigonometric seasonality Box-Cox transformation ARIMA errors Trend Seasonal components model (TBATS)	Linear regression, dynamic regression, ARIMA, exponential time series (TBATS), ANN, and LSTM	Mean absolute percentage error (MAPE), accuracy	ANN, time series, and LSTM models worked well The models outperformed in the order of ARIMA, TBATS, LSTM, ANN, dynamic regression, and linear regression

EMD and gray relational analysis (GRA) along with the optimization method modified particle swarm optimization (MPSO) was utilized to improve the least squares support vector machine (LSSVM) performance in producing an accurate load forecasting. The MPSO plays a major role in enhancing the accuracy of the forecasting. The ability of the model was tested by utilizing different datasets. The result showed that the EMD–GRA–MPSO–LSSVM model produces the least error.

Saber et al. [69] developed the load forecasting system where the load and weather data utilized for the forecasting are collected from smart meters through online. It performs the forecasting by using NN and the optimization techniques are utilized to tune the NN. The swarm-based PSO produces promising results compared to NN. Zhao et al. [70] presented a model for forecasting the annual load by introducing the novel nature-inspired meta-heuristic antlion optimizer (ALO) algorithm with the gray modeling (GM). The model utilizes the ALO intelligent optimization for finding the parameters of GM on the rolling basis. The experiments with regional- and national-level datasets prove that the hybrid GM surpasses the GM, PSO–GM, ALO–GM, generalized regression neural network (GRNN), rolling–GM, and rolling–PSO–GM. The result demonstrates that the ALO outperforms the PSO in the annual load forecasting. Olagoke et al. [71] discussed the bio-inspired GA and designed a model that improves the accuracy of the day-ahead load forecasting. The GA optimizes the ANN network design by tuning the parameters. The load and temperature data of Nigeria are utilized for the experiment. The result shows that the ANN with GA reduces the forecasting error greatly. Sun et al. [72] introduced the hybrid model for STLF where the combination of wavelet transformation, LSSVM, and fruit fly algorithm was utilized. The fruit fly algorithm greatly improves the accuracy of the forecasting by tuning the parameters of LSSVM. Table 11.2 shows the summary of the research work carried out by various researchers in load forecasting using different bio-inspired computational intelligence algorithms.

11.8 CONCLUSION

The operational activities and the functioning of the power system and smart building depend on the accurate load forecasting. The bio-inspired computational intelligence algorithms have significant roles in optimizing the network configurations for the machine learning and help to achieve the improved forecasting results compared to the traditional methods. Many researchers had improved the accuracy of the load forecasting by using the bio-inspired algorithms along with the machine learning such as SVM with ACO, BPNN with bees algorithm, LSTM with BA, SVM with MFO, SVR with PSO, BPNN with PSO, MLP with GA, MLP with PSO, GM with ALO, NN with BBO, NN with EHO, LSSVM with fruit fly algorithm, ANN with GA, and fuzzy logic with PSO. These hybrid methods greatly enhanced the results of load forecasting.

REFERENCES

[1] Flax, B. (1991). Intelligent buildings. *IEEE Communications Magazine* 29, 24–27.
[2] Directive 2010/31/EU (2010) Directive 2010/31/EU of the European Parliament and of the Council of 19 May 2010 on the energy performance of buildings—(recast). *Official Journal of the European Union* L153: 13–35.
[3] Shah, A. S., Nasir, H., Fayaz, M., Lajis, A., & Shah, A. (2019). A review on energy consumption optimization techniques in IoT based smart building environments. *Information* 10(3), 108.
[4] Chen, H., Cong, T. N., Yang, W., Tan, C., Li, Y., & Ding, Y. (2009). Progress in electrical energy storage system: a critical review, *Progress in Natural Science* 19(3), 291–312.
[5] Kiruthika, V. G., Arutchudar, V., & Senthil Kumar, P. (2014). Highest humidity prediction using data mining techniques, *International Journal of Applied Engineering Research* 9(16), 3259–3264.
[6] Swaroop, G., Senthil Kumar, P., & Muthamil Selvan, T. (2014). An efficient model for share market prediction using data mining techniques, *International Journal of Applied Engineering Research* 9(17), 3807–3812.

[7] Paramasivan, S. K. (2017). A review of soft computing techniques in short-term load forecasting, *International Journal of Applied Engineering Research* 12(18), 7202–7206.
[8] Subbiah, S. S., & Chinnappan, J. (2020). An improved short term load forecasting with ranker based feature selection technique. *Journal of Intelligent & Fuzzy Systems* 39(5), 6783–6800.
[9] Paramasivan, S. K., & Lopez, D. (2016). Forecasting of wind speed using feature selection and neural networks. *International Journal of Renewable Energy Research* 6(3), 833–837.
[10] Senthil Kumar, P. (2019). Improved prediction of wind speed using machine learning. *EAI Endorsed Transactions Energy Web* 6(23), 1–7.
[11] Kumar, S., and Lopez, D. (2015). Feature selection used for wind speed forecasting with data driven approaches. *Journal of Engineering Science and Technology Review* 8(5), 124–127.
[12] Nayak, D. R., Mahapatra, A., & Mishra, P. (2013). A survey on rainfall prediction using artificial neural network. *International Journal of Computer Applications* 72(16), 32–40.
[13] Karmel, A., Adhithiyan, M., & Senthil, K. P. (2018). Machine learning based approach for pothole detection. *International Journal of Civil Engineering and Technology (IJCIET)* 9(5), 882–888.
[14] Diviya, M., Malathi, G., & Karmel, A. (2019). Regression based model for prediction of heart disease recumbent. *International Journal of Recent Technology and Engineering* 8(4), 6639–6642.
[15] Agila, N., & Senthil Kumar, P. (2020). An efficient crop identification using deep learning. *International Journal of Scientific & Technology Research* 9(1), 2805–2808.
[16] Rahman, I., & Mohamad-Saleh, J. (2018). Hybrid bio-inspired computational intelligence techniques for solving power system optimization problems: A comprehensive survey. *Applied Soft Computing* 69, 72–130.
[17] Khurana, D., Koli, A., Khatter, K., & Singh, S. (2017). Natural language processing: State of the art, current trends and challenges. arXiv preprint arXiv 170805148.
[18] Nassif, A. B., Shahin, I., Attili, I., Azzeh, M., & Shaalan, K. (2019). Speech recognition using deep neural networks: a systematic review. *IEEE Access* 7, 19143–19165.
[19] Han, X., & Du, Q. (2018). Research on face recognition based on deep learning. *Sixth IEEE International Conference on Digital Information, Networking, and Wireless Communications (DINWC)*, pp. 53–58.
[20] Khourdifi, Y., & Bahaj, M. (2018). Applying best machine learning algorithms for breast cancer prediction and classification. *IEEE International Conference on Electronics, Control, Optimization and Computer Science (ICECOCS)*, pp. 1–5.
[21] Sivasankari S., Baggiya Lakshmi T. (2016). Operational analysis of various text mining tools in bigdata, *International Journal of Pharmacy & Technology (IJPT)*, 8(2), 4087–4091.
[22] Vamathevan, J., Clark, D., Czodrowski, P., Dunham, I., Ferran, E., Lee, G.,... & Zhao, S. (2019). Applications of machine learning in drug discovery and development. *Nature Reviews Drug Discovery* 18(6), 463–477.
[23] Adhithiyan, M., & Karmel, A. (2019). Novel approach of deep learning in toxicity prediction. *International Journal of Recent Technology and Engineering* 7(54), 698–704.
[24] Paramasivan, S. K. (2021). Deep learning based recurrent neural networks to enhance the performance of wind energy forecasting: A review. *Revue d'Intelligence Artificielle* 35(1), 1–10.
[25] Subbiah, S. S., & Chinnappan, J. (2021). Opportunities and challenges of feature selection methods for high dimensional data: A review. *Ingénierie des Systèmes d'Information* 26(1), 67–77.
[26] Subbiah, S. S., & Chinnappan, J. (2020). A review of short term load forecasting using deep learning. *International Journal on Emerging Technologies* 11(2), 378–384.

[27] Panapakidis, I., Skiadopoulos, N., & Christoforidis, G., (2020). Combining machine learning algorithms for short-term bus load forecasting. *IET Generation, Transmission & Distribution* 14(18), 3652–3664.
[28] Paramasivan, S. K., & Lopez, D. (2016). A review on feature selection methods for high dimensional data, *International Journal of Engineering & Technology* 8(2), 669–672.
[29] Darwish, A. (2018). Bio-inspired computing: Algorithms review, deep analysis, and the scope of applications. *Future Computing and Informatics Journal* 3(2), 231–246.
[30] Mishra, S., & Patra, S. K. (2008). Short term load forecasting using neural network trained with genetic algorithm & particle swarm optimization. *First IEEE International Conference on Emerging Trends in Engineering and Technology*, pp. 606–611.
[31] Choudhury, H. A., Sinha, N., & Saikia, M. (2020). Application of nature-inspired algorithms (NIA) for optimization of video compression. *Journal of Intelligent & Fuzzy Systems* 38(3), 1–25.
[32] Goel, L. (2020). An extensive review of computational intelligence-based optimization algorithms: trends and applications. *Soft Computing* DOI: 10.1080/09540090210144948.
[33] Parpinelli, R. S., & Lopes, H. S. (2011). An eco-inspired evolutionary algorithm applied to numerical optimization. *IEEE Third World Congress on Nature and Biologically Inspired Computing*, pp. 466–471.
[34] Lin, C. D., Anderson-Cook, C. M., Hamada, M. S., Moore, L. M., & Sitter, R. R. (2015). Using genetic algorithms to design experiments: a review. *Quality and Reliability Engineering International* 31(2), 155–167.
[35] Binitha, S., & Sathya, S. S. (2012). A survey of bio inspired optimization algorithms. *International Journal of Soft Computing and Engineering* 2(2), 137–151.
[36] Amjady, N., Keynia, F., & Zareipour, H. (2010). Short-term load forecast of microgrids by a new bilevel prediction strategy. *IEEE Transactions on Smart Grid* 1(3), 286–294.
[37] Huang, Z., & Chen, Y. (2013). An improved differential evolution algorithm based on adaptive parameter. *Journal of Control Science and Engineering* 2013, 1–5.
[38] Kennedy, J. (2006). Swarm intelligence. In *Handbook of Nature-Inspired and Innovative Computing*, Springer, Boston, pp. 187–219.
[39] Bonabeau, E., Dorigo, M., & Theraulaz, G. (1999). Swarm intelligence: From natural to artificial systems. *Connection Science* 14(2), 163–164.
[40] Del Ser, J., Osaba, E., Molina, D., Yang, X. S., Salcedo-Sanz, S., Camacho, D.,... & Herrera, F. (2019). Bio-inspired computation: where we stand and what's next. *Swarm and Evolutionary Computation* 48, 220–250.
[41] Karmel, A., & Jayakumar, C. (2015). Recurrent ant colony optimization for optimal path convergence in mobile Ad Hoc networks. *KSII Transactions on Internet & Information Systems* 9(9), 3496–3514.
[42] Karaboga, D. (2005). An idea based on honey bee swarm for numerical optimization. Technical report, Erciyes University, Engineering Faculty Computer Engineering Department, 200, pp. 1–10.
[43] Pham, D. T., Ghanbarzadeh, A., Koc, E., Otri, S., & Zaidi, M. (2006). The bees algorithm - a novel tool for complex optimisation problems, *Elsevier International Conference on Intelligent Production Machines and Systems (IPROMS 2006)*, pp. 454–459.
[44] Pham, D. T., Soroka, A. J., Ghanbarzadeh, A., and Koc, E. (2006). Optimising neural networks for identification of wood defects using the bees algorithm, *IEEE International Conference on Industrial Informatics*, pp. 1346–1351.
[45] Davidović, T., (2016). Bee colony optimization Part I: The algorithm overview. *Yugoslav Journal of Operations Research* 25(1), 33–56.
[46] Rajeswari, M., Amudhavel, J., Pothula, S., & Dhavachelvan, P. (2017). Directed bee colony optimization algorithm to solve the nurse rostering problem. *Computational Intelligence and Neuroscience* 2017, 1–26.

[47] Yang, X. S. (2013). Bat algorithm and cuckoo search: a tutorial. In *Artificial Intelligence, Evolutionary Computing and Metaheuristics*, Springer, pp. 421–434.
[48] Ma, X. X., & Wang, J. S. (2018). Optimized parameter settings of binary bat algorithm for solving function optimization problems. *Journal of Electrical and Computer Engineering* 2018, 1–10.
[49] Wang, J. S., & Li, S. X. (2019). An improved grey wolf optimizer based on differential evolution and elimination mechanism. *Scientific Reports* 9(1), 1–21.
[50] Hamid, M. A., & Rahman, T. A. (2010). Short term load forecasting using an artificial neural network trained by artificial immune system learning algorithm, *12th IEEE International Conferençe on Computer Modelling and Simulation*, pp. 408–413.
[51] Dudek, G. (2008). Artificial immune system for short-term electric load forecasting. *Springer International Conference on Artificial Intelligence and Soft Computing*, pp. 1007–1017.
[52] Adika, C. O., & Wang, L. (2012). Short term energy consumption prediction using bio-inspired fuzzy systems. *IEEE North American Power Symposium (NAPS)*, pp. 1–6.
[53] Nguyen, T. H., Nguyen, L. V., Jung, J. J., Agbehadji, I. E., Frimpong, S. O., & Millham, R. C. (2020). Bio-inspired approaches for smart energy management: state of the art and challenges. *Sustainability* 12(20), 8495.
[54] Ozerdem, O. C., Olaniyi, E. O., & Oyedotun, O. K. (2017). Short term load forecasting using particle swarm optimization neural network. *Procedia Computer Science* 120, 382–393.
[55] Reddy, S. S. (2018). Bat algorithm-based back propagation approach for short-term load forecasting considering weather factors. *Electrical Engineering* 100(3), 1297–1303.
[56] Sarhani, M., & El Afia, A. (2015). Electric load forecasting using hybrid machine learning approach incorporating feature selection. *International Conference on Big Data Cloud and Applications (BDCA)*, pp. 1–7.
[57] Tian, C., & Hao, Y. (2018). A novel nonlinear combined forecasting system for short-term load forecasting. *Energies* 11(4), 712.
[58] Bento, P., Pombo, J., Mariano, S., & do Rosario Calado, M. (2018). Short-term load forecasting using optimized LSTM networks via improved bat algorithm. *IEEE International Conference on Intelligent Systems (IS)*, pp. 351–357.
[59] Wenbin, M. (2008). Power system short -term load forecasting based on improved support vector machine. *IEEE International Symposium on Knowledge Acquisition and Modeling*, pp. 658–662.
[60] Ghiasi, M., Irani Jam, M., Teimourian, M., Zarrabi, H., & Yousefi, N. (2019). A new prediction model of electricity load based on hybrid forecast engine. *International Journal of Ambient Energy* 40(2), 179–186.
[61] Zeng, N., Zhang, H., Liu, W., Liang, J., & Alsaadi, F. E. (2017). A switching delayed PSO optimized extreme learning machine for short-term load forecasting. *Neurocomputing* 240, 175–182.
[62] Zhiping, F., & Tiansheng, H. (2008). The application of Ant Colony Algorithm in Combined power load forecasting. *IEEE International Conference on MultiMedia and Information Technology*, pp. 90–93.
[63] Ahmad, A., Javaid, N., Mateen, A., Awais, M., & Khan, Z. A. (2019). Short-term load forecasting in smart grids: an intelligent modular approach. *Energies* 12(1), 164.
[64] Alhmoud, L., & Nawafleh, Q. (2019). Short-term load forecasting for Jordan's power system using neural network based different. *IEEE International Conference on Environment and Electrical Engineering and IEEE Industrial and Commercial Power Systems Europe (EEEIC/I&CPS Europe)*, pp. 1–6.
[65] Abeyrathna, K. D., & Jeenanunta, C. (2019). Hybrid particle swarm optimization with genetic algorithm to train artificial neural networks for short-term load forecasting. *International Journal of Swarm Intelligence Research* 10(1), 1–14.

[66] Al-Roomi, A. R., & El-Hawary, M. E. (2018). Optimizing load forecasting configurations of computational neural networks. *IEEE Canadian Conference on Electrical & Computer Engineering (CCECE)*, pp. 1–6.
[67] Fallah, S. N., Deo, R. C., Shojafar, M., Conti, M., & Shamshirband, S. (2018). Computational intelligence approaches for energy load forecasting in smart energy management grids: state of the art, future challenges, and research directions. *Energies* 11(3), 596.
[68] Niu, D., & Dai, S. (2017). A short-term load forecasting model with a modified particle swarm optimization algorithm and least squares support vector machine based on the denoising method of empirical mode decomposition and grey relational analysis. *Energies* 10(3), 408.
[69] Saber, A. Y., & Khandelwal, T. (2017). IoT based online load forecasting. *IEEE Ninth Annual IEEE Green Technologies Conference (GreenTech)*, pp. 189–194.
[70] Zhao, H., & Guo, S. (2016). An optimized grey model for annual power load forecasting. *Energy* 107, 272–286.
[71] Olagoke, M. D., Ayeni, A. A., & Hambali, M. A. (2016). Short term electric load forecasting using neural network and genetic algorithm. *International Journal of Applied Information Systems* 10, 22–28.
[72] Sun, W., & Ye, M. (2015). Short-term load forecasting based on wavelet transform and least squares support vector machine optimized by fruit fly optimization algorithm. *Journal of Electrical and Computer Engineering* 2015, 1–9.
[73] Wang, J., Jin, S., Qin, S., & Jiang, H. (2014). Swarm intelligence-based hybrid models for short-term power load prediction. *Mathematical Problems in Engineering* 2014, 1–17.
[74] Alduailij, M. A., Petri, I., Rana, O., Alduailij, M. A., & Aldawood, A. S. (2020). Forecasting peak energy demand for smart buildings. *The Journal of Supercomputing* 1–25.

12 Arduino-Based Fault Detection Schemes for DC Microgrids

Faazila Fathima S and Premalatha L
Vellore Institute of Technology

CONTENTS

ABBREVIATIONS

AOCR	Adaptive Overcurrent Relay
DG	Distributed Generation
LG fault	Line-to-ground Fault
PCC	Point of Common Coupling
PMSG	Permanent Magnet Synchronous Generator
PV	Photovoltaic
SC	Supercapacitor

12.1 INTRODUCTION

As the energy demand is high in recent decades, the importance of sustainable development of smart grids from the conventional grid to implement a clean, less carbon footprint, highly reliable, and secured electricity supply is focused. The traditional

DOI: 10.1201/9781003201069-12

grid is a centralized power generation that depends on manual monitoring, manual restoration, and unidirectional power flow, which have bulk power generation, aged transmission lines, and fossil fuel consumption, leading to an increased carbon footprint in the atmosphere. Implementation of renewable energy resources that are abundant and sustainable resolves the above challenges [1]. Finally, this paves the way to smart grid and smart buildings, the recent trend in this modern era.

Conventional grids are reshaped gradually by using distributed generations (DGs). DGs are small-scale resources that are located nearby the end users that provide lower cost electricity and higher power reliability. Some of the DGs are photovoltaic (PV), small wind turbines, fuel cells, biogas, small hydro turbines, and other sources of energy. Integrating the renewables in the grid results in developing a microgrid that provides better reliability, carbon emission reduction, improvement in power quality and minimizes power loss in the distribution network [2]. DG has many advantages, such as pollution reduction, improved efficiency, a preferred location for installation, and saves operating cost with minimum line losses of transmission [3].

A microgrid is a localized grid that can act in two modes, grid-connected mode and islanded mode, using renewable energy resources and energy storage devices for supplying uninterrupted power to loads. Using a point of common coupling (PCC) as a static switch shifts its operation mode during fault conditions and other disturbances. When a microgrid is disconnected from a utility, it is said to be in "islanded mode" where the DGs continue to supply electricity to the microgrid users without the need for electric power from the utility grid.

In this paper, a simple procedure for integrating renewable energy resources is followed, and a detailed analysis on modeling a direct current (DC) microgrid with a smart fault detection scheme using Arduino is made.

In the first section, a 470 V smart DC microgrid that includes a permanent magnet synchronous generator (PMSG) wind power system and PV system as sources and supercapacitor (SC) bank and battery as energy storages of a smart microgrid is explained. The second section presents PV array modeling where it consists of the Solkar 36 W PV module, and its output was illustrated. Also, wind turbine modeling and its simulation results will be presented. The battery and SC modeling with its corresponding output voltage and current will be discussed. In the last section, modeling of smart DC microgrids with Arduino-based fault detection schemes is illustrated with MATLAB Simulation. Finally, conclusions of the proposed work are briefed out.

12.2 DC MICROGRID CONFIGURATION

A 470 V DC microgrid consists of DGs such as 1 kW wind generation, a 1 kW PV array, a SC, and a battery that supplies a DC load that is interfaced in a common DC bus, as shown in Figure 12.1. Generally, autonomous microgrids operate separately where no connection is made with the primary power grid, and every source and storage in a microgrid is interfaced in a DC bus.

One of the renewables is a 1 kW wind generation system where the presence of PMSG wind turbine with a rectifier is further interfaced in a DC bus. Using PMSG provides better performance with high efficiency and no frequent maintenance

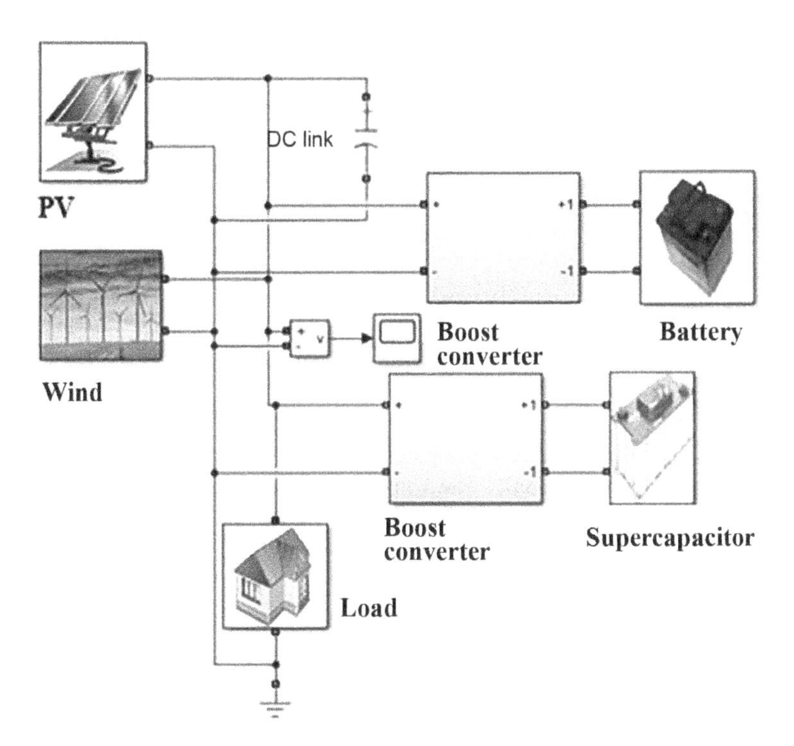

FIGURE 12.1 DC microgrid.

requirement since the absence of rotor current. In PMSG, a gearbox is not mandatory, which reduces the nacelle and economically feasible weight.

The PV system is chosen, which has a PV array combined with a boost converter under varying irradiation and temperature conditions. Battery and SC bank, having bidirectional converter are interfaced in 470 V DC bus that acts as energy storages [4]. After interfacing the sources and energy storages, the microgrid provides 3 kW to supply resistive load. A line-to-ground (LG) fault is applied at each source at different time intervals, and an adaptive overcurrent protection scheme is used to mitigate the fault. During the fault period, the protection device Z-source circuit breaker isolates the faulty section and restores the system quickly. When the fault occurs, a sudden rise in current is detected, indicated by LED glowing, indicating that a fault has occurred. Implementation of hardware is done with the help of Arduino UNO interfaced with MATLAB Simulink.

12.3 MODELING OF DC MICROGRID

12.3.1 Modeling of Photovoltaic Cell

In general, the PV module can be modeled with less complexity which purely depends on the Shockley diode equation. The basic equivalent circuit of the PV cell is shown in Figure 12.2.

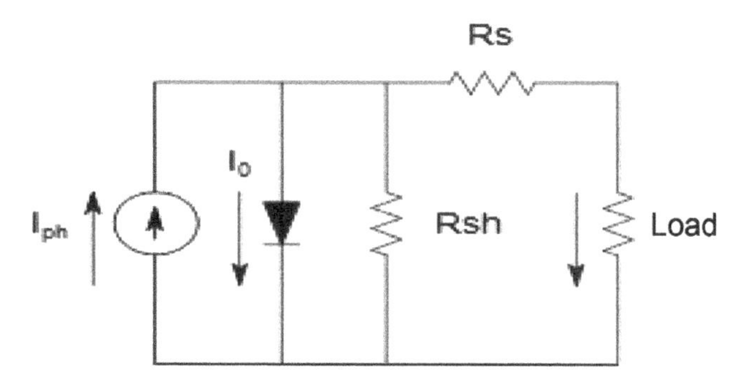

FIGURE 12.2 Equivalent circuit of PV cell.

The I_{ph} denoted the photocurrent of a cell, and R_{sh} and R_s are the shunt and series resistances, respectively. Usually, the value of R_{sh} is greater than that of R_s; hence, they may be neglected to simplify the analysis. PV cells are grouped in a single system called PV modules, and it is then interconnected in a series combination that forms PV arrays [5].

The PV module is designed based on the given equations from (1.1) to (1.3).

$$I_{\text{ph}} = \left[I_{\text{scr}} + K_i (T - 298) * \lambda / 1000 \right] \tag{12.1}$$

$$I_{\text{rs}} = I_{\text{scr}} / \left[\exp\left(qV_{\text{oc}} / N_s kAT \right) - 1 \right] \tag{12.2}$$

$$I_{\text{PV}} = N_p * I_{\text{ph}} - N_p * I_o \left[\exp\left\{ \frac{q * (VPV + IPVRS)}{NS\ AkT} \right\} - 1 \right] \tag{12.3}$$

where

N_p – Number of cells in parallel
N_s – Number of cells in series
I_{rs} - reverse saturation current of a module
I_{PV} - output current of a PV module
V_{PV} - voltage of a PV module
T_r - reference temperature = 298 K
T - module operating temperature
I_o - saturation current of PV module
A - ideality factor = 1.6
$B = 1.6$
$k = 1.3805 \times 10^{-23}$ J/K
$q = 1.6 \times 10^{-19}$ C
I_{scr} - short-circuit current of PV module
K_i - short-circuit current temperature coefficient
$I_{\text{scr}} = 0.0017$ A/°C
λ - illumination of PV module

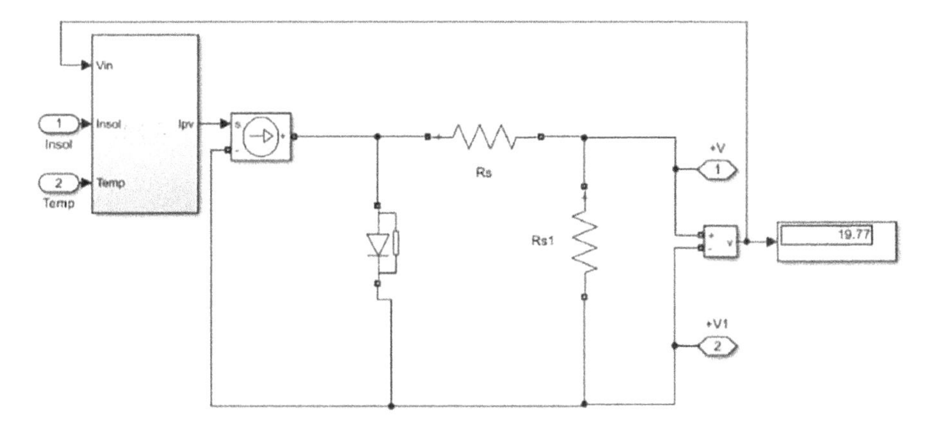

FIGURE 12.3 PV module.

Figure 12.3 shows the PV module in MATLAB Simulink. The PV cell is modeled based on 36 W Solkar PV [6–8] designed with an irradiation level of 1000 W/m^2 and a diode with a snubber circuit, which reduces the voltage spikes in the circuit. The output voltage from each PV cell is 1.9 V. These PV cells are then connected in series combination, thereby maintaining the output voltage at 470 V. Figure 12.4 shows the series combination of PV module, which results in a PV array, and Figure 12.5 shows the simulation results of the PV system.

12.3.2 Modeling of Wind Generation System

Wind power can be estimated using the following equation:

$$P_w = C_p (1/2) \rho A v_w^3 \tag{12.4}$$

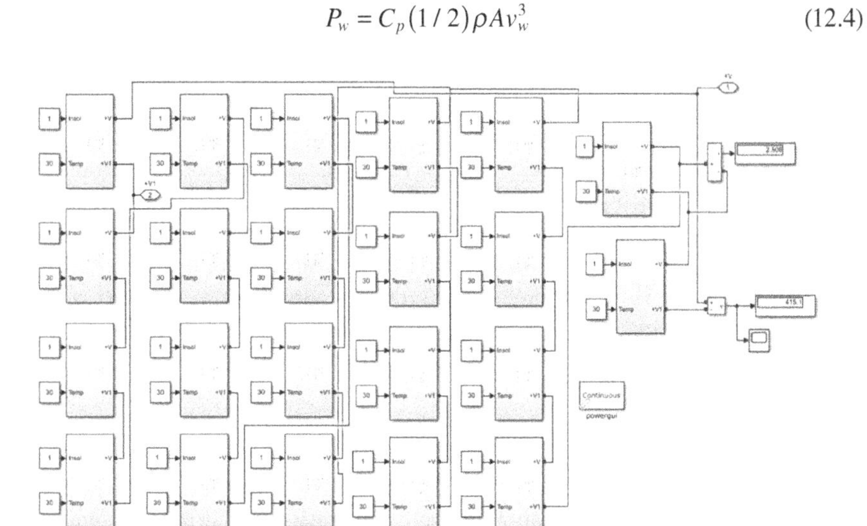

FIGURE 12.4 Modeling of PV array in MATLAB Simulink.

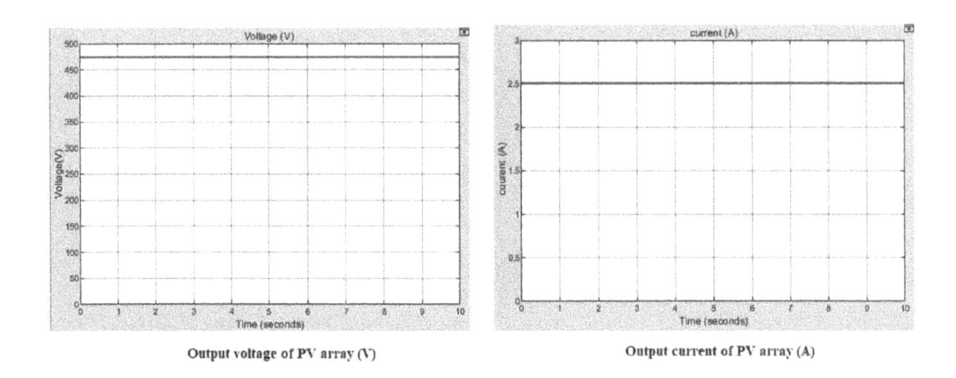

FIGURE 12.5 Simulation results of PV system.

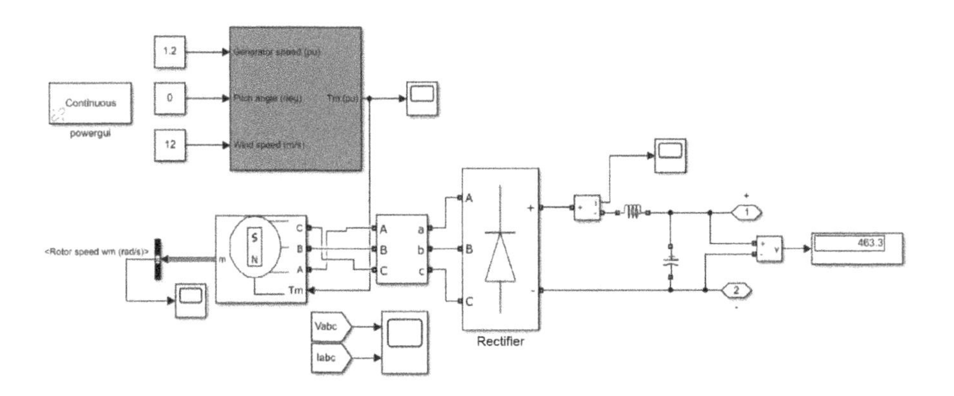

FIGURE 12.6 Modeling of fixed-speed wind generation system in MATLAB Simulink.

where P_w is the output power (Watts), ρ is the air density, C_p is the power coefficient, V_w is the wind velocity (m/s), and A is the rotor covered area. As the rated wind speed is 12 m/s, the input for wind speed is taken as such. The wind generation modeling consists of PMSG with a variable-speed wind turbine, a rectifier, and a filter circuit [9,10]. Modeling of PMSG fixed-speed wind generation system is shown in Figure 12.6.

In a fixed-speed wind turbine, PMSG feeds the generator speed, thereby calculating the torque, power, tip-speed ratio, and C_p. Alternating current (AC)-to-DC conversion is made using the rectifier, and filters are used to reduce the oscillations. Finally, it is interfaced to the smart DC grid with almost 470 V. Simulation for PMSG fixed-speed wind modeling using MATLAB is shown in Figure 12.7.

12.3.3 Modeling of Capacitor Bank

The capacitor bank is connected to a DC–DC converter and finally integrated into a 470 V DC bus. The configuration of the capacitor bank is shown in Figure 12.8. A SC has better efficiency than other types, and it has fast charging and discharging capability. The DC–DC converter consists of metal–oxide–semiconductor

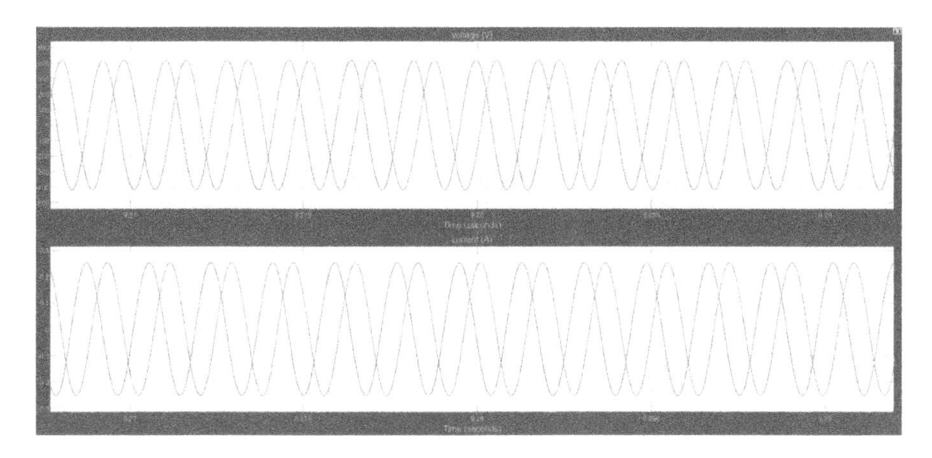

FIGURE 12.7 Performance of fixed-speed wind generation system with PMSG.

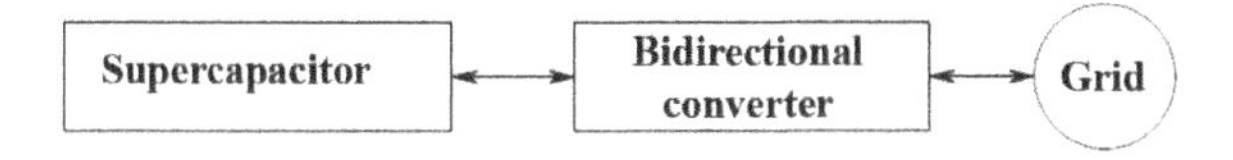

FIGURE 12.8 Configuration of SC bank.

field-effect transistor (MOSFET) with a linear transformer where this arrangement helps for bidirectional power flow from capacitor bank to grid and vice-versa, and each MOSFET conducts using pulse generator [11].

As it has a bidirectional power flow, it can be connected to the grid to supply power and charges itself if there is a presence of excess power after supplying the load.

12.3.4 Modeling of Battery System

The modeling of battery is shown in Figure 12.9. This modeling consists of a 24 V battery with a DC–DC boost converter that is interfaced with the DC grid. The charging and discharging modes are made and connected to a bidirectional converter, and

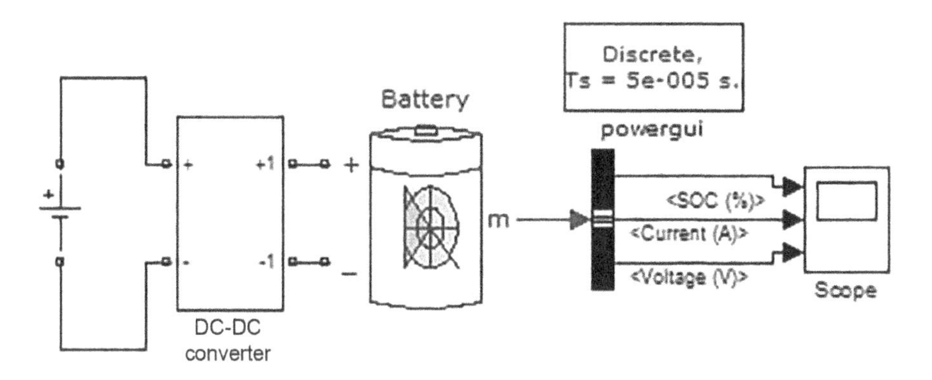

FIGURE 12.9 Modeling of battery (energy storage).

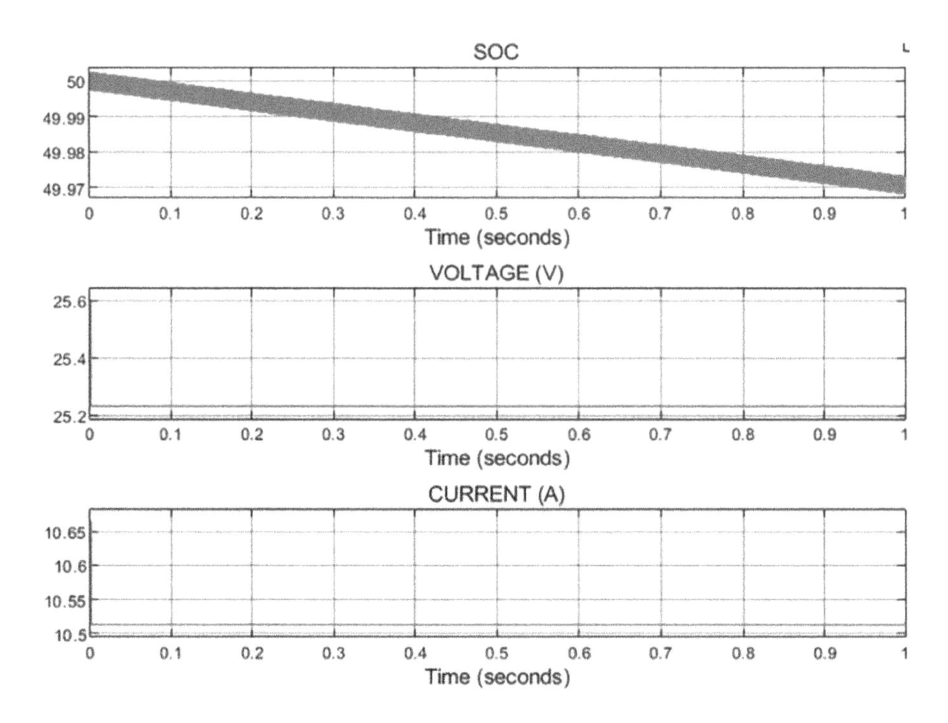

FIGURE 12.10 Charging and discharging mode of battery.

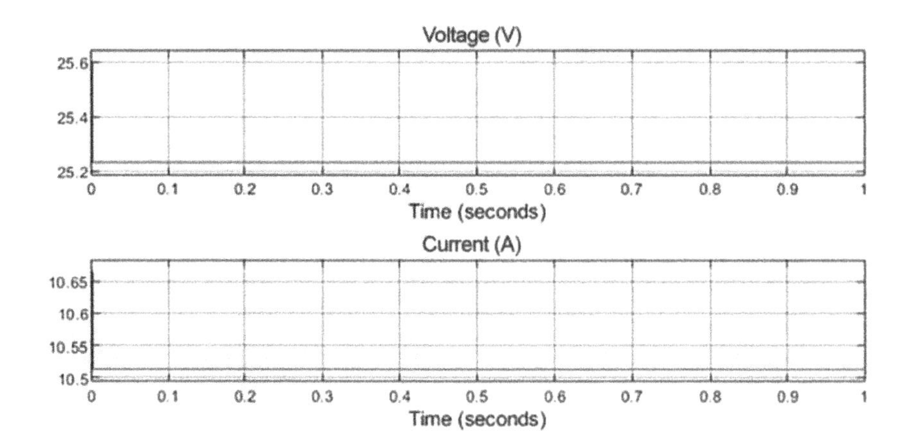

FIGURE 12.11 Output voltage and current of battery.

the state of charge (%), battery current, and voltage simulations, and the mode of battery are shown in Figure 12.10 and 12.11, respectively. The output from battery is further fed to boost the converter to integrate into the 470V DC bus. Since it has bidirectional power flow, it can be connected to the grid to supply power to the grid and it can charge itself in the event of excess power availability after supplying the loads. This can eventually be useful when there is deficit of power to supply load.

12.4 FAULT DETECTION BASED ON RELAY COMMUNICATION IN DC MICROGRID

A 3 kW DC microgrid is designed with a Solkar PV model and a PMSG-based wind generation as sources with SC bank and battery supplying DC loads and AC loads using MATLAB Simulink interfaced with Arduino for relay communication in this proposed work. Based on the requirements, DC–DC boost converters and rectifiers are used where the sources can be connected to a DC bus with common DC voltage as 470 V is illustrated in Figure 12.12.

A 1 kW solar PV model is modeled with 36 PV cells in series and 1 in parallel connection at an irradiation level of 1000 W/m^2 at a reference temperature of 25°C. A single module of PV results with the output voltage of 19.77 V and its corresponding current of 2.5 A.

Similarly, 24 modules have meshed in series combination that results in a voltage of 470 V. Similarly, a fixed-speed wind turbine using a PMSG is one of the generating sources in the proposed microgrid due to its advantages such as higher efficiency and no requirement of external excitation [12,13]. It is proposed for 1 kW generating capacity connected to DC bus through the rectifier supplying DC loads, and by using inverter, it supplies AC loads. Energy storages such as battery and SC bank are interfaced with a bidirectional DC-to-DC converter, integrated into DC bus. Table 12.1 shows the power drawn from the smart DC microgrid system.

A line-to-ground fault (LG fault) is always considered to be hazardous compared to a line-to-line fault, so LG fault analysis is carried out where the adaptive overcurrent detection is made using smart relay communication in microgrid with Arduino UNO. "Arduino UNO" is a microcontroller based on the microchip ATmega328P model, which can be integrated with MATLAB Simulink for fault detection [14].

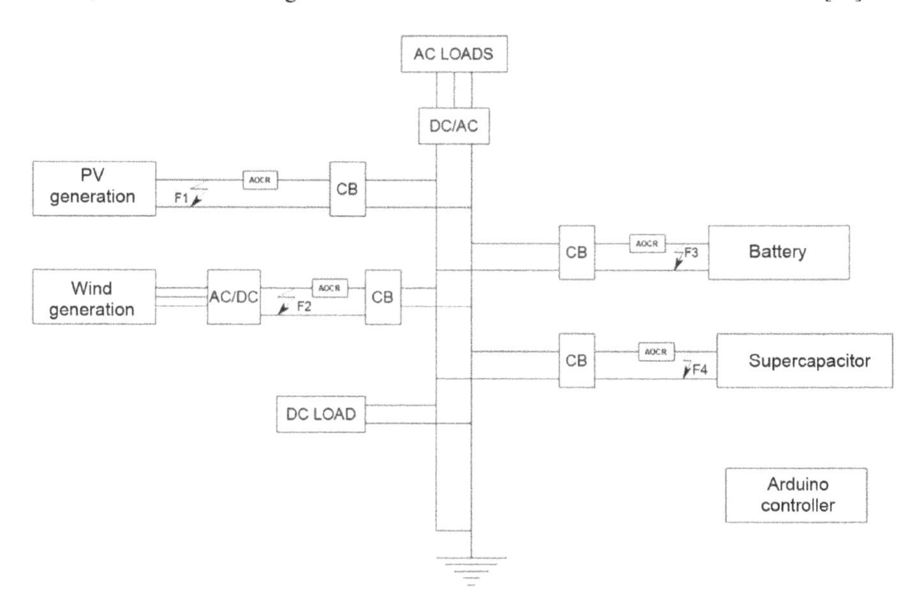

FIGURE 12.12 Fault analysis using Arduino for smart DC microgrid.

TABLE 12.1
Voltage and Current Drawn from Smart DC Microgrid System

Name	Voltage (V)	Current (A)	Power
Microgrid	470	7.3	3.43 kW
Solar	470	2.5	1175 W
Wind	470	2	940 W
Battery	470	2.5	1175 W
Supercapacitor	470	0.3	140 W

A set of analog and digital input/output (I/O) pins present in the board can be interfaced to many circuits to detect the overcurrent during the fault period. Similarly, using Raspberry Pi controller communication between relays for demand management provides better control and reliability. The protection scheme used in the proposed work is adaptive overcurrent relay (AOCR) with a Z-source breaker as a circuit breaker to isolate the source during fault conditions. The fault occurrence is detected by LED, in which the Arduino helps to detect and send a signal to make the LED glow, thereby indicating the presence of a fault. While separating each of the source and storage units, the LED present in Arduino will detect and indicate during fault occurrence, where it is clearly shown in output voltage and output current simulation results in Figures 12.13 and 12.14.

When LG fault F1 occurs at 0.1 seconds nearby solar terminal that connects the DC bus, it has been isolated using the Z-source circuit breaker, and the LED present in Arduino glows represents a fault, which is clearly shown in Figure 12.15.

Similarly, at 0.15 seconds, fault F2 occurs at wind generation connected to DC bus is isolated from the grid to ensure its safety and reliability. Similarly, because of the fault occurrences F3 and F4 at 0.2 and 0.25 seconds, the battery and capacitor bank are isolated from the DC grid, respectively.

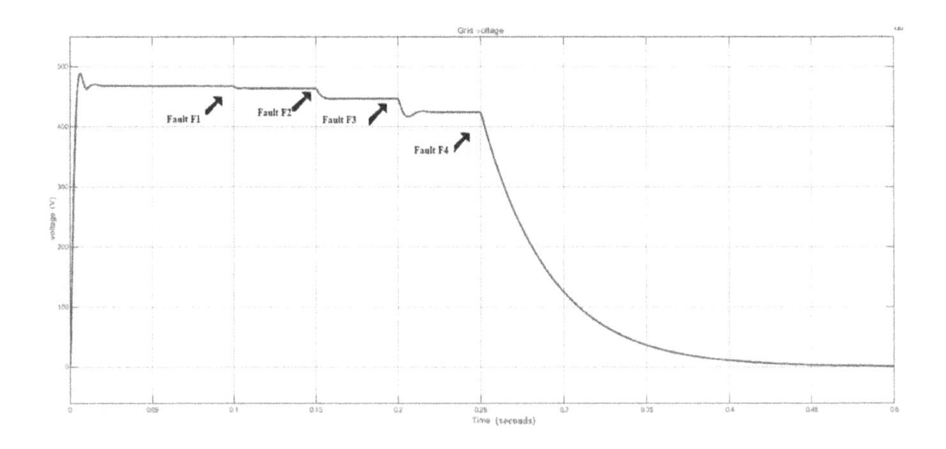

FIGURE 12.13 Output voltage of DC microgrid during fault conditions.

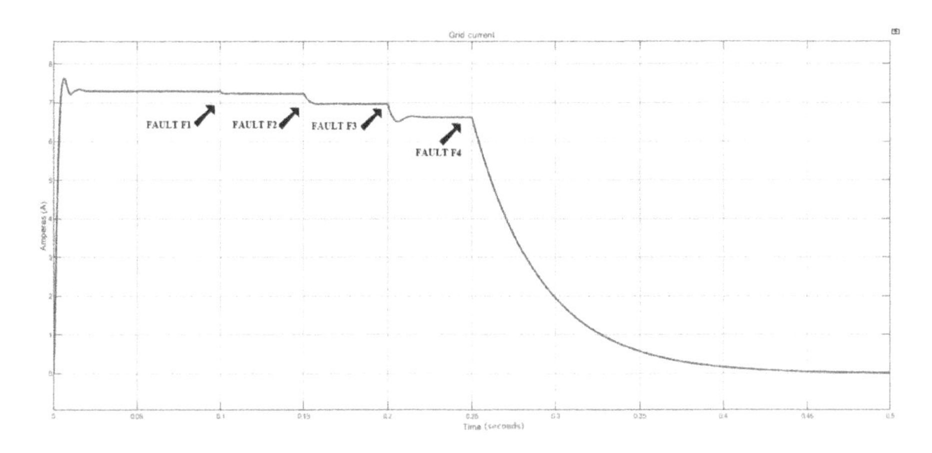

FIGURE 12.14 Output current of DC microgrid during fault conditions.

Occurrence of fault at wind generation terminal

FIGURE 12.15 Event of fault at solar and wind terminals.

The proposed work is ended up with a simple cost analysis for real-time implementation, and it is briefly given in Table 12.2. The fault detection response time for each fault is around 0.02 seconds.

12.5 CONCLUSION AND FUTURE WORK

This paper had been presented the modeling of DC microgrid using MATLAB Simulink, where modeling of each source and energy storage was well explained, and simulation results were analyzed. In this work, solar and wind were used as renewable sources and SC, and the battery was used as storages. It can be improved by adding many renewables such as fuel cells and diesel generators, expanding the solar panels, and integrating large-scale wind turbine. In the future, the present work can be used to analyze the appropriate protection schemes and protective devices to

TABLE 12.2
Cost Analysis of Smart DC Microgrid

S.NO.	Component Name	Specification	Quantity	Cost (in Rupees)
1	PCB	12 × 12 inch	1	150
2	Inductor	2.077 mH 5 A, 162 μH 3–5 A, 1 mH 4–7 A	3	1500
3	Capacitor	20 μF 100 V 31.3 μF 100 V 100 μF 100 V 220 μF 100 V	4	60
4	MOSFET	IRF 540N	3	100
5	Diode	MUR1660	1	50
6	Load resistor	Resistance box	1	30
7	Arduino	UNO	1	500
8	TLP	250	3	50
9	Solar panel	240 V	1	21,000
10	Battery	48 V	4	56,000
11	Wind turbine	400 W 450 V	1	30,000
12	Ultracapacitor	180 V	1	60,000
13	ZS breaker	3 A	1	2000
	Total	-	-	Rs 171,440

achieve a secure and reliable system [5,15]. Also, the stability can be enhanced by analyzing and selecting the suitable compensators [16,17] for the DC microgrid to be considered in the future.

REFERENCES

[1] N. Hatziargyriou, H. Asano, R. Iravani and C. Marnay, Microgrids, *IEEE Power Energy Mag.* 5, 4, 78–94, 2007, doi: 10.1109/MPAE.2007.376583.

[2] H. Nikkhajoei and R. H. Lasseter, Distributed generation interface to the CERTS microgrid, *IEEE Trans. Power Deliv.* 24, 3, 1598–1608, 2009, doi: 10.1109/TPWRD.2009.2021040.

[3] J. Mírez, A modeling and simulation of optimized interconnection between DC microgrids with novel strategies of voltage, power and control, *2017 IEEE Second International Conference on DC Microgrids (ICDCM)*, Nuremburg, 2017, pp. 536–541, doi: 10.1109/ICDCM.2017.8001098.

[4] Z. Fusheng and R. T. Naayagi, Power converters for DC microgrids – modelling and simulation, *2018 IEEE Innovative Smart Grid Technologies - Asia (ISGT Asia)*, Singapore, 2018, pp. 994–999, doi: 10.1109/ISGT-Asia.2018.8467847.

[5] M. Nasir, H. A. Khan, A. Hussain, L. Mateen and N. A. Zaffar, Solar PV-based scalable DC microgrid for rural electrification in developing regions, *IEEE Trans. Sustainable Energy* 9, 1, 2018, 390–399.

[6] X. H. Nguyen and M. P. Nguyen, Mathematical modeling of photovoltaic cell/module/arrays with tags in MATLAB/Simulink. *Environ. Syst. Res.* 4, 24, 2015, doi: 10.1186/s40068-015-0047-9.

[7] N. Pandiarajan and R. Muthu, Mathematical modeling of photovoltaic module with Simulink, *2011 1st International Conference on Electrical Energy Systems*, Newport Beach, CA, 2011, pp. 258–263, doi: 10.1109/ICEES.2011.5725339.
[8] N. Pandiarajan, Photovoltaic generator MATLAB/Simulink model, *2016 3rd International Conference on Electrical Energy Systems (ICEES)*, Chennai, 2016, pp. 91–95, doi: 10.1109/ICEES.2016.7510622.
[9] R. Ben Ali, H. Schulte and A. Mami, Modeling and simulation of a small wind turbine system based on PMSG generator, *2017 Evolving and Adaptive Intelligent Systems (EAIS)*, Ljubljana, 2017, pp. 1–6, doi: 10.1109/EAIS.2017.7954833.
[10] A. Tobías-González, R. Peña-Gallardo, J. Morales-Saldaña and G. Gutiérrez-Urueta, Modeling of a wind turbine with a permanent magnet synchronous generator for real time simulations, *2015 IEEE International Autumn Meeting on Power, Electronics and Computing (ROPEC), Ixtapa*, 2015, pp. 1–6, doi: 10.1109/ROPEC.2015.7395143.
[11] M. C. Argyrou, P. Christodoulides, C. C. Marouchos and S. A. Kalogirou, Hybrid battery-supercapacitor mathematical modeling for PV application using MATLAB/Simulink, *2018 53rd International Universities Power Engineering Conference (UPEC)*, Glasgow, 2018, pp. 1–6, doi: 10.1109/UPEC.2018.8541933.
[12] R. Ben Ali, H. Schulte and A. Mami, Modeling and simulation of a small wind turbine system based on PMSG generator, *2017 Evolving and Adaptive Intelligent Systems (EAIS)*, Ljubljana, Slovenia, 2017, pp. 1–6, doi: 10.1109/EAIS.2017.7954833.
[13] D. Ricchiuto, R. A. Mastromauro, M. Liserre, I. Trintis and S. Munk-Nielsen, Overview of multi-DC-bus solutions for DC microgrids, *2013 4th IEEE International Symposium on Power Electronics for Distributed Generation Systems (PEDG)*, Rogers, AR, 2013, pp. 1–8, doi: 10.1109/PEDG.2013.6785637.
[14] Y. Jaswanth, R. Rachana and B. V. Rao, Protection of microgrids with arduino control scheme, *J. Controller Converters* 4, 3, 43–49, 2019.
[15] S. A. Arefifar, M. Ordonez and Y. A. I. Mohamed, Energy management in multi-microgrid systems—development and assessment, *IEEE Trans. Power Syst.* 32, 2, 910–922, 2017, doi: 10.1109/TPWRS.2016.2568858.
[16] I. Tank and S. Mali, Renewable based DC microgrid with energy management system, in *2015 IEEE Int. Conf. on Signal Process., Informatics, Commun. and Energy Syst.*, Kozhikode, India, 2015.
[17] T. Logenthiran, R. T. Naayagi, W. L. Woo, V.-T. Phan and K. Abidi, Intelligent control system for microgrids using multi-agent system, *IEEE J. Emerg. Select. Top. Power Electron.* 3, 4, 1036–1045, 2015.

13 Characterizing Voltage-Dependent Loads and Frequency-Dependent Loads for Load Stability Analysis

G Naveen Kumar
Andhra Loyola Institute of Engineering and Technology

CONTENTS

13.1 VOLTAGE STABILITY ELUCIDATION

Voltage stability [1,2] defines the capability of an electrical power network in maintaining steady-state voltages at all network buses after they have been subjected to the perturbation from an initial operating condition [3]. The capability that a power system network shows in restoring equilibrium among load demand and supply is load stability or voltage stability. Instability can be a result of load variations that may be, for example, progressive rise or progressive fall of voltages at some of the load buses. Loads are one of the driving forces in retaining the voltage stability. Hence, the loss of load can be resulted in instability [4].

Load stability indices [5] that are simple and computationally inexpensive are useful when determining how close a given work point is to a point of voltage stress

DOI: 10.1201/9781003201069-13

collapse. These can be determined by load stability analysis for both online and off-line studies [6]. Load modeling is one such technique to determine proximity to voltage collapse. It is essential that stability studies address volatility issues for any long-term feeding systems [7].

Modeling of power system loads happens to be a tough task for many reasons, namely the absence of accurate information regarding the compilation of the load that changes with time, changes with seasons, and changes with weather conditions, etc. [8]. Analysts at electrical utilities and their administration need solid evidence of the benefits of better load representation in order to justify the efforts and expenses associated with the collection and processing of load data [9].

Interesting research in load modeling has taken place over years. A number of studies have pointed to the critical effect of load representation in stress-related voltage stability issues [10]. The incorporation of load patterns in the power utility causes a decrease in the voltage profile due to reactive power shortfall. This leads for us to identify precise load models than those traditionally used [8,11]. Artificial intelligence that has become an important tool of application in every part of engineering is considered to make the utilities smart enough to predict and control [12].

13.2 PROBLEM STATEMENT

In this chapter, an address to load stability issues by comparing voltage-dependent load (VDL) model and frequency-dependent load (FDL) model was done. The effect of both load models by installing them in the network and running a power flow routine to determine the voltage profile and loading capability limit in each case was performed, after which the presentation of binary search procedure which is an artificial intelligence approach to optimally size and simultaneously locate a thyristor-controlled series capacitor (TCSC) for addressing load instability caused in the case of formally classified load models is done.

13.3 MATERIAL AND METHOD FOR IMPLEMENTATION

13.3.1 Voltage-Dependant Load Models

"Voltage-dependant loads" [13] such as incandescent lamps, air-conditioners, furnace fans, battery chargers, and fluorescent lights are the loads whose credentials are minimum functions of the bus voltage expressed as follows.

$$P = P_0 \left(V / V_0 \right)^{\alpha \cdot P} \tag{13.1}$$

$$Q = Q_0 \left(V / V_0 \right)^{\alpha \cdot Q} \tag{13.2}$$

The above-mentioned model of the load is a static one. The power depends on the voltage and/or frequency, but not time-dependent. "P" is an active load. "Q" is a reactive load. "P_0" is called base active load. "Q_0" is termed base reactive load. "V" is the load voltage. "V_0" is the base load voltage. Here, "α" is an active load exponent.

The value "α" ranges between 0.08 and 2.59 [13]. This depends upon the load composition used. VDLs used here are directly included in the power flow analysis. "V_0" can have any minimum value and is the starting voltage at the load bus which is obtained by a load flow solution. In this case, as the initial voltage "V_0" is unknown, we assume it to be 1 P.U. (a certain minimum value). Hence, the subsequent equations can be used for the analysis [13].

$$P = P_0 V^{\alpha \cdot p} \tag{13.3}$$

$$Q = Q_0 V^{\alpha \cdot q} \tag{13.4}$$

13.3.2 Frequency-Dependent Load Models

A version of load which has a dependency on frequency is called a FDL. Refrigerators, freezers, air conditioners, water heaters, pumps, and ovens are few examples. This model can be expressed as follows [13]:

$$P = K_p / 100 (V / V_0)^{\alpha p} (1 + \Delta\omega)^{\beta p} \tag{13.5}$$

$$Q = K_q / 100 (V / V_0)^{\alpha q} (1 + \Delta\omega)^{\beta q} \tag{13.6}$$

The value of "β" ranges between 0.31 and 4.06 [13].

"$\Delta\omega$" is representing the frequency deviation near the load bus. This can be determined by differentiating and filtering phase angle "θ."

$$\Delta\omega = x + 1 / 2\pi f_0 + 1 / T_f (\theta - \theta_0) \tag{13.7}$$

$$x = -1 / T_f \left(1 / 2\pi f_0 + 1 / T_f (\theta - \theta_0) + x\right) \tag{13.8}$$

"θ_0" and "V_0" are phase angle and voltage magnitude. They are determined during load flow solution itself. The power rating and voltage rating will be inherited by the FDL if a reactive load is connected to the same [13].

13.3.3 Binary Search Algorithm

Binary search algorithm [14] is one of the types of the common search procedures adopted in most of the real-world applications. It is more of a special algorithm but not a regular sequential search. It uses and exploits the data that are sorted. The basic idea behind binary research is splitting the sorted data into equal halves and then examining the data from the split point. As data are already sorted, it is easy to ignore the first or the second half. This depends on the segment where the data are looked for rather than the data at the split. A binary search is also called a half-range search algorithm that finds the location of a specified input value that is the "search key" in an array.

In binary search, the array must be organized in ascending or descending order. Thereafter, at each step, this algorithm compares the value of the lookup key with the value of the key of the central element of the array.

If the keys correspond, then a corresponding element has been found. Its index and position are returned. If not, if the search key is smaller than the central element key, then the algorithm repeats. It repeats the action on the subarray which is to the left of the central element. If the search key is larger, the action repeats to the right in the subarray. If the array still to be searched is empty, then the key looked up for will not be found. A special indication "not found" comes back.

Binary search halves the number of elements that must be checked at each iteration step. Therefore, the location of an element or the determination of its absence takes about logarithmic time. Hence, this search is also called as "dichotomic divide and conquer search" [15]. A total count of iterations cannot be more than log N. Here, "N" is the number of iterations. Binary search procedure is described through the algorithm that follows below [14].

ALGORITHM

Step 1: Start the solution by choosing a population.
Step 2: Assign the minimum and maximum limits for the population in the solution set X_i to X_n. Here, $i=1$ to n.
Step 3: Inject a population number from the solution set $X_i=X_n$.
Step 4: Check for convergence after step 2.
Step 5: If the output is optimum for the solution target, then finalize the population number.
Step 6: If the output is not optimum for the solution target, then go back to step 2 and readdress the problem.
Step 7: Stop the program and exit.

13.3.4 Thyristor-Controlled Series Capacitor

Technical development in electrical power engineering gave us many technologically advantageous devices to be applicable as solutions to various issues within the power system. One such development is flexible AC transmission systems (FACTS). It is a semiconductor technology component-based control tool. This has many potential benefits. A significant device from the group of FACTS is "TCSC," a series device [6]. The structure is shown in Figure 13.1.

It consists of a series compensating capacitor, which works in side-by- side connection to thyristor-controlled reactor (TCR). This is used to monitor and control the active power flow in the electrical system. It enhances the capacity of the transmission lines. TCSC modifies the impedance of a transmission path, thus allowing for a change in power flows. With TCSC, controlling is fast and efficient [6].

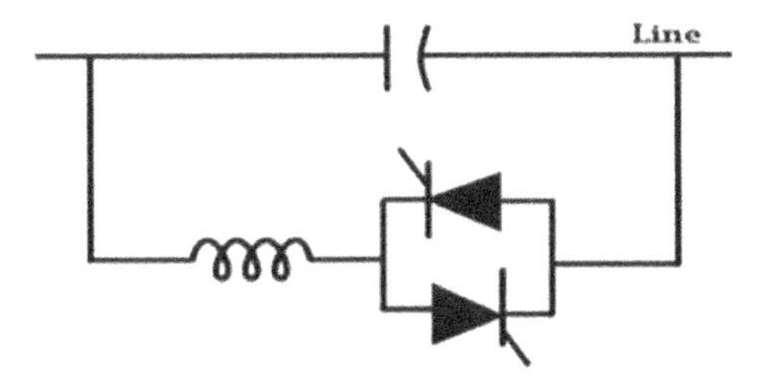

FIGURE 13.1 Structure of TCSC.

13.3.5 Test System

The load flow analysis [16] is performed on IEEE 14-bus network. This power network has 21 counts of branches, 14 counts of buses with 11 numbers of loads. Capacity of the system is 259 MW and 81.4 MVAR. A tolerance of 5% for bus voltages in P.U. is assumed. Slack bus is Bus 1. Twenty counts of iterations were planned and programmed.

13.4 IMPLEMENTATION

The entire investigation is conducted using power system analysis toolkit [13]. Continuation power flow approach was selected with a fast decoupled algorithm for load flow study [16]. The stability limit of the test case network incorporated with VDLs and FDLs is determined along with bus voltage profiles in the form of real power and voltage (P–V) curves with maximum loadability limit. The comparative analysis between the two load models is shown in Table 13.1.

TABLE 13.1
Comparison of VDL and FDL

Bus No.	Voltage Magnitude Profile without Load Classification	Voltage Magnitude Profile with VDLs	Voltage Magnitude Profile with FDLs
01	1.0572	1.0572	1.0572
02	0.93175	0.88923	0.916
03	0.85811	0.74095	0.7672
04	0.77903	0.74086	0.8165
05	0.79614	0.76757	0.8416
06	0.82196	0.83625	0.9437
07	0.79451	0.80221	0.9120
08	0.93818	0.94304	1.009
09	0.720839	0.74587	0.8925
10	0.71213	0.74231	0.8950
11	0.75452	0.77959	0.9159
12	0.7663	0.79402	0.9278
13	0.7445	0.77805	0.9209
14	0.66135	0.71354	0.8890
λ_{max}	2.375	2.7571	3.1718

If looked at the voltage profiles and loading parameters in each case, VDL models are observed to bring down the load stability of the given network. In the case of the effect of FDLs on a power network, they observe to keep the load stability profile of the network under safe limits. FDL models are observed to be better loads than VDL models. Figure 13.2 shows P–V curves of network with unclassified loads. Figure 13.3 draws a comparison of VDL and FDL for the voltage magnitude profile of each bus and also the loading capability limit.

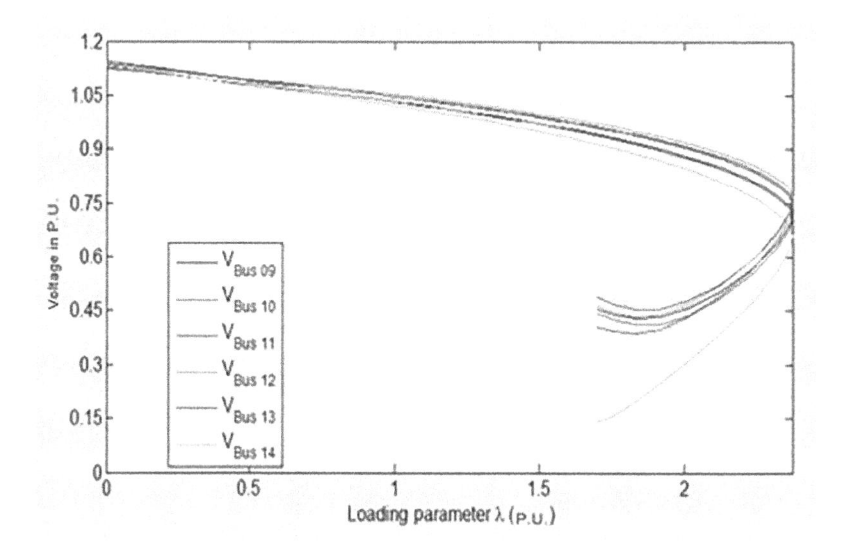

FIGURE 13.2 P–V curves of IEEE 14 bus network with no classified load.

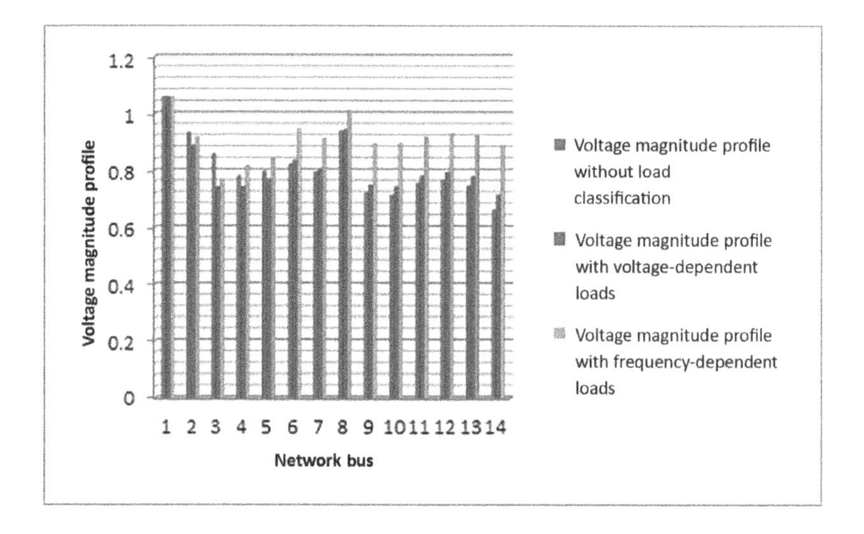

FIGURE 13.3 Comparison of VDL and FDL.

It is understood that the maximum loading parameter in the case of network with unclassified load is 2.375. This is observed to be improved with VDL to a value of 2.7571. This is further enhanced to 3.1718 with FDL. Buses 9 to 14 are exclusive load buses. The voltage magnitude in P.U. at these buses also shows a significant and superior quality improvement with the placement of FDL loads.

As the performance of VDL and FDL is now understood, it can further be established that their safe operation using the placement of TCSC using binary search procedure is possible. The population size and range for binary search to determine the size and location of TCSC FACTS device are shown in Table 13.2. The population range and size are essential for binary searching to scale down the size of TCSC to its appropriate KVAR (kilo volt ampere reactive) value. Finally, it is installed in the system to work for overall benefit.

Observations show a furtherance in a magnitude profile of bus voltages and maximum loading limit in the case of both VDL and FDL as shown in Tables 13.3 and 13.4, respectively.

TABLE 13.2
Population Size

S. No.	Number of Bus Combinations	Range of Population Size
1	2–3	0.2–1.2
2	2–4	0.2–1.2
3	2–5	0.2–1.2
4	3–4	0.2–1.2
5	4–5	0.2–1.2

TABLE 13.3
Power Network with VDL and TCSC

Bus No.	Network with VDL	Network with VDL and TCSC
01	1.0572	1.0572
02	0.88923	0.91217
03	0.74095	0.76217
04	0.74086	0.76347
05	0.76757	0.76722
06	0.83625	0.83433
07	0.80221	0.81243
08	0.94304	0.94882
09	0.74587	0.75282
10	0.74231	0.74699
11	0.77959	0.78075
12	0.79402	0.79131
13	0.77805	0.77566
14	0.71354	0.71458
λ_{max}	2.7571	2.8659

TABLE 13.4
Power Network with FDL and TCSC

Bus No.	Network with FDL	Network with FDL and TCSC
01	1.0572	1.0572
02	0.916	0.9291
03	0.7672	0.7776
04	0.8165	0.8309
05	0.8416	0.8329
06	0.9437	0.9428
07	0.9120	0.9199
08	1.009	1.013
09	0.8925	0.8993
10	0.8950	0.9004
11	0.9159	0.9182
12	0.9278	0.9274
13	0.9209	0.9211
14	0.8890	0.8929
λ_{max}	3.1718	3.2067

Figure 13.4 envisages the fact that operating FDLs are observed as better choices than VDLs for their characteristics to maintain load stability to protect the transmission and distribution network from slipping into an unsafe operating zone in terms of power system network stability. The action of TCSC in inductive mode by modifying equivalent reactance of a transmission line generates the necessary reactive power and thus improving the load stability of the system. Installation of TCSC in the system has improved loading conditions substantially in either case of the loads as shown in Figure 13.4. This is achieved by proper tuning of parameters in the controller.

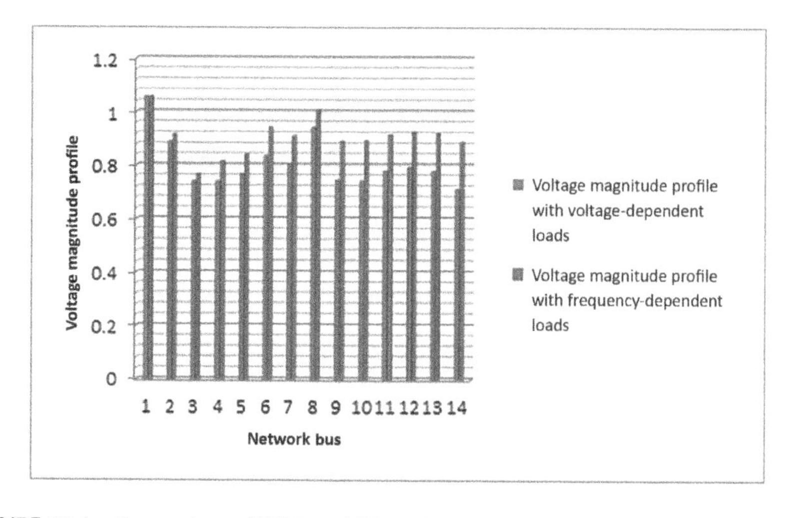

FIGURE 13.4 Comparison of VDL and FDL with the application of TCSC.

13.5 CULMINATION

The research presented in this book chapter details a study of load models for load stability using binary search computational approach. VDL models and FDL models were compared and characterized for loadability in the power system network. Out of the two load models, FDL models were observed to be more reliable comparatively. This was adjudged from the observation of voltage magnitude profiles of load buses and the maximum loading parameter of the power network. Although FDL models were observed to be the best type of loads, they lack in providing complete stability. This instability was addressed by TCSC, a series FACTS tool as found inside many power system-planning applications off late. The optimal placement and size of device were determined using binary search approach. This is a simple but effective procedure in comparison with time-consuming and memory-occupying advanced artificial computational procedures available as applied in smart utilities.

13.6 FURTHER SCOPE FOR RESEARCH

This research is helpful and useful in static voltage stability analysis. Furthermore, the same can also be extended to compare various and different other static and dynamic load models for load stability in practically installed power networks. This work can be extended to be tested in grid-connected renewables for its reliability. This is especially needed in wind power networks where the source of energy is unreliable but abundant. Many latest artificial intelligence techniques can be studied and applied with load models to understand the performance and application in practice.

REFERENCES

[1] P Kundur, *Power System Stability and Control*, New York, McGraw Hill, 1994.

[2] CW Taylor, *Power System Voltage Stability*, New York, McGraw-Hill, 1994.

[3] B Gao, GK Morison, P Kundur, "Voltage stability analysis using static and dynamic approaches", *IEEE Transactions on Power Systems* 8, 3, 1993, 1159–1171.

[4] T Van Cutsem, C Vournas, *Voltage Stability of Electrical Power Systems*, New York, Springer Science, 1998.

[5] GN Kumar, *Investigation of Load Models in Load Stability using UPFC and CSO*, Germany, Lambert Academic Publishers, 2016.

[6] NG Hingorani, L Gyugyi, *Understanding FACTS: Concepts and Technology of Flexible AC Transmission Systems*, New York, IEEE Press, 2000.

[7] GN Kumar, MS Kalavathi, "Static load modeling for voltage stability studies with optimal placement of UPFC using cat swarm optimization", *International Journal of Electrical and Electronics Engineering Research*, 4, 1, 2014, 35–46.

[8] CH Gu, Q Ai, J Wu, "A study of effect of different static load models and system operating constraints on static voltage stability", *Proceedings of the 5th WSEAS/IASME International Conference on Systems Theory and Scientific Computation*, Malta, 2005, pp. 44–49.

[9] P Kundur, J Paserba, V Ajjarapu, G Anderson, A Bose, C Canizares, N Hatiziargyriou, D Hill, A Stankovic, C Taylor, V Vittal, T Van Cutsem, "Definition and classification of power system stability", *IEEE Transactions on Power Systems* 19, 2, 2004, 1387–1401.

[10] GN Kumar, MS Kalavathi, "Dynamic load models for voltage stability studies with a solution of UPFC using CSO", *International Journal of Computer Applications* 116, 10, 2015, 27–32.
[11] I Musirin, TK Abdul Rahman, "Estimating maximum loadability for weak bus identification using FVSI", *IEEE Power Engineering Review* 2002, 50–52.
[12] H Feng, The application of artificial intelligence in electrical automation control, In *First International Conference on Advanced Algorithms and Control Engineering*, IOP Publishing Limited, 2018, 1–6.
[13] Power system analysis toolbox documentation for PSAT version 2.0.0 β, 2007.
[14] A Oommen, C Pal, "Binary search algorithm", *IJIRT* 1, 5, 2014, 800–803.
[15] V Ajjarapu, *Computational Techniques for Voltage Stability Assessment and Control*, New York, Springer Science, 2006.
[16] IA Hisken, Power flow analysis, In *Department of Electrical and Computer Engineering (Vol. 6)*. University of Wisconsin-Madison, 2003.

14 Enabling Technologies for Smart Buildings
High Power Density Power Electronic Converters

M Mahesh and K Vinoth Kumar
New Horizon College of Engineering

M Prabhakar
Vellore Institute of Technology

CONTENTS

14.1 INTRODUCTION: BACKGROUND AND DRIVING FORCES

The aim of the miniaturization of power converters/sources with superior performance for various applications has brought about a revolution in the power electronic (PE) industries that strive to adopt new and advanced technologies. Continued growth of some technologies is expected to have far-reaching impacts by the way in which converters are designed and developed, leading to newer trends within PE industries as well as allied manufacturing industries. One of the most asked questions in PE domain is: Why is the miniaturization of power supplies/converters essential? The most recognizable answer is that some of the applications such as biomedical appliances, aerospace, and satellite equipment demand less space and/or low-weight power supplies. The next motivation arises from the novel technology architectures that can be conceived in order to fulfill the higher power density requirements. The third

DOI: 10.1201/9781003201069-14

motivation is that the present customers demand very portable power supply products such as uninterruptible power supplies (UPSs); power conditioners for domestic and commercial applications; power supply to desktop/laptops; portable battery charging equipment; power supplies to telecom, data servers, and information technology applications.

A small volume requirement permits a greater and flexible design freedom at a lower capital investment [1]. A lower weight and size of converter typically indicates a reduced amount of materials used, and further, most of the applications require simple installation, easy maintenance, and handling; they are especially significant for locomotive systems such as electric aircraft, hybrid vehicles, and electric vehicles [2].

Achieving and managing high power density signifies effective utilization of state of the art of device manufacturing and packing technology, recent topological developments in power conversation, leading edge method of control and avant-garde thermal management techniques. In addition to the size and volume of power supplies, the power supply design engineers serving in any industrial sector strive to meet the high efficiency, high reliability, and lower price of power converters for any given application.

High efficiency is needed to meet the assertive and stringent international standards recommended by government or industry. Reliability is the fundamental requirement essentially demanded by all types of customers across the globe. One of the well-known and key aspects of power converters is thermal management, which determines the reliability as well as their operating performance and power density of converters [3]. Hence, current researches on high power density converters are progressing in the direction of efficiency, reliability, and cost that is compatible with the ongoing customer and market demand. Hence, the trade-off among power density, improved performance with respect to efficiency, mean time between failures (MTBF), and cost of the power supply must be judiciously met. Figure 14.1 depicts the collaborative relationship between height size, volume, cost, losses, and MTBF. Thus, the recent trend in manufacturing, thermal, and nanotechnology is progressing. Hence, based on the market/industrial demand, advancements in technologies by taking care of the chaos of the trade-offs faced by the power supply design engineers. The continuous pressure on market cost is mitigated by minimizing the risks and employing matured technologies based on the reduction in materials and component prices year-on-year.

14.2 DEPENDENCY AND PRACTICAL ISSUES: TO ENABLE HIGH POWER DENSITY

There are some hindrances that must be traversed to overcome in order to achieve high power density while maintaining a better performance in power conversion system, which include driver circuit power consumption, increased switching energy losses, limitations of switching frequency, synthesis of high-Q passive components, electromagnetic interference (EMI) effects, and adverse temperature effects in converters. Many approaches such as zero voltage/zero current switching (ZVS/ZCS) have been introduced by researchers to reduce the power consumed by the switching devices and the gate driving circuit with an increased operation speed of power converters [4–8].

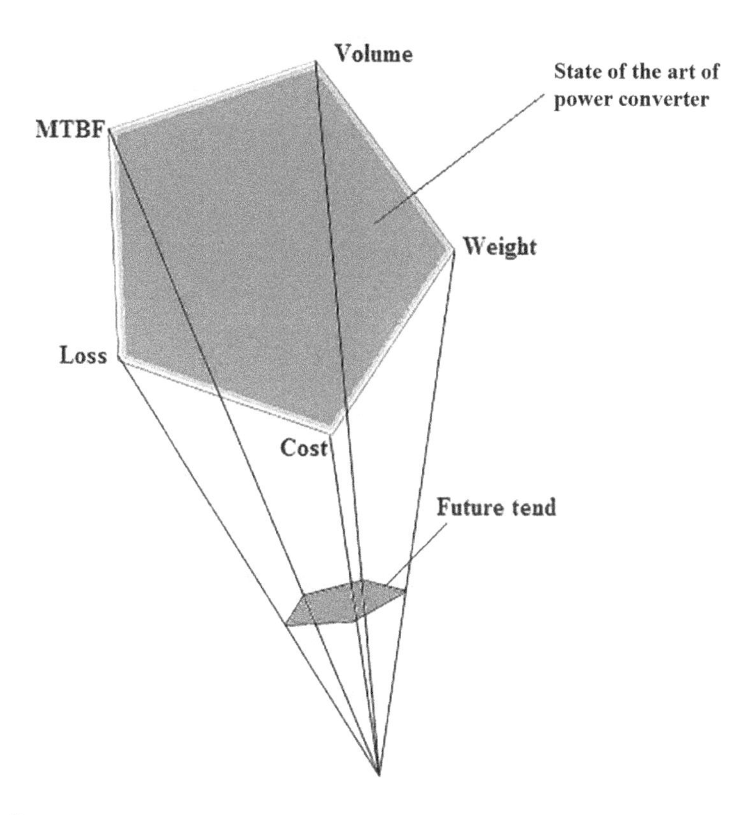

FIGURE 14.1 Progressing trends in power converters for various applications.

One practical challenge is the substantial power consumption of the device driving circuit due to large input capacitance of devices at high switching frequency of operation. The concept of resonant gate drive techniques has been proposed and reported to essentially reduce the energy consumed by the driving circuit [9–11]. It has been noticed in the literature that the progress of researched a matured level practically operating of high density converters while considering EMI effects, inductor core and eddy current losses, ripple compensation. However, there are emerging sectors that compensate and provide solutions to the above issues in high power density converters. Figure 14.2 depicts the relationship among emerging technologies and their bimutual relationship to achieve an optimized design for the miniaturization of power converters. The effort is made in highlighting the emerging fields of research, especially in PE to achieve high power density of converters.

There are four sectors which are emerging in the direction of high power density converters:

1. Integrated power device (IPD) technology
2. Wide bandgap technology
3. Embedded microjets for thermal management
4. Micro-electromechanical system (MEMS) inductors.

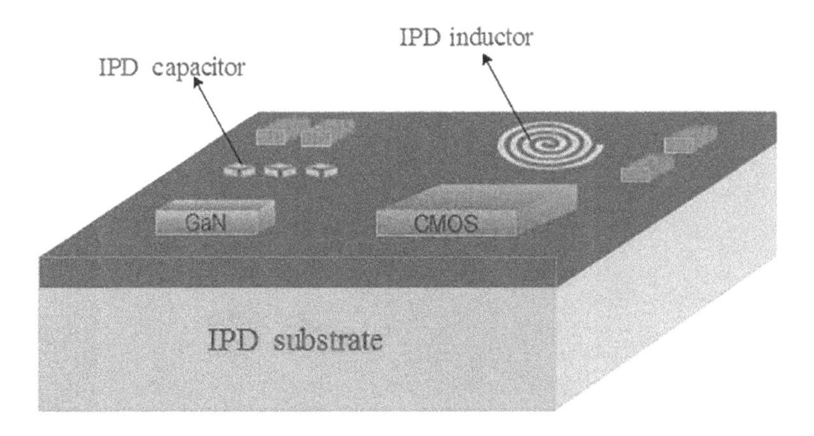

FIGURE 14.2 Emerging technologies to achieve high power density and their relationship.

14.3 INTEGRATED POWER DEVICE TECHNOLOGY

Among the certain technology advances in the miniaturization of power sources, IPD technology plays a vital role to achieve a very high frequency (100s of Mega Hz) with latest silicon carbide (SiC) and gallium nitride (GaN) devices. The further growth in IPD is expected to be a challenging trend as this technology is driven by factors such as increasing adoption of IPD in consumer products (mobiles, digital cameras, and tablets), insect-sized microrobots to provide surveillance and reconnaissance in hostile, integration of IPDs into radiofrequency (RF) applications, and efficient technologies in the electronic industries. Figure 14.3 shows the conceptual structure/layout of (wide bandgap devices) GaN and CMOS circuits/devices in IPD technology. IPDs are classically associated with various passive components in distinct package.

As shown in Figure 14.3, the devices were gradually fabricated on thin films of glass ceramic substrates (which are slightly expensive than glass substrates). Silicon materials are accounted for a major portion of IPD technology and will assist on high-resistivity substrates. This IPD technology is essentially combined with wafer-level packaging, which yields minimal size and reduced costs as this technology does not need a conventional method of plastic package. This is a booming area of advanced technology that supports microfabrication of elements with innovative semiconductor methods to change discrete components in circuit size reduction in addition to the system integration [12]. This power supply in package (PSiP) solution faces challenges due to the predominance of passive components and the fact that their quality factor has to be high to maintain better performance. In general, through this technology, system components and devices of size ranging from 0.15 to 0.3 μm are fabricated. This process of fabrication also includes circuit-like resonant gate drivers with latest devices such as CMOS devices and GaN-high electron mobility transistors (HEMTs). It is reported in the literature that nearly a 5 W DC–DC converter is developed through this technology and has a size of chip area as small as $1 \times 1\ \text{cm}^2$ and power density of around 36 W/cm^3.

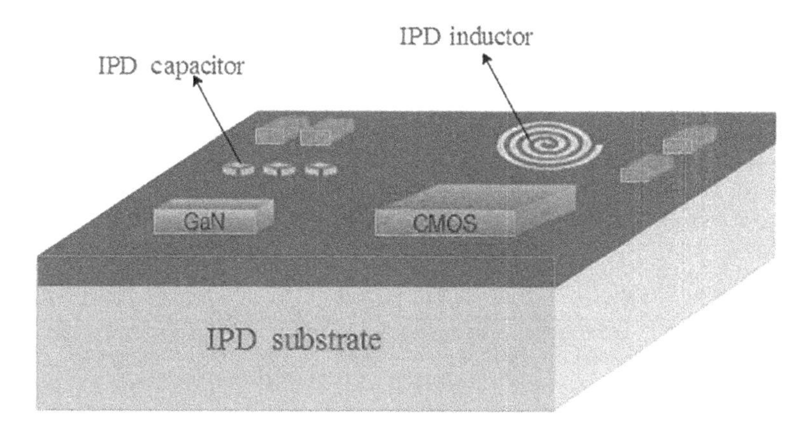

FIGURE 14.3 Connectional layout of IPD technology for high power density.

14.4 WIDE BANDGAP TECHNOLOGY

The efficient and compact power-handling devices that exhibit high critical breakdown fields and high electron mobility are the third generation of semiconductor materials. This semiconductor technology provides relatively wider bandgap (range of 2–4eV) in comparison with conventional semiconductors (wide bandgap range 1–1.5 EV), hence popularly termed as wide bandgap technology. At present scenario, in the miniaturization of power supply, it is highly desirable to have a semiconductor device that exhibits extraordinary wet drift velocity, great critical field breakdown, higher frequency (range of 100s of MHz) of operation, and very high temperature withstanding capacity. These superior advantages of wide bandgap technology driving a hot spot of progress in semiconductor technology research across the globe in research universities as well as in industries. In recent years, two wide bandgap devices, namely GaN-hetero-epitaxial technology and SiC-single-crystal growth technology, are continuing to mature in PE converters for various applications. As GaN substrate's availability is limited, most of the devices are grown on SiC or sapphire substrates. So the family of available SiC devices is SiC-metal–oxide–semiconductor field-effect transistor (MOSFET), SiC-junction field-effect transistor (JFET), and SiC-bipolar junction transistor (BJT), which are manufactured and released in the market to a greater extent. While there are considerable benefits to adopt wide bandgap PEs, still there exists engineering design and economic challenges. Cost of the material is one of the most common issues in the adoption of wide bandgap technology. It is one of the major barriers to overcome, which has been cited by both industrial experts and university researchers [13,14]. Figure 14.3 depicts the average selling price of wide bandgap devices reducing with bumps likely due to the introduction of high-voltage-/high-current-handling devices [15]. This source of indication is that there is a progress in employability of such devices in ongoing projects of PE applications across the globe. The range between health information system's technologyconventional initiation also optimistic forecasts mentioned in the shaded area as shown in Figure 14.4a. Figure 14.4b describes how the average price

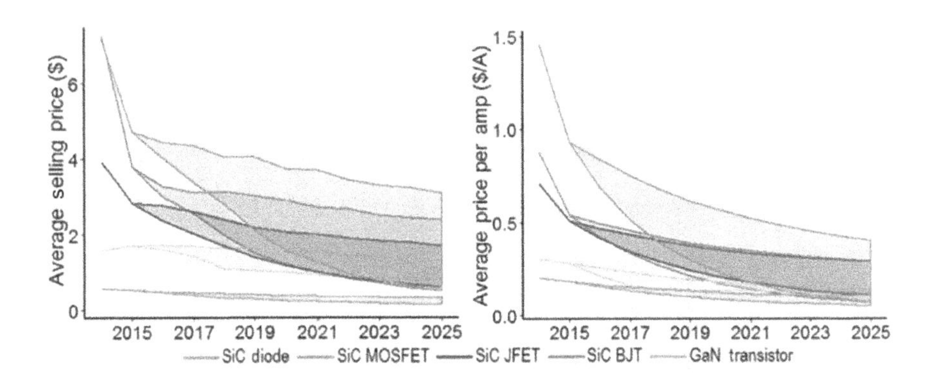

FIGURE 14.4 Wide bandgap discrete's (a) average selling price and (b) price per amp.

per Amp is decreasing very smoothly with years [16]. By comparison, it is understood that GaN transistors are currently priced lower than other SiC devices (except SiC diode), likely due to the much lower voltage capabilities of GaN; the highest rated GaN transistor is 650 V compared to SiCs 1.7 kV as reported is very much lower than SiC. It is noticed that rectifiers/diodes were about $0.06; IGBTs, $0.61; and MOSFETs, $0.14 [17]. This concludes that SiC diodes have ten times the amount of Si diodes, and price variance is greater meant for Si transistors.

14.5 EMBEDDED MICROJETS—THERMAL MANAGEMENT

Developments in the processes, designs, and materials of semiconductor devices have led to the reduction of device measurements from micrometers to nanometers. In progressing, power dissipation has resulted in localized hot spots that directly edict the reliability of device/s and hence the PE systems as well. Hence, a thermal consideration has become a limiting factor in both initial implementation and continued operation of devices. Efficient cooling technologies have been considered as areas of research since 1940 [18]. In achieving high power densities in PE converters, several techniques have grown significantly to handle higher density heat fluxes, which are predicted by thermal road maps noticed/reported by different technical agencies [19–21]. This research in thermal management has overcome certain practical issues and limits, which are driven by the ever-increasing demand of applications, introduction of new advanced cooling technologies. One of the recent cooling technologies is embedded microjet cooling, in which a jet array is fabricated from high-volume, low-price, typical silicon manufacturing techniques. This technology has lower pressure drops, higher heat transfer coefficient, and the ability to maintain uniform heat distribution capacity when arranged in the form of arrays [21]. The layout of embedded microjet impingement integration [22] within the device substrate is presented in Figure 14.5. As shown in the structure, the cooling process will take place at the backside of heat-producing component at the upper stack. Table 14.1 presents the distance between jets, jet diameter, and jet-to-substrate edge distance. In this cooling process, the fluid impacts over narrow passages keen on a fluid-occupied cavity and then leaves through large going away ports as shown in downward arrow marks.

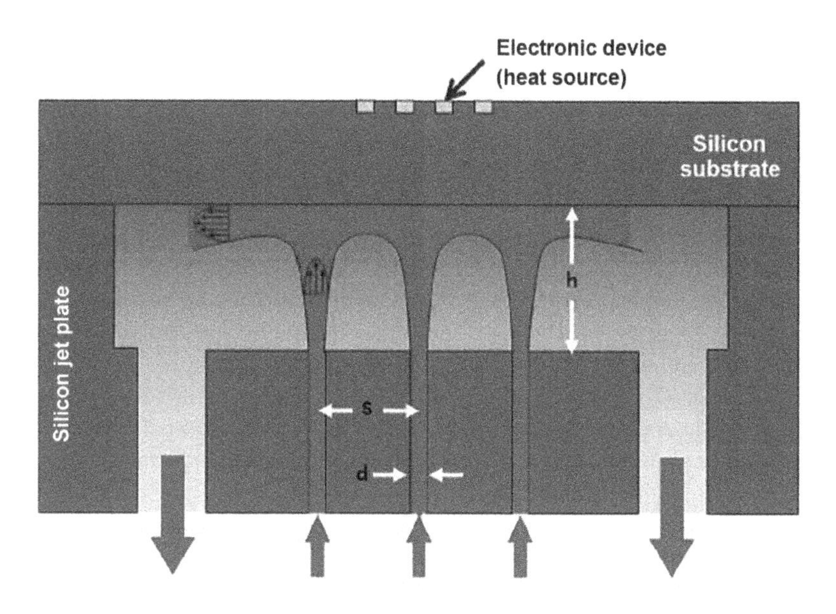

FIGURE 14.5 Structure of embedded microjet impingement thermal management system.

TABLE 14.1
Details of Physical Dimensions of Microjet Impingement

Sl. No.	Notation	Description
1	s	Spacing from jet to jet
2	d	Jet diameter
3	h	Jet-to-target distance

Microjets remain some kinds of jet impingement, which has a portion of liquid with greater velocity than its surroundings also initially less than a millimeter in diameter and hence interact by the solid surface. In this technique, surface makes fluid velocity elect stagnated at a point wherever jet centerline interconnects the wall. Although there is a zone of stagnation, the thermal boundary layer is highly compressed as the pressure increases, and hence, the flow of fluid is accelerated in parallel to the surface [22,23].

14.6 MICRO-ELECTROMECHANICAL SYSTEM (MEMS) INDUCTORS

A promising alternative to the miniaturization of power sources is the utilization of MEMS inductors, which are well suited for very high-frequency power conversion operations. Inductors also transformers remain essential building slabs for all power supplies occupy nearly 60% of the overall volume of the any power supply. Hence, the technology "fabrication of 3D air-core MEMS inductors" is emerging in the field of high power density converters for various applications but specifically finds a scope in the fields of RF MEMS, microactuators, and biosensors [24–26]. In a broad way, MEMS inductor fabrication technology is categorized into dual classes: substrate-embedded inductors and on-substrate inductors.

In substrate-embedded technology, inductors remain embedded classified the silicon substrate then effectively utilize unused substrate volume, and accordingly provide superior advantage that, inductor height can be lowered if it is more in length than substrate surface, and hence finds a scope for improved miniaturization of power converters [26,27]. Figures 14.6 and 14.7 represent inductors embedded with silicon substrate and copper windings [27], which are secured by Si fixtures. This is the 3D air-core inductor fabrication Si-embedded technology suitable for very high-frequency applications. In Figure 14.6, A-A' is the cross section for the fabrication, and input current (I_{in}) and output current (I_{out}) are indicated by arrows [28,29]. Still there exists a challenge for the requirement of a higher aspect ratio of TSVs for compact 3D inductors, in fabrication technology for Si-embedded inductors.

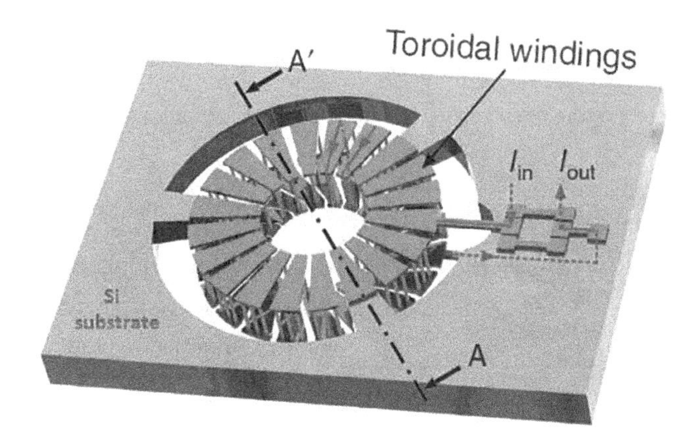

FIGURE 14.6 Physical layout of 3D air-core for solenoidal inductor.

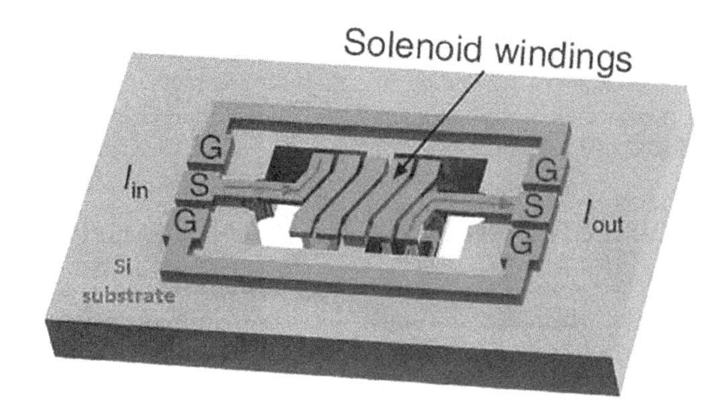

FIGURE 14.7 Physical layout of 3D air-core for toroidal inductor.

The process of perfect design for air-core MEMS inductors includes free-hanging windings wherever the certain silicon portion is far-off from the copper windings [30]. This is possible since the silicon shifts the fundamental frequency (which is also energy conversion efficiency) and causes undesired heating in the system [27]. There are some practical challenges/issues to be taken care of. For instance, besides depreciating the quality factor, the presence of parasitic capacitance also decreases the operation frequency, and also there exists an eddy current loss in the Si core. In this, the resist structures behave as sacrificial layers or electroplating molds or supporting pillars [31,32].

14.7 CONCLUSION

A unique era for the miniaturization in PE systems is developing, just as it did for 5G technique in networking. The defragmentation of wide bandgap and MEMS manufacturers will be a part of this progress. As technologies emerge, mergers and acquisitions will lead to the new enterprises that result in new market trends and new modules of PEs creating better power supplies and enabling applications, which are not currently unseen. The miniaturization of power supplies by emerging technologies discussed in this paper will also come up with new frontiers in terms of integrations and system architectures. For design engineers involved in the design and development of PE systems, the expectation assisted through these technologies such as wide bandgap, MEMS, and embedded microjet cooling will prove to be really beneficial and impactful.

REFERENCES

[1] Yotsumoto, K., Ohashi, Y., Kuwata, Y.: 'Development of an efficient, lightweight switched-mode power supply for telecommunications network use', *IEEE International Telecommunications Energy Conference*, 1986, pp. 25–30.

[2] Homeyer, W. G., Bowles, E. E., Lupan, S. P., Walia, P. S., Maldonado, M. A.: 'Advanced power converters for more electric aircraft applications', *Energy Conversion Engineering Conf. (IECEC'97)*, 1997, pp. 591–596.

[3] Laloya, E., Lucia, O., Sarnago, H., Burdio, J. M.: 'Heat management in power converters: from state of the art to future ultrahigh efficiency systems', *IEEE Trans. Power Electron.* 2016, 31(11), 7896–7908.

[4] Shamsi, P., and Fahimi, B.: 'Design and development of very high frequency resonant DC-DC boost converters', *IEEE Trans. Power Electron.* 2012, 27(8), 3725–3733.

[5] Mahesh, M., Panda, A. K.: 'High-power factor three-phase AC-DC soft-switched converter incorporating zero-voltage transition topology in modular systems for high-power industry applications', *IET-Power Electron.* 2011, 4(9), 1032–1042.

[6] Yu, S., Nguyen, M. Q., and Choi, W.: 'A novel soft-switching battery charge/discharge converter with the zero voltage discharge function', *IEEE Trans. Power Electron.* 2016, 31(7), 5067–5078.

[7] Wen, H., Gong, J., Zhao, X., Yeh, C., and Jih-Sheng L.: 'Analysis of diode reverse recovery effect on ZVS condition for GaN-based LLC resonant converter', *IEEE Trans. Power Electron.* 2019, 3 C4(12), 11952–11963.

[8] You, F., Zhang, B., Hu, Z., and He, S.: 'Analysis of a broadband high efficiency switch-mode delta-sigma supply modulator based on a Class E amplifier and class-E rectifier', *IEEE Trans. Microwave Theory Technol.* 2013, 61(8), 361–369.

[9] Bathily, M., Allard, B., and Hasbani, F.: 'A 200-MHz integrated buck converter with resonant gate drivers for an RF power amplifier', *IEEE Trans. Power Electron.* 2012, 27(2), 610–613.
[10] Wiegman, H. L. N.: 'A resonant pulse gate drive for high frequency applications', *Appl. Power Electronics Conference*, 1992, pp. 738–743.
[11] Chen, Y., Lee, F. C., Amorso, L., and Wu, H. P.: 'A resonant MOSFET gate driver with efficient energy recovery', *IEEE Trans. Power Electron.* 2004, 19(2), 470–477.
[12] Jei Liu, M., and Hsu, S. S. H.: 'A miniature 300-MHz resonant DC-DC converter with GaN and CMOS integrated in IPD technology', *IEEE Trans. Power Electron.* 2018, 33 (11), 9656–9668.
[13] Agarwal, A.: 'WBG revolution in power electronics', *IEEE Workshop on Wide-Bandgap Power Devices & Applications*, Knoxville, TN, 2014.
[14] Armstrong, K., Das, S., and Marlino, L.: 'Wide Bandgap Semiconductor Opportunities in Power Electronics', Technical Report, Oak Ridge National Laboratory, US Department of Energy (DOE) SciTech Connect, 2017, ORNL/TM–2017/702.
[15] Eden, R.: 'IHS Report: The World Market for Silicon Carbide & Gallium Nitride Power Semiconductors', -2016, Edition.
[16] Eden, R.: 'IHS Report: Silicon Carbide and Gallium Nitride Power Semiconductors', -2014, Edition.
[17] Fodale, V., and Richard, E.: 'IHS Report: The World Market for Power Semiconductors', -2015 Edition.
[18] Bergles, A. E.: 'Evolution of cooling technology for electrical, electronic, and microelectronic equipment', *Trans. Compon. Packag. Manuf. Technol.* 2003, 26(1), 6–15.
[19] Chu, R. C.: 'Thermal management roadmap cooling electronic products from handheld devices to supercomputers', presented at the Rohsenow Symposium Future Trends in Heat Transfer, MIT, Cambridge, MA, 2003.
[20] Hannemann, R..: 'Thermal control of electronics: Perspectives and prospects', presented at the Rohsenow Symposium Future Trends Heat Transfer, MIT, Cambridge, MA, 2003.
[21] Layola, E., Lucia, O., Sarnago, H., and Burdio, J. M.: 'Heat management in power converters: from state of the art to future ultrahigh efficiency systems', *IEEE Trans. Power Electron.* 2015, 31(11), 7896–7908.
[22] Stephen, M. W., Malouin, B. A., Browne, E. A., Bagnall, K. R., Wang, E. N., and Smith, J. P.: 'Embedded microjets for thermal management of high power-density electronic devices', *IEEE Trans. Comp. Packag. Manuf. Technol.* 2019, 9(2), 269–278.
[23] Michna, G. J., Browne, E. A., Peles, Y., and Jensen, M. K.: 'Single-phase microscale jet stagnation point heat transfer', *J. Heat Transf.* 131(11), 1–8.
[24] Fulcrand, R., Bancaud, A., and Escriba, C., Qihao, H., Samuel, C., Ali, B., and Anne-Marie, G.: 'On chip magnetic actuator for batch-mode dynamic manipulation of magnetic particles in compact lab-on-chip", *Int. J. – Sci. Direct Sens. Actuat. B: Chem.* 2011, 160(1), 1520–1528.
[25] Olivo, J., Carrara, S., and De Micheli, G.: "Micro-fabrication of high-thickness spiral inductors for the remote powering of implantable biosensors", *J. Microelectron. Eng. Sci. Direct Publ.* 2014, 113, 130–135.
[26] Araghchini, M., Member, S., and Chen. J.: "A technology overview of the power chip development program", *IEEE Trans. Power Electron.* 2003, 28(9), 4182–4201.
[27] Le T., Mizushima H., Nour I., Torben Tang, Y., Knott, P., Ouyang, A., Jensen, Z., and Han, S.: 'Fabrication of 3-D air-core MEMS inductors for very high frequency power conversions', *J. Microsyst. Nanoeng.* 2018, 3, 1–9.
[28] Yu, X., Kim, M., and Herrault, F.: 'Silicon-embedding approaches to 3-D toroidal inductor fabrication', *J. Microelectromech. Syst.* 2013, 22, 580–588.

[29] Feng, Z., Lueck, M., and Temple, D.: 'High-performance solenoidal RF transformers on high-resistivity silicon substrates for 3D integrated circuits', *IEEE Trans. Microwave Theory Tech.* 2012, 60, 2066–2072.
[30] Gu, L., and Li, X.: 'High-Q solenoid inductors with a CMOS-compatible concave-suspending MEMS process', *J. Microelectromech. Syst.* 2007, 16, 1162–1172.
[31] Yoon, Y., Park, J., and Allen, M.: 'Polymer-core conductor approaches for RF MEMS', *J. Microelectromech. Syst.* 2005, 4, 886–894.
[32] Kim, J., Herrault, F., and Yu, X.: 'Microfabrication of air core power inductors with metal-encapsulated polymer vias', *J. Micromech. Microeng.* 2013, 23(3), 350–357.

15 Benefits of Smart Meters in Institutional Building – A Case Study

A.C. Vishnu Dharssini, S. Charles Raja, and T. Karthick
Thiagarajar College of Engineering

CONTENTS

15.1 INTRODUCTION

Smart building is a trending terminology or technology that evolved worldwide in the past decade. The keyword "Smart" in Smart building itself shows that incorporating technologies makes building brainy. Why there exists such a drastic growth in smart building implementation? Why do we need it? What made it more essential? The answer behind these questions is some sort of drawbacks in conventional buildings. A major drawback among those is that conventional building fails to grab consumers' attention on their energy consumption range and also their indirect impacts on energy price. Smart buildings are erected mostly on the concept of optimization in terms of cost minimization. Smart buildings are the buildings converted by automation with the Internet of things (IoT) technology. It is done with the aid of special meters called smart meters – IoT devices that record details of who consumes, how much, and when as continuous time series data to the cloud which can be retrieved for analysis whenever needed [1]. The IoT is a boon to this technical world which makes the universe smart. IoT devices that work with artificial intelligence (AI), machine learning (ML), and deep learning (DL) make it operate on desired, specific, perfect, expected, and optimistic outcomes. For ML-based approaches, selective features are required to be provided as criterion for classification as depicted in Ref. [2]. The features chosen must be properly initialized in the preliminary stage of analysis, following which Data analytics can be taken forward to the training and testing Phases. While in the

DOI: 10.1201/9781003201069-15

DL approach algorithm traces and proceeds further analysis with extracted features without any manual interventions as mentioned in Ref. [3]. Precisely, DL defines the system Data span automatically. For smart buildings, special meters called smart meters – a type of IoT device – are required. Even though erection of such meters is cost-consuming, they give fruitful outcomes. These meter recordings are essential in modeling energy demand, which is well clarified in a model on the basis of energy demand patterns in Bangladesh [4]. They facilitate customers to be aware of their own consumption pattern and reduce their billing by incorporating suitable power- and cost-saving strategies. Analyzing the records of smart meters is a challenging task but a need for both defining existing building energy performance and predicting future demand. Such meters lack appropriateness for computation and need certain modification by data processing as in Ref. [5] for extracting different load profiles. On attaining demand pattern, suitable energy-saving policies and strategies can be formulated for better results [6]. Here, data of merely 43 smart meters of TCE, Madurai, are collected to promote the benefits of smart building technology and to visualize possibilities for suggesting few sustainable energy-saving strategies.

15.2 DATA COLLECTION AND HANDLING

As already said, smart meter data are collected by using ELNet Software, which is a tool to fetch data from smart meters. TCE has erected these meters by 2015 around various laboratories, hostels, and pump houses and also in generation by rooftop PV solar panels. They are uploaded continuously to the cloud, and on requirement, we can fetch them easily. It collects continuous time series data as a csv file with various parameters. For better computation, "kW" total alone is used here. The raw dataset from the meter usually possesses some missing data or else may vary in their format. On proper modification only, we are able to incorporate AI, ML, or DL into them. Figure 15.1 shows the graphical representation of the dataset in two-dimensional axes and also the need of processing the dataset.

Data processing is not a single-step process. It involves five major sub-steps as shown in Figure 15.2. Each one of them is meant for a specific purpose and required for further analysis.

In the data **cleaning** phase of data processing, detection and correction of corrupt or inaccurate data from the dataset are done manually by neglecting and replacing

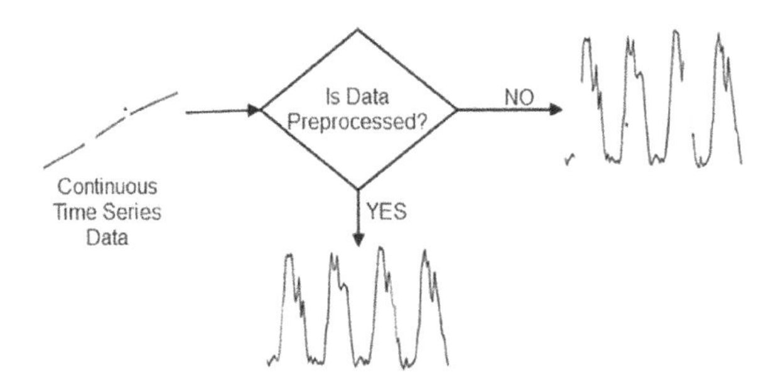

FIGURE 15.1 Representation of data processing.

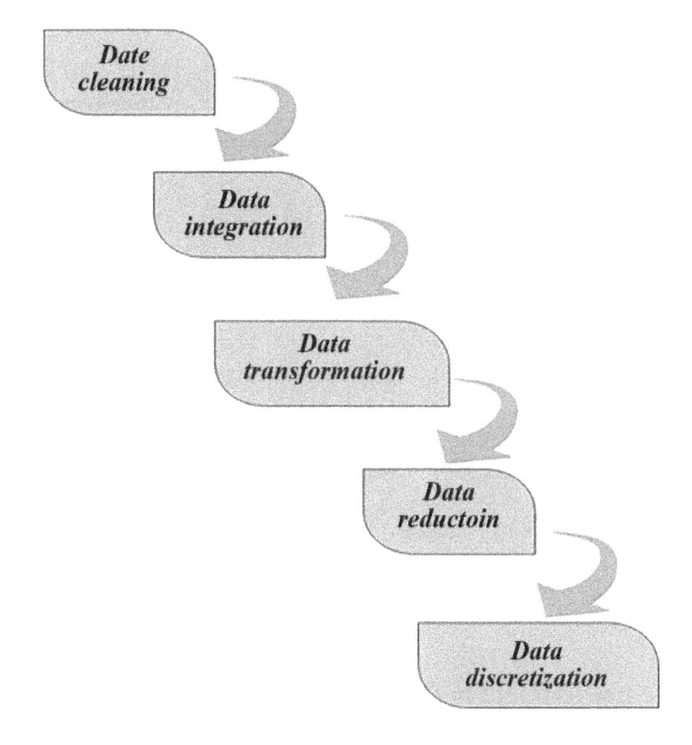

FIGURE 15.2 Phases of data processing.

them. The progress of the next phase is combining various data sources with coherent data sources and gives a unified view. The collections from various laboratories and other workspaces are combined in the **data integration** phase and placed under common format. Next, the process of tracing out lost data while transforming into a unified file and converting these unstructured data into structured data is done. Following that, proper labeling is done in the data **transformation** phase. In the data **reduction** process phase, numerical and alphabetical data are modified into a simplified discrete form for better computations and time-stamping is done for accommodating them to the code. The final one is the data **discretization** phase, which is the process of converting continuous time series data into a finite dataset with finite intervals. For computing hourly analysis, the dataset is modified into an hourly time interval dataset, which is done by means of time-stamping. Here, 1-month data of 2019 are preprocessed and computed for betterment in understanding the underlying uniformity in consumption pattern among various workspaces.

15.3 TOOL AND SOFTWARE

Python is chosen over MATLAB as coding with it is more feasible and reliable for understanding and adapting to various kinds of datasets and also it is user-friendly, while MATLAB is a top-level language highly meant for mathematical computations. Python is run under **Google Colaboratory**, in short Google Colab, as it requires zero configuration, facilitates free access to Graphics Processing Units (GPUs) and

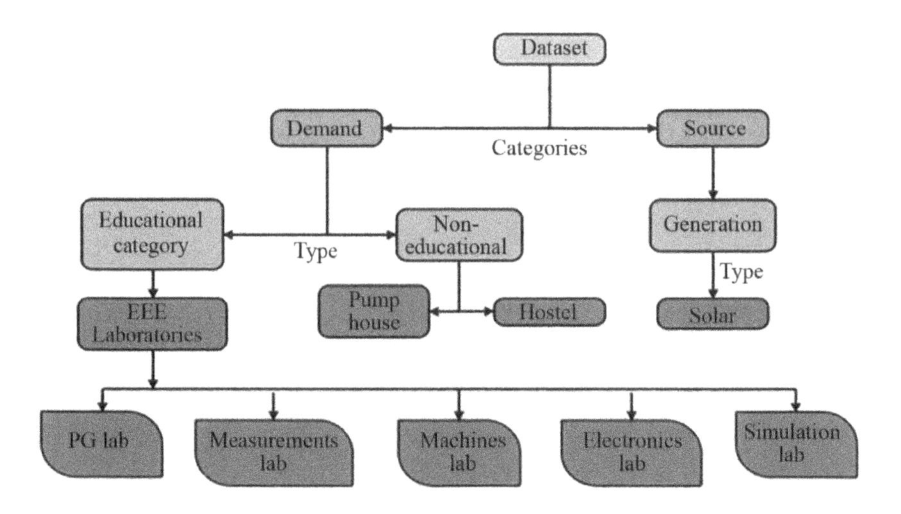

FIGURE 15.3 Categorization of dataset.

enables easy sharing and also is well suited to ML and data analysis and to execute arbitrary Python code through the browser.

15.4 CLASSIFICATION OF DATASET

To analyze and segregate data in terms of load required including demand for initiating generation and Net Energy supply in Building on the basis of category, type, and workspace as in Figure 15.3. Laboratories and classrooms are placed under the educational type of the demand category, while hostels and pump house meter readings fall under the non-educational demand category. By the same way, the power for solar generation comes under the source generation category. It enables us to trace out the ratio of energy generation to energy consumption. In addition, it gives information on the type of workspace that requisite more energy and also the type under which it falls.

15.5 LOAD BEHAVIOR PATTERN

In order to plot and visualize the existing energy demand of the institution in terms of its "type" and "category," a special graph called "**hourly graph**" is used. It utilizes a segregated dataset to plot graphs based on the labels of the processed dataset. Here, a different kind of plot is planned to visualize the demand pattern of TCE, Madurai, by the time-stamping process. By this type of plot, we are able to trace out consumption range in TCE, time of peak hour consumption of each workspace, and also variation in the behavior pattern among workspaces under the same category.

Time-stamping: It is a key tool for plotting the hourly dataset. It is the process of assuming a common date and time format for the entire dataset as it varies from one meter to another. To work with a merged dataset, specific notation or formats are required to call particular workspace consumption details. Figure 15.4 shows the dataset after the time-stamping process. In this process of computing, the average

	Catagory	Type	Name	Energy	Time stamp
0	Educational	PG lab	TX_HOUSTON	0.02	2019-10-01 00:00:00
1	Educational	PG lab	TX_HOUSTON	0.02	2019-10-01 01:00:00
2	Educational	PG lab	TX_HOUSTON	0.02	2019-10-01 02:00:00
3	Educational	PG lab	TX_HOUSTON	0.02	2019-10-01 03:00:00
4	Educational	PG lab	TX_HOUSTON	0.02	2019-10-01 04:00:00

FIGURE 15.4 Dataset after time-stamping.

or mean value of energy consumption in "kW" over the considered continuous time series data is modified with reference to time stamp, by which plotting the consumption rate over a timescale in "day of the month" is feasible.

The 1-month plots of energy consumption in EEE laboratories in Figure 15.5 show the variation in consumption pattern and range among laboratories under the educational category. The plot creates an awareness of peak consumption of each

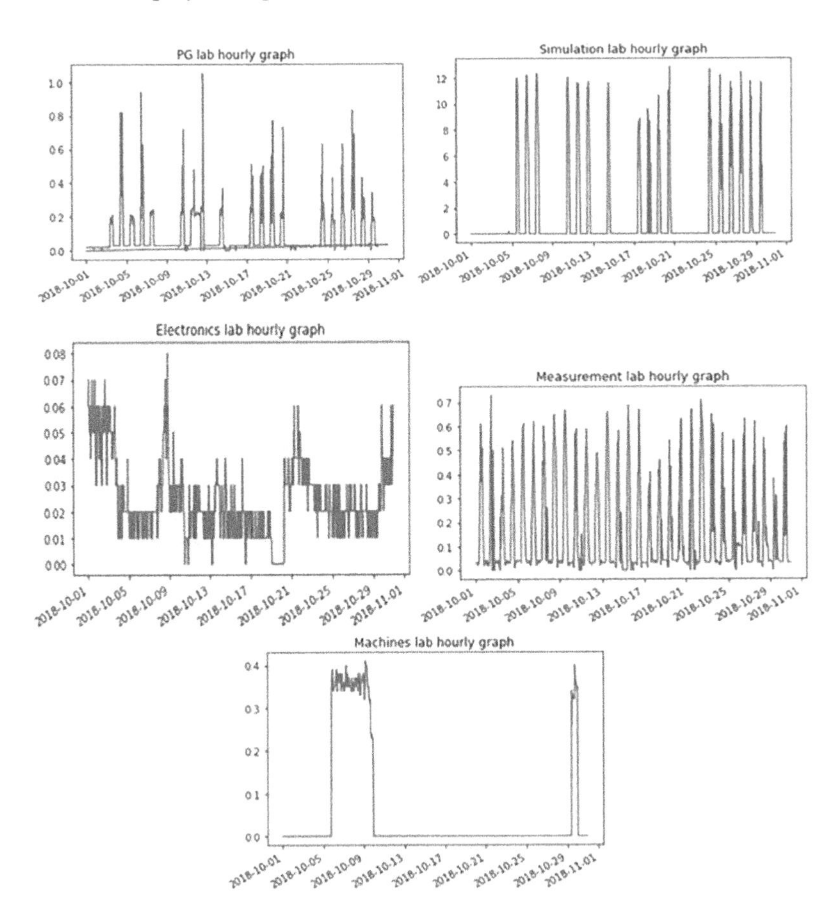

FIGURE 15.5 Hourly graph of various laboratories of the EEE department.

laboratory among consumers, which creates a major direct impact on the maximum demand reach and an indirect impact on billing. It helps in proper scheduling of each workspace and giving equal preference to loads. Among five laboratories, the simulation laboratory consumes more with the peak of 12 kW. While looking into applied electronics laboratory's consumption pattern, it maintains the below-nominal range of 1 kW in consumption mostly. The remaining three laboratories, i.e., measurement, machine, and PG laboratories, consumes moderately on comparing with the above mentioned two laboratories Simulation and Applied Electronics Laboratories.

From this plot, variation in consumption pattern among workspaces within the same category can be visualized. Similarly, variation in generation pattern for 1 month is traced out in order to meet those demands visualized in Figure 15.6. The generation range is about 0.7 kW, but it is quite lower than the consumption pattern. It also makes consumers realize the need for modeling energy demand for an institute.

Average hourly plot: It is also one type of data visualization plot for displaying continuous time series data points as straight-line segments called markers for visualizing a trend in a dataset over an interval of time chronologically. This plot is meant for finding the exact energy demand with respect to time in hour. It is computed by taking the average of continuous time series data of every second and modifying them to hourly data for plotting them correspondingly. The plot shows a wide variation in the energy demand pattern during weekdays and weekends over a timescale of 24 hours with which the need for reducing the probability of reaching maximum demand can be visualized.

The graphs in Figures 15.7 and 15.8 show consumption of TCE during weekends. Pump house and hostel consumption for 1 month of working hours from 6.00 a.m. to 6.00 p.m. is considered as there won't be any educational loads. By this plot, the exact duration of peak hours can be found. During weekends, the maximum demand

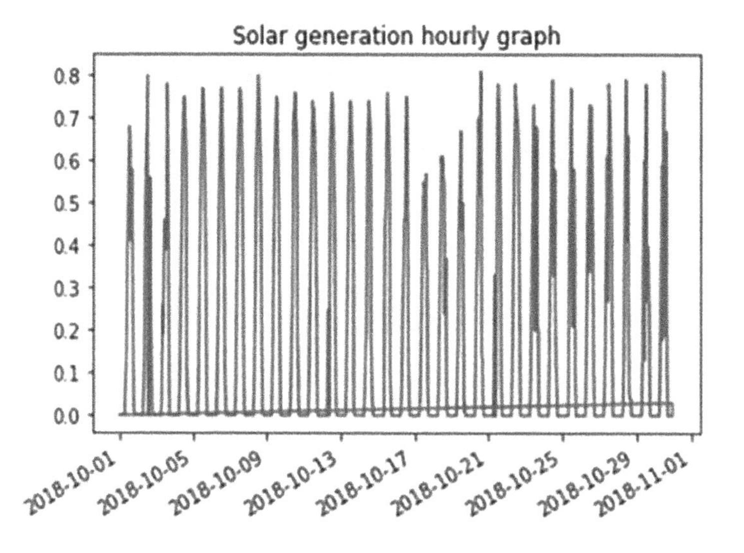

FIGURE 15.6 Generation pattern.

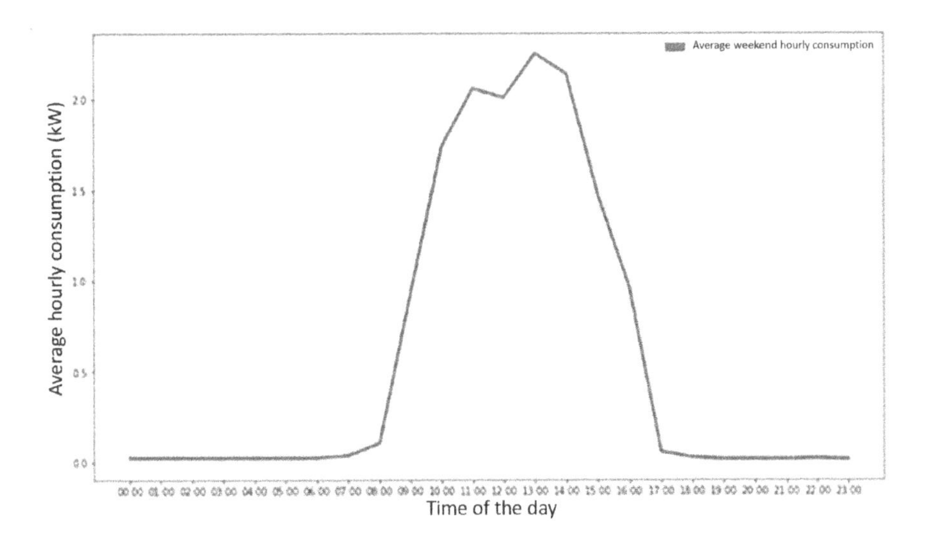

FIGURE 15.7 Weekends' consumption pattern.

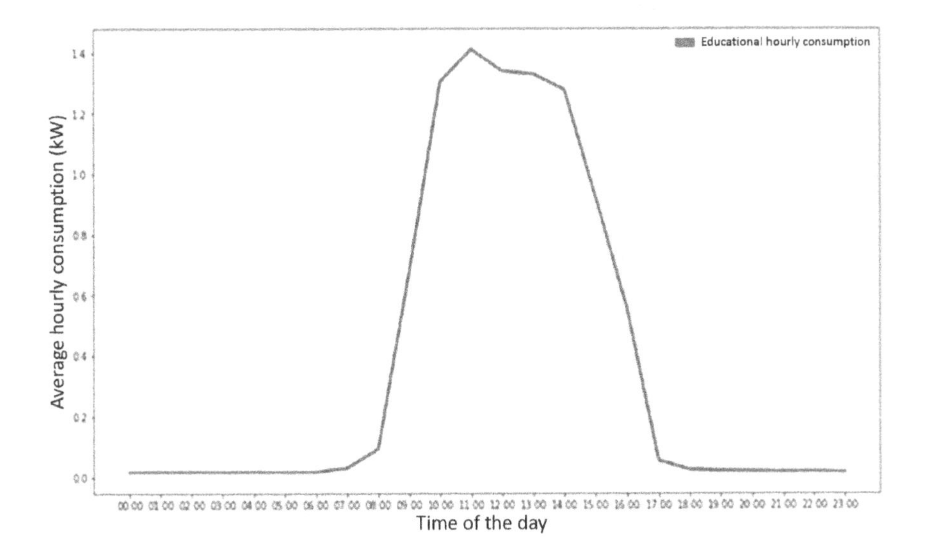

FIGURE 15.8 Weekdays' consumption pattern.

is around 14.00 p.m., and on plotting by the same way, the educational category demand pattern during weekdays' working hours is visualized, from which peak hours are found to be around 11.00 a.m. By using proper energy strategies such as peak clipping, valley filling, and load shifting, it is possible to reduce the probable possibility of maximum demand reach.

Thus, the data analysis with smart meters of Thiagarajar College of Engineering (TCE) which make it a smart building enables us to promote building energy policies in various aspects and interact with consumers to evolve active participation in order to be aware of their own energy consumption pattern. The hourly plot with time-stamping shows the variation in peak demand and also the need for observing a relation between load behavior pattern and generation pattern, while the average hourly plot over a 24-hour timescale shows the exact duration of peak time and visualizes the possibilities to avoid maximum demand reach. Further analysis of smart buildings of TCE with past smart meter records facilitates and ensures the possibilities to trace the existing demand patterns and also to predict future demand.

REFERENCES

[1] G. Trotta, "An empirical analysis of domestic electricity load profiles: who consumes? How much and when?", *Applied Energy* 275(C), 2020.
[2] S. Bourhnane, M. R. Abid, R. Lghoul, K. Z. Dine, N. Elkamoun, and D. Benhaddou, "Machine learning for energy consumption prediction and scheduling in smart buildings", *SN Applied Science* 2(2), 1–10, 2020.
[3] A. Ullah, K. Haydarov, I. U. Haq, K. Muhammad, S. Rho, M. Lee, and S. W. Baik, "Deep learning assisted buildings energy consumption profiling using smart meter data", *Sensors* 20(3), 873, 2020.
[4] S. B. Amin and F. Khan, "Modeling energy demand in Bangladesh: an empirical analysis", *The Journal of Developing Areas* 54(1), 2020.
[5] T. Alquthami, A. AlAmoudi, A. M. Alsubaie, A. B. Jaber, N. Alshlwan, M. Anwar, and S. A. Husaien, "Analytics framework for optimal smart meters data processing", *Electrical Engineering* 102(3), 1241–1251, 2020.
[6] D. Zhang, N. Shah, and L. G. Papageorgiou, "Efficient energy consumption and operation management in a smart building with microgrid", *Energy Conservation and Management* 74, 209–222, 2013.

16 Placement of Distributed Generation (DG) and Reconfiguration in Radial Distribution Systems – A Review in View of the Smart Building Concept

S. Angalaeswari and K. Jamuna
Vellore Institute of Technology

CONTENTS

16.1 INTRODUCTION

In the current world, the power generated is not sufficient to satisfy the needs of the power due to the non-availability of expected power from the existing power generation structure, additional cost required for the expansion of new conventional energy resources, considerable loss in the transmission lines, etc. One of the solutions to meet the power balance equation without disturbing the radial condition of the power system is the microgrid concept. The requirement of more flexible electrical systems, savings in the energy, and the impact of environmental factors are the necessary motivations to the development of microgrid [1]. Microgrid is generally considered as a system that can meet the major portion of the demand with renewable sources. Generally, the microgrid consists of the energy resources such as distributed generators, energy storage devices, and loads.

DOI: 10.1201/9781003201069-16

The energy sources that can distribute the power to the nearby loads from the generating point itself, thereby reducing the transmission distance and losses, are known as distributed energy resources (DERs). Owing to the benefits of DERs, such as improved reliability, maximum utilization of grid asset, reducing environmental pollution, and management between energy and load, these sources are preferred for the microgrid.

Generally, most of the losses in the power field occur in the distribution lines. The total power loss occurred in the radial distribution system comprises of active and reactive components. The radial distribution lines have high R/X ratio, which leads to higher contribution of I2R losses in the total amount of losses. Hence, it is most important to reduce the active power losses in order to enhance the efficacy of the distribution lines.

This chapter has been organized as follows: Section 16.2 discusses the concept of microgrids, need of microgrids, and modes of operation in microgrids. Section 16.3 discusses about the radial distribution network, load flow methods used in radial distribution network, optimal power flow (OPF), and constraints. Section 16.4 discusses the power loss minimization methods and comparison table for different algorithms' results. Section 16.5 discusses the conclusion of this chapter. Section 16.6 gives the references.

16.2 MICROGRIDS

The combination of distributed sources and various storage systems with critical and noncritical loads are named as microgrids. The main advantages of microgrids are the utilization of naturally available sources such as sun and wind, reducing the gas pollutions, combined heat and power transfer, meeting the power balance equation, continuous backup support, etc. [2]. These microgrids can be operated in three types of modes: grid-connected mode, islanded or autonomous mode, and transition mode of operation. In grid-connected mode of operation, the utility grid (UG) is active and it is connected to the microgrid through the static switch, whereas, in autonomous mode of operation, the microgrid is operated in standalone condition by satisfying the demand. In the transition mode, the microgrid is isolated from UG by opening the static switch after occurrence of any fault and it will be reconnected to the main grid once the fault is cleared [3].

In the microgrid formed in Ref. [4], the wind turbine and the photovoltaic system are connected together. The wind turbine has been equipped with an induction generator, and the photovoltaic generator is fitted with the tracker for maximum power point tracking (MPPT) and inverter control system. The battery with inverter control loop is applied for storage purpose and used as a constant voltage source when power from distributed generation (DG) is not available. In order to discuss the operating modes, the microgrid has been taken in the islanded mode of operation for 70 seconds, and then, it is coupled to the UG for the next 70 seconds. Then, it is disconnected again for the next 70 seconds. The simulation studies showed that the frequency and voltage are maintained to the rated value for different loads and climate changes in the autonomous mode. In both the modes of operation, the stability has been ensured. Owing to the intermittent power supply from the renewable sources, the power extracted from the microgrid and the efficiency are less. Hence, more focus is given to the loss minimization in the distribution network as it is more compared to the transmission networks. Also, the deployment of DG in the existing distribution network is preferred for the power loss minimization, which is discussed in the further sections.

16.3 RADIAL DISTRIBUTION STRUCTURE/NETWORK

The high cost of the transmission network, loss occurrence in the lines, constraints in the real and reactive powers, non-reusability of the conventional resources, advantages of the distributed energy sources, and reduction in loss and cost lead to the expansion of distributed sources for the past two decades [5]. Based on the structure of the distribution network, it is classified as

1. Radial structure.
2. Ring structure.
3. Interconnected structure.

Since the power is generated at the common utility and transmitted to the loads connected in the feeder, the radial structure is followed in the practical case. These systems are considered as the weak systems as they have high resistance-to-reactance ratio, distributed nature of generation, with variable load. To decide the power flow method in the network, existing load flow methods like Newton Raphson and fast decoupled load flow are not considered as it is not efficient and effective. Therefore, various algorithms are proposed in the literature such as forward/backward (FW/BW) sweep method, vector method, primitive impedance, current injection method, and ladder theory.

The FS/BS method applied in IEEE 15- and 33-bus systems has been used to calculate powers, voltage magnitudes at different nodes, and voltage mismatches at the last node. The algorithm is very robust and considered as numerically efficient one for convergence of distribution network [6]. The various summation methods such as current, power, and admittance methods are presented, and the result of using the power method for finding power loss is adopted on IEEE 33-bus system using MATLAB with fast convergence ability [7]. In the admittance summation method, the elements of vectors are determined by processing the branches one by one started from the branch n (number of branches) and ended with branch 1 (backward sweep) [8]. The node voltage for all the nodes was calculated in the forward sweep method. The method is more competitive with the other existing methods for weak and radial network analysis.

In the vector-based distribution load flow method [9], one-dimensional vector is used instead of two-dimensional arrays to store the value of all the line details going out from the path considering the path line. By this scheme, there is a huge memory reduction and also in CPU time. The authors of Ref. [10] proposed the effective primitive impedance method to identify the lines that are happening to the path among the feeding bus and the designated bus for calculating impedance. By this method, the elements of the matrix are calculated and stored in single dimension vectors, thereby reducing the memory for large size of the distribution system. This method is time-efficient and robust in nature and finds greater application in the distribution automation.

In the current injection method [11], the conventional method of Newton Raphson has been utilized for solving the power flow equations of unbalanced power networks. The Jacobian matrix is formed for constant impedance and constant power load models. This method is very robust, and it is getting converged in a smaller number of iterations than the other method for heavily loaded systems. The ladder network methods [12] are suitable for the radial system feeding at one end with high R/X ratio, and this method has fast convergence ability to the polynomial loading conditions. The main advantages of ladder network model are highlighted as the lower sensitivity for high resistance-to-reactance ratio; it is simple to formulate the power flow equations, robust for heavy loads, and highly suitable for reflecting the dependency of the node voltage with the level of the load. The limitation of this method is its simple tree structure and is suitable for only the systems having one source. The following table shows the different load flow methods popularly used in radial distribution networks.

The above load flow methods can be used to find the variables such as node voltages, currents in the branch, and finally the power loss in the distribution network. The FW/BW load flow has been widely used in many of the research papers because the formation of load flow equation is simple in nature; it uses the basic Kirchhoff's laws for finding voltage and current.

16.3.1 Optimal Power Flow

OPF aims to optimize an objective function considering the network limitations and various working limits. The objective function is considered as power loss minimization in the entire research analysis. The basic and necessary condition of any system is to optimize the operation of the system under various operating conditions. OPF was presented by Carpentier in 1962 [13], which is defined as the method of determining the optimal solution for the condition given to the objective function. In general, the optimization is being considered to be minimization of objective function and the maximization could be solved by taking the negative of the minimization function [14]. Different algorithms are developed and followed to optimize the objective function.

The OPF may be unconstrained or constrained depending upon the constraints, single objective or multi-objective based on the number of objectives, static (parameter) or dynamic (trajectory) optimization due to the nature of the decision variables, optimal control or nonoptimal control based on the nature of the problem, linear, nonlinear, geometric, and quadratic programming (QP) problems depending upon equations involved and constraints, integer or real-valued programming problems found in the design, deterministic or stochastic programming due to the settled behavior of the control variables, and separable/non-separable programming established on the nature of separability [14].

The OPF methods are mostly classified as conventional/classical and the artificial intelligent methods. The conventional methods comprise the lambda iteration, gradient, linear programming, Newton, QP, and interior point method. The intelligent techniques include genetic algorithm (GA), particle swarm optimization (PSO), simulated annealing (SA), harmony search algorithm, ant colony, and bee algorithm. [15].

In an OPF method, some of the control variables have to be optimized for the chosen objective function. In the power field, the active power or reactive power minimization is chosen as main objectives. Some of the active power objectives can be specified as follows:

i. Economic dispatch problem for the minimization of fuel cost:

$$\text{Min } F(P_G) = \sum_{i=1}^{NG} (\propto_i + \beta_i P_{Gi} + \gamma_i P_{Gi}^2) \tag{16.1}$$

where $F(P_G)$ is the total fuel cost, NG is the number of generators, α_i, β_i, and γ_i β_i are the coefficients, and P_{Gi} is the generated power from bus i.

ii. For the real power loss minimization:

$$\text{Min } P_L = \sum_{i=1}^{Ni} g_k \left[\left(V_i^2 + V_j^2 - 2V_i V_j \cos(\delta_i - \delta_j) \right) \right] \tag{16.2}$$

where PL is the total real power loss in the system, Vi is the magnitude of the voltage at bus i, Vj is the magnitude of the voltage at bus j, and δ_i, δ_j, and e are the phase angles of the voltages at buses i and j, respectively. The power objectives are MW and MVAR loss minimization. Among these, the commonly used objectives are fuel cost optimization and the active power loss minimization.

16.3.2 Constraints

The constraints are the one that validates the OPF. The OPF has to be simulated for the system till the convergence has reached. The convergence criteria may be the number of iterations or the bus voltage deviation between the successive iterations. The constraints in the power system are equality and inequality in nature [16].

1. The power balance equation is the equality constraint

$$P_{gi} - P_{di} - \sum_{j=1}^{NB} |V_i||V_j||Y_{ij}| \cos(\theta_{ij} - \delta_i + \delta_j) = 0 \tag{16.3}$$

$$Q_{gi} - Q_{di} + \sum_{j=1}^{NB} |V_i||V_j||Y_{ij}| \sin(\theta_{ij} - \delta_i + \delta_j) = 0 \tag{16.4}$$

2. Inequality constraints [17]
   i. Generation constraints

      To maintain stable voltages, active and reactive outputs are limited by the upper and lower boundaries as follows:

$$V_{Gi}^{\min} \leq V_{Gi} \leq V_{Gi}^{\max} \; i = 1,2\ldots N \tag{16.5}$$

$$P_{Gi}^{\min} \leq P_{Gi} \leq P_{Gi}^{\max} \; i = 1,2\ldots N \tag{16.6}$$

$$Q_{Gi}^{\min} \leq Q_{Gi} \leq Q_{Gi}^{\max} \; i = 1,2\ldots N \tag{16.7}$$

   ii. Transformer constraints

$$T_i^{\min} \leq T_i \leq T_i^{\max} \; i = 1,2\ldots N_T \tag{16.8}$$

      where T_i is the transformer tap settings; N_T is the number of regulating transformers.

   iii. Security constraints

$$V_{Li}^{\min} \leq V_{Li} \leq V_{Li}^{\max} \; i = 1,2\ldots N_B \tag{16.9}$$

$$S_{li} \leq S_{li}^{\max} \; i = 1,2\ldots N_L \tag{16.10}$$

      where N_L is the transmission lines.

16.4 POWER LOSS MINIMIZATION

The OPF is playing the major role in the power field. There are different algorithms proposed by many authors for meeting the objective of OPF. To meet out the power demand and to ensure the world is more eco-friendly, the power sectors are moving toward the use of nonconventional sources now a day. Once the distributed sources are located in the same location of the load, it considerably decreases the losses and lessens the use of power electronic stages. The real power minimization is of great concern, since the Q loss could be decreased by using the controllers in the nearby location. The different methods implemented for the real power loss reduction can be taken into two cases as follows:

Case 1: Real power loss minimization by optimal placement and sizing of DG.

Different algorithms, methods, and formulae are used for solving the optimization problems in power networks. One of the ways is the introduction of distributed energy sources in the system. The optimum placement and sizing of the DGs are the real task in front of the researchers. There are plenty of research papers showing the considerable reduction in power loss by the optimum placement and rating of the DGs. In most of the papers, the real power losses are determined by the following [18,19]:

Minimizing

$$P_L = \sum_{i=1}^{N}\sum_{j=1}^{N}\left[\alpha_{ij}\left(P_iP_j + Q_iQ_j\right) + \beta_{ij}\left(Q_iP_j - P_iQ_j\right)\right] \tag{16.11}$$

where

$$\alpha_{ij} = \frac{r_{ij}}{V_iV_j}\cos\left(\delta_i - \delta_j\right) \tag{16.12}$$

$$\beta_{ij} = \frac{r_{ij}}{V_iV_j}\sin\left(\delta_i - \delta_j\right) \tag{16.13}$$

$$Z_{ij} = r_{ij} + jx_{ij} \tag{16.14}$$

where P_L is the active power loss in kW; N is the bus count; r_{ij}, x_{ij}, and Z_{ij} are resistance, reactance, and impedance for the nodes i and j; V_i and V_j and i and j are voltage magnitudes and angles at nodes i and j, respectively; and P_i and P_j and Q_i and Q_j are active and reactive power injections at nodes i and j, respectively.

In Ref. [20], the authors proposed an analytical expression for finding the loss of currents. The analysis was done without DG and with single DG, and multi-DG placed at different locations. The assumptions made in that paper are the distribution system fed at one end, radial, balanced one, and constant load level. The extreme value of the DG rating for different trial systems is considered to be equal to the total load in the assumed test system. The constraint has been taken as the upper and lower voltage limits with 0.9 and 1.05 pu. It has been tested in various radial systems to validate the results. The proposed method has taken less number of iterations and less computation time.

The authors of Ref. [21] proposed a hybrid optimization algorithm known as artificial immune bee colony (AIBC) for solving the coordination of DG and capacitors. The authors have implemented their algorithm on 33-bus radial network under varying conditions. The primary objective is placing single DG with optimal size and reducing the real power loss by the integration of single DG at bus 6. The results prove that the algorithm gave better solution compared with various methods.

In Ref. [18], the PSO method is implemented for the best location of DGs. The authors have taken three types of DGs depending on the true and reactive power injection and absorption. Two case studies are considered for analysis like independent location of DGs and the simultaneous placement of DGs. From the results, the real power loss by the real power injecting DG from case 1 is taken for comparison. This algorithm is tested on IEEE 33- and IEEE 69-bus systems, and the results show that the algorithm has reduction in size of DGs within voltage limits.

The analytical method for active power loss minimization of network is given in Ref. [22]. The advantage of the above method is non-calculation of Z bus matrix, inverse of Y bus, or Jacobian matrix. The algorithm is implemented on 33-bus network and showed that the computation time is less, and reduced loss with improved voltage profile. The authors of Ref. [23] proposed a multi-objective approach considering the fitness function of finding the weakest voltage bus and weakest link in the system.

PSO is used to solve the OPF and applied in 12-bus, 30-bus, 33-bus, and 69-bus networks. This algorithm proves that the power system losses were reduced, increasing power factor, improved stability, and enhanced bus voltage. The method of finding the feasible placing and size of the DGs was determined using loss sensitivity factor corresponding to current injection [24]. The bus injection to branch current and branch current to bus voltage values are utilized finding the power loss in the system. The analytical method discussed in the paper finds easy to be implemented in the system and gives fast results for given accuracy.

The authors use a software package tool [25] for finding the intimacy of individual bus and the critical bus. The bus that is sensitive to the voltage failure in any distribution system is considered as the critical bus. The package also found the optimal location and size of source and shunt capacitor for power system. Golden search and grid search algorithms are used for power loss minimization. The package known as voltage stability and optimization (VSOP) with one main window for solving power flow solution finds the weak bus to the voltage failure. Since the package discussed in Ref. [25] has been designed in MATLAB GUI environment, it is simple to use and allows the users to analyze stability of voltage and suitable placing of DG, and capacitor in radial distribution systems.

The authors of Ref. [19] used BIBC and BCBV matrices to solve the distribution load flow analysis. The line stability indices were implemented to analyze and improve the power transfer capacity. The losses have been calculated for the IEEE 33- and IEEE 30-bus systems. The output showed that the proposed method was efficient for the increased voltage profile, with good stability. Table 16.1 shows the comparison between the loss reductions algorithms tested on the 33- and 69-bus systems. The optimal location of DG in 33-bus system has been identified in many research papers as bus 6, and for the IEEE 69-bus system, the optimum location has been identified as bus 61.

From the above results highlighted in the table, each method finds its own way to minimize the losses. Some authors considered the loss sensitivity factors [24], and most of them considered voltage stability as their main criteria. In most of the analysis, the optimum place of the DG in 33-bus system has been identified as bus 6. The sizing of the DG has been varied from 2 to 3.15 MW in various results. The percentage reduction in the loss has been identified in the range of 35%–68%. Some papers considered the central processing unit (CPU) time for getting convergence in terms of seconds. For IEEE 69-bus system, the optimal location has been identified as bus 61 with the DG size from 1.5 to 2.02 MW.

Case 2: Reconfiguration of Radial Distribution System

The distribution networks have sectional switches as shown in Figure 16.1 [26]. The network reconfiguration is nothing but the alteration in the condition of the switches. This has been done for dropping the power loss and also balancing the load in the system [27]. Most of the researchers are doing their research in the reconfiguration of radial distribution network using different algorithms and tested in various test systems. Many of the papers showed that the reconfiguration of the system greatly reduced the power loss and improved the voltage profile.

The evolutionary programming (EP) method [26] is used to reconfigure the redial distribution network considering the power loss minimization. The same authors use the fuzzy mutated genetic algorithm (FMGA) for the same purpose of power loss minimization using reconfiguration. They have tested in 33- and 69-bus systems to validate their results. From the results, it is inferred that the FMGA method is able to find the good switching options, whereas EP took longer time for getting converged.

The authors of Ref. [28] presented an efficient method called adopted ant colony optimization (AACO) method for minimizing the power loss in distribution systems. In the conventional ant colony method, during the evolutionary process, the radiality constraint imposed the hurdle that the appearance of large number of infeasible individuals will occur during the initialization and at intermediate stages of the process. This is rectified in the AACO by creating only the feasible solutions by graph theory. The results are tested on various test systems and prove that it is a good tool in reconfiguration of system, and this could be applicable for multi-objective problem.

By following the heuristic technique, the reconfiguration has been done on radial distribution networks [29] based on the direction of power flows. The switches in the system are closed in the initial position, and then, one by one, only one switch is closed to form a loop. The results prove that the system losses closer to global optimum solutions have been attained. The authors of Ref. [30] used fuzzy multi-objective approach for network reconfiguration. The objective function chosen is the minimization of real power loss, minimization of deviation of node voltages, and branch current constraint violation, balancing the load among the feeders. The algorithm reduces the number of tie switch operations, search space, and computational time.

TABLE 16.1
Comparison of Active Power Loss with and without DGs in 33- and 69-Bus Systems

	Plots in kW IEEE 33-Bus				Plots in kW IEEE 69-Bus			
Algorithm Used	Without DG	With DG	DG Size in MW	DG at Bus	Without DG	With DG	DG Size in MW	DG at Bus
Analytical method [20]	• 197.94	• 139.16	• 2.96	• 6	• -	• -	• -	• -
AIBC [21]	• 203.19	• 104.38	• 2.58	• 6				
PSO [18]	• 211	• 115.29	• 3.15	• 6	• 225	• 83.37	• 1.80	• 61
Analytical method [22]	• 211.20	• 67.97	• 2.53	• 6	• -	• -	• -	• -
PSO [23]	• 211	• 114.89	• 2.89	• 7	• 225	• 84	• 2.02	• 61
Analytical method [24]	• 211	• 111.17	• 2.49	• 6	• 225	• 83.37	• 1.80	• 61
Grid search [25]	• 211	• 111.03	• 2.60	• 6	• 225	• 83.22	• 1.86	• 61
BIBC and BCBV [19]	• 210	• 110.63	• 2.48	• 6	• -	• -	• -	• -

For minimization of system loss, a method of genetic algorithm and search algorithm (GA + SA) [31] is proposed to find the optimal pattern of reconfiguration by improving the voltage. In this chapter, the DG and capacitor placement and reconfiguration have been taken in different cases. From the reconfiguration of the system, the results show that the optimal on/off patterns of the switches could be identified for power loss reduction by satisfying the voltage constraints. GA is used to obtain the total system loss in radial network in an effective way [32]. This chapter discusses the effect of placement of capacitor, DGs, and the reconfiguration in the radial distribution system. Even though different case studies have been discussed in the chapter, the power loss after the reconfiguration is considered for comparison. The algorithm is adopted in a 33-bus system, and the results are comparable with other methods.

The changes in loads in distribution systems usually come to a balanced condition by the utility using reconfiguration technique. Different load models like constant current, constant impedance, and composite type of load are considered for optimal operation [33] using harmony search algorithm. The algorithm is tested in IEEE 33-bus system for two different lines and load data. The test result showed that the configuration offers reduced power loss for the particular type of line and load data of IEEE 33-bus system.

The load balancing index and the loss index [34] are considered for optimizing the multi-objective function with loss reduction and balancing of load with fuzzy and ant colony optimization (ACO) algorithm. The reconfiguration has been done on 33 and 69 systems. The ant colony is applied to create a search space large. The obtained values are closely associated with the standard results. The plant growth simulation algorithm (PGSA) [35] takes the objective function and the constraints separately to avoid the trouble to determine the barrier factors. The external parameters such as crossover rate and mutation rate are not required in this method as in GA. It provides a guiding search direction, which that continuously changes as there is change in the required function. The algorithm is being tested on 33- and 84-bus systems, and the results are comparable with the other methods. This method could be helpful for operation of the existing system and the planning of any future system.

The authors of Ref. [36] presented GA to carry out the reconfiguration of the system. The optimization problem has been formulated as a multi-objective one by taking both normal and contingency into account. The method is being tested on 16- and 33-bus systems. The results infer that GA could effectively do the reconfiguration of the system. The refined genetic algorithm (RGA) proposed in Ref. [37] uses the distribution load flow to determine the branch current and system loss. The refinement is performed on chromosome coding, mutation pattern, and fitness function. The method is tested on IEEE 16-bus and IEEE 33-bus systems, the advantage of this method is the prevention of premature convergence, and the convergence is smooth with the reduced memories ensured with search efficiency. The authors simulated the algorithm using GA [36] and RGA [37] implemented on 33- and 69-bus systems, which showed that the solutions are comparable with the standard one.

The maximum load ability index is taken as the important criteria for optimal network configuration [38]. The fuzzy adaptation method of EP is used to set the objectives of maximization of margin load ability and maximum voltage profile. This is implemented on IEEE 33-bus radial distribution network. The reconfiguration and expansion planning problems of distribution systems are considered as important one for the testing and verification of the radiality constraints [39]. The reconfiguration (DSR) and expansion with planning problem are the known problems in distribution systems. The authors modeled the DSR with the minimization of real power loss objective and the DSP problem as minimization of the annual investment and operation cost. These problems are modeled as mixed-integer nonlinear programming problem (MINLP) with radial constraints.

The authors of Ref. [40] used the meta-heuristic harmony search algorithm (HSA) for the reconfiguration and placement of DG in the distribution system for minimizing the real power loss and improving the voltage profile in the system. This method is tested on 33- and 69-bus systems under different load levels in different scenarios. The reconfiguration case alone is considered for comparison. The modified honey bee mating optimization (MHBMO) has been used in multi-objective distribution feeder reconfiguration [41]. The honey bee mating technique has been modified with some factors such as crossover and mutation, temperature reduction factor heuristic function application, and updating methods. The modified method is most effective and efficient, and the global optimal solution could be attained with this algorithm. The network reconfiguration for the DG with rooftop solar cells and wind turbines is considered for power loss minimization [42].

The modified plant growth simulation algorithm (MPGSA) is very much suitable for power loss minimization as both the objectives and constraints are solved separately. The authors have considered five different cases including the reconfiguration and DG placement and tested on 33-bus system, and the results are comparable with other methods.

The branch statuses that are represented by continuous functions are initially considered as closed one [43]. The sensitivity analysis-based heuristic technique has been used to find the loop, which has to be broken next by opening one switch. The process has to be repeated till all the loops have been broken and make the distribution radial. The algorithm is being tested on IEEE 33-bus system, and the number of power flows has been reduced with the incorporated network constraints. The PSO using graph theory was introduced in Ref. [44], and the number of loops or meshes has been considered as the number of cycles in the graph theory. GA with graph theory has been considered for the reduction in power loss in the radial distribution network. The algorithm is tested on IEEE 33-bus system, and the results prove that GA with graph theory produces better results than PSO with graph theory. The PSO converged prematurely without finding the local optimum when the problem becomes complex. The authors are working on the guaranteed convergence PSO to overcome the premature convergence (Table 16.2).

The authors of Ref. [45] proposed an algorithm called selective particle swarm optimization (SPSO) for distribution network reconfiguration (DNR) problem. The steps involved in the method are the identification of search spaces after closing all switches and identify the switches that have to be opened. The algorithm has been tested on 33- and 69-bus systems with the results proved to be good for the capacitor placement and sizing. The authors work on the capacitor placement with sizing and reconfiguration simultaneously. A new heuristic population-based group search

TABLE 16.2
Power Loss Minimization after Reconfiguration of the Radial Distribution Network

	Plots in kW IEEE 33-Bus		Plots in kW IEEE 69-Bus	
Algorithm Used	**Base Case**	**After Reconfiguration**	**Base Case**	**After Reconfiguration**
EP [26]	207.92	129.70	226.92	137.66
FMGA [26]	207.92	129.76	226.92	136.23
Ant colony [28]	202.68	139.55	227.53	202.19
Heuristic approach [29]	202.68	139.55		
Fuzzy [30]	-	-	227.53	205.320
GA + search [31]	202.70	146.50	-	-
GA [32]	202.61	138.10	-	-
Harmony search [33]	202.67	139.55	-	-
Fuzzy ACO [34]	202.74	136.80	-	-
PGA [35]	202.70	139.50	-	-
GA [36]	202.74	141.61	-	-
RGA [37]	202.67	139.53	-	-
Fuzzy EP [38]	202.74	139.98	-	-
DSR [39]	202.70	139.55	-	-
HSA [40]	202.67	138.06	225	99.350
GA [40]	202.67	141.60	225	103.29
RGA [40]	202.67	139.46	225	100.28
MHBMO [41]	202.67	134.26	-	-
MPGSA [42]	202.67	139.50	-	-
Sensitivity analysis [43]	202.68	136.66	-	-
PSO and GA graph theory [44]	204.50	143.70	-	-
SPSO [45]	202.60	139.79	224.96	125.97
GSO [46]	202.4	137.26		
HC-ACO [47]	202.67	136.30		
ACSA [48]	202.68	139.98	224.89	98.59
SAI [49]	-	-	225.00	99.62
ABC [50]	202.71	139.50		

optimization (GSO) is used to reconfigure the radial distribution network [46]. The reconfiguration is done on 33-bus system with proved to be efficient for the optimization problem.

A paper [47] presented a new algorithm hypercube ant colony optimization (HC-ACO) for the reconfiguration of radial distribution network. Four different cases are considered in the paper including reconfiguration and DG placement. The hypercube framework is a new one based on changing the pheromone update rules used in the ant colony optimization algorithms. The reconfiguration based on the above method has been implemented on 33-bus system for validation of the algorithm. The results prove that the scaling of the objective functions yielded fast optimum

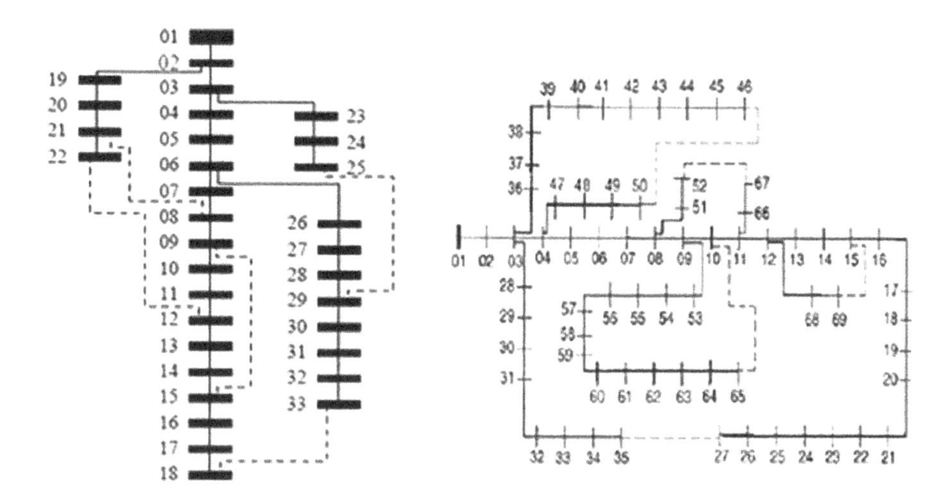

FIGURE 16.1 Single line diagram of IEEE 33- and IEEE 69-bus radial distribution system.

convergence with good accuracy. Adaptive cuckoo search algorithm in Ref. [48] was proposed to solve the power loss minimization problem. The algorithm basically inspired from the nature created cuckoo species. Graph theory is also used to find the search space, which could reduce the infeasible network configuration in the reconfiguration process. Different scenarios are taken for analysis, and the algorithm is tested on IEEE 33-, 69-, and 119-bus systems. The obtained simulation results proved that the method is more effective in reducing the power loss and improving the voltage profile.

The authors of Ref. [49] proposed simulated annealing immune (SAI) by using the loop encoding technique. By introducing a refined vaccine extraction method in this paper, the performance of solution and convergence of the algorithm have been improved a lot. The paper in Ref. [50] discussed the algorithm called artificial bee colony for finding the sensationalizing switch to be operated to solve the loss problem in radial distribution systems. The main advantage of this algorithm is that the parameters like crossover rate and mutation rate are not required in this method. The algorithm has been implemented in 14-, 33-, and 119-bus systems, and the efficiency of the algorithm is much better than the other methods.

16.5 CONCLUSION

The power loss minimization in radial distribution networks has become an interesting and essential research area since the development of electrical network systems implemented. More advancement has been made after the inclusion of distribution generations in the radial distribution systems. The chapter has presented various algorithms for power loss minimization developed in the past 20 years of research area. In the majority of the papers, the voltage profile improvement by the minimization of real power loss has been taken as the main objective. There are various parameters considered for the OPF such as voltage magnitude, phase angle, real power and reactive power injection at the buses, real power generation limits, reactive power limits, and voltage minimum and maximum limits. The results are compared with the other existing methods by taking various factors such as real power loss in IEEE 33- and IEEE 69-bus systems, percentage reduction in the loss compared with the base loss, computational time, number of iterations, and size and location of DGs. Each method has its own considerations and methodology to arrive the objective function. It is not being reasonable to come to a common conclusion with all these methods. The algorithms discussed in the chapter provide the path for further improvement in the field of power loss minimization to the young researchers. Also, the renewable source inclusion in the existing building and power flow analysis makes the smart building concept, which is much required for future generation.

REFERENCES

[1] F. A. Mohamed and H. N. Koivo, Multi objective optimization using mesh adaptive direct search for power dispatch problem of micro grid, *Electrical Power and Energy Systems* 42, 2012, 728–735.

[2] S. Koohi-Kamali, N. A. Rahim, and H. Mokhlis, Smart power management algorithm in micro grid consisting of photovoltaic, diesel, and battery storage plants considering variations in sunlight, temperature, and load, *Energy Conversion and Management* 84, 2014, 562–582.

[3] P. Sivachandran and R. Muthukumar, An overview of micro grid system, *International Journal of Applied Engineering Research* 9, 22, 2014, 12353–12376.

[4] F. D. Kanellos, A. I. Tsouchnikas, and N. D. Hatziargyriou, Micro-grid simulation during grid-connected and islanded modes of operation, *International Conference on Power Systems Transients (IPST05) in Montreal*, Canada 2005.

[5] D. Bhujel, B. Adhikary, and A. K. Mishra, A Load flow algorithm for radial distribution system with distributed generation, *3rd International conference on Sustainable Energy Technologies (ICSET)*, 2012, pp. 375–380.

[6] A. D. Rana, J. B. Darji, and M. Pandya, Backward/forward sweep load flow algorithm for radial distribution system, *International Journal for Scientific Research & Development* 2, 01, 2014, 398–400.

[7] J. A. Michline Rupa and S. Ganesh, Power flow analysis for radial distribution system using backward/forward sweep method, *International Journal of Electrical, Computer, Electronics and Communication Engineering* 8, 10, 2014, 1540–1544.

[8] D. Rajicic and R. Taleski, Two novel methods for radial and weakly meshed network *Analysis Electric Power Systems Research* 48, 1998, 79–87.

[9] T. Ramana, V. Ganesh, and S. Sivanagaraju, Simple and fast load flow solution for electrical power distribution systems, *International Journal on Electrical Engineering and Informatics* 5, 3, 2013, 245–255.

[10] K. Prakash and M. Sydulu, An effective topological and primitive impedance based three phase load flow method for radial distribution systems, *TENCON 2008- IEEE Conference*, 2008, pp. 1–6.

[11] P. A. N. Garcia, J. L. R. Pereira, S. Carneiro, V. M. da Costa, N. Martins, Three-phase power flow calculations using the current injection method, *IEEE Transactions on Power Systems* 15, 2, 2000, 508–514.

[12] J. Liu, M. M. A. Salama, and R. R. Mansour, An efficient power flow algorithm for distribution systems with polynomial load Inter- national, *Journal of Electrical Engineering Education* 39, 4, 2002, 371–386.

[13] M. Huneault and F. D. Galiana, A survey of the optimal power flow literature, *IEEE Transactions on Power Systems* 6, 2, 1991, 762–770.

[14] S. S. Rao, *Engineering Optimization*, A Wiley-Inter Science Publication John Wiley & Sons, Inc.
[15] B. E. Turkay and R. I. Cabadag, Optimal power flow solution using particle swarm optimization algorithm, In *EUROCON*, IEEE, 2013, pp. 1418–1424.
[16] U. Kwannetr, U. Leeton, and T. Kulworawanichpong, Optimal power flow using artificial Bees algorithm, *International Conference on Advances in Energy Engineering (ICAEE)* 19, 2010, 215–218.
[17] S. Anantasate and P. Bhasaputra, A multi-objective Bees algorithm for multi-objective optimal power flow problem, *8th International Conference on Electrical Engineering/ Electronics, Computer, Telecommunications and Information Technology (ECTI-CON)*, 2011, pp. 852–856.
[18] S. Kansal, V. Kumar, and B. Tyagi, Optimal placement of different type of DG sources in distribution, *Networks Electrical Power and Energy Systems* 53, 2013, 752–760.
[19] A. Parizad, A. Khazali, and M. Kalantar, Optimal placement of distributed generation with sensitivity factors considering voltage stability and losses indices, *18th Iranian Conference on Electrical Engineering*, 2010, pp. 848–855.
[20] R. Viral, D. K. Khatod, An analytical approach for sizing and siting of DGs in balanced radial distribution networks for loss minimization, *Electrical Power and Energy Systems* 67, 2015, 191–201.
[21] M. N. B. Muhtazaruddin, N. D. Tuyen, G. Fujita, and J. J. B. Jamian, Optimal distributed generation and capacitor coordination for power loss minimization, *IEEE PES T&D Conference and Exposition*, 2014, pp. 1–5.
[22] S. G. Naik, D. K. Khatod, and M. P. Sharma, Sizing and siting of distributed generation in distribution networks for real power loss minimization using analytical approach, *International Conference on Power, Energy and Control (ICPEC)* 2013, pp. 740–745.
[23] M. M. Aman, G. B. Jasmon, A. H. A. Bakar, and H. Mokhlis, A new approach for optimum DG placement and sizing based on voltage stability maximization and minimization of power losses, *Energy Conversion and Management* 70, 2013, 202–210.
[24] T. Gzel and M. H. Hocaoglu, An analytical method for the sizing and siting of distributed generators in radial systems, *Electric Power Systems Research* 79, 2009, 912–918.
[25] T. Gozel, U. Eminoglub, and M. H. Hocaoglu, A tool for voltage stability and optimization (VS&OP) in radial distribution systems using mat lab graphical user interface (GUI), *Simulation Modelling Practice and Theory* 16, 5, 2008, 505–518.
[26] B. Venkatesh, S. Chandramohan, N. Kayalvizhi, and R. K. Devi, Optimal reconfiguration of radial distribution system using artificial intelligence methods, *IEEE Toronto International Conference Science and Technology for Humanity (TIC-STH)*, 2009, pp. 660–665.
[27] M. E. Baran and F. F. Wu, Network reconfiguration in distribution systems for loss reduction and load balancing, *IEEE Transactions on Power Delivery* 4, 2, 1989, 1401–1407.
[28] A. Swarnkar, N. Gupta, and K. R. Niazi, Efficient reconfiguration of distribution systems using ant colony optimization adapted by graph theory, *IEEE Power and Energy Society General Meeting*, 2011, pp. 1–8.
[29] J. A. Martn, A. J. Gil, A new heuristic approach for distribution systems loss reduction, *Electric Power Systems Research* 78, 2008, 1953–1958.
[30] D. Das, Fuzzy multi objective approach for network reconfiguration of distribution systems, *IEEE Transactions on Power Delivery* 21, 1, 2006, 202–209.
[31] N. Rugthaicharoencheep, S. Nedphograw, and W. Wanaratwijit, Distribution system operation for power loss minimization and improved voltage profile with distributed generation and capacitor placements, *4th International Conference on Electric Utility Deregulation and Restructuring and Power Technologies (DRPT)*, 2011, pp. 1185–1189.

[32] A. K. Saonerkari and B. Y. Bagde, Optimized DG placement in radial distribution system with reconfiguration and capacitor placement using genetic algorithm, *2014 IEEE International Conference on Advanced Communication Control and Computing Technologies (TCACCCT)*, 2014, pp. 1077–1083.
[33] P. Kumar and S. Singh, Reconfiguration of radial distribution system with static load models for loss minimization, *IEEE International Conference on Power Electronics, Drives and Energy Systems (PEDES)*, 2014, pp. 1–5.
[34] A. Saffar, R. Hooshmand, and A. Khodabakhshian, A new fuzzy optimal reconfiguration of distribution systems for loss reduction and load balancing using ant colony search-based algorithm, *Applied Soft Computing* 11, 2011, 4021–4028.
[35] C. Wang and H. Z. Cheng, Optimization of network configuration in large distribution systems using plant growth simulation algorithm, *IEEE Transactions on Power Systems* 23, 1, 2008, 119–126.
[36] Y.-Y. Hong and S.-Y. Ho, Determination of network configuration considering multi objective in distribution systems using genetic algorithms, *IEEE Transactions on Power Systems* 20, 2, 2005, 1062–1069.
[37] J. Z. Zhu, Optimal reconfiguration of electrical distribution network using the refined genetic algorithm, *Electric Power Systems Research* 62, 2002, 37–42.
[38] B. Venkatesh, R. Ranjan, and H. B. Gooi, Optimal reconfiguration of radial distribution systems to maximize load ability, *IEEE Transactions on Power Systems* 19, 1, 2004, 260–266.
[39] M. Lavorato, J. F. Franco, M. J. Rider, and R. Romero, Imposing radiality constraints in distribution system optimization problems, *IEEE Transactions on Power Systems* 27, 1, 2012, 172–180.
[40] R. S. Rao, K. Ravindra, K. Satish, and S. V. L. Narasimham, Power loss minimization in distribution system using network reconfiguration in the presence of distributed generation, *IEEE Transactions on Power Systems* 28, 1, 2013, 317–325.
[41] J. Olamaei, T. Niknam, and S. B. Arefi, Distribution feeder reconfiguration for loss minimization based on modified honey Bee mating optimization algorithm, *Energy Procedia* 14, 2012, 304311.
[42] R. Rajaram, K. Sathish Kumar, and N. Rajasekar, Power system reconfiguration in a radial distribution network for reducing losses and to improve voltage profile using modified plant Growth simulation algorithm with Distributed Generation (DG) Energy Reports 1, 2015, p. 116122.
[43] F. V. Gomes, S. Carneiro, Jr, J. L. R. Pereira, M. P. Vinagre, P. A. N. Garcia, and L. R. de Araujo, A new distribution system reconfiguration approach using optimum power flow and sensitivity analysis for loss reduction, *IEEE Transactions on Power Systems* 21, 4, 2006, 1616–1623.
[44] M. Assadian, M. M. Farsangi, and H. Nezamabadipour, Optimal reconfiguration of distribution system by PSO and GA using graph theory, *Proceedings of the 6th WSEAS International Conference on Applications of Electrical Engineering*, Istanbul, Turkey, 2007, pp. 83–88.
[45] T. M. Khalil and A. V. Gorpinich, Reconfiguration for loss reduction of distribution systems using selective particle swarm optimization, *International Journal of Multidisciplinary Sciences and Engineering* 3, 6, 2012, 16–21.
[46] Y. Mohamed Shuaib and M. Surya Kalavathi, Optimal reconfiguration in radial distribution system using GSO algorithm IET Chennai, *Fourth International Conference on Sustainable Energy and Intelligent Systems (SEISCON 2013)*, 2013, pp. 50–56.
[47] M. R. Nayak, Optimal feeder reconfiguration of distribution system with distributed generation units using HC-ACO, *International Journal on Electrical Engineering and Informatics*, 6, 1, 2014, 107–128.

[48] T. T. Nguyen, A. V. Truong, and T. A. Phung, A novel method based on adaptive cuckoo search for optimal network reconfiguration and distributed generation allocation in distribution network, *Electrical Power and Energy Systems* 78, 2016, 801–815.
[49] J. Chen, F. Zhang, and Y. Zhang, Distribution network reconfiguration based on simulated annealing immune algorithm, *Energy Procedia* 12, 2011, 271–277.
[50] R. Srinivasa Rao, S. V. L. Narasimham, and M. Ramalingaraju, Optimization of distribution network configuration for loss reduction using artificial bee colony algorithm world academy of science, *Engineering and Technology* 45, 2008, 708–714.

17 Photovoltaic System-Integrated Smart Buildings

A Mini Review

Aadyasha Patel and O.V. Gnana Swathika
Vellore Institute of Technology

CONTENTS

ABBREVIATIONS

AC Alternative Current
AI Artificial Intelligence
ANN Artificial Neural Network
BESS Battery Energy Storage System
BIPV Building Integrated Photovoltaic
CPC Cascaded Predictive Control
DC Direct Current
DG Distributed Generation
ENN Elman Neural Network
EOD Efficiency Optimized Design
EV Electric Vehicle
FLC Fuzzy Logic Control
FPV Flexible PV
FSM Fuzzy Satisfaction Method
HESS Hybrid Energy Storage System
IBBA Improved Binary Bat Algorithm
INC Incremental Conductance

DOI: 10.1201/9781003201069-17

IoT	Internet of Things
ITSMC	Integral Terminal Sliding Mode Control
LCI	Line Commutated Inverter
LCOD	Lifetime Cost Optimized Design
MG	Microgrid
MPP	Maximum Power Point
MPPT	Maximum Power Point Tracking
MRC	Modified Repetitive Control
P&O	Perturb and Observe
PEI	Power Electronic Interface
PEV	Plug-In Electric Vehicle
PFM	Pulse-Frequency Modulation
PI	Proportional Integral
PID	Proportional Integral Derivative
PR	Performance Ratio
PV	Photovoltaic
PWM	Pulse-Width Modulation
RBFN	Radial Basis Function Network
SAPV	Stand-Alone Photovoltaic
SOC	State of Charge
SPVSS	SAPV System Simulator
SPWM	Sinusoidal Pulse-Width Modulation
SWT	Scanning Window Technique
WT	Wind Turbine

17.1 INTRODUCTION

There is a change taking place in the worldwide electricity system. Demand is increasing on a global level for affordable, reliable, scalable, clean, and green electricity. Renewable technologies, one of them being solar photovoltaic (PV) system, is being looked upon as the solution. The focus on such systems is mainly due to environmental concerns so as to reduce greenhouse gas emission. Sunlight is directly converted to electricity using PVs. Such devices require very little maintenance and are simple in design and rugged in construction. Stand-alone systems are installed to supply output in the range of few microwatts to megawatts. Few applications include solar home systems, smart buildings, communications, space vehicles, satellites, and water pumping. References [1,2] are guides recommended to test, evaluate, and size lead–acid batteries that are used in PV systems. Reference [3] presents and discusses an advanced MPPT method to extract maximum obtainable power from a PV system regardless of load variances, solar irradiation, and temperature with the help of IoT-based wireless sensor nodes. An AI technique is employed to find the fault ranking of PV modules. The critical faults are accessed using fuzzy logic [4]. Reference [5] suggests data acquisition from an installed setup using a data logger and evaluation by proper performance monitoring of the system, and also using an IoT-based Wi-Fi module for energy management system.

Reference [6] presents a statistical investigation using a periodic autoregressive model for the development of stand-alone systems. Mock sequences are generated from the past solar irradiance; an energy steadiness of a typical suburban load is made by varying the capacity of the batteries and power of the PV system. Arduino is used here to confirm the purpose of P&O for a SAPV system during continual climatic circumstances and step disparities in the load connected to it [7]. This paper provides an all-inclusive analysis of solar PV technology in terms of globally leading countries, PV materials' efficiency, funding, research and development activities, driving policies, cost analysis in terms of project cost, balance of system cost, and PV module cost [8]. References [9,10] discuss PV system design techniques such as analytical, numerical, and intuitive techniques. The complete-history persistence ensemble is projected as a common standardized technique for solar prediction as it exploits complete measured history and forms practical disseminations of the estimate that is for a particular period of the day [11]. A new hybrid forecasting approach is proposed and evaluated in Ref. [12], resulting in a combination of the utmost well-performing prediction models. A hybrid improved multi-verse optimizer algorithm is proposed to enhance support of trajectory for PV yield estimation [13]. This method is helpful in the calculation of output power and maintenance of the steadiness of the power system and conduces to the economic dispatch of the network. A machine learning method for predictive maintenance is presented in Ref. [14] that allows implementation of dynamical verdict guidelines for maintenance supervision which are used for clear cut facts and high-dimensional complications.

17.2 STAND-ALONE AND GRID-CONNECTED PV SYSTEMS

A fuzzy multiple-objective optimization procedure is offered in Ref. [15] for plotting power generation schemes of stand-alone systems considering three key objectives – societal effects, technology fee, and environment. A system dependability index is assessed along the period of the venture for each practicable result of the Pareto set. The decision-making process utilizes FSM, which accounts at the same time for social, economic, methodical, and conservational performance indexes. Originality of the suggestion belongs to the insertion of social effects in the FSM used here to select more fitting answer, when earlier only two of the four indexes were considered. This paper proposes a smart, distributed, SAPV MG structure appropriate for islands as a non-renewable power system becomes expensive to install. The proposed scheme offers development of scheme dependability and competence for the suggested system which is analyzed with DC–DC boost converter, single-phase full-bridge inverter and backup and battery discharge state. MATLAB/Simulink is used to simulate the MG models [16]. A DC MG stand-alone system is simulated and analyzed in this paper using MATLAB/Simulink. The integration of present utility grids and deployment of power generation plants based on renewable energy together give rise to the notion of smart grid and MG. The main source to the grid is solar PV system with BESS. The intended arrangement is simulated under several load variations and input settings to analyze and study the entire system performance [17]. This paper uses data attained from HOMER software to present a method concerning optimization of lifetime cost and operational efficiency by consequently sizing the storage agent and PV system. EOD and LCOD help in restructuring the arrangement to make best use of surplus energy and improving the efficiency while not allowing the performance of the system to degrade and also maintaining its lifetime cost. A

9.15% increase in operational efficiency and a 17.18% increase in cost savings are observed in the EOD system and the LCOD system, respectively [18].

DG capacity configuration is a vital part in the design and planning of MG whose advantages and disadvantages directly affect the power supply reliability and economy of MG and react on the environment. The storage of energy in flywheel and supercapacitor-based systems cannot be optimally configured for longer durations. The combined arrangement of diesel generator, PV system, wind power, and HESS is difficult to configure. The solution to this problem is proposed as a configuration model consisting of two-stage and double period scale for stand-alone type of MG. PV–wind–diesel–battery configuration outcome is cracked in the primary stage; energy storage configuration outcomes based on results of the primary stage are taken care of in the secondary stage [19]. This article presents the modeling of a DC–DC boost-type converter and design of its control loops in the discontinuous conduction mode and the average current control scheme, respectively. The designed controllers are validated using simulation and verified to justify the necessities of maximum overshoot and settling period. The results attained show that the designed controllers have a satisfactory transient response to disturbances in the system input [20]. For the anticipated MG to function for 20 or more years, demand data and techno-economics from the commencement of mission are required to improve system configuration. System component pricing, demand fluctuations, fuel, and technological advances along the timeline are not measured in these studies, leading to improbable results. With the aim of addressing the above-mentioned limitations, the design of the system is adjusted in three legs in view of the fluctuations of demand and system component market values [21].

Reference [22] presents an optimal control design, under numerous environmental conditions, for a generic grid-connected and SAPV system. For extraction of power from a solar PV system, many control points are inspected and output voltage is adjusted in the grid-connected mode and the stand-alone mode, respectively. Here, MPPT is implemented using P&O algorithm. A linear quadratic regulator is ideally used to implement voltage controller. Along with load demand fluctuations, the performance of the system in various climatic situations and the efficiency of the planned method are shown in the simulation outcome. DC MG has some advantages over AC MG, such as improved power quality, a decrease in energy consumption, and a decrease in other costs. Initially, multi-loads and multi-sources of DC MG are analyzed. Then, its coordinated control structure and energy management are studied. Finally, the focus is on HESS topology [23]. A grid-connected PV system with a single-phase transformer-less inverter is introduced in Ref. [24] working on the principle of Ćuk converter and also allowing bidirectional current flow. This arrangement is suitable for stand-alone purposes as well. Stochastic characteristic of load, WT, and PV is established considering a multi-type DG scheduling model to install DG correctly in the stand-alone MG. The total yearly cost includes objective functions, which are maintenance charge, environment compensation charge, investment charge of DG, and fuel charge, with constraints such as SOC of battery storage limit and node voltage limit. Monte Carlo method-based probability power flow is used to calculate the voltage violation ratio of nodes in MG, according to the probability density function of load, WT, and PV. Lastly, the optimization model is resolved by the genetic algorithm. The proposed strategy is economic with good performance and is verified using simulation of the 33-bus MG system [25].

A flexible and instinctive explanation is proposed in Ref. [26] via a price-based style for power administration of SAPV systems with centralized DC bus which is taken as a market setting to fabricate energy price depending on energy insufficiency. The advantages of the proposed method are intuitive programming effort and scalability, to help designers of off-grid PV systems. The experimental results proved the effectiveness of the system. There is inadequate information and description of what precisely constitutes an off-grid renewable energy system despite the rising market opportunities and attention. The International Renewable Energy Agency recognizes a number of significant areas to address this challenge where methodological enhancements are sought, which include the following: (i) system outline; (ii) existing data source identification, compilation of their limitations, and consistency creation; (iii) constant pointers to compare, evaluate, differentiate, and aggregate data on hybrid and stand-alone non-conventional energy systems; and (iv) application and system design-based categorization of stand-alone non-conventional energy systems [27]. Reference [28] aims at pulling out maximum power and feeding it to a stand-alone system and single-phase utility grid simultaneously using a LCI and a multilevel boost converter. In the proposed study, for a fixed firing angle of LCI, maximum power is tracked while the duty ratio remains unchanged irrespective of irradiation variations. A 110-V single-phase grid is fed by a 230-V, 100-W, DC motor and an 80-V, 9.4-A PV array. The maximum power is extracted from the PV array, feeding a bigger percentage to the utility grid through LCI and the smaller percentage to a DC motor. The effectiveness of the proposed system is proved by correlating experimental, simulation, and theoretical results.

The international off-grid renewable energy conference report presents the key findings and references that arose from the roundtable negotiations. It says that accepting an effective strategy and regulatory agenda along with tailored business and funding representations and adapting skills to the rural setting are all critical factors in accelerating the positioning of off-grid renewable energy. The unconstrained political assurance to rural electrification along with a strong institutional context is vital to attracting private sector contribution [29]. A stand-alone hybrid power system is proposed in Ref. [30]. The dynamic model is built and simulated in MATLAB/Simulink. The intelligent controller contains an upgraded ENN and RBFN to attain a steady and quick reaction from the real power control. The WT pitch angle is controlled by ENN, while to achieve MPPT, RBFN is used. Also, the DC–DC boost converter is controlled by the output signal. IBBA-based capacity configuration optimization model for stand-alone hybrid MG is studied in Ref. [31]. The proposal of IBBA answers various questions regarding selection, mutation, and crossover processes.

17.3 SAPV SYSTEM

For a stand-alone DC MG, a control structure of nonlinear type for a PV–supercapacitor–battery system is offered in Ref. [32]. This also takes care of limits such as supercapacitor voltage regulation, multiple controllers' designing conflicts, and stability in a small area of linear PI-control structure. For a DC source of the SAPV system, a five-level PV inverter topology is studied in Ref. [33]. BESS controls the DC link voltage and handles energy from the battery. Improving the efficiency of the system and dealing with fractional PV power are taken care of by the DC–DC buck converter. A DC SAPV MG system is designed, modeled, and simulated in Ref. [34]. The results show reduced system losses and increased efficiency. In Ref. [35], the design specifications of a multi-stage-type PEI are provided, which include a single-phase voltage source inverter and a current-fed full-bridge isolated converter of active clamp type. PEI processes power delivery and low output voltage from PV module to the stand-alone load. The converter is controlled by P&O algorithm, whereas the inverter is controlled by the fixed-frequency sliding-type method. Reference [36] focuses on the experimental validation results of a SAPV system comprising PV panel/inverter/battery with charge controller and AC load. SAPV arrays are incorporated in two stages using MPPT in Ref. [37]. To attain appropriate PWM firing pulse, voltage–frequency control is recommended. A general MPPT scheme for application of partially shaded state on the PV panels is presented in Ref. [38]. Also, flower pollination AI algorithm-based perturbation of random variables is discussed. Reference [39] offers a comparison between two diverse MPPT techniques, namely P&O and INC, with varying irradiation. Under any environmental and faulty situation, to extract MPP from a PV array, a MPPT technique called ITSMC is introduced in Ref. [40]. Lyapunov criterion presents the controllers' stability analysis. ITSMC performance is compared with the performance of P&O and PID techniques, the former being a nonlinear control technique and the latter a predictable technique. Size optimization of the SAPV system is proposed in Ref. [41] by applying grey wolf optimization algorithm whose inputs are radiation from sun, load data, and ambient temperature. The objective function of the algorithm is taken as the life cycle cost of the system.

A SAPV system installed with a single-phase inverter is studied and compared for both unipolar and bipolar switching structures in Ref. [42]. The MPPT algorithms such as INC and variable-step-size INC algorithms are systematically scrutinized for both transient and steady state behavior. The functionality of the unipolar and bipolar SPWM is observed at an irradiation of 210 W/m^2, confirming that the switching performance of unipolar SPWM is better than that of bipolar SPWM. P&O and INC MPPT algorithms for an independent PV system are compared, examined, and studied in Ref. [43]. A test center setup for the SAPV system is established using MPPT algorithm and boost converter, which is executed in a ten-bit Arduino mega 2560 microcontroller. By looking at P&O and INC algorithms from perspectives such as duty cycle and irradiance, the latter showcases healthier performance than the former. Using MATLAB/Simulink tools, I-V and P-V characteristics of PV array are investigated with varying loads in Ref. [44]. PV radiation under variable and fixed conditions to attain all-out operating point of energy is the key objective of this study. In Ref. [45], the design of a 2-kW SAPV system is analyzed. The switching control algorithm is realized with proportional and integral controllers. The proposed scheme is explained with fewer stages of converter, high solar MPPT, and battery with high level of control with constant load voltage [46]. The stand-alone mode of operation of a single-phase PV inverter is presented in Ref. [47] with the multi-loop and MRC-based hybrid control strategy. MRC with sinusoidal reference attains zero steady state error and implements a multi-loop control, which in turn increases the dynamic performance of the system. An adaptive linear neuron strategy-based method is proposed where assessment of performance is carried out via simulation following standard EN50530 test approvals for diverse irradiance profiles. Also, under dissimilar operational conditions, a traditional P&O algorithm is compared with the proposed system [48]. For the purpose of maximum power generation tracked by MPPT for a SAPV system, a buck–boost converter is primarily developed. To control the converter, a microcontroller is programmed and loaded with adaptive neuro-fuzzy inference-based MPPT algorithm [49].

The inspection and assessment of batteries and supercapacitors is explained in Ref. [50]. The supercapacitors perform better than conventional batteries because of factors such as rapid charging, less charging time, high power density, high discharging capability, and improved performance characteristic with enhanced system efficiency. A SAPV system sizing optimization technique is presented in Ref. [51] to make the most of the system PR by influencing the charge controllers, inverters, optimum PV modules, and batteries. The outcomes disclosed that dolphin echolocation outpaced classical evolutionary programming and fast evolutionary programming in making the highest PR. In this work, two battery/supercapacitor HESS arrangements are examined. The conducted simulation studied in the MATLAB/Simulink setting permitted to defend the appropriate structures of the energy shaping control systems for each of the HESS configurations and proved that both systems accomplish acceptable management strategies [52]. The goal of this paper is launching the system's optimal capacity strategy model with the aim of increasing the renewable energy penetration ratio of the system as approximately as imaginable. The weighted average method is used in transforming from a multi- to single-objective problem, and the genetic algorithm is employed to obtain the optimal solution [53]. Reference [54] studies the stability analysis and nonlinear dynamics in the battery charging mode of a nonlinear PV generator-fed DC–DC SEPIC converter. Initially, discrete and continuous time system modeling is carried out thoroughly and precisely. In addition to it, a scrutiny of its bifurcation behavior and nonlinear dynamics is presented. The integral nonlinearities and joint optimization problem are explained in Ref. [55] by proposing a method based on ANN, which is user task accessible, with conformability to temporal resolution and nonlinearities. The intention of this paper is testing the SAPV system inverter's performance evolved by the test center of B2TKE PV system. The results present that peak inverter efficiency is reached at 25% of the resistive load [56]. Some of the SAPV projects commissioned in India are shown in Table 17.1 below.

The original orientation of DC voltage is added with the required amount of oscillation of second harmonic voltage in the proposed system to attain a modified indication to the intermediate bus capacitor voltage. The proposed method is easy to apply in each operational mode of the power system, and it proves beneficial due to overpowering the second harmonic current effectually without losing the dynamic performance of the DC–DC converters [57]. The SAPV system design along with battery energy storage is elaborately studied in Ref. [58]. In order to accomplish both DC–AC conversion and voltage boosting simultaneously, the full-bridge DC–AC

TABLE 17.1
SAPV Projects in India

S. No.	Location	Capacity	S. No.	Location	Capacity
1	Ladakh	1 MW	29	Dell International	350 kW
2	CREDA, Chhattisgarh	100+ solar microgrids	30	Tropical Flavours	1.2 MW
3	Sundarbans, West Bengal	110 kW	31	Niketan Solar Solutions	3 MW
4	Hanle Observatory, Leh	35 kWp	32	Mangalore Port	4 MW
5	Nyoma, Leh	40 kWp	33	Kerala State Electricity Board	500 kW
6	Durbuk	100 kWp	34	Kerala State Electricity Board	1 MW
7	Sub-District Hospital, Moreh, Manipur	1.25 kWp	35	Cochin Airport	14.4 MW
8	District Hospitals, Manipur	7×25 kWp	36	Cochin Airport	11 MW
9	State Academy of Training, Manipur	25 kWp	37	ANERT	2 MW
10	MANIREDA office, Imphal West, Manipur	7 kWp	38	Gorich Energy	1 MW
11	Imphal Airport, Manipur	3×5 kWp	39	Visakha Dairy	1.65 MW
12	Deputy Commissioner's Offices, Manipur	9×25 kW	40	Southern Rocks	1 MW
13	TR Energy	2.1 MW	41	Bangalore Airport	2.9 MW
14	Krishna Automobiles	120 kW	42	MTR Food	30 kW
15	Tynor Orthotics	180 kW	43	Himalaya Drugs	100 kW
16	Honda Motorcycles	600 kW	44	Wonderla	30 kW
17	Monte Carlo	352 kW	45	Carbonaire	200 kW
18	Oswal Woollen Mills	240 kW	46	Laxmi Agro	200 kW
19	Nahar Paper	205 kW	47	Sri Vinayaga	5 MW
20	Speedways Tyres	100 kW	48	Pavagada, Karnataka	300 MWp
21	LPS Bossard	180 kW	49	Noamundi, Jharkhand	3 MW
22	Jolly Grant Hospital	500 kW	50	Kovvur, Andhra Pradesh	3 MW
23	Maruti Suzuki	1 MW	51	Anantapur, Andhra Pradesh	100 MW
24	Escorts	1.5 MW	52	Chitradurga, Karnataka	10 MW
25	DS Group	412.5 kW	53	Kasaragod Solar Park, Kerala	50 MW
26	Delhi Public School	874 kW	54	Dhuvaran, Gujarat	95 MW
27	Sterling Tools	500 kW	55	Mithapur, Gujarat	17 MW
28	Bosch	10 MW	56	Mulshi, Maharashtra	3 MW

inverter and DC–DC buck–boost converter are integrated together, resulting in the core element which is a boost converter. A PFM and PMW hybrid modified three-port converter incorporating storage battery, load, and PV source is suggested for a SAPV–battery system. The power transfer analysis and topology derivation are presented. Zero-voltage switching, gain, and input current ripple are examined and compared [59]. This report talks about a method to make progress on a regression model intended for estimating SAPV system and also forecasting the operational necessities of the SAPV system meant for a specific site and load conditions. The comparative outcome of experimental results and simulation provides an assurance level of 92% [60]. The study was planned to investigate the SAPV system for size-matching of batteries and solar array by using the SAPV hardware simulator system or the SPVSS. The whole simulator is controlled and supervised by a computer with the help of LabVIEW [61]. The PV technology is reviewed in Ref. [62]. The various dependability assessment models and existing performance, grid connection and distribution, sizing, and control are also deliberated. The multilevel converters with the very popular network topology are compiled and presented in Ref. [63].

17.4 ENERGY STORAGE AND MANAGEMENT IN PV SYSTEMS

HESS, being the finest solution for the SAPV systems, as studied in Ref. [64], is a mix of supercapacitor and battery. HESS configuration model of multiple-converter type is simulated using MATLAB/Simulink and is also examined subjected to diverse settings of input radiation [64]. FLC is applied to excerpt MPPT from PV panel in Ref. [65]. The advantage of implementing FLC in MPPT is that the system responds faster under deviations in environments when open to temperature and radiation, which is also demonstrated by simulation. A power flow management system to manage the maximum capacity of a Li–ion battery charging system is studied in Ref. [66] with the battery cells of varying storage capacity and SOC. Reference [67] discusses the complete MG prototype built on commercially obtainable devices and specific topologies facilitating a full analysis of the situation and bearing in mind the operating circumstances of the MG. The tool makes available an improved understanding of MGs of stand-alone nature, eliminating the difference between industrial implementation and ideal explanation. The focus of work in Ref. [68] is electrical fault analysis in the SAPV system by reducing the number of sensors installed for recognizing and sorting out the faults. The investigation done in Ref. [69] shows that a non-conventional source such as solar PV is combined through a wireless power transfer interface for stand-alone and grid-connected applications, even though the system requirements demand adjustments conforming to the demands of the real world. A comprehensive financial investigation comprising operation, replacements, and contribution to determine expenses and the most ideal configuration size of PV system using evolutionary optimization approaches is discussed in Ref. [70].

Battery supercapacitor HESS of semi-active and passive kind is presented in Ref. [71] for SAPV systems. The extended lifespan with reduced stressed condition of the battery are also discussed. Reference [72] proposes and investigates a user-centric real-time control algorithm for SAPV systems with its communication requirements by minimizing the average cumulative system cost. Reference [73] presents a

MATLAB model of a SAPV system along with electrochemical storage. Reference [74] elaborates on the SAPV MG system by throwing light on an efficient energy management structure. The proposed fractional order PID- and PI-based energy management structure includes two control loops, inner and outer loops, to outpace a SAPV system with acceptable response. This report gives out a control strategy and sizing of BESSs for transmitting a PV generation farm in 1 hour in advance and 1 day in advance markets. For instructing a neural network of feed-forward type in forecasting load power consumption and solar irradiation, the Levenberg–Marquardt backpropagation learning algorithm is used [75]. The demonstration of a load-managing PV system over a typical PV system is studied in Ref. [76] with the former pointedly decreasing the levelized electricity price. A transformer-coupled dual-input converter is proposed to understand battery charge control and MPPT at the same time keeping suitable load-side voltage level. An appropriate control strategy and an operation scheme are also proposed, verified, and simulated with the help of a small-signal mathematical model [77].

Reference [78] introduces a new controller based on a recently developed MPPT technique permitting very fast maximum power point capture and employing a constant-current, constant-voltage charging system to decrease the charging time of battery while also permitting access to all system parameters remotely for administration and monitoring purposes. Reference [79] proposes a combined buck with a buck–boost converter which results in reduced recurrent power processing while improving the conversion efficiency. For stabilization and efficient employment of PV power flow to load and battery, Refs. [80,81] show the controller design and the modeling of PV charger system implemented with SEPIC converter, which also provides three phases of battery charging. In Ref. [82], the P&O technique is simulated and compared with practical results. In brief, the advantage of a double-integral sliding-mode controller is taken as a target in designing the MPPT for the PV system. At the same time, a new sliding surface is selected for minimizing the disadvantages of slow transient response and chattering [83,84].

17.5 CLIMATIC EFFECTS ON PV SYSTEMS

Reference [85] shows a new way of employing finite set model predictive control for progressive control approaches of PV emulators. The first part of the study proposes and verifies a predictive PV emulator based on buck converter under tough climatic situations and load disparities. An effectual CPC process is recommended and enforced in the subsequent investigation on stand-alone and grid-connected systems. The conclusion after the extensive experimentation is that the existence of distorted grid voltages does not impact the effectiveness and correctness of the suggested CPC under tough environmental settings. The numerous arrangements of PV arrays are examined and investigated in Ref. [86] along with their conduct, operation, and effectiveness under settings of various patterns of shading. For unchanging irradiation levels, the topologies reveal identical workings and effectiveness, whereas the total cross-tied and honey-comb formations offer enhanced performances in addition to higher efficiency in comparison with the other array topologies under partial shading conditions in spite of their high interconnectedness to intricacies. The proposition of a cross-technique for an off-grid DC solar power structure through merging of the INC method and shuffled frog leaping algorithm is explained in Ref. [87]. To verify the proposed method, the experimental circuit is implemented in MATLAB simulation under partial shading conditions. The field measurements estimate how the distortion fluctuates with power originated by a contemporary single-phase PV inverter [88]. When working as a stand-alone system, the nature and trait of supply voltage are scrutinized under dissimilar loading environments with regard to its harmonic constitution. The proposed method comprises modeling curved FPV segments and enhancing the power yield using a new SWT [89]. As the fill factor for curved FPV is highly dynamic, SWT proves to be exceedingly effective, resulting in fast and accurate MPPT. This study shows a new schematic to find the global MPP established on regulating a DC–DC converter such that it acts as a continuous input to power load. The proposed and existing global MPP techniques assure convergence for any fractional shading circumstances, which is investigated in Ref. [90].

17.6 CASE STUDY ON REAL-TIME PV APPLICATIONS

Reference [91] suggests electricity provision to low-voltage rural consumers by harvesting solar energy. Each module used is designed individually, then combined, simulated, and analyzed under different environmental conditions with varying loads. The P&O and Herman Beta methods are implemented for MPPT and to predict the load requirements of the village, respectively. This study contemplates three different energy management approaches applied to an off-grid district MG situated in Boston [92]. Within the MG, every time when an energy generation system of nonconventional type is operated, the management system distresses on the quantity of clean energy produced. This also disturbs the input and output specifications of the system. To ignore the incorrect information in the overseeing of a solar PV plant, Ref. [93] has come up with the idea to carry out firm integrity checks. The received data are separated out into a triangle ranking order of uppermost to lowermost precedence. A grid-tied 6.4-kW test PV plant and 271-kW PV plant provide fresh statistics to perform part of the planned checks. SAPV structure for online monitoring of working conditions based on Wi-Fi is analyzed in Ref. [94]. The system is implanted on the posterior of each PV panel to make available quick data on the operating point and also on the power generation of the apparatus. TerraSAS PV simulator is used to simulate the PV panels. Reference [95] presents an assessment of SAPV structure mounted on the rooftop of the EN Department building of KIET Group of Institutions, Ghaziabad, aiming to inspire the use of small SAPV systems to deliver power to research laboratory in countryside districts and inaccessible sites. An IoT- and Wi-Fi-based cost-effective energy management solution is developed for remote data monitoring and logging applications.

A boost inverter-fed induction motor for an off-grid PV water pumping system is proposed in Ref. [96] with specifications of 1 hp, three phases, 415 V, and star connection with a switching frequency of 20 KHz. For a three-phase, single-stage, DC–AC conversion using a boost inverter system, the minimum accessible DC input voltage is given to the induction motor to emphasize on its drivability. The parking lots for EVs depending on SAPV in the supply side are presented in Ref. [97] with an all-inclusive design method. A step-down DC–DC converter offers essential voltage to produce accessible peak power from the PV arrangement. A bidirectional DC–DC converter is accountable to sustain the appropriate voltage profile at the DC bus with a controller that assures constant operation during abrupt alteration of load and PV supply, for the entire working section. The latter leg is a voltage source converter that receives its input from the key DC bus along with a competent algorithm for filter design for a healthier trade-off between filtering and damping. To meet the electrical energy demand of a suburban household in the district of Faisalabad, Pakistan, Ref. [98] scrutinizes the viability of the SAPV system by introducing a broad design procedure granted with its monetary breakdown in terms of life cycle pricing. Reference [99] confirms the probability of PV–battery integrated module as an explanation for stand-alone systems in evolving nations. Reference [100] considers the fluctuations in solar intensities and their corresponding varying solar cell temperatures, and the operation and conduct of PV-powered permanent-magnet DC motor paired with a centrifugal pump is investigated. It is observed that manual tracking is found to be 20% more efficient when correlated with immovable slanted PV array.

Smart buildings include smart appliances, EV, energy storage systems, and most importantly a rooftop PV as in Refs. [101,102]. The energy management system minimizes the total cost factor toward the overall energy utilization of the smart home. In the course of low-demand hours, the EV is charged. Excess energy generated is stored or fed back to the grid when the power demand is at its peak. Figure 17.1 shows the block diagram of a smart home connected to PV arrays and the utility grid. An arrangement for PEV charging is available. Depending on the load demand of the home, the smart home EMS sends and receives signal from the various smart devices installed and hence manages power flow in the system. The focus of Refs. [103,104] is on the smart home energy management consisting of a PV array along with PEV energy storage. The objective is to decrease the energy expenditure of the home while also settling the PEV and home energy demands keeping in mind the inconsistent solar power. A random-variable prototype is initially evolved. Later, mathematical formulation of a hypothetical control problem is done to look at the flow of power in a smart home. Subsequently, based on the changing prices of electricity, the

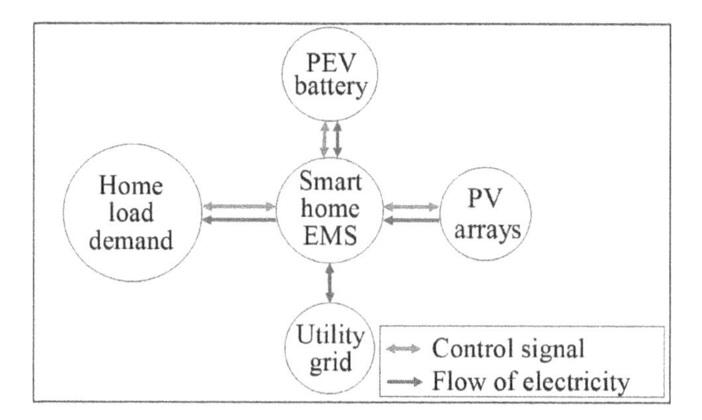

FIGURE 17.1 Block diagram of a smart home.

above system is studied and analyzed. A BIPV is proposed in Ref. [105] for the city structures to self-feed using PV arrays. A hierarchical controller, in the form of an interface, is designed to exchange information between the smart grid and the BIPV. The BIPV can also provide power to a tertiary structure via a smart grid. Smart wireless devices installed at homes and buildings are energy-efficient and operate for quite a long time duration without calling for maintenance. Reference [106] gives an all-inclusive study of such devices.

17.7 CONCLUSION

Worldwide energy consumption is growing every year, and several technologies are used to meet the energy demand. One of the evolving technologies, namely solar PV, which has been rapidly growing in the past decade, is reviewed here. Even though PV has not attained widespread development, few policymakers in some countries have its attention. In conclusion, stand-alone and grid-connected PV systems are reviewed here along with their energy storage and management systems. Their performance in different shading and climatic conditions is also talked about. Looking at all the key aspects covered in this piece, it is tough to extract a precise global pattern. All the perceptions covered in this chapter are useful to researchers, academicians, and solar PV system installers.

REFERENCES

[1] D. Generation and E. Storage, "IEEE recommended practice for sizing lead-acid batteries for stand-alone photovoltaic (PV) systems," *IEEE Std 1013–2007 (Revision of IEEE Std 1013–2000)*, vol. 1013, pp. 1–55, 2007, doi: 10.1109/ieeestd.2007.4280849.

[2] IEEE, "IEEE guide for test and evaluation of lead-acid batteries used in photovoltaic (PV) hybrid power systems," *IEEE Std 1661–2007*, pp. 1–18, 2008, doi: 10.1109/IEEESTD.2008.4449092.

[3] A. Sharma, Y. Koraz, and M. Youssef, "A novel control methodology for stand-alone photovoltaic systems utilizing maximum power point tracking," *2019 IEEE Canadian Conference of Electrical and Computer Engineering, CCECE 2019*. 2019, doi: 10.1109/CCECE.2019.8861548.

[4] S. Perveen, H. Ashfaq, and M. Asjad, "Fault ranking in PV module based on artificial intelligence technique (AIT)," *2019 International Conference on Power Electronics, Control and Automation, ICPECA 2019- Proceedings*, vol. 2019, 2019, doi: 10.1109/ICPECA47973.2019.8975619.

[5] A. K. Singh, K. Pal, and N. K. Gupta, "Performance evaluation of a 4kW isolated solar powered lab with IoT energy management system," *2019 2nd International Conference on Power Energy, Environment and Intelligent Control (PEEIC)*, pp. 418–423, 2019.

[6] G. Rostegui, L. Timana, and M. Gemignani, "Planning of stand-alone systems through statistical analysis," *8th International Conference on Renewable Energy Research and Applications, ICRERA 2019*, pp. 253–258, 2019, doi: 10.1109/ICRERA47325.2019.8997106.

[7] A. Al-Gizi, M. Al-Saadi, S. Al-Chlaihawi, A. Craciunescu, and M. A. Fadel, "Experimental installation of photovoltaic MPPT controller using arduino board," *2018 International Conference on Applied and Theoretical Electricity, ICATE 2018- Proceedings*, 2018, doi: 10.1109/ICATE.2018.8551397.

[8] M. Gul, Y. Kotak, and T. Muneer, "Review on recent trend of solar photovoltaic technology," *Energy Explor. Exploit.* vol. 34, no. 4, 2016.
[9] H. A. Kazem, A. M. S. Al-aisaee, K. Sopian, A. S. Albusaidi, M. H. Albadi, and T. He, "Design and evaluation of photovoltaic systems using different techniques," *Int. Conf. Adv. Electr. Electron. Eng.* 75–79, 2014.
[10] A. Grantham, Y. R. Gel, and J. Boland, "Nonparametric short-term probabilistic forecasting for solar radiation," *Sol. Energy* vol. 133, 465–475, 2016, doi: 10.1016/j.solener.2016.04.011.
[11] D. Yang, "A universal benchmarking method for probabilistic solar irradiance forecasting," *Sol. Energy* vol. 184, 410–416, 2019, doi: 10.1016/j.solener.2019.04.018.
[12] D. Su, E. Batzelis, and B. Pal, "Machine learning algorithms in forecasting of photovoltaic power generation," *SEST 2019-2nd International Conference on Smart Energy Systems and Technologies*, 2019, doi: 10.1109/SEST.2019.8849106.
[13] L. L. Li, S. Y. Wen, M. L. Tseng, and C. S. Wang, "Renewable energy prediction: A novel short-term prediction model of photovoltaic output power," *J. Clean. Prod.* vol. 228, 359–375, 2019, doi: 10.1016/j.jclepro.2019.04.331.
[14] G. A. Susto, A. Schirru, S. Pampuri, S. McLoone, and A. Beghi, "Machine learning for predictive maintenance: A multiple classifier approach," *IEEE Trans. Ind. Inform.* vol. 11, no. 3, 812–820, 2015, doi: 10.1109/TII.2014.2349359.
[15] J. D. Rivera-Niquepa, P. M. De Oliveira-De Jesus, J. C. Castro-Galeano, and D. Hernández-Torres, "Planning stand-alone electricity generation systems, a multiple objective optimization and fuzzy decision making approach," *Heliyon* vol. 6, no. 3, e03534, 2020, doi: 10.1016/j.heliyon.2020.e03534.
[16] A. Saha, S. Misra, and P. M. Progya, "Design and simulation based stand-alone solar micro grid system for island areas," *2019 5th Int. Conf. Adv. Electr. Eng. ICAEE 2019*, pp. 229–234, 2019, doi: 10.1109/ICAEE48663.2019.8975488.
[17] K. Jm, S. Sheik Mohammed, T. P. I. Ahamed, and M. Shafeeque, "Design and simulation of stand-alone DC microgrid with energy storage system," *IEEE International Conference on Intelligent Techniques in Control, Optimization and Signal Processing, INCOS 2019*, 2019, doi: 10.1109/INCOS45849.2019.8951384.
[18] S. Shankar, A. C. Sridhar, A. Gopikanna, V. K. Shankar, and V. Vijayaraghavan, "Efficiency-cost design optimization for a stand-alone rural microgrid," *2019 IEEE Power Energy Conf. Illinois, PECI 2019*, pp. 1–6, 2019, doi: 10.1109/PECI.2019.8698906.
[19] X. Huang, "Capacity optimization of distributed generation for stand-alone microgrid considering hybrid energy storage systems," *Zhongguo Dianji Gongcheng Xuebao/Proc. Chinese Soc. Electr. Eng.* vol. 38, no. 7, 1962–1970, 2018, doi: 10.13334/j.0258-8013.pcsee.170128.
[20] M. A. Abundis, O. Carranza, J. J. Rodriguez, R. Ortega, and J. V. Chavez, "DC/DC converter for a PV system operating in stand-alone and grid-tied modes," *31st International Summer Meeting on Power And Industrial Applications, RVP-AI 2018*, pp. 64–69, 2018, doi: 10.1109/RVPAI.2018.8469781.
[21] A. T. D. Perera, J. L. Scartezzini, and N. A. Iliadis, "Multi-stage integration of renewable energy technologies into standalone energy systems," *Proc. 2018 5th Int. Symp. Environ. Energies Appl. EFEA 2018*, pp. 1–5, 2019, doi: 10.1109/EFEA.2018.8617047.
[22] S. Batiyah, N. Zohrabi, S. Abdelwahed, T. Qunais, and M. Mousa, "Optimal control design of a voltage controller for stand-alone and grid-connected PV converter," *2018 IEEE Texas Power and Energy Conference, TPEC 2018*, vol. 2018, pp. 1–6, 2018, doi: 10.1109/TPEC.2018.8312094.
[23] Z. Lan-Lan, Z. Jian-Ping, L. Hong-Qing, L. Xin-Yu, H. Cheng-Yi, D. Yu-Jun, G. Yu-Jiao, "Research progress and strategy on stand-alone DC micro-grid with multi-sources and multi-loads," *Proceedings of the 30th Chinese Control and Decision Conference, CCDC 2018*, pp. 5126–5130, 2018, doi: 10.1109/CCDC.2018.8408020.

[24] S. Sheng and J. Zhang, "Capacity configuration optimisation for stand-alone micro-grid based on an improved binary bat algorithm," *J. Eng.* vol. 2017, no. 13, 2083–2087, 2017, doi: 10.1049/joe.2017.0696.
[25] W. Fang, H. Liu, F. Chen, H. Zheng, G. Hua, and W. He, "DG planning in stand-alone microgrid considering stochastic characteristic," *J. Eng.* vol. 2017, no. 13, 1181–1185, 2017, doi: 10.1049/joe.2017.0515.
[26] L. V. Bellinaso, C. D. Schwertner, and L. Michels, "Price-based power management of off-grid photovoltaic systems with centralised dc bus," *IET Renewable Power Gen.* vol. 10, no. 8, 1132–1139, 2016, doi: 10.1049/iet-rpg.2015.0472.
[27] R. Kempener, O. Lavagne, D. Saygin, J. Skeer, S. Vinci, and D. Gielen, "Off-grid renewable energy systems: status and methodological issues," *Irena* vol. 29, 2015.
[28] S. Krithiga and N. G. A. Gounden, "Power electronic configuration for the operation of PV system in combined grid-connected and stand-alone modes," *IET Power Electron.* vol. 7, no. 3, 640–647, 2014, doi: 10.1049/iet-pel.2013.0107.
[29] IRENA, "IOREC 2012 international off-grid renewable energy conference," *Int. Off-grid Renew. Energy Conf.*, 2012, [Online]. Available: http://www.irena.org/DocumentDownloads/Publications/IOREC_KeyFindingsandRecommendations.pdf.
[30] W. M. Lin, C. M. Hong, and C. H. Chen, "Neural-network-based MPPT control of a stand-alone hybrid power generation system," *IEEE Trans. Power Electron.* vol. 26, no. 12, 3571–3581, 2011, doi: 10.1109/TPEL.2011.2161775.
[31] S. Ghosh, K. Nathan, T. Long, P. Tripathi, and Y. Siwakoti, "Single phase integrated ĆUK transformerless SiC inverter for grid-connected PV systems," *2018 1st Workshop on Wide Bandgap Power Devices and Applications in Asia, WiPDA Asia 2018*, pp. 18–22, 2018, doi: 10.1109/WiPDAAsia.2018.8734602.
[32] B. R. Ravada and N. R. Tummuru, "Control of a supercapacitor-battery-PV based stand-alone DC-microgrid," *IEEE Trans. Energy Convers.* 35, 3, 1268–1277, 2020, doi: 10.1109/TEC.2020.2982425.
[33] M. Farhadi-Kangarlu and M. G. Marangalu, "A single DC-source five-level inverter applied in stand-alone photovoltaic systems considering MPPT capability," *2019 10th International Power Electronics, Drive Systems and Technologies Conference, PEDSTC 2019*, pp. 338–342, 2019, doi: 10.1109/PEDSTC.2019.8697896.
[34] S. Sumaiya, A. El-Shahat, R. Haddad, H. Ramadan, and M. Becherif, "A stand-alone PV-micro-grid efficiency enhancement," *Conference Proceedings - IEEE SOUTHEASTCON*, 2019, doi: 10.1109/SoutheastCon42311.2019.9020543.
[35] S. Prakash, M. Mohanty, and S. Padhee, "Design of multi-staged power electronic interface for stand-alone application powered by photovoltaic module," *2019 IEEE Students Conference on Engineering and Systems, SCES 2019*, 2019, doi: 10.1109/SCES46477.2019.8977210.
[36] S. Guesmi, K. Jamoussi, and M. Ghariani, "Experimental and simulation study of a stand-alone photovoltaic system with storage battery," *19th International Conference on Sciences and Techniques of Automatic Control and Computer Engineering, STA 2019*, pp. 442–448, 2019, doi: 10.1109/STA.2019.8717199.
[37] S. Chakraborty, P. Arvind, and D. Kumar, "Integrated solar PV MPPT and V-f control for stand-alone microgrid," *Proc. -2019 Int. Conf. Electr. Electron. Comput. Eng. UPCON 2019*, no. 2, pp. 7–12, 2019, doi: 10.1109/UPCON47278.2019.8980045.
[38] N. M. Elbehairy, R. A. Swief, A. M. Abdin, and T. S. Abdelsalam, "Maximum power point tracking for a stand-alone PV system under shading conditions using flower pollination algorithm," *2019 21st International Middle East Power Systems Conference, MEPCON 2019- Proceedings*, pp. 840–845, 2019, doi: 10.1109/MEPCON47431.2019.9008230.

[39] M. A. E. Eid, A. A. Elbaset, H. A. Ibrahim, and S. A. M. Abdelwahab, "Modelling, simulation of MPPT using perturb and observe and incremental conductance techniques for stand-alone PV systems," *2019 21st International Middle East Power Systems Conference, MEPCON 2019- Proceedings*, pp. 429–434, 2019, doi: 10.1109/MEPCON47431.2019.9007962.

[40] Z. A. Khan, L. Khan, Q. Khan, U. H. Khan, F. W. Karam, and M. A. Khan, "Neuro based integral terminal sliding mode nonlinear mppt control paradigms for stand-alone photovoltaic system," *Proceedings -22nd International Multitopic Conference, INMIC 2019*, 2019, doi: 10.1109/INMIC48123.2019.9022751.

[41] A. Khalil and A. Asheibi, "Optimal sizing of stand-alone PV system using grey wolf optimization," *2019 International Conference on Electrical Engineering Research and Practice, iCEERP 2019*, 2019, doi: 10.1109/ICEERP49088.2019.8956979.

[42] P. K. Behera, S. Das, and M. Pattnaik, "Performance comparison between bipolar and unipolar switching scheme for a single-phase inverter based stand-alone photovoltaic system," *2019 IEEE 16th India Council International Conference, INDICON 2019- Symposium Proceedings*, 2019, doi: 10.1109/INDICON47234.2019.9030323.

[43] J. Mishra, S. Das, D. Kumar, and M. Pattnaik, "Performance comparison of PO and INC MPPT algorithm for a stand-alone PV system," *2019 Innovations in Power and Advanced Computing Technologies, i-PACT 2019*, 2019, doi: 10.1109/i-PACT44901.2019.8960005.

[44] M. Alghassab, "Performance enhancement of stand-alone photovoltaic systems with household loads," *2nd International Conference on Computer Applications and Information Security, ICCAIS 2019*, 2019, doi: 10.1109/CAIS.2019.8769553.

[45] S. M. Mahmood and M. E. Khan, "Photovoltaic based application for domestic load," *2019 International Conference on Power Electronics, Control and Automation, ICPECA 2019- Proceedings*, 2019, doi: 10.1109/ICPECA47973.2019.8975501.

[46] K. Bharathi, S. Sakthi, and M. Sasikumar, "Power optimization of embedded controller PV powered stand alone system for rural electrification," *5th Int. Conf. Sci. Technol. Eng. Math. ICONSTEM 2019*, vol. 1, pp. 362–367, 2019, doi: 10.1109/ICONSTEM.2019.8918855.

[47] B. Guo, M. Su, J. Yang, J. Ou, Z. Tang, B. Cheng, and M. Liu, "A hybrid control strategy based on modified repetitive control for single-phase photovoltaic inverter in stand-alone mode," *Proceedings -2018 IEEE International Conference on Industrial Electronics for Sustainable Energy Systems, IESES 2018*, pp. 308–313, 2018, doi: 10.1109/IESES.2018.8349894.

[48] Y. Triki, A. Bechouche, H. Seddiki, D. O. Abdeslam, and P. Wira, "ADALINE based maximum power point tracking methods for stand-alone PV systems control," *Proceedings of the IEEE International Conference on Industrial Technology*, pp. 880–885, 2018, doi: 10.1109/ICIT.2018.8352294.

[49] N. Priyadarshi, V. K. Ramachandaramurthy, S. Padmanaban, F. Azam, A. K. Sharma, and J. P. Kesari, "An ANFIS artificial technique based maximum power tracker for standalone photovoltaic power generation," *2018 2nd IEEE International Conference on Power Electronics, Intelligent Control and Energy Systems, ICPEICES 2018*, pp. 102–107, 2018, doi: 10.1109/ICPEICES.2018.8897386.

[50] A. Pareek, P. Singh, and P. N. Rao, "Analysis and comparison of charging time between battery and supercapacitor for 300W stand-alone PV system," *Proceedings of the 2018 International Conference on Current Trends towards Converging Technologies, ICCTCT 2018*. 2018, doi: 10.1109/ICCTCT.2018.8551164.

[51] Z. Othman, S. I. Sulaiman, I. Musirin, A. M. Omar, and S. Shaari, "Dolphin Echolocation - Based sizing algorithm for stand-alone photovoltaic system," *Proceedings of 4th IEEE International Conference on Applied System Innovation 2018, ICASI 2018*, pp. 1284–1287, 2018, doi: 10.1109/ICASI.2018.8394527.

[52] I. Shchur and Y. Biletskyi, "Interconnection and damping assignment passivity-based control of semi-active and active battery/supercapacitor hybrid energy storage systems for stand-alone photovoltaic installations," *14th Int. Conf. Adv. Trends Radioelectron. Telecommun. Comput. Eng. TCSET 2018- Proc.*, pp. 324–329, 2018, doi: 10.1109/TCSET.2018.8336212.

[53] L. Zhang, D. Mu, Z. He, and J. Sun, "Multi-objective capacity optimal design of stand-alone PV DC microgrid system," *2018 8th Int. Conf. Power Energy Syst. ICPES 2018*, pp. 273–277, 2019, doi: 10.1109/ICPESYS.2018.8626892.

[54] M. Zhioua, A. El Aroudi, and S. Belghith, "Nonlinear dynamics and stability analysis of a SEPIC converter for stand-alone PV systems," *2018 15th International Multi-Conference on Systems, Signals and Devices, SSD 2018*, pp. 1139–1143, 2018, doi: 10.1109/SSD.2018.8570406.

[55] A. Ahmad and J. Y. Khan, "Stand-alone distributed PV systems: maximizing self consumption and user comfort using ANNs," *2018 IEEE International Conference on Communications, Control, and Computing Technologies for Smart Grids, SmartGridComm 2018*, 2018, doi: 10.1109/SmartGridComm.2018.8587531.

[56] O. A. Rosyid, N. M. Lande, and F. M. Rizanulhaq, "Validation of solar inverter testing procedure for stand-alone PV systems," *2018 Electrical Power, Electronics, Communications, Controls and Informatics Seminar, EECCIS 2018*, pp. 42–45, 2018, doi: 10.1109/EECCIS.2018.8692977.

[57] W. Wang and X. Ruan, "A modified reference of an intermediate bus capacitor voltage-based second-harmonic current reduction method for a standalone photovoltaic power system," *IEEE Trans. Power Electron.* vol. 31, no. 8, pp. 5562–5573, 2016, doi: 10.1109/TPEL.2015.2497314.

[58] D. Debnath and K. Chatterjee, "Solar photovoltaic-based stand-alone scheme incorporating a new boost inverter," *IET Power Electron.* vol. 9, no. 4, pp. 621–630, 2016, doi: 10.1049/iet-pel.2015.0112.

[59] X. Sun, Y. Shen, W. Li, and H. Wu, "A PWM and PFM hybrid modulated three-port converter for a standalone PV/battery power system," *IEEE J. Emerg. Sel. Top. Power Electron.* vol. 3, no. 4, pp. 984–1000, 2015, doi: 10.1109/JESTPE.2015.2424718.

[60] P. G. Nikhil and D. Subhakar, "Approaches for developing a regression model for sizing a stand-alone photovoltaic system," *IEEE J. Photovoltaics* vol. 5, no. 1. pp. 250–257, 2015, doi: 10.1109/JPHOTOV.2014.2368711.

[61] W. Shen and A. S. K. Bin, "Investigation of standalone photovoltaic systems," *Proc. 2011 6th IEEE Conf. Ind. Electron. Appl. ICIEA 2011*, pp. 2651–2656, 2011, doi: 10.1109/ICIEA.2011.5976044.

[62] B. Parida, S. Iniyan, and R. Goic, "A review of solar photovoltaic technologies," *Renewable Sustainable Energy Rev.* vol. 15, no. 3, pp. 1625–1636, 2011, doi: 10.1016/j.rser.2010.11.032.

[63] S. Daher, J. Schmid, and F. L. M. Antunes, "Multilevel inverter topologies for stand-alone PV systems," *IEEE Trans. Ind. Electron.* vol. 55, no. 7. pp. 2703–2712, 2008, doi: 10.1109/TIE.2008.922601.

[64] K. Javed, H. Ashfaq, and R. Singh, "Application of supercapacitor as hybrid energy storage device in stand-alone PV system," *2019 International Conference on Power Electronics, Control and Automation, ICPECA 2019- Proceedings*, 2019, doi: 10.1109/ICPECA47973.2019.8975650.

[65] O. S. S. Hussian, H. M. Elsayed, and M. A. Moustafa Hassan, "Fuzzy logic control for a stand-alone PV system with PI controller for battery charging based on evolutionary technique," *Proceedings of the 2019 10th IEEE International Conference on Intelligent Data Acquisition and Advanced Computing Systems: Technology and Applications, IDAACS 2019*, vol. 2. pp. 889–894, 2019, doi: 10.1109/IDAACS.2019.8924269.

[66] U. K. Das, K. S. Tey, M. Y. Idna Idris, and S. Mekhilef, "Maximum power flow management for stand-alone PV based battery charging system," *ICPE 2019- ECCE Asia -10th Int. Conf. Power Electron. - ECCE Asia*, vol. 2030, pp. 1599–1604, 2019.
[67] G. N. Bogado, F. Paz, I. G. Zurbriggen, and M. Ordonez, "Optimal sizing of a PV and battery storage system using a detailed model of the microgrid for stand-alone applications," *Conference Proceedings - IEEE Applied Power Electronics Conference and Exposition - APEC*, vol. 2019, pp. 555–560, 2019, doi: 10.1109/APEC.2019.8722113.
[68] S. Sarkar, K. U. Rao, J. Bhargav, S. Sheshaprasad, and A. Sharma, "Signature analysis of electrical faults in standalone PV systems with storage," *2019 3rd International Conference on Recent Developments in Control, Automation and Power Engineering, RDCAPE 2019*, pp. 472–476, 2019, doi: 10.1109/RDCAPE47089.2019.8979080.
[69] A. Ghosh, A. Ukil, and A. P. Hu, "Integration of rooftop solar PV generation with wireless power transfer," *Asia-Pacific Power and Energy Engineering Conference, APPEEC*, 2019, doi: 10.1109/APPEEC45492.2019.8994668.
[70] M. Elloumi, R. Kallel, and G. Boukettaya, "A comparative study of GA and APSO algorithm for an optimal design of a standalone PV/battery system," *2018 15th International Multi-Conference on Systems, Signals and Devices, SSD 2018*, pp. 1104–1109, 2018, doi: 10.1109/SSD.2018.8570449.
[71] T. Rout, M. K. Maharana, A. Chowdhury, and S. Samal, "A comparative study of standalone photo-voltaic system with battery storage system and battery supercapacitor storage system," *Proceedings of the 4th International Conference on Electrical Energy Systems, ICEES 2018*, pp. 77–81, 2018, doi: 10.1109/ICEES.2018.8442346.
[72] A. Ahmad and J. Y. Khan, "A joint real time optimization of household loads, energy storage and peak generator for stand-alone distributed PV systems," *IEEE International Conference on Communications*, 2018, doi: 10.1109/ICC.2018.8422977.
[73] D. A. Ciupageanu and G. Lazaroiu, "Dynamic simulation of a stand-Alone photovoltaic/battery energy storage system," *2018 Int. Symp. Fundam. Electr. Eng. ISFEE 2018*, 2018, doi: 10.1109/ISFEE.2018.8742478.
[74] A. M. Betti, M. A. Ebrahim, and M. A. Mustafa Hassan, "Modeling and Control of Stand-alone PV System Based on Fractional-Order PID Controller," *2018 20th Int. Middle East Power Syst. Conf. MEPCON 2018- Proc.*, no. I, pp. 377–382, 2019, doi: 10.1109/MEPCON.2018.8635293.
[75] M. Brenna, F. Foiadelli, M. Longo, and D. Zaninelli, "Energy storage control for dispatching photovoltaic power," *IEEE Trans. Smart Grid* vol. 9, no. 4, pp. 2419–2428, 2018, doi: 10.1109/TSG.2016.2611999.
[76] J. A. Azzolini and M. Tao, "Simulation of a Load-Managing Photovoltaic System," *2018 IEEE 7th World Conference on Photovoltaic Energy Conversion, WCPEC 2018- A Joint Conference of 45th IEEE PVSC, 28th PVSEC and 34th EU PVSEC*, pp. 1158–1162, 2018, doi: 10.1109/PVSC.2018.8547717.
[77] D. Debnath and K. Chatterjee, "Two-stage solar photovoltaic-based stand-alone scheme having battery as energy storage element for rural deployment," *IEEE Trans. Ind. Electron.* vol. 62, no. 7, pp. 4148–4157, 2015, doi: 10.1109/TIE.2014.2379584.
[78] Y. E. Abu Eldahab, N. H. Saad, and A. Zekry, "Enhancing the design of battery charging controllers for photovoltaic systems," *Renew. Sustain. Energy Rev.* vol. 58, no. 2018, pp. 646–655, 2016, doi: 10.1016/j.rser.2015.12.061.
[79] L. An and D. D. C. Lu, "Design of a single-switch DC/DC converter for a PV-battery-powered pump system with PFM+PWM control," *IEEE Trans. Ind. Electron.* vol. 62, no. 2, pp. 910–921, 2015, doi: 10.1109/TIE.2014.2359414.
[80] S. J. Chiang, H. J. Shieh, and M. C. Chen, "Modeling and control of PV charger system with SEPIC converter," *IEEE Trans. Ind. Electron.* vol. 56, no. 11, pp. 4344–4353, 2009, doi: 10.1109/TIE.2008.2005144.

[81] N. Bianchi and M. Dai Pre, "Novel battery charging regulation system for photovoltaic applications," *IEE Proc.-Electric Power Appl.* vol. 150, no. 2, pp. 139–145, 2003, doi: 10.1049/ip-epa:20040219.
[82] S. Alweheshi, A. Abdelali, M. Albarassi, A. Hammoda, and A. Mohamed, "Simulation and hardware implementation of photovoltaic maximum power point tracking system," *5th International Conference on Power Generation Systems and Renewable Energy Technologies, PGSRET 2019*, 2019, doi: 10.1109/PGSRET.2019.8882739.
[83] R. Pradhan and B. Subudhi, "Double integral sliding mode MPPT control of a photovoltaic system," *IEEE Trans. Control Syst. Technol.* vol. 24, no. 1, pp. 285–292, 2016, doi: 10.1109/TCST.2015.2420674.
[84] R. Abid, F. Masmoudi, F. Ben Salem, and N. Derbel, "Design and realisation of a photovoltaic system controlled by the MPPT algorithm," *16th Int. Conf. Sci. Tech. Autom. Control Comput. Eng. STA 2015*, pp. 664–671, 2016, doi: 10.1109/STA.2015.7505121.
[85] S. E. I. Remache, A. Y. Cherif, and K. Barra, "Optimal cascaded predictive control for photovoltaic systems: Application based on predictive emulator," *IET Renewable Power Gen.* vol. 13, no. 15. pp. 2740–2751, 2019, doi: 10.1049/iet-rpg.2019.0068.
[86] A. Gbadega Peter and A. K. Saha, "Effects and performance indicators evaluation of PV array topologies on PV Ations," *Proc. -2019 South. African Univ. Power Eng. Conf. Mechatronics/Pattern Recognit. Assoc. South Africa, SAUPEC/RobMech/PRASA 2019*, pp. 322–327, 2019, doi: 10.1109/RoboMech.2019.8704823.
[87] N. Sy, C. S. Chiu, and W. E. Shao, "Mppt design for a dc stand-Alone solar power system with partial shaded pv modules," *Proceedings of 2019 International Conference on System Science and Engineering, ICSSE 2019*, pp. 31–36, 2019, doi: 10.1109/ICSSE.2019.8823469.
[88] S. De, O. G. Swathika, N. Tewari, A. K. Venkatesan, U. Subramaniam, M. S. Bhaskar, S. Padmanaban, Z. Leonowicz, and M. Mitolo, "Implementation of designed PV integrated controlled converter system," *IEEE Access* vol. 8, pp. 100905–100915, 2020.
[89] P. Sharma, S. P. Duttagupta, and V. Agarwal, "A novel approach for maximum power tracking from curved thin-film solar photovoltaic arrays under changing environmental conditions," *IEEE Trans. Ind. Appl.* vol. 50, no. 6. pp. 4142–4151, 2014, doi: 10.1109/TIA.2014.2322136.
[90] E. Koutroulis and F. Blaabjerg, "A new technique for tracking the global maximum power point of PV arrays operating under partial-shading conditions," *IEEE J. Photovoltaics* vol. 2, no. 2, pp. 184–190, 2012, doi: 10.1109/JPHOTOV.2012.2183578.
[91] N. K. Gupta, A. Kumar Singh, A. D. Thombre, and K. Pal, "Smart solar energy management to power computer lab in rural areas," *3rd Int. Conf. Innov. Appl. Comput. Intell. Power, Energy Control. with their Impact Humanit. CIPECH 2018*, pp. 76–80, 2018, doi: 10.1109/CIPECH.2018.8724133.
[92] S. Abu-Elzait and R. Parkin, "Energy management for a community microgrid in the city of boston," *2019 IEEE Green Energy and Smart Systems Conference, IGESSC 2019*, 2019, doi: 10.1109/IGESSC47875.2019.9042384.
[93] M. Matam and J. Walters, "Data-integrity checks and balances in monitoring of a solar PV system," *Conference Record of the IEEE Photovoltaic Specialists Conference*, pp. 1276–1281, 2019, doi: 10.1109/PVSC40753.2019.8980693.
[94] L. Antonino, L. G. Maria, and R. Martina, "A real-time MCU-based wireless system for PV applications," *2019 AEIT International Annual Conference, AEIT 2019*, 2019, doi: 10.23919/AEIT.2019.8893319.
[95] N. Ngubane and S. Chowdhury, "Performance analysis of a stand-alone solar PV battery system for supplying low voltage rural customers in South Africa," *2019 10th International Renewable Energy Congress, IREC 2019*, 2019, doi: 10.1109/IREC.2019.8754563.

[96] M. K. Barwar, P. R. Tripathi, and P. R. Thakura, "Boost inverter fed three phase induction motor for off grid PV based water pumping system," *Proceedings of the 4th IEEE International Conference on Advances in Electrical and Electronics, Information, Communication and Bio-Informatics, AEEICB 2018*, 2018, doi: 10.1109/AEEICB.2018.8480940.

[97] A. H. Yazdavar, M. A. Azzouz, and E. F. El-Saadany, "Design, modeling and simulation for stand-alone electric vehicle parking lots fed by photovoltaic systems," *2018 IEEE Electrical Power and Energy Conference, EPEC 2018*, 2018, doi: 10.1109/EPEC.2018.8598354.

[98] M. Ali, A. Yousaf, and F. G. Seharan, "Feasibility evaluation of stand-alone photovoltaic systems for residential loads," *2018 9th International Renewable Energy Congress, IREC 2018*. pp. 1–4, 2018, doi: 10.1109/IREC.2018.8362463.

[99] V. Vega-Garita, D. De Lucia, N. Narayan, L. Ramirez-Elizondo, and P. Bauer, "PV-battery integrated module as a solution for off-grid applications in the developing world," *2018 IEEE International Energy Conference, ENERGYCON 2018*, pp. 1–6, 2018, doi: 10.1109/ENERGYCON.2018.8398764.

[100] M. Kolhe, J. C. Joshi, and D. P. Kothari, "Performance analysis of a directly coupled photovoltaic water-pumping system," *IEEE Trans. Energy Convers.* vol. 19, no. 3. pp. 613–618, 2004, doi: 10.1109/TEC.2004.827032.

[101] S. Lee and D. H. Choi, "Energy management of smart home with home appliances, energy storage system and electric vehicle: A hierarchical deep reinforcement learning approach," *Sensors* vol. 20, no. 7, 2020, doi: 10.3390/s20072157.

[102] O. G. Swathika and K. T. M. U. Hemapala, "IoT based energy management system for standalone PV systems," *J. Electr. Eng. Technol.* vol. 14, no.5, pp. 1811–1821, 2019.

[103] X. Wu, X. Hu, S. Moura, X. Yin, and V. Pickert, "Stochastic control of smart home energy management with plug-in electric vehicle battery energy storage and photovoltaic array," *J. Power Sources* vol. 333, pp. 203–212, 2016, doi: 10.1016/j.jpowsour.2016.09.157.

[104] Y. M. Wi, J. U. Lee, and S. K. Joo, "Electric vehicle charging method for smart homes/buildings with a photovoltaic system," *IEEE Trans. Consum. Electron.* vol. 59, no. 2, pp. 323–328, 2013, doi: 10.1109/TCE.2013.6531113.

[105] M. Sechilariu, B. Wang, and F. Locment, "Building integrated photovoltaic system with energy storage and smart grid communication," *IEEE Trans. Ind. Electron.* vol. 60, no. 4, pp. 1607–1618, 2013, doi: 10.1109/TIE.2012.2222852.

[106] N. C. Batista, R. Melício, J. C. O. Matias, and J. P. S. Catalão, "Photovoltaic and wind energy systems monitoring and building/home energy management using ZigBee devices within a smart grid," *Energy* vol. 49, no. 1, pp. 306–315, 2013, doi: 10.1016/j.energy.2012.11.002.

18 Design of a Hybrid Photovoltaic and Battery Energy Storage System Using HOMER Software

J. Nishanthy and S. Charles Raja
Thiagarajar College of Engineering

J. Jeslin Drusila Nesamalar
Kamaraj College of Engineering and Technology

CONTENTS

18.1 INTRODUCTION

The integrating renewable energy source for the purpose of charging is most essential for sustainable development and social development for enhancing the life of individuals in the society [1]. The renewable energy resources are clean and more useful to the consumers while contributing level in benefits of hybrid power system analyzing towards solar, wind, photovoltaic, and other sources evaluated the optimal cost profit of hybrid renewable energy sources and therefore, required to determine the sensitivity analysis based on wind speed, solar radiation, temperature, etc., by using the HOMER software performs. Forecasting by analyzing the techno–economical benefit to be reliable of PV/BESS – diesel of off-grid and hybrid to meet out the load demand with unmet load by ensuring carbon emissions [2,3]. The National Renewable Energy Laboratory's (NREL) HOMER simulation software is used while considering the enhancement of energy demand by using renewable energy sources including wind and solar in stand-alone applications with storage capacity where

DOI: 10.1201/9781003201069-18

excess electricity production process would more reliable [4]. While concerning the environment impact [5], global warming and fossil fuel depletion are the main reason for the Renewable Energy (RE) growth, therefore, hybrid photovoltaic diesel battery system proceeds load demand with low Net Present Cost (NPC) and Levelized Cost of Energy (LCOE) contributes to economic and environmental benefits when using NREL and software HOMER. The evaluation of techno-economic analysis of hybrid PV–diesel battery utilization of electrical energy system to meet out the load and also examined the NPC and cost of energy Cost of Energy (COE) enhanced [6].

This chapter evaluates the cost analysis by the hybrid design of a photovoltaic and battery energy storage system. The demand of energy is growing day by day in the whole world. The renewable energy resources of solar will play an important role in the future. Solar energy contribution significantly increases the primary energy demand to reduce carbon emissions and pollution. The main objective is to maintain the profit utility as more affordable and more efficient in the charging process. The complete energy from solar receives form sunlight supplies energy to the load as well as battery. During peak hours, if the solar energy is unavailable abundantly then the load requirements are met using the battery storage. While to charge AC load from similar working of inverter form battery/charger combines together to supplies energy to the DC load. For charging AC load from similar process of inverter to the battery/charger to supply energy to the load.

18.2 ECONOMIC UTILITY

Evaluate the study of economic utility of the off-grid system simulate the cost and identify the best design of PV system that needs to calculate the life cycle of the cost which is NPC. Therefore, examines all the combinations for the entire system in a single run and determines the least-cost options from base case cost option for the entire systems. Moreover, the profit utility shows to calculate the final simulation evaluate NPC, Internal Rate of Return (IRR), Return on Investment (ROI), and simple payback period. The following process in HOMER software is required to determine the real discount rate from the expected inflation rate and nominal discount.

$$i = i' - f \div 1 + f \tag{18.1}$$

where i is the real discount rate, i' is the nominal discount rate, and f is the expected inflation rate.

TABLE 18.1
Discount Rate

Economic Utility	• Rate (%)
Nominal discount rate	8
Expected inflation rate	3.5
Real discount rate	4.35

As shown in Table 18.1 below, in HOMER to obtain the real discount rate from the net present cost and also the real discount rate is the conversion between one-time costs and Annual costs.

18.2.1 Definition

Net present cost is the measure of economic cash flow project planning analysis into minimum level by the difference into cash income and outcome. **Internal rate of return (IRR)** performs each investment in terms of a rate of return. **The net present** benefits are equal to zero. **The net present** benefits are equal to zero. Therefore, the criteria for the investment to be chosen with the highest rate of return. **Rate of investment** denotes the overall return (annual return) from the project. **Simple payback period** refers to the duration of the years about to get back the cost of the initial investment.

18.2.2 Assumptions

- To assume that the design of hybrid photovoltaic battery energy storage system should be economically reliable when the conventional fossil supply come into the existence.
- Moreover, the cost of electricity should be decreased when compared to on grid and diesel generators energy production costs.
- While considering the battery storage system is highly efficient during power outages and power blackout.

18.3 ENVIRONMENTAL IMPACTS

The solar renewable resources play a vital role by reducing the global warming and fossil fuel depletion. Moreover, the dependency of electricity is inversely proportional to the generation of electricity. Therefore, the total emissions in Madurai are increasing while using conventional sources with complete enhancing in demand extension and CO_2 emission. Therefore, the annual parameters of emission for the city of Madurai during the year 2018 to 2021 are shown in Table 18.2 below, the city has highly utilization of the solar radiation in the energetic criteria is obtained since the power consumption is good and increased due to maximum production of PV generation. HOMER software is performed by giving the requirements of components such as solar, battery and generator parameters. Moreover, the emissions allow for the specify cost penalty associated with a pollutant such as CO_2, particulate matter, SO_2, NO, etc., For example, the cost penalty of emissions in HOMER estimates the emissions level for the designed optimal system for their production of CO_2 emission capacity. Therefore, it is used to determine the emissions penalties for the calculation of emission level in the diesel generator when compared to the solar energy resources.

$$C_{\text{main \& other}} = C_{\text{main \& other}} + C_{\text{cs}} + C_{\text{emissions}} \tag{18.2}$$

As per the above equation, there is a need to calculate cost penalty for emissions to evaluate the environmental benefits. Therefore, the emissions analysis is satisfied

TABLE 18.2
Yearly Emission Level in Madurai

Years	• Transport (t/y)	Residential (t/y)	Industry (t/y)	All Dust (t/y)	Waste Burn (t/y)	DG Sets (t/y)
2018	1800	2195	2250	3250	4810	5350
2019	1900	2188	2300	3360	4825	5480
2020	2000	2170	2325	3500	4836	5640
2021	2100	2160	2450	3700	4850	5950

when the conditions for the constraints system are applicable. HOMER prevents the entire system that does not satisfy the specified constraints and the capacity shortage for the constraint is to calculate the penalty in HOMER.

$$C_{cs} = C_{cs} \,.\, E_{cs} \tag{18.3}$$

18.4 APPLICATION OF HOMER

The software applications are used to design and evaluate technically and economically the options of on-grid and off-grid power systems for monitoring stand-alone and distributed generation applications. HOMER software has been used to perform

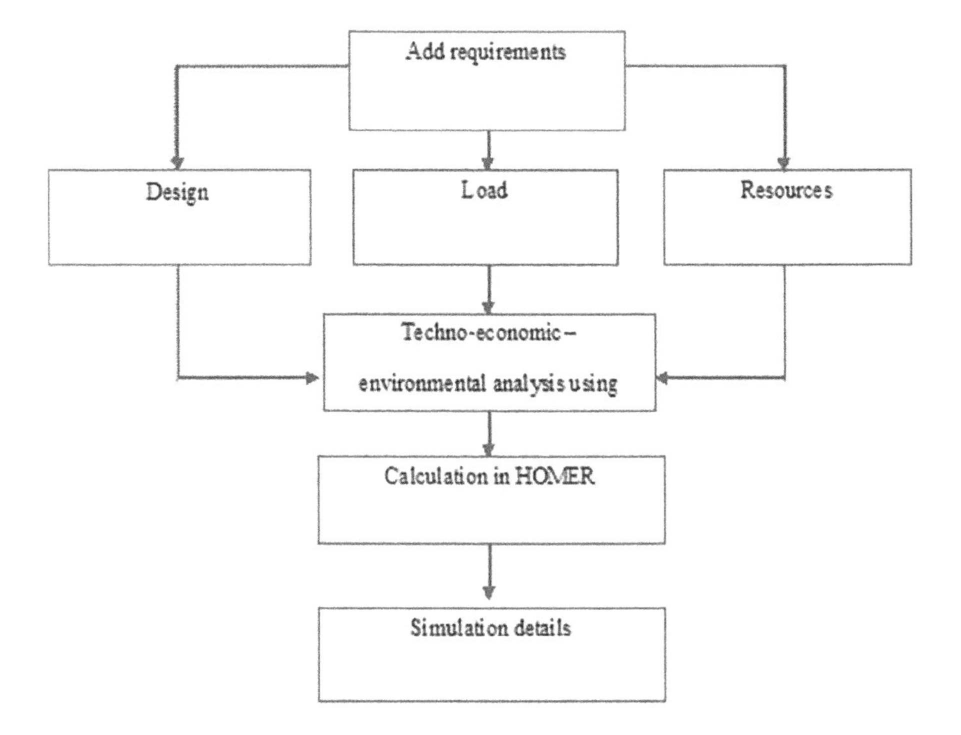

FIGURE 18.1 HOMER process.

the optimization and determine the best configuration. Indeed, HOMER simulates the operation of the considered micro-grid for an entire year, in time steps from 1 minute to 1 hour.

18.5 PERFORMANCE OF HOMER

In Figure 18.1 shows the process of HOMER software for the optimization of the estimated system to be in optimal solution based on the cost effective analysis and environmental benefits. Therefore, in HOMER which requires the input parameters for the design of the solar PV/BESS to optimize including components are generator, the solar PV, battery storage system.

18.6 METRICS FOR DESIGN AND CONSEQUENCE

The design of the solar photovoltaic and battery energy storage system needs the parameters for the proposed system should be given in HOMER for the location of city Madurai and the latitude = 9°53.6′N, longitude = 78°6.4′W. Moreover, the scaled annual average load is 165.44 kWh/day with solar radiation from the sunlight emit is 5.61 kWh/m^2/day, and the solar ambient temperature is at 30°C per day. Indeed, a component denotes the equipment which is a part of the power system. So, the solar photovoltaic of the proposed system is 5 kW with the capacity of single solar PV is Rs. 80,354 at 18% efficiency and the battery capacity is Rs. 14,158 at 88%, and then the inverter capacity of 1 kW is Rs. 60,000. The diesel generator is 5 kW in which fuel price is Rs. 80 per liter and therefore, the evaluation of economic utilities are good and positive which means NPC is Rs. 1, 96,174 of the designed model system and is lower compared to the base case system analysis which is Rs. 3, 07,823 in HOMER tool. Moreover, the IRR is 14%, ROI is 11%, and simple payback period is almost 6 years. Figure 18.2 shows that the vital design of the photovoltaic and battery energy storage system is crucial for economic utility and environmental benefit and the cost analyses

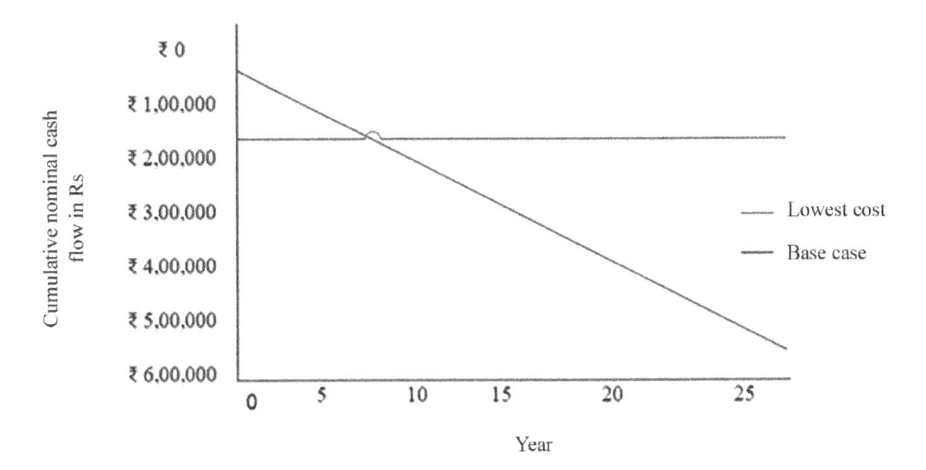

FIGURE 18.2 Nominal cash flow.

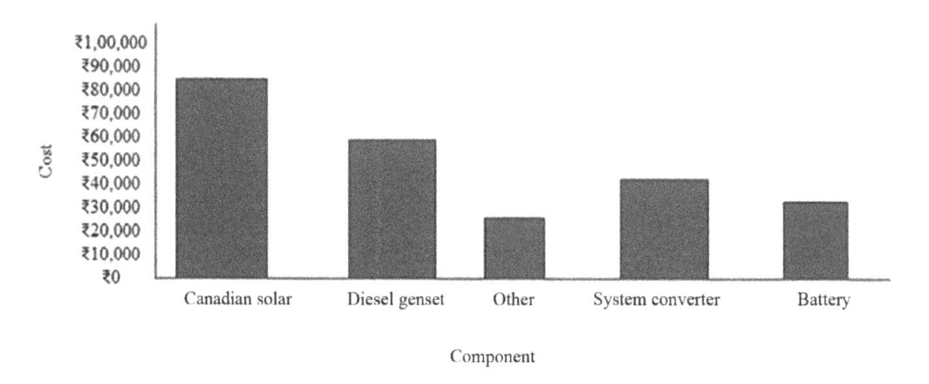

FIGURE 18.3 Life cycle cost.

of the overall system are sustainable and the NPC is lower than base; then, IRR is positive, and ROI is quite good. The life cycle cost of a component is the present value of all the costs of installing and operating the component over the project lifetime.

The annualized cost of a component to be occurred equally in every year of the project lifetime would provide the same net present value of the actual cash flow sequence associated with that component. Figure 18.3 shows the solar PV electrical production of model Canadian solar max power and is 70, 262 kWh per year at 71 % and also the diesel generator energy production is 23,775 kWh per year at 29%. Therefore, the above parameters configures the total production of electrical energy integration of the estimated system is 94,037kWh/year with 100 % which refers the total production is the amount of energy produced by the proposed system per year and also the satisfy AC load consumption is 60,386 kWh per year.

The solar power output capacity using HOMER tool for the proposed designed representation shows that the month of February and March is almost enhanced compared to other months. Moreover, the capacity of the production increases based on the weather forecasting conditions but the production of energy in the city of Madurai is highly utilized. Therefore, the overall renewable power output energy production of the designed system is shown in Figure 18.4, the development and integration of renewable energy systems which helps to reduce the greenhouse gas emissions and particulates matters of emissions from the combustion of fossil fuel from the integrating renewable energy system.

The excess electricity production capacity from the solar renewable sources after it meets out the load is requirement of 6,156 kWh/year is stored in the battery. This is observed when the generator exceeds the minimum output to the load and the battery. It appears when the electrical demand exceeds the supply. For the cost analysis from the simulation details, the energy production, components used, cash flow, and overall emissions are found to be more sustainable and feasible. Therefore, the outcome of the estimated designed system of PV–BESS satisfies the electricity demand and attain the goal of technical analysis economically viable and environmentally reliable based on NPC and COE.

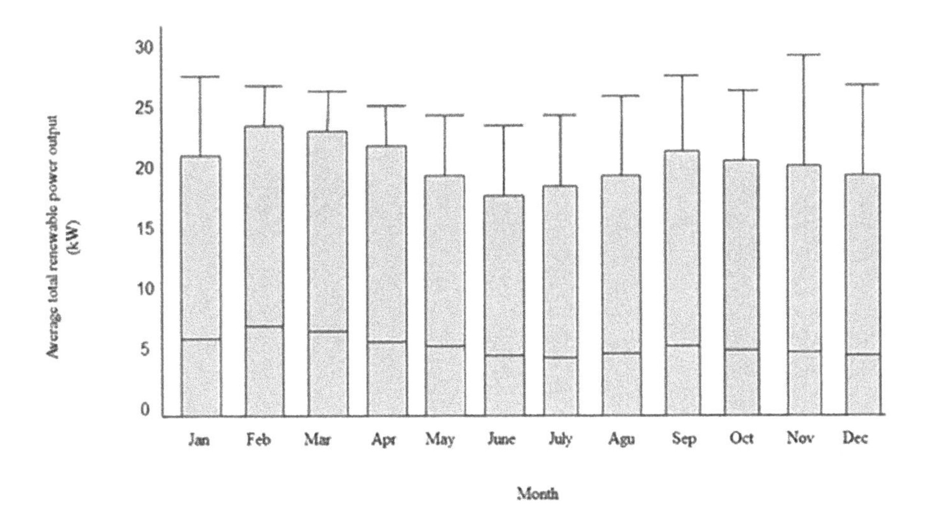

FIGURE 18.4 Total renewable power output.

REFERENCES

[1] KY Lau, MFM Yousof, SNM Arshad, M Anwari, AHM Yatim, "Performance analysis of hybrid photovoltaic/diesel energy system under Malaysian conditions," *Energy* 35, 3245–3255, 2010.

[2] SM Shaahid, MA Elhadidy, "Technical and economic assessment of grid-independent hybrid photovoltaic-diesel-battery power systems for commercial loads in desert environments," *Renewable and Sustainable Energy* 11, 1794–1810, 2007.

[3] SM Shaahid, MA Elhadidy, "Economic analysis of hybrid photovoltaic-diesel-battery power system for residential loads in hot regions–A step to clean future," *Renewable and Sustainable Energy* 12, 488–503, 2008.

[4] SM Shaahid, I El-Amin, "Techno-economic analysis of off-grid hybrid photovoltaic-diesel-battery power system for rural electrification in Saudi Arabia-a way forward for sustainable," *Renewable and Sustainable Energy* 13, 625–633, 2009.

[5] SM Shaahid, LM Al-Hadharmi, MK Rahman, "Review of economic assessment of hybrid photovoltaic-diesel-battery power systems for residential loads for different provinces of Saudi Arabia," *Renewable and Sustainable Energy* 31, 174–181, 2014.

[6] U Sureshkumar, PS Manoharan, APS Ramalakshmi, "Economic cost analysis of hybrid renewable energy system using HOMER," *IEEE - Advances in Engineering, Science and Management*, pp. 174–181, 2012.

19 AI Applications to Renewable Energy – An Analysis

G Naveen Kumar
Andhra Loyola Institute of Engineering and Technology

O.V. Gnana Swathika
Vellore Institute of Technology

CONTENTS

19.1 INTRODUCTION

Renewable energies such as solar and wind are in high demand. There are challenges in the renewable energy sector which need to be addressed. Technologies such as artificial intelligence (AI) are turning out to be an effective scheme for analyzing, predicting, controlling, and monitoring the generation and distribution of electricity generated through renewable energy sources. These applications combined with traditional schemes are now termed smart schemes or smart utilities or smart buildings or smart cities wherever found to be fit. In this chapter, we try to explore and present to readers the role that AI is playing and is yet to play in the upcoming renewable energy sector.

When community-level renewable energy generators are added to the main grid, it becomes difficult to control the operation of energy flow. In this scenario, we could take the help of AI-powered control systems to solve congestion issues in distribution. We can provide improved safety, efficiency, sustainability, and reliability by understanding energy consumption patterns. This reduces energy leakage and theft in the grid.

DOI: 10.1201/9781003201069-19

Also, operators can intelligently adjust the supply and demand. We can develop integrated microgrids using AI. We can build smart control centers. The energy grid in renewable energy can generate data. These data, when coupled with AI, can give new insights to grid operators for better control operations. AI can help us expand the market. Energy storage systems can be improved with new intelligence methods. People have developed techniques that can help reduce failures before they could occur in real time. The way energy is produced and consumed has changed a lot. It is now a well-known fact that Google is using AI to predict power output in wind farms across the United States.

We have tried though not at a large scale but to make a survey and review about how the aforementioned facts have taken shape. A few of these methods are brought together for the reader to understand the increase in demand of AI usage for energy-efficient renewable systems, and also how there is an open ground for electrical and computer engineers to research further to improve the quality of human living and make these technologies available to common people.

19.2 LATEST RESEARCH OF AI IN RENEWABLES

The benefits of renewable energy where it is understood as energy that is sustainable and low in environmental pollution are presented in Ref. [1]. The authors highlighted the efficiency of AI in bulk power distribution, consumption, and its control. It was shown that AI works better compared to data mining and machine learning tools. Two AI-based techniques, namely Polak–Ribiere gradient backpropagation neural networks and gradient with descent adaptive learning rate and momentum backpropagation neural networks, are applied, and a detailed analysis is presented. Polak–Ribiere gradient backpropagation is a prediction method integrated with neural networks. In this work, data were processed using backpropagation standards and optimized using the gradient Polak–Ribiere neural network approach. Also, this is compared with another technique, namely the adaptive learning method with the backpropagation concept for neural networks. The 'backpropagation' concept deals with the goal of minimizing the objective function of a network, which is called a gradient descent approach. Backpropagation is a concept where previous changes in the weights should influence the current direction of movement in weight space.

This will help the scholars to dig into energy prediction analysis for utilities where outlier detection is also possible for energy efficiency. The simulation algorithms presented by the authors in Ref. [1] are not only fast, but also accurate. These AI-based models have achieved reliable and precise predictions for medium-term and long-term load management. Further, it was stated by the authors that these methods can be used for demand-side management, optimal control strategies, peak load prediction, etc.

In solving power supply problems, along with load-side management using renewables, battery is another crucial component that allows storing the excess power generated from renewable energy. The next two reviews are related to battery management in renewables. In Ref. [2], the authors stressed the importance of adopting new energy policies in the wake of increasing consumable energy resources. It was presented that heuristic approaches can be applied to evaluate lead–acid battery for optimal power generation. This was illustrated in a stand-alone hybrid wind–solar renewable power delivery system. Two mathematically modified heuristic methods, namely tuned genetic algorithm and improved colliding body optimization, were illustrated.

In the real coded tuned genetic algorithm, a set of good solutions are selected probabilistically from the firstly initiated random population based on their fitness value that identifies the best solution. As told by the authors, colliding body optimization is a metaheuristic approach where the operation starts with generation of a set of population. The population is divided into two equal groups. Stationary bodies constitute the best ones. Moving bodies constitute the worst ones. After the collision and settlement, the initial velocities are updated by considering the coefficient of restitution. This process continues for finding new positions and updated velocities. Then, based on the fitness function, the best solution is selected. These were illustrated for specific winter and summer load demands in India. It was observed by the authors of Ref. [2] that more optimized power is generated by the renewable distributed energy sources when evaluated by improved colliding body optimization than by the tuned genetic algorithm as they were comparing both approaches. This also resulted in a low average value of state of charge. The low values of state of charge prevent the battery from malfunctioning for a longer period. Also, the authors have carried out parametric studies of modified algorithms, whose results are useful for real-time load profiles. Better results were established in terms of state of charge of the energy storage system. They were obtained by the application of improved colliding body optimization over tuned genetic algorithm. These were about 13% and 17% better than those obtained by the linear programming method. We understand that by parametric variation of heuristic techniques, certain uncertainties and approximations of renewable energy sources can be optimized with accuracy.

In Ref. [3], the authors evaluated the Java 500-kV Indonesian grid for resilient wide-area multi-mode controllers' performance. This analysis was carried out for this grid as it was integrated with renewables. Renewables, such as wind and solar, are unpredictable. This results in power system stability problems when integrated with battery storage. Power electronic schemes control the charging and discharging times of such a battery. In this scenario, the authors successfully verified the bat algorithm to infuse the parameter input to a resilient wide-area multi-mode controller for successfully managing challenges such as power oscillation damping. Bat optimization algorithm is an approach based on the metaheuristic process for global optimization. It was inspired by the echolocation behavior of microbats which was developed by X S Yang in 2010 [4]. Microbats have varying pulse rates of emission and loudness. This is one potential algorithm for scholars exploring worth.

Wave energy is an important source of power generation developed in the recent past. In the work of Ref. [5], two mathematical models based on soft computing techniques for the forecasting of wave energy in the Macaronesian region are exposed. The intelligent systems proposed by the authors for the wave energy prediction are artificial neural networks and fuzzy inference systems. Neural networks are based on the functioning of neurons in human brain, and fuzzy logic is a mathematical process of computing based on degrees of truth rather than true or false in general [6]. These intelligent systems as mentioned by the authors constituted an effective tool in computing the wave power quickly and accurately at any point in oceanic deep waters. Oceanic energies could play a prominent role in renewable energies soon for the enhancement of electric power systems, and as both approaches have achieved satisfactory results, this is a possible topic of research further. As told by the authors of this practical approach being implemented and validated with and by datasets from two different buoys located near the Canary Islands, we see this to be effective.

Weighted-additive fuzzy multi-choice goal programming model for renewable energy site selection is presented in Ref. [7]. The main contribution of this model is its use as an objective function which minimizes the weighted-additive summation of the normalized deviations. The application of the model was also verified using real data. The authors proposed the weighted-additive fuzzy multi-choice goal programming model that includes fuzzy goal programming, multi-choice goal programming, and weighted goal programming forms by taking a novel fuzzy goal programming added with the multi-choice goal programming approach. It was seen that this model has supported empirical decisions of selecting the best location for wind-farm expansion. Since the effect of randomness was unexplored in the above-mentioned empirical case study, we feel that this would be a topic that is worthy enough for researchers to explore further.

Hybrid renewables are being implemented in multiples to make the best benefit of two or more than two renewables at the same time along with conventional power generation schemes. The next two reviews presented are about hybrid renewables. Methods were compared to realize the full potential of one such hybrid nonconventional power system at a lower cost in Ref. [8]. Here, the authors have shown the benefit of applying and comparing three different swarm intelligence methods, namely Jaya, harmony search, and particle swarm. Jaya search is a population-based approach that repeatedly modifies a set of population of individual solutions which is a gradient-free optimization process. Harmony search is a metaheuristic approach where we mimic the improvisation process of musicians for finding a pleasant harmony as a search procedure. Particle swarm is inspired from swarm behavioral intelligence such as bird flocking and schooling in nature [8].

From what the authors have demonstrated, we understood that the AI approaches they characterized led them in zeroing down to one beneficial approach best suited for increasing the efficiency of hybrid renewables. The authors cleared a roadblock for future research in choosing the optimal sizing of hybrid renewables for realizing their full potential at an economic benefit. Also, every utility is moving toward green revolution. So, this literature adds to a step toward reducing environmental pollutants. This work has shown that harmony search has the potential for faster convergence to the optimal solutions and is more efficient.

In Ref. [9], the authors have talked about renewable energy sources being integrated to serve as an autonomous trigeneration-integrated cooling, heating, and power production. Cogeneration process where combining heat and power cycles was already observed and proved to be an effective way of producing heat and power simultaneously. In the recent times, an additional cooling cycle is used which is called as trigeneration concept [10]. This is one of the essential entities in renewables, especially when we are generating electricity through solar collector and biogas [11,12]. It has emerged as a potential source of research where not only benefits of steam generation and power production, but also cooling benefits are added to increase the efficiency of the overall system. Moreover, trigeneration systems are considered for implementation in warmer climates. Hence, this area opens potential area for research including AI and similar approaches combined with it when we want to implement these in warmer climates such as those of India. The contributors for this research developed a simulation model for meeting cooling, heating, and electrical loads using an evolutionary particle swarm optimization approach that we see having a potential for research prospects in this line.

As recorded in Ref. [13], an improved particle swarm optimization has been applied as a master control scheme for controlling the power of the sources in a hybrid, centralized, and distributed renewable energy system consisting of AC/DC microgrids. The power grid simulated and tested consisted of 100 kW PV, fuel cells, and 100 kW wind. This was designed to supply continuous load power. The control strategy is based on interlinking converter control. The authors have satisfactorily demonstrated droop control for both AC and DC microgrids to achieve control of renewable energy and power sharing process. We observe and understand that improved particle swarm optimization is an effective way to study and implement master–slave control for integrated AC and DC microgrids for harnessing maximum power. This area shows a potential area of research with more advanced AI methods replacing the explored approach.

Load scheduling is one of the important concerns considering the uncertainty of power generation in unpredictable renewables such as wind and solar. The modified personal best particle swarm optimization method is presented in Ref. [14] for these types of problems. The authors have applied this approach for renewable generation scheduling in the uncertainty of load scenario. Unlike the authors of Ref. [13], the authors here have concentrated on power sharing optimally in a microgrid for a cogeneration scheme rather than trigeneration scheme. The results demonstrated by the modified personal best particle swarm optimization method were better in comparison with memory-based genetic algorithm, particle swarm optimization with constriction factor, and particle swarm optimization with inertia weight. This research throws light for any researcher to explore a particular intelligence approach to the level of its benchmark for validating their achievements which is very much necessary.

Wind energy is generally an unpredictable quantity. Hence, power production using this source also makes it unreliable. The authors in Ref. [15] have addressed this problem for increasing stable operation of wind farms using combined application of improved dragonfly algorithm and support vector machine. The optimization approach here is improved by introducing the differential evolution strategy and adaptive learning factor in the traditional approach. This improved version is used to decide the optimal parameters necessary to feed in to support vector machine. The importance of mentioning this study is that the research was practically applied to the La Haute Borne wind farm in France. This makes the results 100% accurate for application in real time. The authors proved that this approach is better than Gaussian process regression and backpropagation neural networks. Now, this work can further be explored using other swarm intelligence approaches for practical wind farms in service.

Maximum power point tracking is a method to harness maximum output of a source within its limited availability. This was initially applied for solar energy tracking but later moved to be implemented in other renewables as well. This approach, as applied in two different scenarios, was reviewed and presented here. In Ref. [16], on-time adjustment of a boost converter using modified sine–cosine algorithm was addressed by the corresponding authors. The system for application was a grid connected photovoltaic system which was partially shaded. The maximum power was tracked using the modified sine–cosine approach in comparison with genetic algorithm, particle swarm optimization, grey wolf optimization, moth flame optimization, and sine–cosine algorithm that were already implemented and tabulated for their performance. This was done alongside the perturb-and-observe method, which is a common approach.

In Ref. [17], a continuing study from the same series of publishers, we observed another interesting research where adaptive fuzzy logic was implemented to track maximum power. Here, the approach was applied to boost converter again. This was applied to generate gating pulses of an interleaved soft switching boost converter that is connected to a stand-alone photovoltaic system unlike the grid-integrated one in Ref. [16]. It was observed by the authors of Ref. [17] that the efficiency was improved by 50% with losses due to reduced switching. The short circuit output current has exhibited minimum ripples with an expected open circuit voltage. Now, we see an open ground here as to why not we can implement more such AI methods for tracking solar power in both stand-alone and grid-integrated types of systems under normal and shaded conditions. This can also be implemented in power generation schemes using wind energy if we are correct.

AI can also be combined with other technologies such as embedded systems and Internet of things for better utilization as depicted in Ref. [18]. Here, the authors have developed an Internet of things–AI process to combine and utilize piezoelectric sensor, body to heat convertor, and solar panels for power storage circuit in generation of electrical energy. The contributors of Ref. [18] used an adaptive network-based fuzzy inference system and artificial neural networks for power output predictions. This work shows how different technologies can be combined to gain maximum benefit out of a product.

Biomass is a potential source for energy production [19]. In countries like India, biomass is available in large scale it seems to be a potential source. Also, energy generation through biomass can be considered as an alternative to conventional energy combined with other renewables in the desert arenas, for example, where we find date palm as the primary source of biofuel. This is a very generally known fact. We need to precisely know the calorific value of the biomass from which energy needs to be extracted. We need to estimate the efficiency of steam turbine and generators. We try to highlight how research was conducted in this area for improvements.

In Ref. [20], the researchers have done an analysis to determine the heating value of the date palm biomass using artificial neural networks, especially the multilayer perceptron model. Biogas, generally known as green gas, can be used to generate electricity. So, using AI is something noteworthy here. Agri-based countries in the Asian region have seen a rise in biomass plants. Variations in size, which result in variation of quality of biogas plant boilers, have resulted in some restrictions.

The authors of Ref. [21] have addressed that these restrictions could be overcome using artificial neural networks for them to be operated. This is to cope up with the variation of materials used in biomass that is effecting boilers efficiency. A multilayer perceptron architecture with backpropagation artificial neural networks has been exploited by the authors.

Similarly, in Ref. [22], the use of Internet of things and machine learning for data collection and its analysis to effectively predict the scenario of agricultural biomass that is available for regenerating clean energy has been addressed. Large quantities of leftovers biomass after harvesting, residual matters, etc., cannot be managed usually easily in populated countries like India. Hence, some predictive analysis needs to be made for collection and proper utilization of the same for cleaner energy along with a clean environment. As we limit to a small survey here, we see that there is a

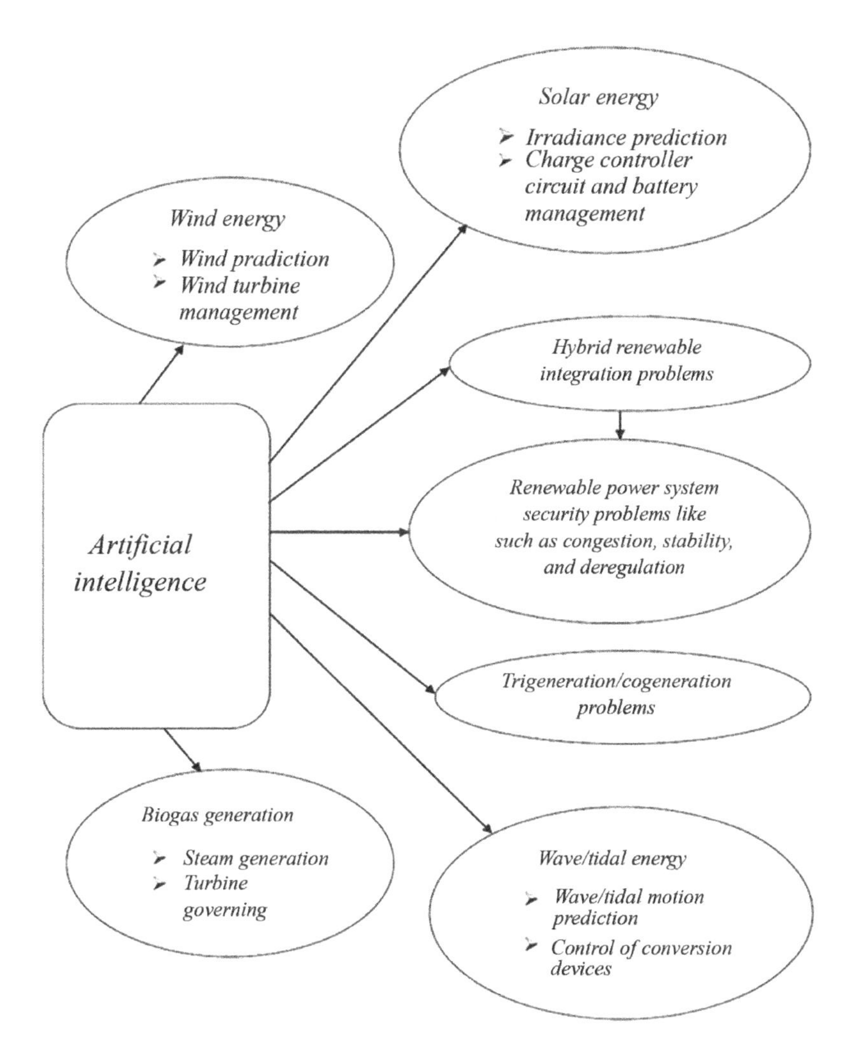

FIGURE 19.1 Possible listing of AI applications to renewables.

potential area of research in this field with the application of different AI methods apart from artificial neural networks that we observed to be applied more to further develop the biomass technology.

19.3 POTENTIAL SCOPE FOR RESEARCH

We have listed different areas of renewables where potential application of AI has been successfully made possible by various researchers. These areas can be explored further, which include wave energy predictions, hybrid renewables that may be standalone or grid-integrated maximum solar energy tracking under general and partial shaded conditions, wind energy harnessing, cogeneration, trigeneration, and biomass energy generation, to mention a few. Apart from this research made in certain energy management applications such as battery and storage device management used for renewable energy generated power, load scheduling for power system stability in renewables was observed.

This review or analysis leads us to one question. What is the potential for doing research in AI applications to renewables? Our answer is a lot. A large scale of AI methods is available which can be taken help of to improve the quality and quantity of power generated from non-conventional energy sources. Also, difficult areas for electrical power management and monitoring such as stability, congestion, deregulation, and battery storage can be resolved.

In Figure 19.1, we have listed a few topics in renewables and integrated renewables that can be explored for improvising the efficiency using AI. The list in practice is an exhaustive one. The readers must understand that this is a possible list but not a limited one.

19.4 CONCLUSION

We are not the first to emphasize the importance of AI to renewables. We have only added to the review literature already existing to throw some light on the need-of-the-hour problems we are facing and the possible solutions many researchers have shown in their work. We have reviewed research articles from recent years to present some interesting points that are noteworthy for readers in a single stand. From the review made, it is understood that there is a huge potential and scope for the application of AI in renewables to improvise the existing schemes to strive further for better solutions. Applications include an add-on to existing methods and technologies of future which can be called smart renewables.

REFERENCES

[1] T. Ahmad, H. Chen, W. A. Shah, "Effective bulk energy consumption control and management for power utilities using artificial intelligence techniques under conventional and renewable energy resources", *International Journal of Electrical Power & Energy Systems* 109, 2019, 242–258.

[2] T. Som, M. Dwivedi, C. Dubey, A. Sharma, "Parametric studies on artificial intelligence techniques for battery SOC management and optimization of renewable power", *Procedia Computer Science* 167, 2020, 353–362.

[3] H. Setiadi, N. Mithulananthan, R. Shah, K. Y. Lee, A. U. Krismanto, "Resilient wide-area multi-mode controller design based on Bat algorithm for power systems with renewable power generation and battery energy storage systems", *IET Generation, Transmission & Distribution* 13, 10, 2019, 1884–1894.
[4] X. S. Yang, "A new metaheuristic bat-inspired algorithm, in: nature inspired cooperative strategies for optimization (NISCO 2010)", *Studies in Computational Intelligence* 284, 65–74.
[5] D. Avila, G. N. Marichal, I. Padron, R. Quiza, A. Hernandez, "Forecasting of wave energy in Canary Islands based on artificial intelligence", *Applied Ocean Research* 101, 2020.
[6] F. J. Pelletier, "Review of metamathematics of fuzzy logics", *The Bulletin of Symbolic Logic* 6, 3, 2014, 342–346.
[7] A. Hocine, Z. Zheng-Yun, N. Kouaissah, L. Der-Chiang, "Weighted-additive fuzzy multi-choice goal programming (WA-FMCGP) for supporting renewable energy site selection decisions", *European Journal of Operational Research* 285, 2, 2020, 642–654.
[8] N. Alshammari, J. Asumadu, "Optimum unit sizing of hybrid renewable energy system utilizing harmony search, Jaya and particle swarm optimization algorithms", *Sustainable Cities and Society* 50, 2020.
[9] A. Lorestani, M. M. Ardehali, "Optimal integration of renewable energy sources for autonomous trigeneration combined cooling, heating and power system based on evolutionary particle swarm optimization algorithm", *Energy* 145, 2018, 839–855.
[10] R. Marwan, L. Chawki, "Review of cogeneration and trigeneration systems", *African Journal of Engineering Research* 6, 2018, 39–54.
[11] S. K. Deb, B. C. Sarma, "Trigeneration solar thermal system", *Procedia Computer Science* 111, 2017, 427–434.
[12] G. Leonzio, "An innovative trigeneration system using biogas as renewable energy", *Chinese Journal of Chemical Engineering* 26, 5, 2018, 1179–1191.
[13] N. H. Saad, A. A. El-Sattar, A. El-Aziz, M. Mansour, "A novel control strategy for grid connected hybrid renewable energy systems using improved particle swarm optimization", *Ain Shams Engineering Journal* 9, 4, 2018, 2195–2214.
[14] K. Gholami, E. Dehnavi, "A modified particle swarm optimization algorithm for scheduling renewable generation in a micro-grid under load uncertainty", *Applied Soft Computing* 78, 2019, 496–514.
[15] L.-L. Li, X. Zhao, M.-L. Tseng, R. R. Tan, "Short-term wind power forecasting based on support vector machine with improved dragonfly algorithm", *Journal of Cleaner Production* 242, 2020.
[16] S. Behera, I. Pattnaik, A. Meher, "MPP tracking of grid- integrated PV system under partial shading using MSCA", *Journal of Institution of Engineers (India), Series B* 101, 4, 2020, 389–395.
[17] M. Mohapatra, A. K. Panda, B. P. Panigrahi, "Real-time implementation of interleaved soft-switching boost converter connected to stand-alone photovoltaic system using adaptive fuzzy MPPT", *Journal of Institution of Engineers (India), Series B* 101, 4, 2020, 397–409.
[18] A. C. Serban, M. D. Lytras, "Artificial intelligence for smart renewable energy sector in europe - smart energy infrastructures for next generation smart cities", *IEEE Access* 8, 2020, 77364–77377.
[19] M. Balat, G. Ayar, "Biomass energy in the world, use of biomass and potential trends", *Energy Sources* 27, 10, 2005, 931–940.
[20] B. Khalida, Z. Mohamed, S. Belaid, H. O. Samir, K. Sobhi, S. Midane, "Prediction of higher heating value HHV of date palm biomass fuel using artificial intelligence method", *8th International Conference on Renewable Energy Research and Applications (ICRERA)*, Brasov, Romania, 2019, pp. 59–62.

[21] C. Pornsing, A. Watanasungsuit, "Steam generating prediction of a biomass boiler using artificial neural network," *2nd International Conference on Control, Automation and Robotics (ICCAR)*, Hong Kong, 2016, pp. 281–284.

[22] P. Mahajan, C. Naik, "Development of Integrated IoT and Machine Learning based data collection and analysis system for the effective prediction of agricultural residue/ biomass availability to regenerate clean energy", *2019 9thInternational Conference on Emerging Trends in Engineering and Technology - Signal and Information Processing (ICETET-SIP-19)*, Nagpur, India, 2019, pp. 1–5.

20 Development of UAV-Based Aerial Observation Platform to Monitor Medium-Voltage Networks in Urban Areas

K.T.M.U. Hemapala and D.H. Ranasinghe
University of Moratuwa

O.V. Gnana Swathika
Vellore Institute of Technology

CONTENTS

DOI: 10.1201/9781003201069-20

20.1 INTRODUCTION

20.1.1 Background

Urban infrastructure systems, such as electricity networks, are the backbone of modern societies. In Sri Lankan context, the electricity network plays the most vital role in ensuring the smooth function of almost all the socioeconomic systems. Not like in rural areas, where the electricity is used mostly for lightning purposes, in urban areas, the efficiency of most of the functions, starting from ventilating the office premises, up to traffic handling and maintaining security systems, depends on the reliability of the electricity network. When it comes to maintaining the reliability of the connection supplied to the end customer, healthy operation of the electricity distribution network plays a key role. Reliability data of Lanka Electricity Company (Pvt) Ltd, one of the power distribution utilities operating in Sri Lankan urban areas, verify the fact. Therefore, the continuous monitoring of the power distribution lines and early identification of faults have become vital requirements. While this consumes a lot of time, effort, and man power, unmanned aerial vehicle (UAV) provides a practical solution for effective and efficient monitoring of the electricity network. Considering the rapid urbanization trends in Sri Lanka and the popularity in commercial adoption of UAV, electricity utilities will be no exception in commercially utilizing UAV in near future. This research focuses on developing such a UAV-based aerial observation platform to monitor medium-voltage electricity network in urban areas.

20.1.1.1 Sri Lankan Distribution Network

The distribution network of Sri Lanka is almost all overhead, operates in medium voltages of 33 and 11 kV and a low voltage of 400/230 V. As a regulator in Sri Lankan energy sector, PUCSL has issued five licenses for electricity distribution in Sri Lanka. Out of these five, CEB has four and one license is issued to LECO. PUCSL has provided guidelines and regulations to the utilities on maintaining quality of supply and set goals on reducing energy losses in the network.

The structure of the country's distribution network has not been changed significantly from its formation in early 50 seconds until recent past. The conventional distribution network included only the typical items such as primary substations, MV feeders, distribution transformers, low-voltage feeders, and protection and metering mechanisms. The power flow was vertically downward from grid substation to the customer premises through primary substation, MV network, distribution transformer, and LV network.

20.1.2 Problem Statement

Feeder line inspection is essential for an electrical distribution utility for operational and maintenance purposes in both planned maintenance and breakdown clearing. In the present situation, this is a manual process with the involvement of human intervention. In addition to the related safety issues, inspection process creates more outage time, which has an impact on distribution utility performance indices.

In practice, tools used in inspection process are very few in distribution networks. Generally, inspection process in Sri Lanka is totally done only by skilled technicians, and very often, HV line gets de-energized during the process. Usually, during this process, the electricity supply is interrupted minimum for 8 hours for a planned maintenance activity.

To make the process of locating the fault effective and accurate, the observation platform should provide clear and real-time statuses of the feeder line. Fault identification has to be faster as much as possible to clear the breakdown in a short time. However, depending on the nature of the fault, it is not detected in the early stages and outage continues until technicians manually check every pole top assembly in the feeder.

Although commercial drones such as remote controlled quadcopters and planes are available to automate inspections and logistical activities in other industries, it is yet to become popular in the electricity distribution network. Substantially high electromagnetic interference in MV distribution lines has critical impacts on radio and electronic controller units and creates challenges in achieving the flying stability in such kind of environment. Therefore, most of the drone project has failed to fulfill economic feasibility to automate inspection process.

20.1.3 Objectives of the Study

To develop hardware platform to perform aerial inspection in urban medium-voltage distribution feeders with the following features:

- Capability to handle in highly congested areas
- Easy detection of faults
- Reduce human intervention and improve safety of inspection operation

20.1.4 Motivation

This research enables to improve the effectiveness of MV line inspection process while improving the human safety as it minimizes the human movement closer to energized equipment.

- Reduce outage time
- Reduce time to investigate defects
- Provide aerial view and a convenient platform to monitor pole top accessories
- Highlight abnormal spots on equipment
- Study the demand elasticity with tariff revisions
- Reduce human intervention and improve safety of inspection process by providing remote operation

If updated information about the customers and relevant load profiles is available in the databases, the above activities can be implemented by the utility.

20.1.5 Methodology

Major activities of this research can be ordered as follows:

- Literature survey/background study
  - Investigating the work that has been already carried out under MV line inspection.
  - Identifying the most optimum method for medium-scale urban distribution MV lines.
- Developing the platform for aerial imaging and identifying faults
- Field testing
- Reporting

20.2 LITERATURE REVIEW

The overhead MV electrical feeders have become the link between modern industrial and urban communities. Maintenance, breakdowns, and services are often in service for these power lines as suggested in Figures 20.1 and 20.2.

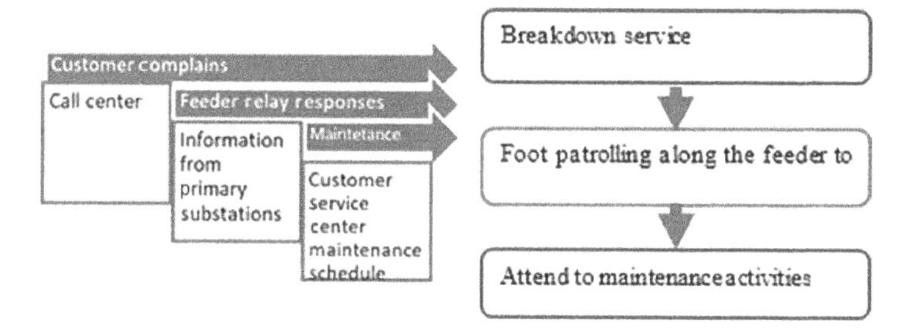

FIGURE 20.1 Flowchart of the maintenance process.

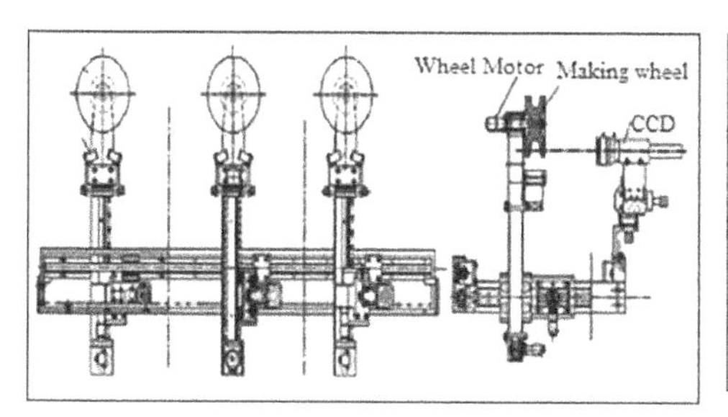

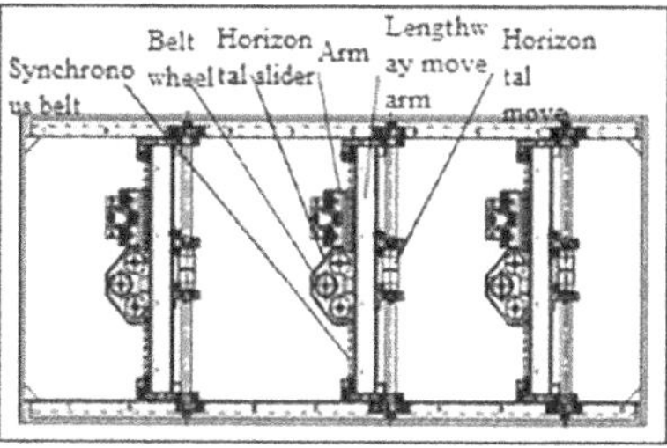

FIGURE 20.2 Front, left, and platform views of the robust chart.

Commonly used current inspection methods are people online method, telescope, and using a helicopter for inspections. As these methods take time and effort a lot, different innovations have been carried out in order to overcome those difficulties over the tower due to the complex of the structure and control. A mobile robot design is created and developed for overhead power line inspection and a control to avoid obstacles which is composed of three suspended arms along with the 03 rolling wheel machine which is coordinated with each other, 03 nodes CAN bus system and use of a camera system which can transmit images with wireless CCD. The walking module structure over an obstacle is designed in three axles with the idea of modulation and has three arms which are connected to moving three hanging axles. This consists of moving structure, horizontal and vertical flex arms, and horizontal moving structure. The walking structure consists of movable wheel, driving motor with hinges, and fix-up bracket. Control system design and implementation have been carried out on three-phase bare conductor lines and grounding cables on tower. In this design, three suspension arms have been fixed in order to fasten the frame by the steering gear. The upright flexible arm along with the horizontal flex arm is fixed perpendicularly [1]. In this design, vertical arms are used to move the machines break away or move up along the conductor cables, while the horizontal flexible arm is used to connect vertical arms and move machine along the plane. The plane moving body has pinion and rack steering gear and guide, driving upright and horizontal flex arms by rolling bearing [1]. This makes easy for the three flex arms to move separately along X, Y, and Z directions. Therefore, the robot can move over obstacles along the conductor pathway. Optical sensors and touch sensors that are mounted on the right and the left of each flex arm help in detecting obstacles. These sensors detect obstacles at a 10 cm distance, although the driving motor, which is connected to walking wheel, slows down to stop when touch sensors detect obstacles in the front. In the design and implementation stage, the object that has been selected is a suspension tower, not a strain tower, which consists of a three-phase electrical line and grounding wire cable on the tower. As described in Figure 20.3, the obstacles on the electrical lines are split clapboards with intervals of 10–20 m. The obstacle near the electrical tower is wire clip hanging on suspension insulator string, and wire clip and vibration damper are the obstacles seen in the grounding wire. As implemented here, the robot can walk over these obstacles, which is indicated with wire clip 3 and vibration dampers (1, 2, 4, and 5) where suspension tower is of rating 220–500 kV. As shown in Figure 20.4, the robot is moving where it can move along the suspension line, which contains three obstacles with the same size. This robot takes the size that is larger than the two obstacles. The intervals between the obstacles can accommodate two moving wheels of the robot. The system electric design system has modules in both online and downline. The online module consists of CCD optic imaging and wireless image emission along with three-node wireless controlling and a battery for the CAN bus. The downline module has a wireless receiving unit and an image processing section, a battery unit, and a controlling system (Figure 20.5).

Broken strands, bulk shares, surface corrosions, and conductor splits can be detected from the CCD camera, which has been used to identify those surface geometric failures of conductors and optical cable. The images were transmitted online and received and processed by receiving ground station control machine. This system replaces the current inspection method and detecting method of using telescope by manpower along a wire.

This robot designed for overhead power line inspection can save a lot of labor and increases the detection efficiency and accuracy. Even though this is a successful method to walk through the suspended line and use optical sensors and touch sensors to detect obstacles, the MV distribution line design of LECO, in the current context, has post insulators with cross-arms. Therefore, with the development of this methodology, the robot structure will be bulky and heavy for these line designs.

The lines are always operated at an extreme level, and there are no reserves or any other termination process to compensate breakdowns. Protective maintenance is therefore of extreme importance. High-voltage networks usually running across

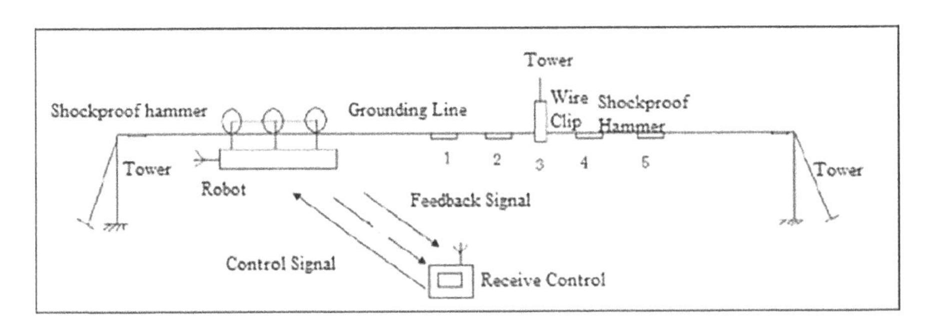

FIGURE 20.3 Placement of the robot over obstacle.

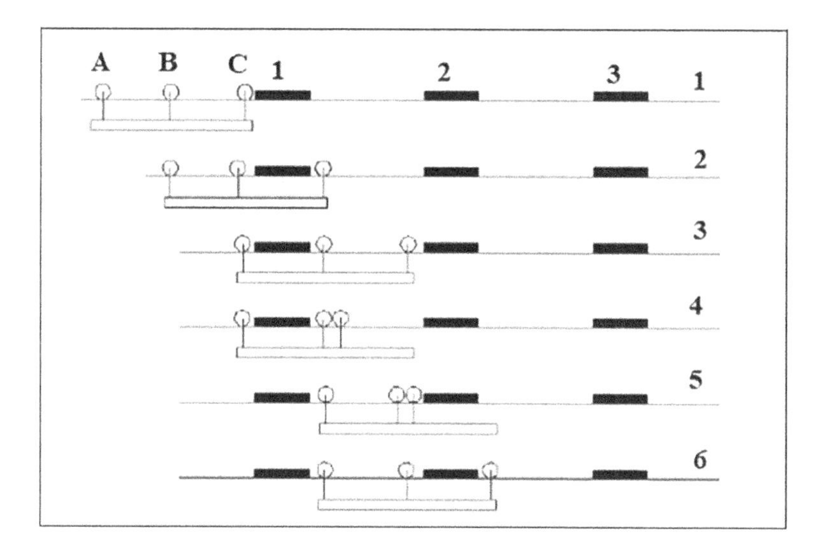

FIGURE 20.4 State chart of robot pace over obstacle.

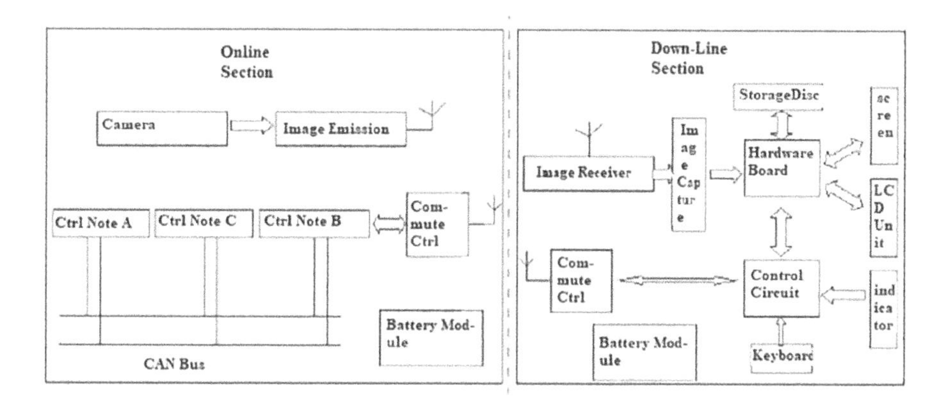

FIGURE 20.5 Electrical system of robot.

suburban environments, forest, mountains, and coastal areas are often exposed for a long period to vigorous working conditions such as thermal excursions, heavy rain, wind-induced vibration, and heavy temperatures. These extreme climatic events vulnerable for corrosion and other failures induce fatigue ruptures, which reduce the life span of the lines, and it gives high losses to the company.

Addressing the stated problems, a state-of-art solution is presented for two main categories of robots offering a solution of automation (Table 20.1). There are [2]

TABLE 20.1
Comparison of Robot Categories

Method	Advantages	Disadvantages
Rolling-on-Wire robots (line-following robots/line scouts)  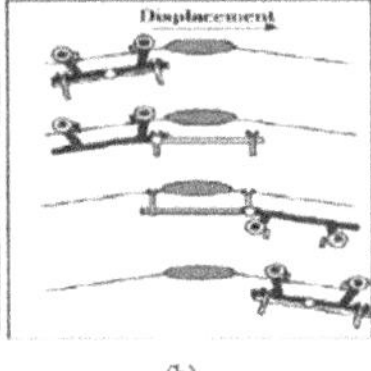 (a) (b) Line-following robots	• Operate very close to conductors and therefore can detect conductor faults • Can cross damper spheres, corona rings, double insulator rings, etc. • Usually carry weights up to 100 kg • Not limited to a specific distance between adjacent obstacles	• Crossing dead-end assemblies and post insulators are not considered • Slow operation due to significant time taken to avoid obstacle • Radial imaging is not possible in order to inspect line assemblies • High installation time on cables prior operation (approximately 2 hours) • Not good for short span lines on post insulators
VTOL heavy-weight UAVs (unman commercial helicopters)   (a) (b) Unmanned commercial helicopters	• Imaging is possible in wide operational range • Fuel-operated UAVs have high flight time • Microturbine-powered UAVs can carry around 12 kg • Can carry specified sensors such as corona probes and HD cameras Thermal images as both power and weight can be tolerated	• High cost of operation • Need a skilled pilot to operate the UAV • Cannot get closer to power line accessories.
VTOL lightweight UAVs (small-scale multirotors)	• Low cost of operation • Image processing and feature tracking are possible • High mobility • Easy to deploy	• Low payload (<2 kg) • Flight time constraints • Power source issues • Cannot get closer to power line accessories. • EMI on electronic and RF communication

- Vertical takeoff and landing (VTOL)
- Unmanned aerial vehicles (UVAs)
- Rolling-on-Wire robots (RWR)

This research creates a simple roadmap that can guide researchers and industries in the implementation of a live line power line inspection. This is based on a completely autonomous mobile platform that consists of the following:

- Compatible payload
- Power line data management system

which includes specific tool for image and signal data processing to automatically detect defects and other abnormal conditions. This is to create a reliable electrical power supply system and at the same time to reduce the cost and time.

The main categories of power line inspection robots, such as VTOL, UAVs, and RWR, consumed different robotic technologies and operating systems, which have been developed through time. Advantages and disadvantages of these categories are as follows [2]:

In the above assignment, the main fundamental was to develop a data management system including specific tool for image and signal data processing to automatically detect defects or abnormal conditions. These automated systems are capable to elaborate all the data stored that give an essential additional value to optimize the advantages making further difference with respect to the traditional inspection methods [2].

Even though these technologies were developed to maintain a better power supply system, in the current context, the LECO MV distribution line designs have short spans of about 35–40 m and conductors are placed on post insulators and cost for the above operations will be high. Addressing these problems, a small-scale multirotor (quadcopter) will be sufficient as the aerial platform in designing.

These multirotor projects dedicated to completely autonomous inspection of power line are still an emerging technology, which needs further improvements for better concrete results. Projects that are considered in particular specific constraints for a completely autonomous live line inspection can be seen in different areas. Visual surveying supports power line tracking, obstacle detection, and avoidance (especially during a crash in live line, this is important for a reliable autonomous inspection system). Robust control algorithms for flight dynamics ensure a very high stability and positioning capability for close and precise inspections in case of adverse weather conditions like strong lateral wind and rain [2]. Thus, automated systems are more advantageous than the traditional system. A theoretical development study is carried out on takeoff constraint thrust equation for a drone or a multirotor and the results with Web simulation were validated. These theory equations are useful for the drone application in the extra feature design during the fly, which consists of a camera, thermal sensor, wireless sensor, and other sensor application [3–6]. A drone consists of a pair of diagonal propeller, which rotates clockwise, while another pair will rotate counterclockwise. This movement helps in controlling the direction and achieving the movement of the drone. A quadcopter requires a gyroscope, Global

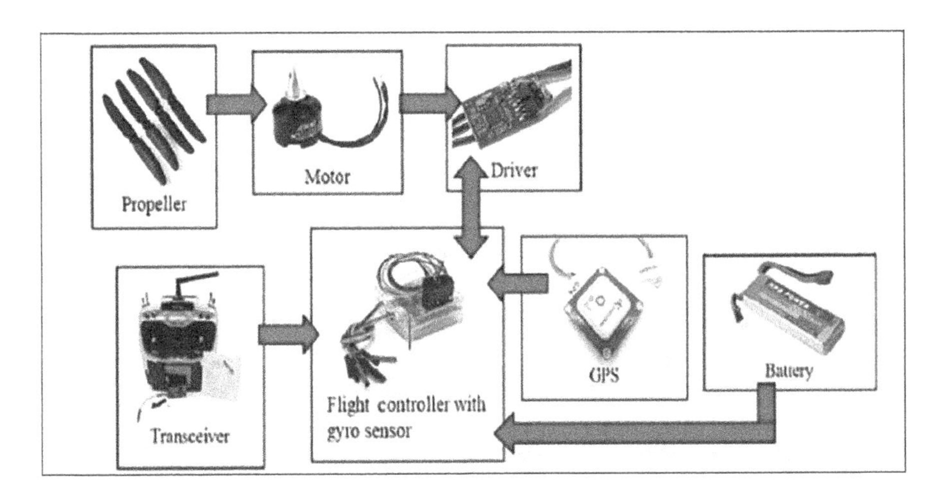

FIGURE 20.6 Setup of fundamental components.

Positioning System (GPS), flight controller, transceiver, motor speed driver, flight controller, LiPo battery, brushless DC motor, propeller, and quadcopter airframe. The fundamental components of a drone setup are as in Figure 20.6.

20.3 DESIGN AND DEVELOPMENT

The design component of the research was cascaded into two sections in order to identify abnormalities in the network components and development of a quadcopter drone, respectively.

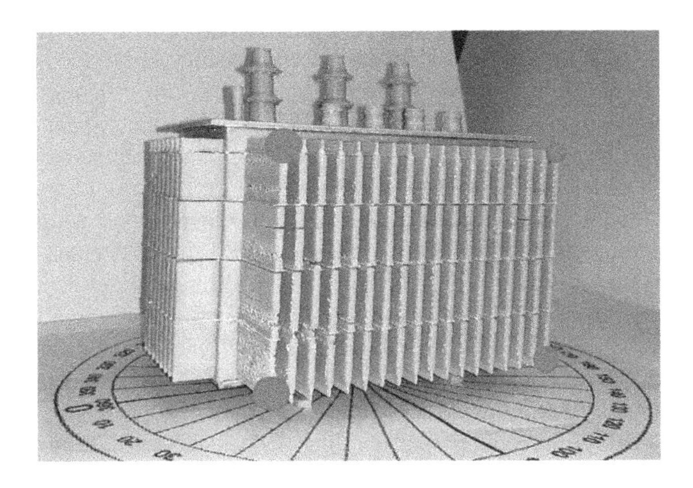

FIGURE 20.7 Model transformer used in algorithm.

20.3.1 Fault Identification

a. Identification of reference points

It is required to identify the particular area for further processing with reference to the predetermined demarcations of an equipment. In order to develop this algorithm, a model transformer is selected as in Figure 20.7. The reference points are considered as red points (RGB: 273, 70, 75) as of the used model. In practical conditions, predetermined demarcations in the transformer can be considered as the references.

1. The image matrices are cascaded to three 2D matrices for each color property as in Figure 20.8. The corresponding value is subtracted from each color plane. When the 2D matrices are combined together to regenerate the image again, the intensity level of reference points becomes close to zero, and therefore, these points become black spots.

b. Identifying Location of Referenced Points

The grayscale image of the previous image was obtained by adding intensities of all color plains together.

$$g(x,y) = \sum_{x=1}^{n} \sum_{y=1}^{m} \left(\text{RedPlan}(x,y) + \text{GreenPlan}(x,y) + \text{BluePlan}(x,y) \right)$$

As the intensity of the reference points in all color plains is close to zero, it will appear as black patches in the grayscale image as in Figure 20.9.

FIGURE 20.8 Differentiation of reference color from background.

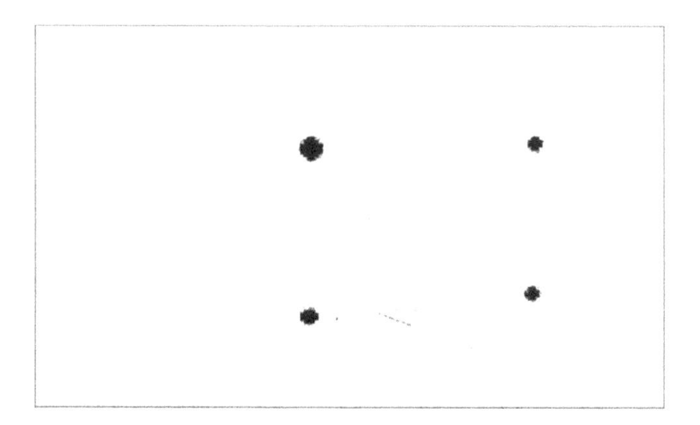

FIGURE 20.9 Image after filtering reference points from the background.

2. Removing the noise in the grayscale image
   During the image transformation process, some registers related to pixels' values overflow and become empty due to matrix operations. This becomes a noise in the image, and it could negatively impact the accuracy of the calculations. Impulse noise, shot noise, spike noise, and dropout noise can be categorized as salt (white pixels) and pepper (black pixels), which usually create bigger impact comparing to other types of noises. There are many methods to eliminate these salt and paper noises, and depending on the requirement of high-speed image processing, the median filter is used. The median filter replaces the pixel value with the median value of the adjacent pixels. This function is usually a 3×3 kernel, which moves from first to last pixels while eliminating the noises. The kernel operator (T[]) could be any size, and the elements could be weighted forward or backward if necessary.

Kernel

T[] =

1/9	1/9	1/9
1/9	1/9	1/9
1/9	1/9	1/9

Kernel Operation

Image matrix (V) T[V]

1	5	4
2	100	12
11	3	16

T[] →

	17	

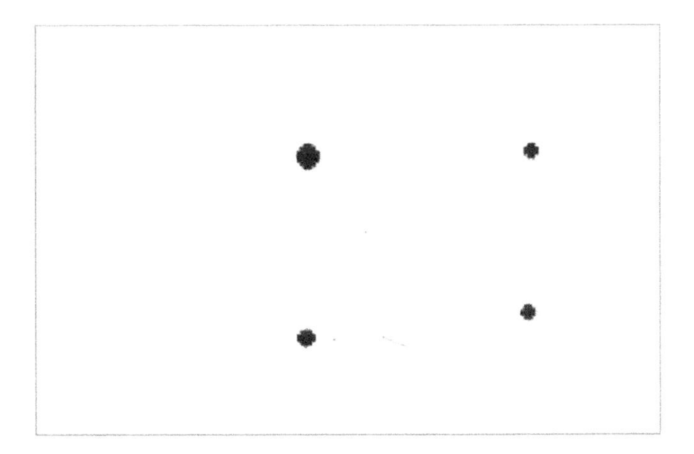

FIGURE 20.10 Image after filtering noise pixels (high-pass filter).

Therefore, low-frequency pixels in the image are eliminated by moving the kernel through the grayscale image as in Figure 20.10.

$$g\text{Average}(x, y) = \sum_{x=1}^{n}\sum_{y=1}^{n}\left(\begin{pmatrix} g(x,y)+g(x+1,y+1)+g(x,y+1)+g(x-1,y+1)+ \\ g(x+1,y)+g(x,y)+g(x-1,y)+g(x+1,y-1)+ \\ g(x,y-1)+g(x-1,y-1) \end{pmatrix}/9\right)$$

Depending on the required level of accuracy, this operation can be done several times using the same kernel or different kernels. Owing to the nature of the grayscale images used for the project, the same kernel was used in repeat operations for five times.

$$g\text{Average}(x, y) = \sum_{R=1}^{5}\sum_{x=1}^{n}\sum_{y=1}^{n}\begin{pmatrix} g(x,y)+g(x+1,y+1)+g(x,y+1)+ \\ g(x-1,y-1)+g(x+1,y)+g(x,y)+ \\ g(x-1,y)+g(x+1,y-1)+g(x,y-1)+g(x-1,y-1) \end{pmatrix}/9$$

As the image is clearly separated with black and white pixels, the location of the reference points can be obtained by identifying the gravity of the black pixels in each section of image. The inverse of the picture gives the exact location of the most significant pixels, and location of these significant pixels is calculated.

Generally, the object is captured covering more than 80% of the background, and reference points of the object are placed in each quadrant of the image as shown in Figure 20.11. Therefore, coordinates of reference points in each quadrant are calculated.

Image matrix $= g(m, n)$

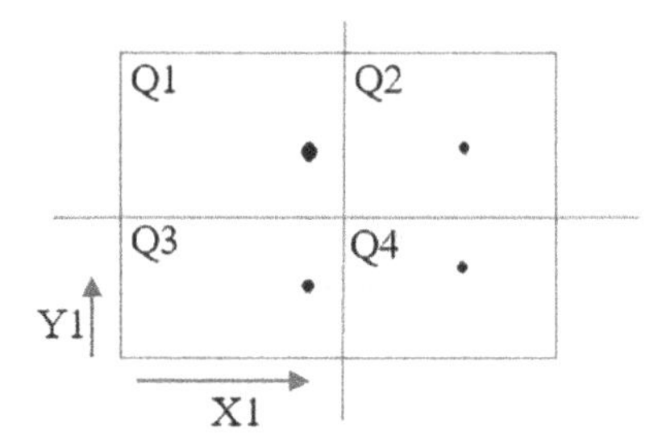

FIGURE 20.11 Reference points in each quadrant.

$$Q1 = g\left[0;\frac{m}{2},\frac{n}{2}:n\right] \qquad Q2 = g\left[\frac{m}{2}:m,\frac{n}{2}:n\right]$$

$$Q3 = g\left[0:\frac{m}{2}0,\frac{n}{2}\right] \quad Q4 = g\left[\frac{m}{2}:m,0,\frac{n}{2}\right]$$

$$\text{inverse image metrix}\left(\widehat{g}(m,n)\right) = 255 - g(m,n)$$

Coordinates of the reference point in Q3 are

$$X_1 = \frac{\sum_{j=1}^{n/2}\left(\left(\sum_{i=1}^{m/2}\widehat{g}(i,j)\right)\times j\right)}{\sum_{j=1}^{n/2}\sum_{i=1}^{m/2}\widehat{g}(i,j)}$$

Likewise, Y_1 also can be expressed as

$$Y_1 = \frac{\sum_{i=1}^{m/2}\left(\left(\sum_{j=1}^{n/2}\widehat{g}(i,j)\right)\times i\right)}{\sum_{j=1}^{n/2}\sum_{i=1}^{m/2}\widehat{g}(i,j)}$$

Therefore, the reference points in the model transformer are obtained as tabulated as in Table 20.2. These coordinates are calculated in each frame, and algorithm execution speed directly impacts on the frame rate for image capturing as in Figure 20.12.

TABLE 20.2
Coordinates of the Reference Points in Model Transformer

Reference Points	X-Coordinate	Y-Coordinate
(x1,y1)	488	928
(x2,y2)	482	1888
(x3,y3)	1162	1881
(x4,y4)	1225	925

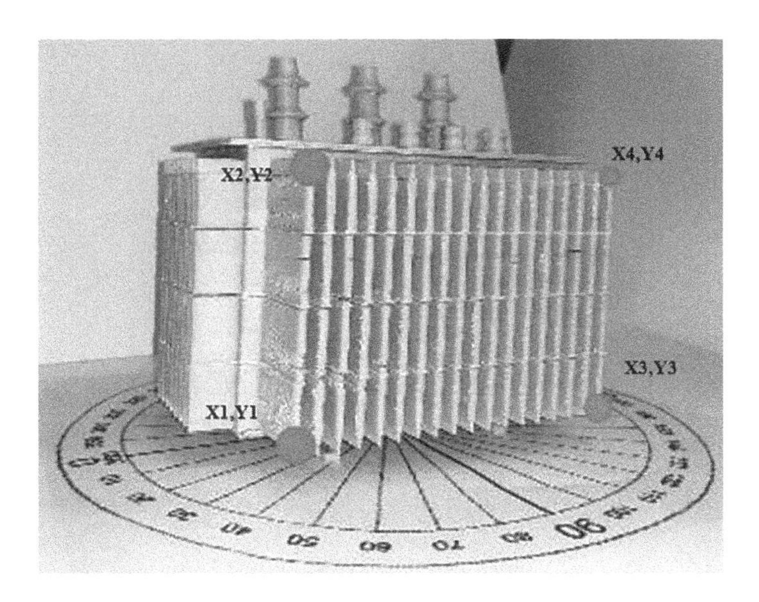

FIGURE 20.12 Coordinates of the reference points in model transformer.

20.3.1.1 Correction of Object Perspective due to Different Capturing Angle

When processing images to identify the faults, it is important to isolate the relevant object from the background, which is captured in the frame. Although the shape and the size of this object are known, it becomes difficult to filter this object out of the image background if it is oriented in a different angle. Owing to the nature of the drone imaging, this angle of orientation changes from image to image. The practical difficulties in the field are vegetation obstacles, flight protocols, and safety clearance regulations, and it is not possible to always capture images of the objects in the same favorable direction. But orientation has to be identical in order to analyze the comparison with reference images.

20.3.1.1.1 Approach

The capturing angle of the image can be considered as a rotated image of the 3D object of the equipment. As the reference points of the equipment are known, coordinates of the original equipment boundaries of the front elevation of the image can be obtained using 3D coordinate transformation method.

In general, the conversion effect on a 2D or 3D object does not change the shape or the size of the object but varies from a simple change in location and to a uniform change in scale. Ultimately, changes in shape and size triggers varying degrees of nonlinearity. Therefore, Helmert transformation is used to obtain the coordinates of corrected reference points (DEAKIN, 1998).

20.3.1.1.2 Helmert Transformation

$$\begin{bmatrix} x' \\ y' \\ z' \end{bmatrix} = \lambda R_{K\phi\omega} \begin{bmatrix} X \\ Y \\ Z \end{bmatrix} + \begin{bmatrix} R \\ P \\ Q \end{bmatrix}$$

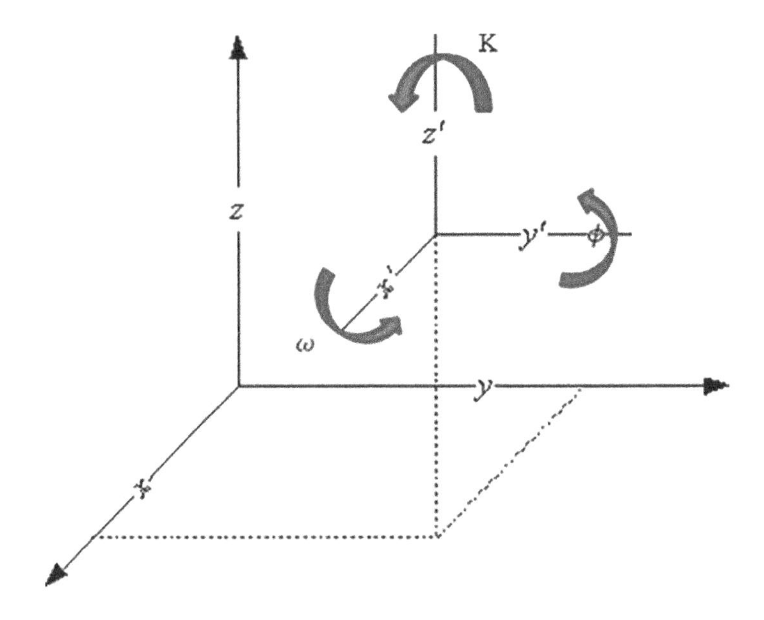

FIGURE 20.13 Axis of rotation.

where $R_{K\phi\omega}$ is a rotation matrix (the product of rotations ω, φ, and K about the X, Y, and Z axes in turn) as in Figure 20.13.

Considering the nature of matrix, $R_{K\phi\omega}$, it is not possible to solve directly the each rotation of K,ϕ, and ω axis. Therefore, first the equation is derived for a transformation between two planes as in Figure 20.14.

Gaussian complex expression of the transformation from two planes can be denoted by

$$y + ix = f(\chi + i\omega)$$

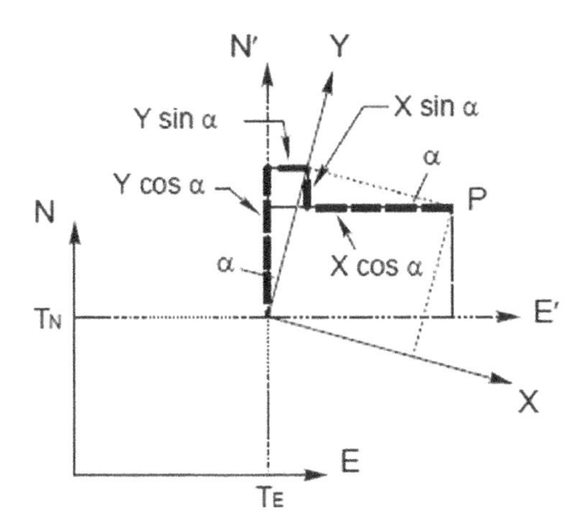

FIGURE 20.14 Rotation over 2D plane.

Here, i is a complex number and $f(\chi + i\omega)$ is analytic function and parameters X and Y are the dimensions of the object. If the function is analytic, it is a necessary condition to satisfy the Cauchy–Riemann equation. Then, it is also considered as a polynomial function, and therefore, the function can be represented as

$$y' + \mathrm{i}x' = \sum_{k=0}^{n} (a_k + ib_k)(Y + iX)^k$$

for the condition $k = 1$ equating the real and imaginary parts

$$y' = a_0 + a_1 Y - b_1 X$$

$$x' = b_0 + a_1 X + b_1 Y$$

This equation is represented by a matrix

$$\begin{bmatrix} y' \\ x' \end{bmatrix} = \begin{bmatrix} a_1 & -b_1 \\ b_1 & a_1 \end{bmatrix} \begin{bmatrix} Y \\ X \end{bmatrix} + \begin{bmatrix} b_0 \\ a_0 \end{bmatrix}$$

where a_0 and b_0 are considered as the transformation of the origin, and b_1 is considered as function of scale factor and rotation angle between coordinate axes.

$$a_1 = \lambda \cos \alpha$$

$$b_1 = \lambda \sin \alpha$$

Therefore, transformation in 2D can be represented by scaling factor and rotational angle as follows:

$$\begin{bmatrix} y' \\ x' \end{bmatrix} = \lambda \begin{bmatrix} \cos \alpha & -\sin \alpha \\ \sin \alpha & \cos \alpha \end{bmatrix} \begin{bmatrix} Y \\ X \end{bmatrix} + \begin{bmatrix} b_0 \\ a_0 \end{bmatrix}$$

The rotational matrix (R_α) for 2D plane,

$$R_\alpha = \begin{bmatrix} \cos \alpha & -\sin \alpha \\ \sin \alpha & \cos \alpha \end{bmatrix}$$

20.3.1.1.3 Transformation in 3D Axis

A 3D transformation can be considered as three subsequent transformations between 2D planes.

Step 1

Rotation of ω about X-axis changes Y and Z to y' and z' with X-axis to x'. Coordinates of the new system will be given by

$$\begin{bmatrix} x' \\ y' \\ z' \end{bmatrix} = \left[\underbrace{\begin{matrix} 1 & 0 & 0 \\ 0 & \cos\omega & \sin\omega \\ 0 & -\sin\omega & \cos\omega \end{matrix}}_{R_\omega} \right] \begin{bmatrix} X \\ Y \\ Z \end{bmatrix}$$

Step 2

Transformation of x', y', z' system to x'', y'', z'' system with the rotation of ϕ about new y' axis.

$$\begin{bmatrix} x'' \\ y'' \\ z'' \end{bmatrix} = \left[\underbrace{\begin{matrix} \cos\phi & 0 & -\sin\phi \\ 0 & 1 & 0 \\ \sin\phi & 0 & \cos\phi \end{matrix}}_{R_\phi} \right] \begin{bmatrix} x' \\ y' \\ z' \end{bmatrix}$$

Step 3

Transformation of x'', y'', z'' system to x''', y''', z''' system with the rotation of Đ about new z'' axis.

$$\begin{bmatrix} x''' \\ y''' \\ z''' \end{bmatrix} = \left[\underbrace{\begin{matrix} \cos \mathrm{K} & \sin K & 0 \\ -\sin K & \cos K & 0 \\ \sin\phi & 0 & 1 \end{matrix}}_{R_K} \right] \begin{bmatrix} x'' \\ y'' \\ z'' \end{bmatrix}$$

Therefore, 3D rotational matrix can be obtained by multiplying co-efficient matrices of the above three steps.

$$\begin{bmatrix} x''' \\ y''' \\ z''' \end{bmatrix} = R_\omega \quad R_\phi \quad R_K \begin{bmatrix} X \\ Y \\ X \end{bmatrix}$$

Rotational matrix for 3D transformation,

$$R_{\omega\phi K} = R_\omega R_\phi R_K = \begin{bmatrix} C_\phi C_K & C_\omega S_K + S_\omega S_\phi C_K & S_\omega S_K - C_\omega S_\phi C_K \\ -C_\varphi S_K & C_\omega C_K - S_\omega S_\phi C_K & S_\omega C_K + C_\omega S_\phi S_K \\ S_\phi & -S_\omega C_\phi & C_\omega C_\phi \end{bmatrix}$$

20.3.1.1.4 Obtaining the Parameters to Transform Images

Quadcopter is designed to always operate in a leveled position to minimize the rolling angle due to the nature of its flight dynamics as in Figure 20.15. Therefore, the rotation around *Z*-axis is negligible and can be considered as zero. Rotation over X-axis (ω) depends on the drone flying height and type of the observation and detail

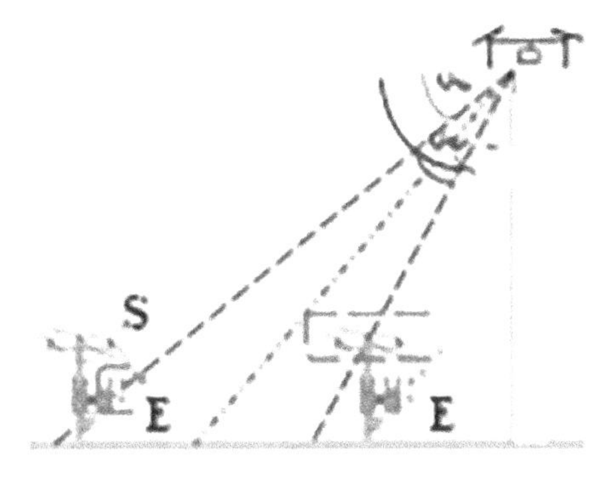

FIGURE 20.15 Orientation of the capturing angle in the space.

requirements. With respect to the below image, if the drone is used to monitor top part of assembles such as cable preforms and top section of insulators, it is required to increase camera angle and keep the drone at higher position (ωB). When it is used to monitor lower elements such as transformer components and cross-arm fittings, the camera angle will be low (ωA), and the flying height will be kept at lower level.

In this case study, the drone will be used to monitor transformer components and it will be kept at the same level as the transformer while keeping the camera at horizontal position. Therefore, the rotation over X-axis (ω) is very minimal and can be neglected.

Owing to the restrictions in flying regulations and other obstacles, it is almost impossible to keep the drone straight to the object while avoiding roads and pedestrian ways in urban areas. Hence, images were taken at angle and the object has rotation over Y-axis as φ.

20.3.1.1.5 Obtaining the Correct Rotational Angle over Y-Axis (Φ) to Correct the Given Image

As described in the section, for designing the platform, the rotational angles of three axes of the drone are continuously monitored to perform the flight as in Figure 20.16. Yaw angle is measured by an accurate, high-speed compass in order to obtain the drone orientation with respect to the north pole. These real-time data are received to the ground station via the telemetry unit, and this can be used to calculate the image rotational angle over Y-axis. Similarly, the rotation of drone around X-axis is depicted in Figure 20.17.

During the initial takeoff, drone is kept in the same orientation as the object, and therefore, any rotation in Y-axis during the flight is represented by the difference in

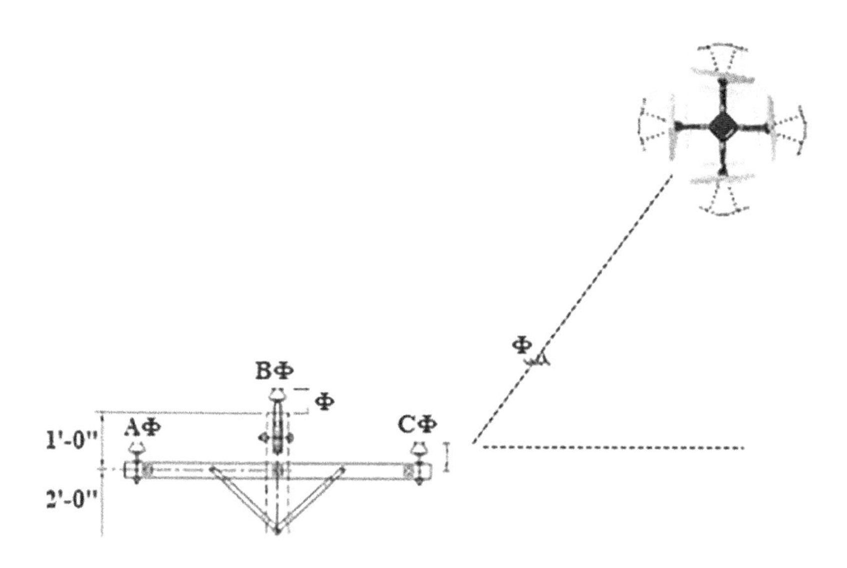

FIGURE 20.16 Rotation over Y-axis graph.

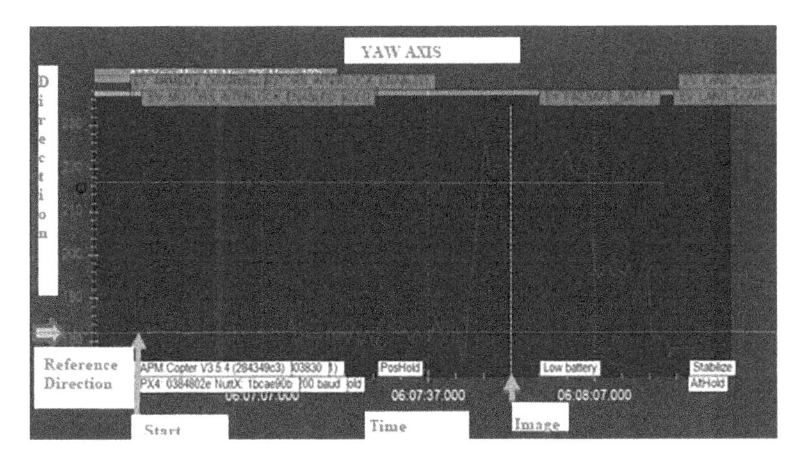

FIGURE 20.17 Rotation of the drone around X-axis.

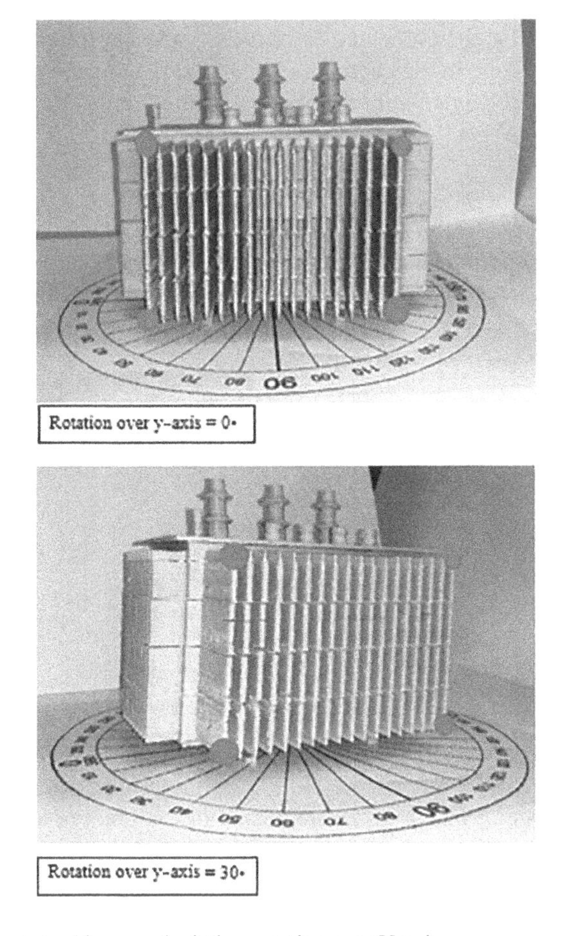

FIGURE 20.18 Actual images depicting rotation over Y-axis.

3D point cloud for object

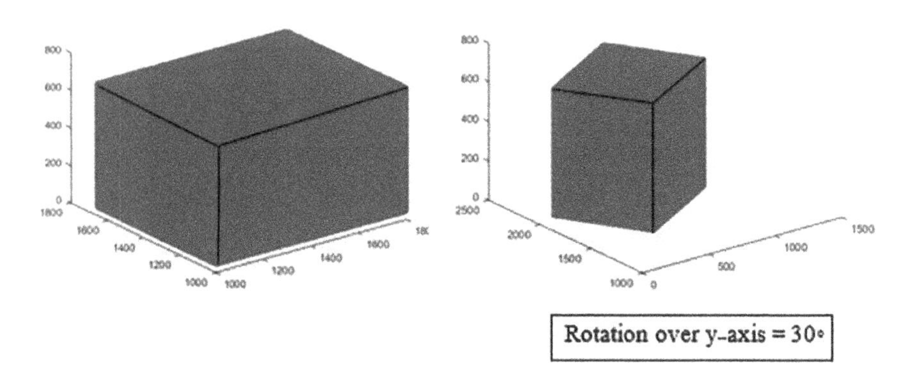

FIGURE 20.19 3D model for rotation over Y-axis.

the yaw angle. Usually, the drone and camera are started at the same time, and the time domain is the same in the captured images and data received from the drone. Hence, the rotation in Y-axis for an image as in Figure 20.18, which is taken at time "t," can be obtained as φA.

20.3.1.1.6 Filtering Object from Image Background

As the location and the size of the object are known from Methodology 01, it is possible to create a 3D point cloud for the same object as in Figure 20.19. The closet reference point ($x1$,$y1$) is considered as the origin of 3D point cloud object, and the dimensions are taken as proportional to the height of the object in the captured image ($x1$,$y1$ and $x2$,$y2$).

20.3.1.1.7 Base Image for Algorithm

Rotational matrix R for $k=0$, $\omega=0$, and $\varphi=30$.

$$R=\begin{bmatrix} 0.8660 & 0 & 0.5000 \\ 0 & 1.00000 & 0 \\ -0.5000 & 0 & 0.8660 \end{bmatrix}$$

Rotated point cloud $= R\ x\ M^T$

20.3.1.1.8 X-Z Plane View of the Object

This projection of the rotated 3D cloud plane is projected X-Z plane as the captured image in 2D plane is shown in Figure 20.20. Superimposing the projection on X-Z plane with the captured image gives the details of the object excluding the background data.

20.3.1.1.9 Filtered Image after Processing

Filtered image after processing is shown in Figure 20.21.

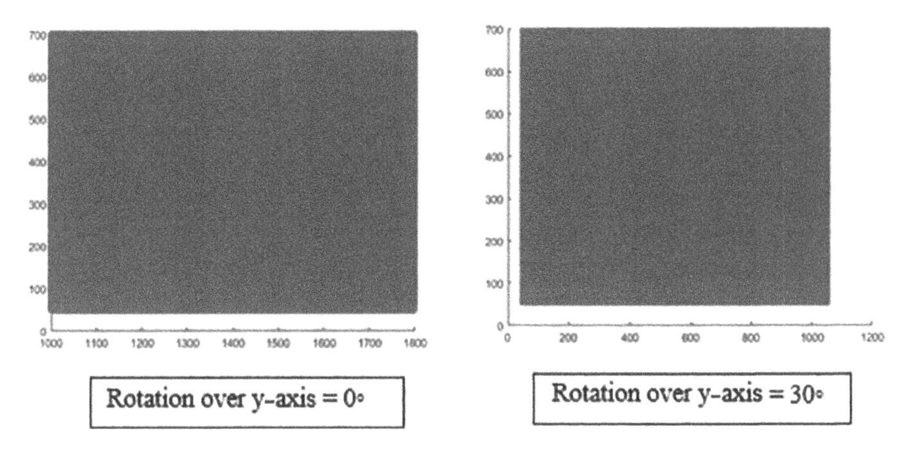

FIGURE 20.20 Projection of 3D object on X-Z plane.

FIGURE 20.21 Filtered image after processing.

20.3.1.2 Pattern Recognition

After isolating specific areas of the object as per the above steps, the specific visible fault can be located through recognizing pixel patterns. As the first step, the image can be broken down into three planes such as most significant bit plane (MSB plane), center bit plane, and least significant bit plane (LSB plane). Categorizing an image into these planes can help to easily identify the major pixels, which contributes identical color patches in the picture (Arefin).

Bit plane slicing eliminates noise in the image

$$\text{Bit plane k} = \text{Remainder}\left\{\frac{1}{2}\text{floor}\left[\frac{1}{2^{k-1}}\text{Im age}\right]\right\}$$

Slicing is done to identify the most significant and least significant bit planes for analysis.

$$\begin{matrix} 6 & 7 & 6 & 6 & 7 \\ 0 & 0 & 0 & 1 & 2 \\ 1 & 1 & 1 & 2 & 3 \\ 4 & 5 & 5 & 4 & 2 \\ 6 & 6 & 6 & 7 & 7 \end{matrix} \Rightarrow \underset{\text{MSB plane}}{\begin{matrix} 1 & 1 & 1 & 1 & 1 \\ 0 & 0 & 0 & 0 & 0 \\ 0 & 0 & 0 & 0 & 0 \\ 1 & 1 & 1 & 1 & 0 \\ 1 & 1 & 1 & 1 & 1 \end{matrix}} \quad \underset{\text{Centre bit plane}}{\begin{matrix} 1 & 1 & 1 & 1 & 1 \\ 0 & 0 & 0 & 0 & 1 \\ 0 & 0 & 0 & 1 & 1 \\ 0 & 0 & 0 & 0 & 1 \\ 1 & 1 & 1 & 1 & 1 \end{matrix}} \quad \underset{\text{LSB plane}}{\begin{matrix} 0 & 1 & 0 & 0 & 1 \\ 0 & 0 & 0 & 1 & 0 \\ 1 & 1 & 1 & 0 & 1 \\ 0 & 1 & 1 & 0 & 0 \\ 0 & 0 & 0 & 1 & 1 \end{matrix}}$$

As an advantage of segregating the image using bit planes, the algorithms can do the analysis faster. Therefore, this methodology can be used to process live streaming data in order to analyze the image on time.

20.3.1.3 Pattern Clustering

20.3.1.3.1 Hough Transform

The Hough transform is a dominant tool to find straight lines and functions hidden in pixel clusters. This technique is widely used in image processing as a prominent method to find straight lines. In order to detect lines, the pixels in the image are initially binarized using some thresholding method and then the positive instances are cataloged in an example dataset.

20.3.1.3.2 Basic Functions

Small radius range is defined for better accuracy.

$$\text{Range: rmax} < 3 * \text{rmin and } (\text{rmax-rmin}) < 100$$

The accuracy of function increases when the value of radius is larger than 5.

Both computation methods, "phase code" and "two stage," are limited in their ability to detect concentric circles. The results for concentric circles can vary depending on the input image.

Clustering function does not find circles with centers outside the domain of the image. It preprocesses images in binary (logical) patterns to improve the result accuracy. In order to do so, the function automatically converts the true color image to grayscale before processing them.

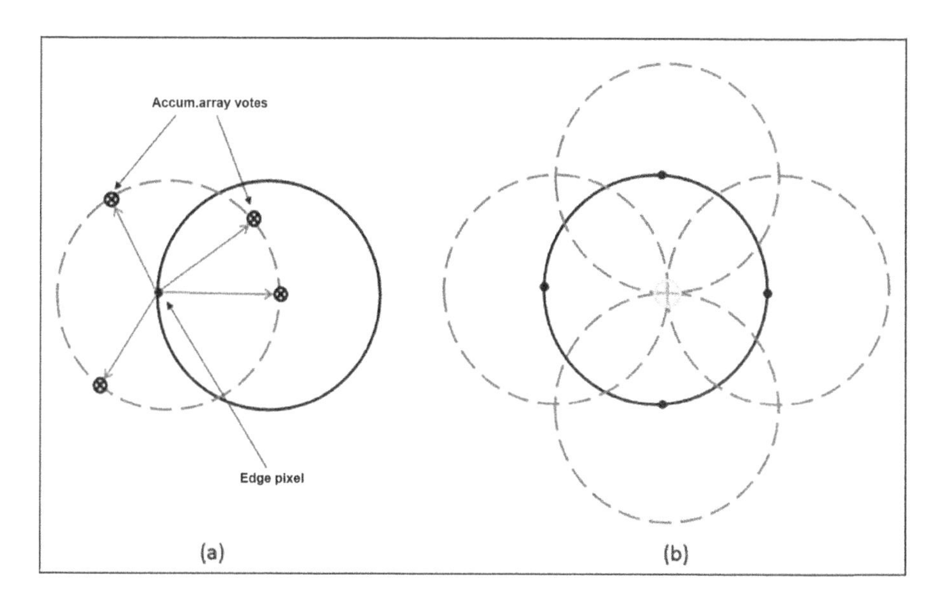

FIGURE 20.22 Circular Hough transform.

20.3.1.3.3 Algorithms

Clustering function uses a circular Hough transform (CHT)-based algorithm for finding circles in images as shown in Figure 20.22. This approach is used because of its robustness in the presence of noise, occlusion, and varying illumination.

20.3.1.3.4 Classical CHT Voting Pattern

The pixels belonging to an image circle tend to gather at the accumulator array according to the circle's center. Therefore, the circle centers are predicted by detecting the peaks in the accumulator array.

20.3.2 Development of the Quadcopter

The drone has been designed to inspect energized HV lines and pole top accessories as a remote aerial inspection platform. Due to high magnetizing issues in the MV lines in the distribution networks, this drone is designed to fly stable close to the energized HV power lines by eliminating other stability issues in the commercial drones.

20.3.2.1 Design Inputs

Lifting capacity: 500 g; flying time: 10 minutes; maximum speed: 10 m/s; and size (approximately): 500×500 mm.

20.3.2.2 Design Calculations

The balance of a quadcopter frame is achieved by adjusting the angular velocities of the rotors, which are spun by four electric motors as in Figure 20.23. It has six degrees of freedom in both translational and rotational directions, which are controlled by those four independent motor signals. In order to achieve such mobility,

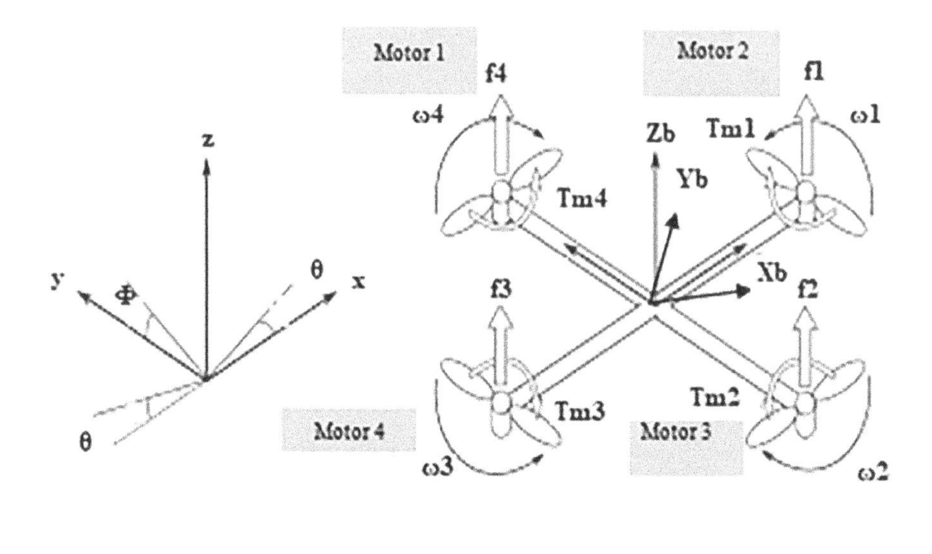

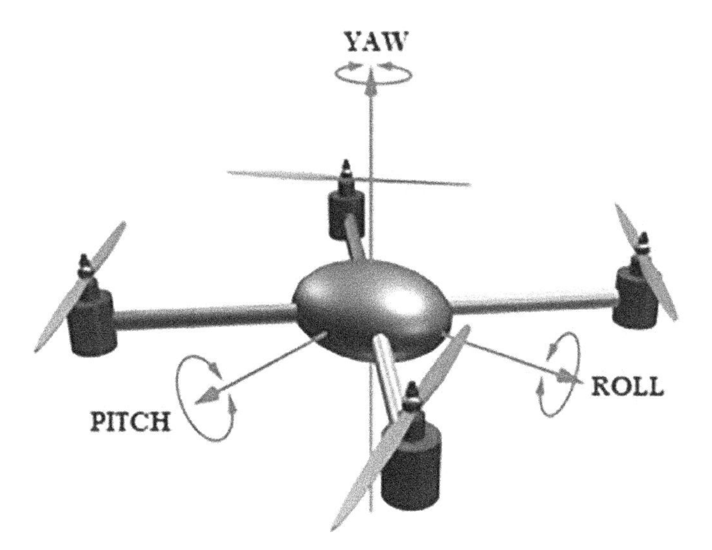

FIGURE 20.23 Inertial and body frames of a quadcopter.

rotational motion and translational motion are coupled. The resulting dynamics are highly nonlinear, especially after accounting for the complicated aerodynamic effects. Unlike ground vehicles, quadcopters have very little friction to prevent their motion. Therefore, during the flight, quadcopters must have their own damping in order to stop moving and remain stable.

When the quadcopter motors spin propellers, it generates a torque that affects the quadcopter's body in the opposite direction. Hence, if all motors rotate in the same direction, the resulting force will continuously turn the quadcopter in one direction. In order to counterpart this torque effect, two of the motors are designed to rotate in the opposite direction. Torques are balanced if all propellers are spinning at the same rate. Therefore, the speed difference in the motor pairs, which rotate in the same direction, will create a resultant torque on the quadcopter body. This mechanism is used to rotate quadcopter in the horizontal plane, and this is called yaw of the quadcopter.

The spinning propellers create a thrust on the quadcopter body, and when the resultant force ($f1+f2+f3+f4$) exceeds overall weight, it starts moving upward. This process is used to change the altitude of the quadcopter during the flight, and this is called as throttling. While the quadcopter is leveled at the horizontal plane, the resultant force (z_B) will be parallel to the gravitational force. When the quadcopter is banked at any particular direction, the resultant force (z_B) will create an additional horizontal force component, which will make the frame to drift in that particular direction. This principle is used to move quadcopter forward, backward, and side to side, which is called pitching and rolling, respectively. The entire quadcopter dynamics is achieved by controlling motor pairs in different combinations as in the below diagram, and the remote controller has four principle servo signals dedicated for this purpose as in Figure 20.24.

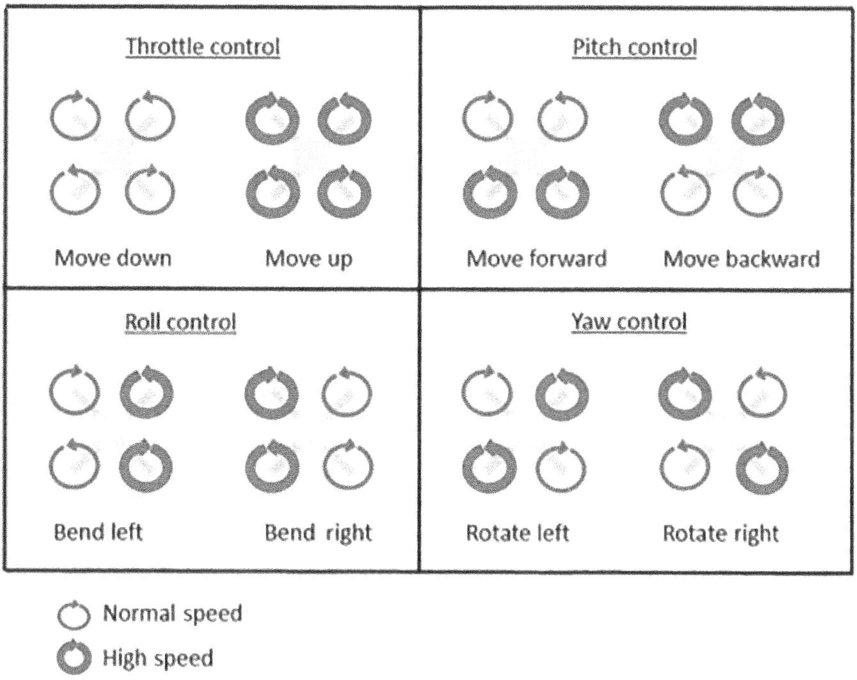

FIGURE 20.24 Quadcopter movements.

20.3.2.3 Kinematics

The position and the velocity of the quadcopter in the inertial frame are considered as $x = (x, y, z)^T$ and $\dot{x} = (\dot{x}, \dot{y}, \dot{z})^T$, respectively. Similarly, the roll, pitch, and yaw angles in the body frames are defined as $\theta = (\phi, \theta, \varphi)^T$ with corresponding angular velocity equal to $\dot{\theta} = (\dot{\phi}, \dot{\theta}, \dot{\varphi})^T$. The vector of the angular velocity () is pointing along the axis of rotation, whereas $\dot{\theta}$ gives the time derivatives of roll, pitch, and yaw axis. Therefore, the relationship can be obtained from trigonometry calculation as follows:

$$\omega = \begin{bmatrix} 1 & 0 & -\sin\theta \\ 0 & \cos\phi & \cos\theta, \sin\phi \\ 0 & -\cos\phi & \cos\theta, \cos\phi \end{bmatrix} \dot{\theta}$$

In order to relate body frame movements in the inertial frame, matrix R can be used, which is defined as follows:

$$R = \begin{bmatrix} \cos\phi.\cos\varphi - \cos\theta.\sin\phi.\sin\varphi & -\cos\varphi.\cos\phi - \cos\phi.\cos\theta.\sin\varphi & \sin\theta.\sin\varphi \\ \cos\theta.\cos\varphi.\sin\phi + \cos\phi.\sin\varphi & \cos\phi.\cos\theta.\cos\varphi - \sin\phi.\sin\varphi & -\cos\varphi.\sin\theta \\ \sin\phi.\sin\theta & \cos\phi.\sin\theta & \cos\theta \end{bmatrix}$$

Using this conversion matrix, vector in body frame is reflected by $R\vec{v}$ vector in the inertial frame.

20.3.2.4 Electrical Forces (Motors)

The torque () produced in the electric motors is given by

$$\tau = K_t (I - I_0)$$

where K_t, I, and I_0 is denoted by torque proportionality constant, input current, and the no load current, respectively. The voltage across the motor () is sum of the back EMF () $(K_v \omega)$ and resistive loss (IR_m), where R_m is the motor resistance, and K_v is a proportionality constant (back EMF generated per RPM) and is angular velocity of the motor.

$$V = IR_m + K_v \omega$$

Therefore, power of the motor (P) is derived from

$$P = VI = \frac{(\tau + K_t I_0)(K_t I_0 R_M + \tau R_m + K_t K_v \omega)}{K_t^2}$$

Assuming the motor resistance as negligible, power becomes proportional to the angular velocity.

$$P \approx \frac{(\tau + K_t I_0) K_v \omega}{K_t}$$

In practical situations, no load torque is >>very minimal, and therefore, $(\tau + K_t I_0)$ can be assumed as.

Hence,

$$P \approx \frac{K_v}{K_t} \tau_\omega$$

20.3.2.5 Aerodynamic Forces

By the law of conservation of energy, the power exerted from the motors is used to keep the quadcopter loitering in the air. The energy that motors spend in a specific time period is the force exerted on the propellers multiplied by the displacement distance of the air it moves.

$$P = F \frac{dx}{dt}$$

Therefore, power is equal to the trust (T) time air velocity (v_n)

$$P = T v_n$$

At an equilibrium point of the quadcopter in the mid-air, air velocity can be considered as function of thrust as follows:

$$\psi_n = \sqrt{\frac{T}{2\rho A}}$$

where ρ is the density of the surrounding air and A is the area swept by the rotor. Therefore, the power (P) can be simplified as follows:

$$P = \frac{K_v}{K_t} \tau\omega = \frac{K_v K_\tau}{K_t} T\omega = \frac{T^{\frac{3}{2}}}{\sqrt{2\rho A}}$$

Generally, torque is equal to the cross product of force into the distance vectors, and in quadcopter aerodynamic calculations, it is proportional to the thrust. The ratio (K_τ) is determined by the propeller parameters and the blade configuration. The trust is proportional to the square of angular speed.

$$T = \left(\frac{K_v K_\tau \sqrt{2\rho A}}{K_t} \omega \right)^2 = k\omega^2$$

where k is a constant. Considering all four motors, the total trust of the quadcopter (on body frame) is derived from

$$T_B = \sum_{i=1}^{4} T_i = k \begin{bmatrix} 0 \\ 0 \\ \sum \omega_i^2 \end{bmatrix}$$

The additional force on the quadcopter body due to fluid friction is considered as

$$F_D = \begin{bmatrix} -k_d \dot{x} \\ -k_d \dot{y} \\ -k_d \dot{z} \end{bmatrix}$$

The drag equation from fluid dynamics is derived as

$$F_D = \frac{1}{2} \rho C_D A v^2$$

where ρ is the surrounding fluid density, C_D is dimensional constant, and A is the propeller cross-sectional area. This implies that the torque due to drag (R) is given as a function of A where the radius of the propeller ($C_D \rho$) is given as follows:

$$\tau_D = \frac{1}{2} R \rho C_D A v^2 = \frac{1}{2} R \rho C_D A (\omega R)^2 = b \omega^2$$

where C_D is defined as some appropriate dimensional constant.

The complete torque about the Z-axis is the sum of the torque due to drag and the product of moment of inertia (I_M) and angular acceleration ($\dot{\omega}$).

$$\tau_z = b \omega^2 + I_M \dot{\omega}$$

In the steady-state flight (with no vertical movement of the quadcopter in mid-air), the propellers are spinning at a nearly constant speed, and therefore, torque due to inertial acceleration can be considered as negligible. Therefore, in the steady-state flight, the torque about the Z-axis of the ith motor is derived as

$$\tau_z = (-1)^{i+1} b \omega_i^2$$

As half of the motors are spinning in the opposite direction, term $(-1)^{i+1}$ becomes positive for the ith propeller which is spinning in the clockwise and it becomes negative if it is spinning in the counterclockwise direction. Considering all the motors, the total torque (τ_φ) on the quadcopter body is given by

$$\tau_\varphi = b\left(\omega_1^2 - \omega_2^2 + \omega_3^2 - \omega_4^2\right)$$

The roll and the pitch torques are derived from the same standard mechanism. As shown in "Figures 20.3–20.17: Quadcopter Movements," the roll axis movement identically controls motor pairs 1 and 4 and 2 and 3, separately. Therefore, torque on the roll axis

$$\tau_\phi = \sum r \times T = L\left(\left(k\omega_1^2 - k\omega_3^2\right) + \left(k\omega_4^2 - k\omega_2^2\right)\right)$$

$$= Lk\left(\left(\omega_1^2 - \omega_3^2\right) + \left(\omega_4^2 - \omega_2^2\right)\right)$$

Similarly, the torque on the pitch axis can be derived as

$$\tau_\theta = Lk\left(\left(\omega_1^2 - \omega_3^2\right) + \left(\omega_2^2 - \omega_4^2\right)\right)$$

where L is the distance from the center of the quadcopter to any of the propeller. All together, the total torque in the body frame is as follows:

$$\tau_B = \begin{bmatrix} Lk\left(\left(\omega_1^2 - \omega_3^2\right) + \left(\omega_4^2 - \omega_2^2\right)\right) \\ Lk\left(\left(\omega_1^2 - \omega_3^2\right) + \left(\omega_2^2 - \omega_4^2\right)\right) \\ b\left(\omega_1^2 - \omega_2^2 + \omega_3^2 - \omega_4^2\right) \end{bmatrix}$$

20.3.2.6 Dynamics of the Quadcopter

The acceleration of the quadcopter in the inertial frame is based on the trust, gravity, and the linear friction of the air drift. Therefore, using rotational matrix R, the linear motion of the quadcopter can be summarized as

$$m\ddot{x} = \begin{bmatrix} 0 \\ 0 \\ -mg \end{bmatrix} + RT_B + F_D$$

where $\vec{x}$ is the position of the quadcopter, m is the acceleration due to gravity, F_D is the drag force, and T_B is the trust vector in the body frame.

Based on Euler's equation, the rigid body dynamics is expressed in vector forms as follows:

$$I\dot{\omega} + \omega \times (I\omega) = \tau$$

The angular acceleration vector on quadcopter body frame is mentioned as follows:

$$\dot{\omega} = \begin{bmatrix} \dot{\omega}_x \\ \dot{\omega}_y \\ \dot{\omega}_z \end{bmatrix} = I^{-1}\left(\tau - \omega \times (I\omega)\right)$$

ω is the inertial matrix and τ is a vector of external torques.

Considering the quadcopter body structure, the frame can be considered as four-point masses (motors) connected to the corners of two thin uniform rods, which are crossed at the center point of each other. Therefore, the inertia matrix is given by

$$I = \begin{bmatrix} I_{xx} & 0 & 0 \\ 0 & I_{yy} & 0 \\ 0 & 0 & I_{zz} \end{bmatrix}$$

The final result for the body frame rotational equation of motion is given by

$$\dot{\omega} = \begin{bmatrix} \tau_{\phi} I_{xx}^{-1} \\ \tau_{\theta} I_{yy}^{-1} \\ \tau_{\varphi} I_{zz}^{-1} \end{bmatrix} - \begin{pmatrix} \frac{I_{yy} - I_{zz}}{I_{xx}} \omega_y \omega_z \\ \frac{I_{zz} - I_{xx}}{I_{yy}} \omega_x \omega_z \\ \frac{I_{xx} - I_{yy}}{I_{zz}} \omega_x \omega_y \end{pmatrix}$$

20.3.2.7 Components Used in the Design

20.3.2.7.1 Flight Controller

Flight controller usually operates to maintain a reference for the orientations of the quadcopter with respect to the ground during the entire flight time. In fact, the controller should be able to run the equations as mentioned above and control motor speed accordingly at a high frequency. In addition to that, the controller acts as the bridge between remote controller and the motors, which generates control signal with respect to the user inputs. As the quadcopter responses are very fast, usually flight controller has high-speed processers with higher clock speeds in order to process the controlling signal at almost instantly to maintain the precise levels.

20.3.2.7.2 Gyroscopes and Accelerometers

The development of gyroscopes is based upon mechanical spinning devices, which have axles, actuators, and gimbals to various materializations of electro-optical devices. Generally, multicomputer uses "vibrating structure gyroscope" as in Figure 20.25 to measure orientations.

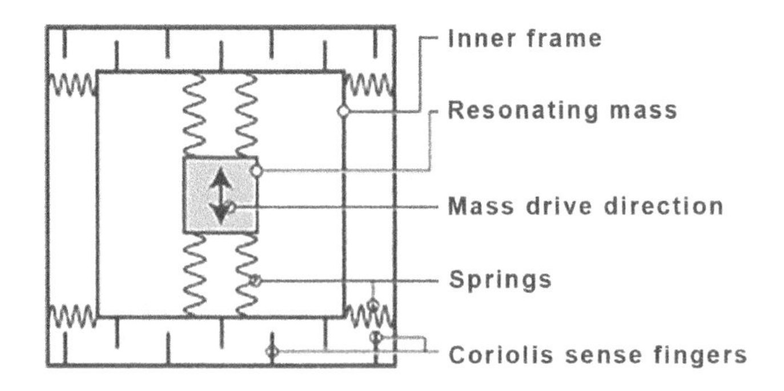

FIGURE 20.25 Vibrating structure gyroscopes.

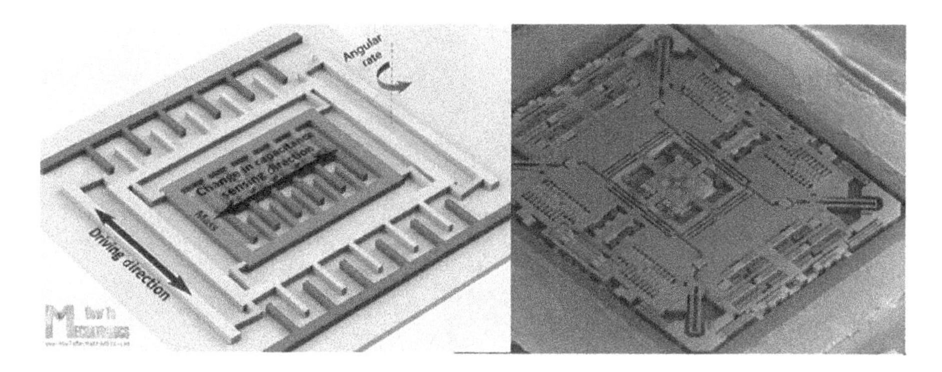

FIGURE 20.26 Semiconductor wafer architecture (left) and the real wafer structure (right) of an MEMS accelerometer.

Vibrating structure gyroscopes are known as MEMS (micro-electromechanical systems) devices, which have the ability to operate under the Coriolis force fundamentals. Every point in a rotary system has the same angular velocity. The angular velocity remains constant at the point of axis of rotation of the system, whereas the speed decreases along the direction, which is perpendicular to the axis of rotation. Therefore, in order to keep the same angular position of the body, it is required to increase or decrease the lateral speed of the system. Hence, the movement should maintain in a straight line in or out from the axis of rotation. During the decrease or increase in the speed, the Coriolis force is generated as acceleration times the mass of the object in order to maintain the direction. The Coriolis force proportionally depends on velocity of the object which is moving in and out from the axis of rotation and the angular velocity.

There is a micromass inside vibrating structure gyroscopes, and it is combined to outer structure by springs. This outer structure also has other orthogonal springs, which are connected to the external circuit board. The mass is constantly going through a sinusoidal movement by the first set of springs. The Coriolis acceleration, which is induced by rotation of the system, will push the mass toward the direction of the circuit board. The movement of the mass due to the Coriolis forces is always perpendicular as it is pushed away from the axis of rotation.

The capacitive sense fingers are used to detect Coriolis that are mounted along the mass housing and the rigid structure. As the mass is moved by the Coriolis force, sensing fingers are brought closer and differential capacitance will be detected. Therefore, the sensor can recognize both direction and magnitude of the angular velocity of the system. The details are given in Figure 20.26.

20.3.2.7.3 Actuators – Brushless DC (BLDC) Motors

Brushless DC motor is a type of electronically commuted motor, which does not have brushes. These motors are much efficient in producing large amount of torque at very high-speed range. In these kinds of motors, there is a permanent magnet that rotates around a fixed armature and it avoids the problem of connecting current to the armature. Commutation of the armature is done by power electronics, and therefore,

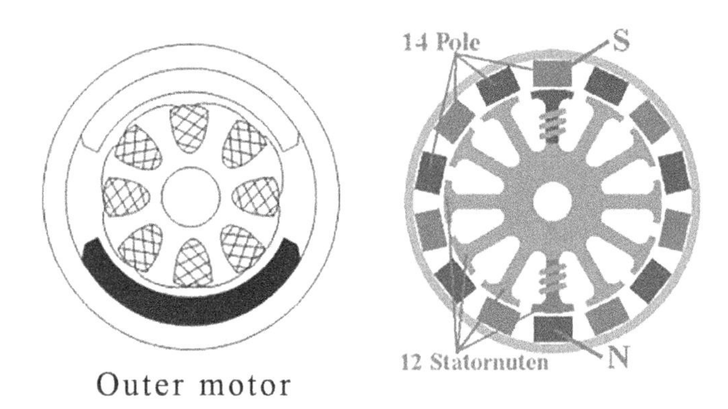

FIGURE 20.27 Rotor design.

it has large scope of capabilities and flexibility such as smooth operation, and holding torque when stationary.

20.3.2.7.4 Outer Rotor Design

This type of design has a rotor around the winding, which is located in the core of the motor as in Figure 20.27. The heat generated by the motor armature gets trapped inside the motor due to magnet in the rotor. This motor design operates at low current and has low clogging torque as well.

Velocity of BLDC motors is determined by the frequency at which the current is supplied, and therefore, it is highly efficient in operation. As there are no brushes, mechanical energy loss due to friction is very minimal and it has high lifetime and maintenance-free operation. It has no ionizing sparks, and therefore, electromagnetic interferences are also minimum. Due to low rotor inertia, it can be easily accelerated and decelerated with the control signal.

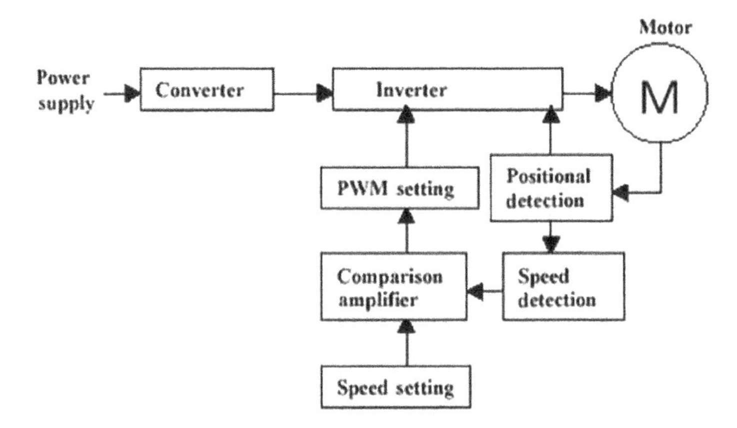

FIGURE 20.28 Flow diagram of the speed-controlling mechanism in ESC.

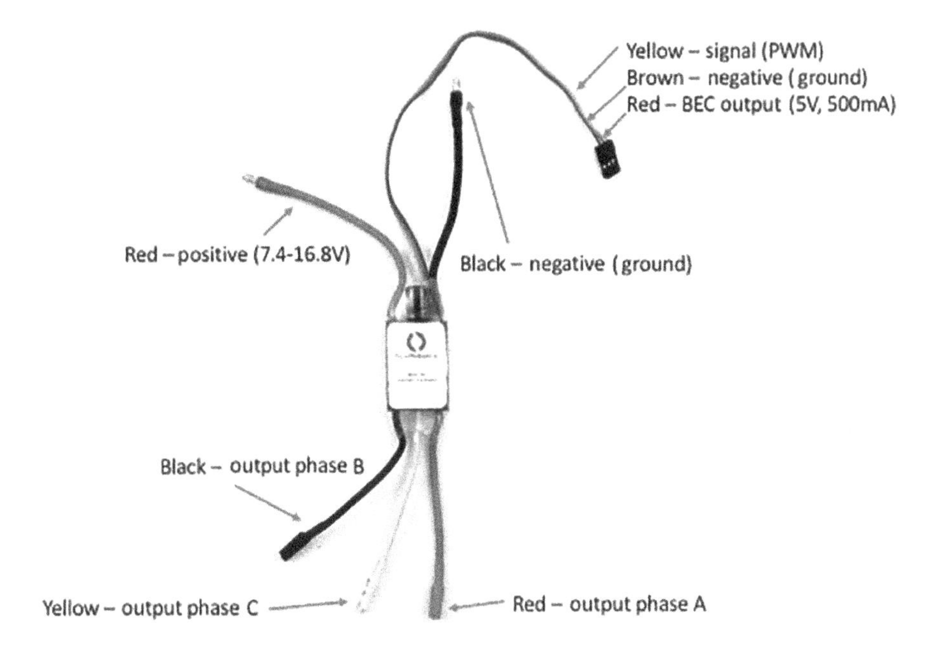

FIGURE 20.29 General image of an ESC.

20.3.2.7.5 Electronic Speed Controllers

Electronic speed controllers (ESCs) act as drivers of BLDC motors used in quadcopter, and it offers high-frequency, high-resolution three-phase AC power to the motors in an extremely compact, lightweight, and less space-consuming small package as in Figures 20.28 and 20.29. The dynamics of the craft totally depends on varying speed of the motors, which drive the propellers. In order to achieve a smooth flight, it is necessary to provide quadcopter propellers a wide RPM variation and fine PWM control.

Generally, quadcopter ESCs can use higher frequencies compared to the standard 50 Hz signal, which is used in other remote controlling appliances. Modern ESC protocols have the ability to communicate higher than 37.5 KHz with DSHOT2400 frame. ESCs are usually specified according to the operating voltage range and the maximum current it can handle.

20.3.2.7.6 Radio Transmitter and Receiver

Radio transmitter generally uses radio signals to send commands over to the receiver through set of radiofrequency. The transmitter and the receiver should operate in the same set of frequencies in order to maintain the communication.

Quadcopter radio transmitter send commands via channels. Each channel carries the instruction for an individual action for the quadcopter. Fundamental commands for quadcopter control such as throttle, yaw, pitch, and roll signals have dedicated channels, and hence, there should be a minimum of four channels to operate the quadcopter. Each channel is allocated to a separate control switch such as slider or knob on the transmitter. The extra channels are used to send the additional information through the receiver.

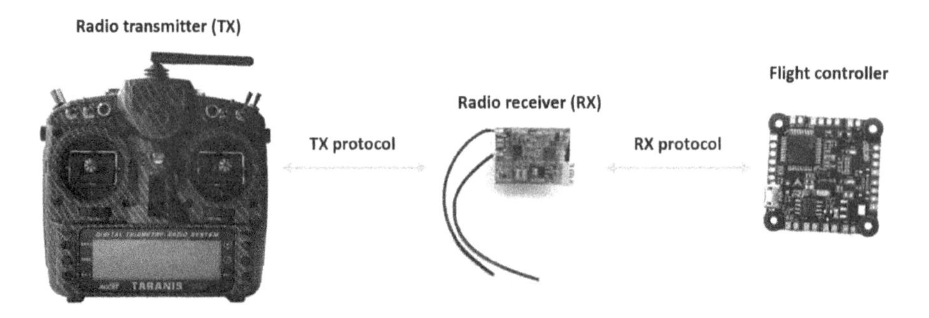

FIGURE 20.30 Radio Tx Rx protocol.

Transmitters generally use radiofrequencies such as 27, 72, 433, 900 MHz, 1.3, and 2.4 GHz to communicate with receiver. For long-range communications, 433 MHz, 900 MHz, and 1.3 GHz frequencies are usually used in first-person view remote controlled systems. Very low frequencies such as 27 and 72 MHz are no longer available in operations.

Nowadays, 2.4 GHz is the most popular frequency in almost all remote controlling devices. It is a novel technology, and it has the ability to do "frequency hopping," which enables to manage transmitting multiple users' frequency at the same time. Considering the space constraints of quadcopter design layouts, 2.4 GHz is a good fit as the antenna is very small in size.

Some transmitter has the ability to connect external transmitter modules and operate simultaneously. Therefore, it is possible to use a different frequency in the same application with a different receiver from another brand/protocol.

Radio communications mainly have two sets of protocols as in Figure 20.30 as follows:

TX protocols between radio transmitter and radio receiver.

RX protocols between radio receiver and flight controller.

Tx protocols basically depend on the brand or the manufacturer, and D8, D16, LR12, DSM, DSM2, DSMX, AFHDS, AFHDS 2A, etc., protocols are commonly used in quadcopters. Generally, receivers have universal protocols, but there are brand-specified protocols as well. PCM, PWM, PPM, SBUS, and iBUS are among these protocols.

20.3.2.7.7 Power Source – LiPo Battery

Lithium polymer batteries (LiPos) are commonly used power source for remote-guided vehicles such as quadcopters as in Figure 20.31. In this battery type, lithium ions are from a positive electrode and negative electrode material, and therefore, it works on the principle of intercalation and de-intercalation of the ion. A liquid electrolyte provides conductive medium for these negative and positive ions. In order to prevent the direct contact of these ions, a microporous separator is placed in between the materials and it allows only the ions to migrate from one side to another while making a barrier for electrode particles.

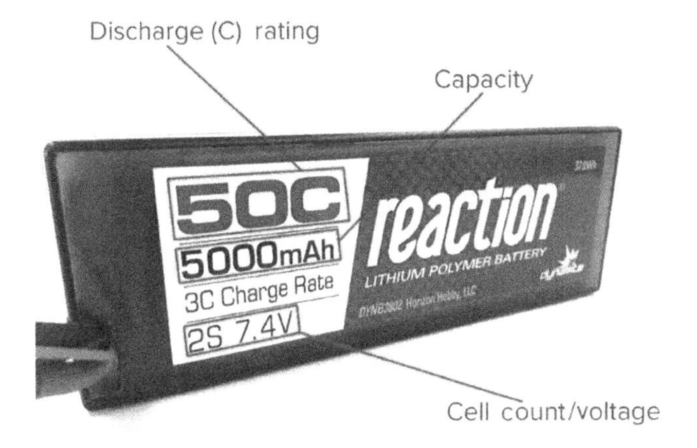

FIGURE 20.31 LiPo battery rating.

Lithium ion cylindrical and prismatic cells have a rigid metal case, whereas LiPo cells have a flexible, foil-type (polymer laminate) case. Hence, they are relatively unconstrained. Apparently, cylindrical cells are about 20% heavier than equivalent LiPo cells of the same capacity. Therefore, this lightweight provides an advantage for the applications such as quadcopter, which requires low-weight electronics. However, the pressure on the stack of layers, which make the cells, increases the contacts between the components, and thus, cell impedance and degradation are maximized. On the other hand, it reduces delamination and deformation of cells. Therefore, the pressure on the stack increases the capacity retention.

20.3.2.7.8 Cell Count/Voltage

A LiPo cell has a nominal voltage of 3.7 V., and the formation of cells defines the terminal voltage and maximum discharge current of a battery. The number of cells, which are connected in series, defines the terminal voltage, and the number of cells, which are connected in parallel, defines the discharge current. Hence, a two-cell (2S) pack will have an operating voltage of 7.4 V, a three-cell (3S) pack will have 11.1 V, and so on.

20.3.2.7.9 Capacity

The capacity of a battery is basically a measure of how much energy that the battery can provide, and the unit of measure here is milliamp hours (mAh). When the rating is high, it provides a long run time, but it increases the weight of the battery pack.

20.3.2.7.10 Discharge Rating ("C" Rating)

The "C" rating indicates maximum output current of the battery, which can be discharged safely and without harming the battery. The maximum discharging rate is calculated using the "C" rating and the battery capacity as follows:

$$50\text{ C} = 50 \times \text{Capacity}\left(\text{in Amps}\right)$$

$$50 \times 5\text{ A} = 250\text{ A}$$

Likewise, for 35C battery, which has a 5500 mAh capacity, the maximum discharging current will be 192.5 A.

20.3.2.7.11 Ground Station (GCS)

The ground station unit serves as virtual cockpit for the operator and displays real-time data on the quadcopter performance, position, and other important data to operate quadcopter. This application communicates with the quadcopter via wireless telemetry. In advance quadcopter and UAVs, the radio transmitting unit is also embedded with ground stations, and therefore, it is used to control the vehicle in flight, upload new mission commands, and set control parameters as well. It is often also used to monitor the live video streams from a UAV's cameras.

20.3.2.7.12 Telemetry Unit

Telemetry units are basically a radio link, which helps the ground station to communicate with the quadcopter to exchange data during the flight. Generally, telemetry units have two frequency ranges as 966 and 433 MHz, which are used based on the regulations of the country.

20.4 TESTING AND VALIDATION

Testing procedure was done near to transformer BZ 3079 assembly and 33 kV feeder lines, which are installed inside the university premises. The transformer is fed by LECO 11 kV feeder, and the assembly has HV components such as DDLOs, surge arresters, insulators, and strands, which are used to mount bare cable to the insulator. In order to identify the flight dynamics near MV distribution lines and line surveying, aerial imaging are used and tested near 33 kV line section inside the university premises.

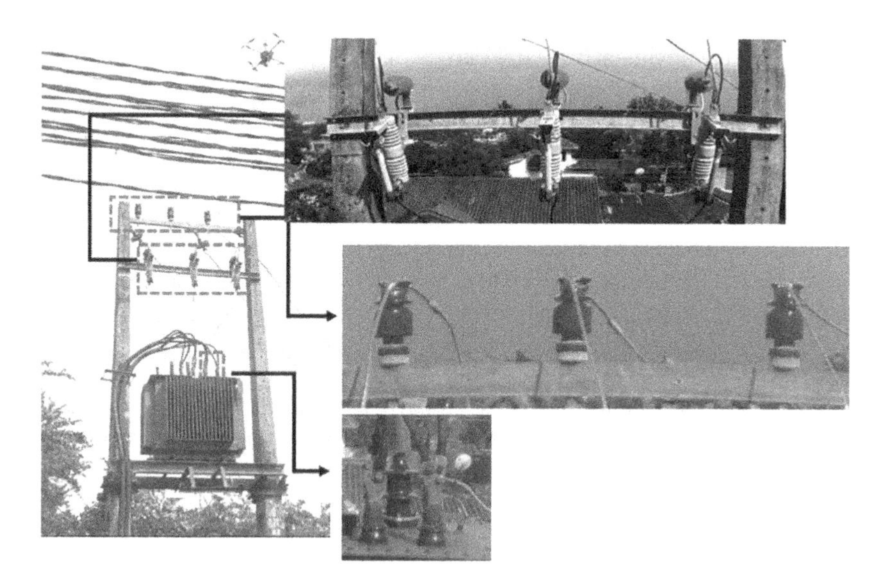

FIGURE 20.32 Components inspected using the aerial imaging platform – BZ3079.

20.4.1 Obtaining Images to Study the Assembly in Details

Regular inspection process, which is done by line patrolling, can only detect the faults and defects by the looks from the ground. But most of the arc flash marks are only visible on the top of insulators. Therefore, those faults can easily be identified using the images taken by the drone. Images were taken as in Figure 20.32 during the test flights, and each element can be clearly observed using the remote platform.

20.4.1.1 Insulation Assembly

Damages due to arc flashes create insulation failures, and the line gets tripped due to the operation of earth fault relays in downstream. In order to restore the power system, it is mandatory to identify the faulty insulator due to arc flash. From line patrolling, it is difficult to locate arc flash marks on insulator tops from ground level, and therefore, efficiency of clearing fault related to this issue is very low. Hence, using information from the precise, aerial images can improve the efficiency of identification of insulation faults.

On the other hand, from the level of details available in the image, the status of the cable ties and preforms can be identified. This feature is also a major advantage of inspection through aerial images vs. the conventional line patrolling method.

20.4.1.2 DDLO and Surge Arrester Assembly

Earth link for surge arrestors is extremely important in order to protect equipment from surges. Poor connection and broken conductors of earth links can create high impedances for short circuit path, and therefore, it will damage the downstream assets such as transformers and consumer goods. Clear information about the status of the earth link connections can be taken from aerial images, and therefore, the accuracy of the inspection is high.

20.4.1.3 Transformer LV Bushing

Owing to the construction of a typical transformer, LV bushings are short in size and it is hardly visible to the ground when it is mounted on top of the pole. Therefore,

FIGURE 20.33 View of the transformer assembly from ground.

FIGURE 20.34 Detailed view of the transformer assembly from aerial imaging.

during general line inspection, the status of this is barely seen. As LV terminals carry high current, poor connection in the flag to lug terminals can cause not only fire hazards due to temperature rise but also power losses in distribution systems. Through aerial imaging, the status of the terminals such as corroded nuts and bolts, broken lugs, and oil leak marks on transformer top can be clearly investigated as in Figures 20.33 and 20.34. Therefore, information that is gathered from aerial imaging is more important to schedule planned maintenance effectively.

20.4.2 Feeder Line Surveying

Prior to HV feeder line rehabilitation project, it is a mandatory requirement to perform a survey to identify the existing arrangement of the feeder. This information is used in the planning stage to identify the obstacles and limitations in order to optimize the construction process. In the current situation, online services such as Google Street Maps and Google Earth are used to do this survey. But aerial imaging provides more accurate and real-time details about the situation, and hence, it can be used to do the survey effectively. Even though using aerial imaging for survey purposes does not directly impact reducing system outages, it adds more values to the operation by giving ability to dynamically observe feeder arrangement in gantry points, vegetation level, line overlapping, and type of the pole used in construction. Image Patch and Defect Identification Algorithm Testing aids in processing of the images subject to the visual demarcations of the equipment boundaries. In the current contest, there is no demarcation in the existing MV lines, and the algorithm was tested for a known item, i.e., the transformer assembly in BZ3079 unit. The accuracy of the algorithm was tested to identify the corroded nuts and bolts in transformer LV terminals. Dimension ratio in the transformer is used to identify each LV terminal. Bit plane slicing algorithm is applied to identify LV terminal image section as in Figure 20.35.

FIGURE 20.35 Line surveying –33 kV feeder section in UoM.

TABLE 20.3
Parameters Used to Identify Corroded Nuts and Bolts

	Nuts in Good Condition	Nuts in Bad Condition
Radius (minimum)/pixel	10	200
Radius (maximum)/pixel	20	250
Sensitivity	91%	97%

The most significant bit plane was used to identify the corroded color patches on the terminals. Table 20.3 indicates the parameters to identify corroded nuts and bolts. Comparison was done between original image and MSB plane in order to identify the accuracy of algorithm in both conditions.

The results reveal that the algorithm reduces number of incorrect detections. Even though this is not the absolute solution to fully automate the fault identification and unman process, this can be used to filter most significant images with defects

FIGURE 20.36 Identification of focus area to be processed.

for further inspection. As in many other object recognition algorithms, it helps to increase the accuracy of inspection process by highlighting areas for operator's attention without wasting much time to evaluate the entire image.

20.4.3 Image Patch and Defect Identification Algorithm Testing

The processing of the images can be done subject to the visual demarcations of the equipment boundaries. In the current contest, there is no demarcation in the existing MV lines, and the algorithm was tested for a known item, i.e., the transformer assembly in BZ3079 unit. The accuracy of the algorithm was tested to identify the corroded nuts and bolts in transformer LV terminals. Sample images are shown in Figures 20.36 and 20.37. Dimension ratio in the transformer is used to identify each LV terminal.

FIGURE 20.37 Bit plane slicing algorithm for LV terminal.

TABLE 20.4
Parameters Used to Identify Corroded Nuts and Bolts

	Nuts in Good Condition	Nuts in Bad Condition
Radius (minimum)/pixel	10	200
Radius (maximum)/pixel	20	250
Sensitivity	91%	97%

Applying bit plane slicing algorithm to identified LV terminal image section, the parameters used to identify corroded nuts and bolts are specified in Table 20.4. The most significant bit plane was used to identify the corroded color patches on the terminals. Comparison was done between original image and MSB plane in order to identify the accuracy of algorithm in both conditions.

The results in Table 20.5 reveal that the algorithm reduces number of incorrect detections. Even though this is not the absolute solution to fully automate the fault identification and unman process, this can be used to filter most significant images with defects for further inspection. As in many other object recognition algorithms, it helps to increase the accuracy of inspection process by highlighting areas for operator's attention without wasting much time to evaluate the entire image.

20.4.4 Quadcopter Testing

20.4.4.1 Tuning the Parameters

The algorithm uses PID control loop mechanism to achieve precise outputs of each motor with respect to the controlling signal. The parameters of the initial design were determined as follows in order to obtain smooth controlling of the drone as in Figure 20.38.

20.4.4.2 Control Signal vs Drone Response with Initial Parameters

The PID values used in quadcopter are indicated in Table 20.6.

20.4.4.3 Control Signal vs Drone Response after Applying the Current Parameters

The alignment of controlling signal and the response are also overlapped for the roll and yaw axis for the abovementioned PID values as in Figure 20.39. Due to the high power consumption of additional stability equipment such as Lidar range finder and flow sensor, the actual flying time of the drone was dropped to approximately about 4 minutes, and therefore, the second drone was designed to overcome the challenges.

With proposed configuration as per the drone design, the optimum speed of the drone is 24 km/h and the expected flight time is 5.5 minutes with the payload. This delivers maximum flight distance of 2000 m, and therefore, the drone can be operated within 1 km span considering the total back and forth traveling distance. Imaging unit can capture 30 frames per second, and therefore, in this operational

TABLE 20.5
Summary of Color Patch Detecting Algorithm Testing

	Case 1 – Raw Image	Case 1 – Processed Image	Case 2 – Raw Image	Case 2 – Processed Image	Case 3 – Raw Image	Case 3 – Processed Image
Sample images	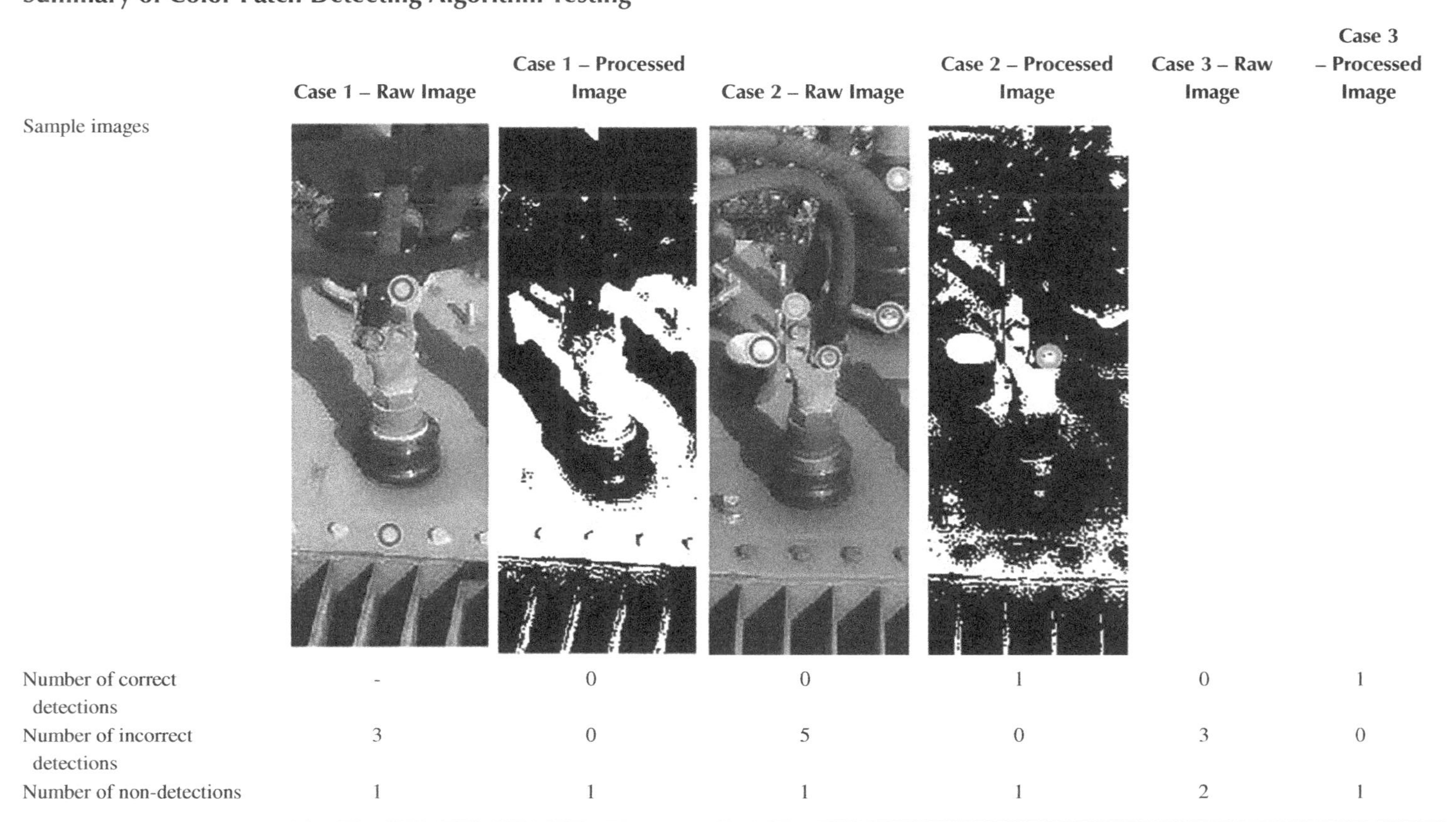					
Number of correct detections	-	0	0	1	0	1
Number of incorrect detections	3	0	5	0	3	0
Number of non-detections	1	1	1	1	2	1

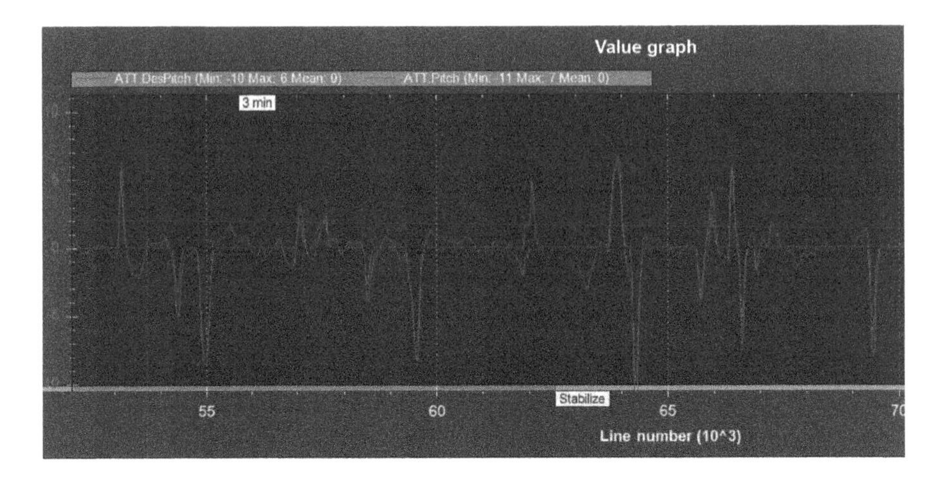

FIGURE 20.38 Before tuning the PID parameters in pitch axis – badly aligned controlling signal and response.

TABLE 20.6
PID Values Used in Quadcopter

Parameter	Rolling Axis	Pitching Axis	Yaw Axis
P :	0.153222	0.17473	1.0480
I :	0.153222	0.17473	0.1048
D :	0.006211	0.006833	0.0000

state, six images can be taken per 1 m of distribution line. This image rate is satisfactory for obtaining relevant information on a feeder line. The flight characteristics are as in Figure 20.40.

20.4.4.4 Altitude Holding Function

As the flight controller get barometer reading from two sensors, better altitude holding was achieved for the new design as in Figure 20.41. Therefore, the maneuvering has become easy for the new drone when flying the "altitude hold" mode.

20.4.4.5 Impact Analysis on Time and Space Requirement for Inspection Process

Table 20.7 indicates the impact analysis and space requirement for the inspection process.

20.4.5 Limitation of the Study

The design of the aerial platform was done to build the hardware within a limited budget. Therefore, the design of the aerial platform was done to build the hardware to run algorithms and check the usability in the practical environment. The existing

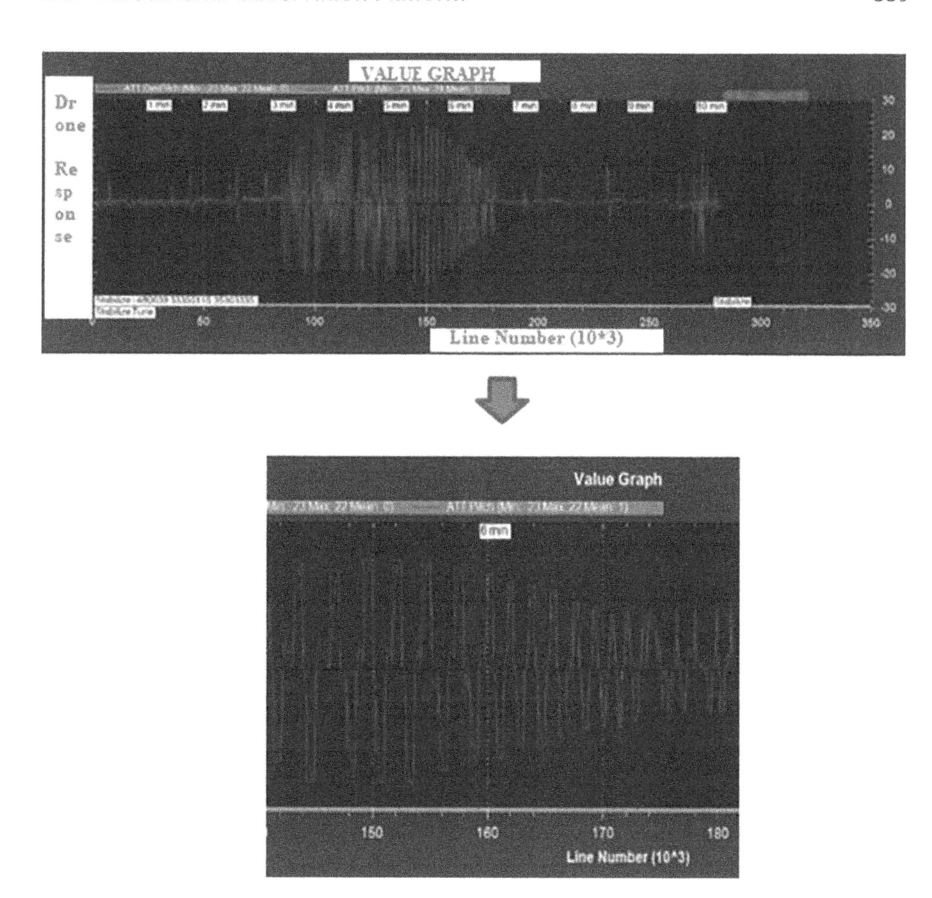

FIGURE 20.39 After tuning PID values in pitch axis – controlling signal and response are substantially overlapped.

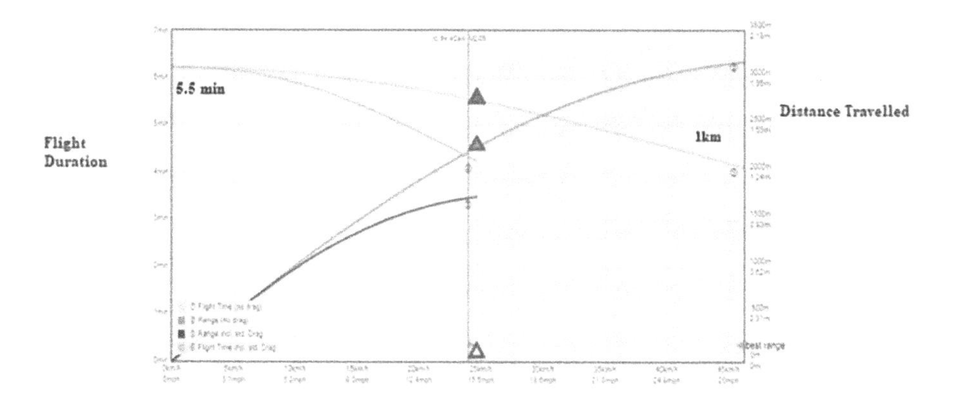

FIGURE 20.40 Flight characteristics of quadcopter.

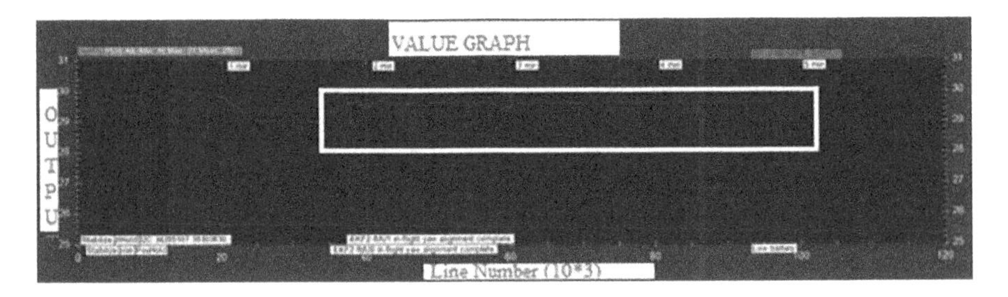

FIGURE 20.41 Altitude remains constant in the "altitude hold" mode.

TABLE 20.7
Impact Analysis on Time and Space Requirement for Inspection Process

	Line Patrolling with Ladders			Bucket Truck Deployment			Aerial Observation Platform		
	Time (min)	Space (m^2)	Network Outage Time (min)	Time (min)	Space (m^2)	Network Outage Time (min)	Time (min)	Space (m^2)	Network Outage Time (min)
Transformer inspection	60	2	20	30	20	10	5	2	0
Line inspection (500 m span)	180	20	180	50	80	0	10	2	0
Insulator inspection	30	2	30	15	15	0	3	2	0

MV lines do not have visual demarcations for equipment boundaries, and therefore, image processing algorithm was tested only for one known equipment, i.e., the transformer assembly in BZ3079 substation. Should the utility use this algorithm for fault identification process, the equipment in the lines shall be demarcated as per the design and algorithm has to be customized for each type of fault. Image processing and analysis algorithms were developed in MATLAB platform in order to identify the accuracy of the results. Hence, real-time processing for an incoming video stream is not possible with selected software platform. The finalized algorithm can be transformed to portable software platforms such as Python or OpenMV, in order to facilitate processing live video feeds.

20.5 CONCLUSION

The energy need of urban community in Sri Lanka is highly dependent on the electricity supply. This consumer behavior and its impact on Sri Lankan economy, the regulatory body, are drastically pushing utilities to reduce outage time. Now, it has come to a stage where a compensation system has been proposed for consumers who undergo more system outages than the nominal level while imposing penalties to utilities.

Mainly, the outages are occurred due to system maintenance and it is considered as an essential element in the operation of distribution system. The maintenance process includes several steps, and among those, inspection is considered as a necessary but non-value adding activity, which cannot be compromised. Considering the advanced technologies used in other industries, there are opportunities to improve the efficiency of this inspection process, which apparently reduces the outage time and increases system reliability.

In this study, the concept of having a remote aerial platform with a camera unit is introduced. As the method of inspection, camera unit and image processing are proposed, and as the aerial platform, the design and the development of a quadcopter are proposed. The design has the capability to capture and process images to identify basic faults and run across the HV lines while mitigating electromagnetic interferences. Case study compression proves that inspection process through the proposed system brings more advantages over conventional, manual inspection process. The ability to take images in 360° scope of view itself brings a lot of benefits over limited eye inspection from ground. Remote operation of the camera unit increases the safety of inception procedure as it minimizes human involvement closer to HV lines. Further, automated fault identification algorithm improves probability of detecting images with defects, and hence, it improves the efficiency of the process.

Depending on the operational requirement such as span of inspection, time of inspection, and nature of the investigation, the design parameters can be selected to increase the flight time, duration, and camera resolution accordingly. Therefore, this concept can be customized to utilize to improve efficiency and quality of any overhead MV line inspection activity in urban areas in Sri Lanka.

REFERENCES

[1] L. Zhang, and S. He, "Mobile robot for overhead powerline inspection and a controlling method for obstacle avoidance", in *2011 International Conference on Electric Information and Control Engineering.*

[2] A. Pagnano, M. Höpf, and R. Teti, "A roadmap for automated power line inspection, Maintenance and repair", in *8th CIRP Conference on Intelligent Computation in Manufacturing Engineering.*

[3] C. Huang Shen, F. Y. C. Albert, C. K. Ang, and D. J. Teck, "Theoretical development and study of takeoff constraint thrust equation for a drone", in *2017 IEEE 15th Student Conference on Research and Development.*

[4] E. A. Niit, and W. J. Smit, "Integration of model reference adaptive control (MRAC) with PX4 firmware for quadcopters", in *2017 24th International Conference on Mechatronics and Machine Vision in Practice (M2VIP).*

[5] D. Kim, J. Park, J. Jung, T. Kim, and J. Paik, "Lens distortion correction and enhancement based on local self-similarity for high-quality consumer imaging systems", *IEEE Transactions on Consumer Electronics* 60, 1, 2014.

[6] E. A. Niit, and W. J. Smit, "VTOL aerial robot for inspection of transmission line", in *2017 24th International Conference on Mechatronics and Machine Vision in Practice (M2VIP).*

Appendix 1

Site Measured Elevator Data – Office Building Complex @ Narahenpita

No.	Utility Side 3ϕ Voltage (V)	DC Bus Voltage (V)	Utility Side 3ϕ Current (A)	Utility Side 3ϕ Power Freq. (Hz)	Elevator Load (kg)	Travelling Direction [Up/Down] (1/0)	Regen. Energy (Wh)
1	401.8	567	–22.0	49	780	0	–42.6
2	400.4	677	15.5	50	160	1	10.1
3	398.5	671	11.0	49	240	1	7.1
4	397.9	675	15.8	49	160	1	20.3
5	402.3	680	6.2	50	320	1	3.9
6	400.9	677	11.3	50	240	1	14.1
7	398.8	560	–20.0	51	90	0	–60.8
8	402.3	680	1.3	49	400	1	2.3
9	399.5	676	17.0	49	160	1	29.1
10	397.8	673	6.1	51	320	1	3.9
11	400.0	561	–25.7	51	810	0	–14.3
12	400.3	561	–28.7	51	860	0	–33.3
13	398.4	564	–20.2	49	750	0	–51.2
14	399.4	678	22.2	49	80	1	12.6
15	398.6	670	3.2	49	470	1	10.5
16	402.1	564	–24.4	49	40	0	–41.6
17	398.5	567	–18.4	49	140	0	–21.8
18	402.3	562	–22.4	49	70	0	–26.5
19	397.6	563	–15.5	50	180	0	–18.7
20	400.0	672	16.3	50	160	1	9.5
21	399.2	567	–34.5	50	980	0	–63.7
22	399.3	564	–24.7	51	830	0	–30.2
23	399.5	569	–23.2	50	790	0	–14.5
24	399.1	561	–21.0	50	760	0	–25.7
25	401.9	568	–20.4	49	760	0	–64.1
26	399.2	671	4.5	50	350	1	10.5
27	400.0	670	10.3	51	250	1	6.5
28	401.9	675	14.3	50	640	1	40.1
29	400.1	676	8.5	51	560	1	15.5
30	400.2	672	16.7	50	680	1	20.3
31	401.6	562	–21.0	50	80	0	–26.7
32	400.8	678	20.3	50	730	1	12.2
33	399.3	562	–35.5	50	990	0	–63.8
34	397.9	679	4.8	49	340	1	6.1
35	398.6	678	26.8	49	0	1	31.2

(Continued)

No.	Utility Side 3ϕ Voltage (V)	DC Bus Voltage (V)	Utility Side 3ϕ Current (A)	Utility Side 3ϕ Power Freq. (Hz)	Elevator Load (kg)	Travelling Direction [Up/Down] (1/0)	Regen. Energy (Wh)
36	402.4	670	15.8	49	170	1	9.5
37	400.3	565	−28.4	50	890	0	−34.2
38	399.6	674	19.6	51	110	1	35.3
39	397.6	673	10.2	51	260	1	24.4
40	397.7	563	−21.7	51	80	0	−37.8
41	400.6	674	25.2	49	840	1	68.9
42	398.6	677	13.7	50	650	1	17.6
43	400.7	673	5.9	50	510	1	6.6
44	401.2	567	−21.1	51	80	0	−24.8
45	400.6	680	19.6	51	110	1	11.8
46	402.3	560	−35.1	49	1000	0	−64.9
47	398.9	570	−29.5	50	880	0	−18.0
48	402.4	564	−24.1	51	790	0	−42.3
49	400.6	671	19.3	51	120	1	32.7
50	400.1	673	18.1	50	720	1	53.5
51	400.2	569	−21.5	50	70	0	−13.4
52	397.6	678	13.6	50	210	1	53.1
53	397.9	671	25.8	49	0	1	63.9
54	402.4	566	−24.6	50	30	0	−56.6
55	402.5	570	−21.4	51	90	0	−37.3
56	401.6	679	10.4	50	590	1	12.3
57	399.3	565	−24.6	50	40	0	−14.6
58	397.5	678	13.2	49	630	1	15.7
59	399.8	565	−19.1	51	130	0	−10.6
60	397.8	675	18.6	49	710	1	42.8
61	397.7	563	−37.1	49	1020	0	−71.1
62	397.6	567	−29.9	51	910	0	−38.6
63	400.7	675	26.0	50	0	1	78.4
64	398.4	671	6.6	50	310	1	20.8
65	402.4	680	20.3	51	110	1	11.2
66	399.6	565	−20.9	51	90	0	−38.1
67	400.0	676	29.5	51	870	1	80.2
68	398.6	676	18.5	51	730	1	33.6
69	400.0	563	−21.8	50	90	0	−12.7
70	401.4	564	−23.7	50	40	0	−41.1
71	400.7	672	12.3	51	610	1	6.9
72	402.2	679	26.9	50	0	1	48.9
73	399.3	568	−26.9	51	840	0	−15.3
74	400.8	561	−18.5	49	710	0	−43.8
75	399.6	677	3.2	49	370	1	7.6
76	401.3	672	12.8	51	630	1	32.6
77	397.8	560	−24.8	51	40	0	−29.0
78	401.3	673	23.6	51	790	1	54.4

(*Continued*)

No.	Utility Side 3ϕ Voltage (V)	DC Bus Voltage (V)	Utility Side 3ϕ Current (A)	Utility Side 3ϕ Power Freq. (Hz)	Elevator Load (kg)	Travelling Direction [Up/ Down] (1/0)	Regen. Energy (Wh)
79	402.2	678	12.5	49	620	1	23.6
80	398.6	561	−13.3	49	200	0	−8.4
81	399.1	561	−23.8	51	800	0	−58.6
82	400.8	670	27.2	51	0	1	48.8
83	399.7	565	−21.7	49	760	0	−26.1
84	398.9	672	11.0	51	250	1	6.1
85	397.8	677	11.9	50	230	1	22.0
86	402.0	560	−24.6	50	40	0	−67.0
87	397.5	561	−21.2	50	70	0	−13.1
88	398.3	566	−20.3	50	110	0	−36.5
89	398.8	674	26.4	50	820	1	45.4
90	400.7	672	33.5	50	930	1	19.8
91	398.4	560	−22.1	51	50	0	−14.4
92	401.8	675	14.7	50	190	1	8.7
93	400.9	569	−26.1	49	830	0	−44.9
94	397.6	676	27.4	50	0	1	32.9
95	401.0	568	−19.4	49	730	0	−11.9
96	401.8	670	8.5	49	290	1	10.1
97	397.5	567	−19.1	50	720	0	−11.8
98	399.4	678	5.2	50	340	1	12.5
99	401.9	674	6.5	50	320	1	19.3
100	398.9	677	14.7	51	180	1	9.4
101	397.8	568	−22.7	50	40	0	−27.4
102	398.1	563	−18.4	49	140	0	−42.8
103	398.5	672	0.0	50	420	1	0.0
104	398.1	670	21.7	51	760	1	73.9
105	401.2	565	−17.1	51	150	0	−20.1
106	400.1	565	−19.8	49	90	0	−12.5
107	402.0	675	16.1	50	670	1	28.0
108	401.0	562	−21.1	50	80	0	−13.3
109	399.4	679	8.7	51	280	1	10.3
110	398.8	677	20.6	50	90	1	25.7
111	397.9	565	−18.1	50	710	0	−21.4
112	399.0	674	0.6	50	410	1	0.4
113	399.2	672	4.4	50	350	1	7.8
114	400.3	673	2.4	50	380	1	6.2
115	402.3	564	−15.6	50	180	0	−27.1
116	401.6	565	−11.5	49	230	0	−28.8
117	397.9	675	4.5	50	490	1	5.4
118	398.7	676	7.6	50	540	1	9.0
119	400.5	672	13.2	50	620	1	7.5
120	400.4	672	25.9	50	850	1	15.7
121	401.7	677	24.0	49	790	1	40.5

(Continued)

No.	Utility Side 3ϕ Voltage (V)	DC Bus Voltage (V)	Utility Side 3ϕ Current (A)	Utility Side 3ϕ Power Freq. (Hz)	Elevator Load (kg)	Travelling Direction [Up/Down] (1/0)	Regen. Energy (Wh)
122	399.4	678	33.7	51	940	1	20.4
123	399.9	566	−24.4	51	40	0	−14.1
124	398.7	675	15.5	50	170	1	9.5
125	401.3	565	−31.3	49	910	0	−18.6
126	400.7	677	0.7	51	430	1	1.3
127	398.2	561	−24.0	49	800	0	−29.0
128	398.4	561	−22.9	49	800	0	−75.0
129	398.6	672	21.6	50	750	1	41.9
130	398.5	570	−20.3	50	750	0	−38.8
131	401.5	679	25.2	49	0	1	49.3
132	400.9	672	12.5	50	620	1	28.7
133	402.3	679	6.9	49	310	1	8.3
134	399.2	674	16.4	51	170	1	18.8
135	399.8	674	16.1	50	150	1	30.5
136	399.4	567	−14.3	50	200	0	−49.3
137	399.8	680	12.5	50	620	1	7.6
138	398.3	673	4.4	51	490	1	10.3
139	398.4	670	1.3	50	400	1	5.9
140	399.3	678	12.7	49	210	1	23.2
141	402.3	680	2.0	50	390	1	2.2
142	399.4	677	20.2	49	730	1	36.8
143	401.0	562	−14.4	49	200	0	−17.3
144	399.7	679	6.5	49	520	1	11.0
145	401.9	567	−14.8	49	180	0	−37.2
146	400.1	560	−25.4	51	840	0	−16.6
147	400.7	674	12.9	49	630	1	15.2
148	398.5	674	3.7	49	360	1	6.8
149	401.7	677	27.2	50	0	1	69.8
150	399.7	677	28.4	49	890	1	92.7
151	399.0	566	−28.3	50	870	0	−33.6
152	399.8	672	5.9	51	330	1	6.7
153	398.4	671	12.9	50	210	1	23.3
154	399.4	678	21.5	50	750	1	51.2
155	402.3	673	3.1	50	370	1	3.7
156	401.4	568	−16.9	50	140	0	−22.1
157	399.2	671	7.4	49	540	1	8.8
158	398.6	675	1.8	49	390	1	3.5
159	400.1	680	18.5	50	120	1	21.7
160	398.4	565	−23.6	49	800	0	−82.6
161	399.1	678	19.0	49	730	1	110.3
162	402.4	675	27.0	49	0	1	99.5
163	399.5	677	14.0	50	650	1	43.9
164	399.0	566	−24.9	51	820	0	−109.5

(Continued)

No.	Utility Side 3ϕ Voltage (V)	DC Bus Voltage (V)	Utility Side 3ϕ Current (A)	Utility Side 3ϕ Power Freq. (Hz)	Elevator Load (kg)	Travelling Direction [Up/Down] (1/0)	Regen. Energy (Wh)
165	402.0	561	−19.1	50	120	0	−61.2
166	401.5	563	−11.4	50	240	0	−20.4
167	399.5	677	1.2	51	400	1	3.4
168	397.7	672	7.8	50	300	1	14.3
169	400.4	679	18.6	51	720	1	78.3
170	397.9	561	−23.3	49	780	0	−83.3
171	401.3	670	10.9	50	590	1	31.9
172	401.9	570	−16.5	50	160	0	−35.3
173	399.4	677	8.1	51	290	1	19.2
174	400.5	675	16.3	50	150	1	30.5
175	399.0	569	−23.2	50	800	0	−41.2
176	398.7	678	27.2	50	0	1	61.8
177	402.2	674	22.6	51	770	1	47.1
178	397.6	562	−17.6	49	150	0	−21.6
179	398.6	562	−23.5	51	800	0	−42.7
180	400.6	671	17.9	50	700	1	67.4
181	398.5	563	−13.2	51	210	0	−24.4
182	398.3	677	27.4	51	0	1	79.4
183	401.0	677	10.9	51	240	1	32.8
184	400.1	675	19.8	50	90	1	26.1
185	400.8	679	25.5	51	830	1	95.0
186	400.0	677	16.8	49	140	1	65.4
187	397.8	677	10.4	50	580	1	12.0
188	398.1	674	21.0	49	740	1	46.5
189	400.0	676	1.9	49	390	1	4.5
190	397.8	678	4.9	50	500	1	6.2
191	398.2	676	29.4	51	870	1	67.7
192	398.1	673	15.0	49	660	1	45.7
193	399.8	673	9.6	49	580	1	6.0
194	399.9	565	−26.5	50	850	0	−110.3
195	400.4	675	0.6	50	430	1	1.1
196	401.7	562	−24.0	50	40	0	−108.4
197	400.8	678	27.4	49	0	1	107.5
198	400.5	562	−10.3	51	260	0	−32.5
199	401.7	678	27.2	50	0	1	79.6
200	398.6	569	−13.9	51	190	0	−25.9
201	398.5	671	20.9	50	740	1	37.2
202	402.1	677	12.9	49	210	1	38.8
203	398.5	563	−27.1	51	870	0	−91.7
204	400.7	567	−16.3	49	150	0	−41.3
205	398.2	563	−24.4	51	790	0	−44.1
206	399.1	679	1.2	50	440	1	2.3
207	402.1	566	−14.7	51	190	0	−25.8

(*Continued*)

No.	Utility Side 3ϕ Voltage (V)	DC Bus Voltage (V)	Utility Side 3ϕ Current (A)	Utility Side 3ϕ Power Freq. (Hz)	Elevator Load (kg)	Travelling Direction [Up/Down] (1/0)	Regen. Energy (Wh)
208	399.6	679	7.2	50	530	1	24.4
209	399.6	672	0.0	50	420	1	0.0
210	398.3	675	5.2	50	340	1	9.5
211	397.9	675	2.4	50	380	1	4.5
212	401.3	560	–26.1	49	20	0	–72.7
213	400.2	563	–25.2	50	820	0	–53.9
214	399.0	565	–17.7	50	150	0	–32.1
215	401.5	675	7.1	50	530	1	15.1
216	400.6	566	–21.2	49	770	0	–63.9
217	398.3	678	8.1	51	290	1	23.4
218	397.8	671	22.4	50	770	1	46.3
219	401.5	677	9.2	50	560	1	20.6
220	398.4	568	–22.3	50	770	0	–46.0
221	400.1	565	–25.0	49	830	0	–60.8
222	397.9	678	1.3	49	400	1	3.0
223	399.3	671	14.6	51	660	1	52.6
224	398.7	678	3.6	50	360	1	9.1
225	398.1	563	–26.0	50	850	0	–68.1
226	398.7	567	–15.9	50	170	0	–73.8
227	402.4	674	8.5	50	280	1	24.8
228	400.7	677	10.8	49	590	1	19.7
229	398.5	679	6.8	50	310	1	13.0
230	397.8	565	–27.4	51	840	0	–46.5
231	402.4	674	38.4	50	1030	1	140.3
232	398.0	562	–26.0	51	850	0	–16.6
233	400.1	679	1.2	50	440	1	3.4
234	400.8	673	2.5	50	380	1	2.9
235	400.8	680	9.0	50	280	1	5.1
236	400.4	567	–12.9	50	220	0	–71.4
237	401.7	674	0.6	51	430	1	2.3
238	401.5	567	–13.8	50	190	0	–30.4
239	400.1	671	2.5	49	460	1	5.3
240	401.8	569	–26.9	50	840	0	–75.8
241	400.1	671	8.4	51	280	1	20.5
242	398.7	560	–23.6	49	790	0	–68.8
243	400.1	675	4.3	49	490	1	23.3
244	399.3	564	–23.6	50	800	0	–28.5
245	400.3	561	–20.5	51	730	0	–41.3
246	402.0	679	30.1	50	890	1	102.7
247	399.1	676	16.2	51	170	1	89.0
248	402.3	678	6.8	50	530	1	19.8
249	397.7	675	9.2	51	570	1	10.9
250	399.2	679	10.9	50	250	1	20.0

(Continued)

No.	Utility Side 3ϕ Voltage (V)	DC Bus Voltage (V)	Utility Side 3ϕ Current (A)	Utility Side 3ϕ Power Freq. (Hz)	Elevator Load (kg)	Travelling Direction [Up/Down] (1/0)	Regen. Energy (Wh)
251	402.2	674	4.4	50	490	1	13.8
252	401.7	568	−12.5	50	220	0	−31.6
253	400.3	569	−17.8	50	710	0	−78.9
254	400.6	678	10.7	50	590	1	40.3
255	401.8	680	10.6	50	260	1	34.1
256	397.7	562	−26.1	49	830	0	−62.1
257	401.6	567	−17.6	51	150	0	−72.9
258	401.8	561	−25.4	51	820	0	−118.4
259	399.6	673	6.0	50	520	1	35.2
260	401.2	680	1.9	50	390	1	6.3
261	398.4	671	7.3	50	540	1	9.5
262	399.0	674	2.5	50	380	1	6.9
263	402.0	567	−10.4	50	250	0	−27.0
264	397.7	672	11.8	50	610	1	34.8
265	398.0	679	10.1	51	260	1	29.0
266	399.9	568	−15.6	51	180	0	−8.8
267	400.9	569	−14.8	49	190	0	−35.7
268	399.0	569	−25.7	51	850	0	−63.7
269	397.9	675	0.0	51	420	1	0.0
270	399.8	673	7.1	50	530	1	12.2
271	398.2	565	−11.7	50	230	0	−34.4
272	400.3	670	9.6	49	260	1	39.4
273	397.8	565	−13.9	50	190	0	−8.6
274	399.0	564	−11.3	50	240	0	−21.4
275	398.2	674	4.9	49	340	1	14.6
276	402.2	676	8.4	50	560	1	19.0
277	402.4	672	0.0	50	420	1	0.0
278	402.1	567	−18.5	49	720	0	−35.1
279	401.6	567	−16.2	49	160	0	−40.2
280	398.6	568	−18.3	50	720	0	−43.8
281	400.5	678	27.9	49	860	1	56.5
282	401.6	672	21.9	51	80	1	79.0
283	399.3	564	−15.7	51	160	0	−39.8
284	397.5	566	−15.7	50	180	0	−26.7
285	402.1	567	−20.6	50	750	0	−65.7
286	400.1	672	3.2	50	470	1	3.9
287	398.4	563	−27.1	50	870	0	−80.6
288	398.5	560	−14.4	50	200	0	−43.6
289	401.1	675	15.4	50	660	1	27.1
290	397.7	567	−23.5	51	780	0	−41.8
291	400.5	561	−19.4	51	740	0	−42.8
292	399.9	679	6.4	51	520	1	15.5
293	400.4	678	6.1	49	520	1	22.8

(Continued)

No.	Utility Side 3ϕ Voltage (V)	DC Bus Voltage (V)	Utility Side 3ϕ Current (A)	Utility Side 3ϕ Power Freq. (Hz)	Elevator Load (kg)	Travelling Direction [Up/Down] (1/0)	Regen. Energy (Wh)
294	397.9	562	−24.9	51	830	0	−81.9
295	397.8	569	−13.7	49	210	0	−7.8
296	398.9	564	−26.5	50	850	0	−79.7
297	400.3	673	1.2	51	400	1	2.3
298	399.2	673	18.4	50	700	1	54.8
299	402.0	567	−12.0	50	230	0	−21.2
300	398.1	678	18.9	50	730	1	60.7
301	400.4	677	17.3	50	140	1	105.1
302	401.2	567	−18.5	50	130	0	−54.7
303	398.0	567	−25.3	51	810	0	−65.3
304	401.5	560	−16.7	50	160	0	−53.4
305	397.6	674	7.4	51	300	1	30.8
306	402.5	675	12.1	49	610	1	33.4
307	400.9	671	3.9	50	360	1	10.8
308	397.9	672	8.4	50	550	1	36.9
309	399.4	678	18.8	49	110	1	87.9
310	398.2	674	5.4	50	510	1	18.9
311	397.9	675	5.8	49	330	1	12.5
312	402.1	567	−28.4	50	860	0	−67.8
313	402.0	673	25.1	50	820	1	95.2
314	401.8	569	−18.1	49	700	0	−69.5
315	402.3	675	5.0	51	500	1	6.0
316	399.9	561	−11.6	50	230	0	−46.6
317	402.1	676	1.3	50	400	1	4.6
318	400.1	566	−13.9	51	200	0	−61.0
319	401.4	561	−26.0	51	820	0	−74.0
320	401.3	679	0.6	49	410	1	1.3
321	399.7	566	−17.3	50	150	0	−73.3
322	401.2	672	1.3	50	400	1	2.4
323	402.1	677	7.4	50	540	1	8.8
324	399.1	561	−27.0	50	860	0	−51.5
325	400.0	672	7.2	49	540	1	13.2
326	400.6	675	8.0	51	290	1	9.6
327	399.3	673	13.1	50	220	1	42.2
328	400.5	560	−16.0	49	170	0	−38.3
329	400.8	562	−16.1	50	170	0	−32.9
330	401.2	561	−21.1	50	750	0	−50.2
331	400.9	680	15.7	50	670	1	63.7
332	399.5	562	−20.2	50	740	0	−76.4
333	400.1	565	−13.8	49	190	0	−26.7
334	399.8	679	6.5	50	320	1	13.6
335	401.5	671	6.4	49	320	1	7.5
336	400.9	567	−27.2	50	860	0	−33.8

(Continued)

No.	Utility Side 3ϕ Voltage (V)	DC Bus Voltage (V)	Utility Side 3ϕ Current (A)	Utility Side 3ϕ Power Freq. (Hz)	Elevator Load (kg)	Travelling Direction [Up/ Down] (1/0)	Regen. Energy (Wh)
337	401.9	679	18.7	49	730	1	89.0
338	400.1	676	10.5	50	590	1	12.6
339	400.4	570	−17.4	50	710	0	−53.6
340	399.7	566	−17.5	51	700	0	−32.6
341	400.2	678	20.8	50	750	1	60.4
342	400.6	569	−25.5	49	810	0	−116.3
343	402.2	565	−15.0	50	170	0	−72.4
344	399.1	679	27.8	51	880	1	17.6
345	400.3	564	−21.2	49	760	0	−39.3
346	398.9	675	21.7	50	770	1	45.5
347	399.3	676	8.4	50	290	1	15.3
348	398.2	673	17.1	51	680	1	9.4
349	398.3	564	−23.4	51	780	0	−95.5
350	398.0	678	7.9	50	550	1	14.3
351	401.4	672	13.0	50	630	1	70.7
352	398.5	680	3.2	50	370	1	13.4
353	400.4	570	−15.5	50	170	0	−38.4
354	402.0	562	−22.9	51	790	0	−41.0
355	398.6	566	−12.8	50	210	0	−15.6
356	400.4	670	9.7	51	270	1	11.7
357	401.3	673	14.6	50	190	1	26.7
358	400.7	674	18.5	49	140	1	54.0
359	399.4	678	22.0	49	60	1	42.3
360	400.6	567	−18.3	51	130	0	−67.8
361	398.5	561	−11.5	49	230	0	−7.2
362	401.8	680	12.8	51	210	1	33.0
363	400.6	672	0.6	50	430	1	1.1
364	401.2	563	−27.3	49	840	0	−16.4
365	400.3	568	−12.7	50	220	0	−54.4
366	401.3	676	14.8	50	190	1	54.5
367	400.9	565	−18.9	50	710	0	−22.1
368	399.5	677	7.2	49	540	1	18.8
369	402.1	570	−13.4	50	200	0	−29.7
370	401.8	569	−30.2	51	910	0	−97.1
371	402.5	566	−25.2	49	840	0	−77.7
372	398.4	673	12.8	51	210	1	23.2
373	401.8	678	17.1	50	690	1	83.4
374	400.8	563	−19.9	51	730	0	−94.7
375	398.5	569	−13.5	51	210	0	−39.2
376	399.1	675	3.1	50	370	1	6.9
377	398.3	567	−10.8	50	240	0	−42.8
378	400.1	678	15.1	50	660	1	9.3
379	400.3	679	20.0	49	90	1	101.8

(*Continued*)

No.	Utility Side 3ϕ Voltage (V)	DC Bus Voltage (V)	Utility Side 3ϕ Current (A)	Utility Side 3ϕ Power Freq. (Hz)	Elevator Load (kg)	Travelling Direction [Up/Down] (1/0)	Regen. Energy (Wh)
380	399.4	569	−13.8	50	210	0	−8.2
381	398.0	674	13.5	50	630	1	28.7
382	401.2	676	10.4	49	590	1	12.6
383	401.4	563	−15.9	49	160	0	−41.0
384	398.2	566	−22.9	50	800	0	−49.1
385	399.8	672	25.6	50	810	1	56.7
386	399.9	567	−21.7	49	760	0	−26.4
387	402.2	676	2.6	49	460	1	4.4
388	402.4	570	−24.7	51	800	0	−136.6
389	399.4	672	32.4	50	960	1	205.6
390	399.9	677	3.1	51	370	1	3.9
391	400.5	567	−21.7	51	760	0	−85.3
392	401.0	567	−16.6	50	150	0	−29.4
393	398.3	567	−24.0	50	810	0	−61.1
394	399.2	677	6.2	51	520	1	14.5
395	400.7	561	−15.0	50	170	0	−9.4
396	398.1	565	−23.4	51	780	0	−49.4
397	397.8	671	9.1	50	560	1	22.8
398	402.3	677	22.6	50	60	1	67.8
399	402.2	678	28.0	49	850	1	93.0
400	399.5	672	18.7	51	120	1	56.9
401	398.0	672	7.5	50	540	1	13.5
402	398.7	568	−17.5	50	150	0	−61.3
403	399.0	567	−20.2	50	740	0	−49.5
404	401.2	568	−22.3	51	780	0	−54.9
405	397.6	676	4.9	50	340	1	2.9
406	399.7	569	−24.2	50	810	0	−29.8
407	401.7	671	4.4	50	490	1	7.7
408	399.3	565	−19.9	51	740	0	−50.2
409	400.7	677	13.9	51	650	1	25.6
410	397.6	673	23.7	51	810	1	60.8
411	401.4	568	−17.1	49	160	0	−43.2
412	401.4	567	−23.1	49	790	0	−29.1
413	399.9	673	0.7	50	410	1	0.4
414	397.7	673	12.9	51	630	1	16.5
415	397.9	565	−32.4	49	930	0	−77.4
416	397.7	679	19.3	49	720	1	23.3
417	399.3	563	−23.3	50	790	0	−13.6
418	402.3	678	6.4	51	320	1	7.8
419	397.8	568	−20.0	50	740	0	−12.1
420	399.9	676	1.3	49	400	1	2.3
421	399.7	678	11.2	51	240	1	7.2
422	399.7	680	17.7	50	150	1	20.1

(Continued)

No.	Utility Side 3ϕ Voltage (V)	DC Bus Voltage (V)	Utility Side 3ϕ Current (A)	Utility Side 3ϕ Power Freq. (Hz)	Elevator Load (kg)	Travelling Direction [Up/Down] (1/0)	Regen. Energy (Wh)
423	399.0	676	19.9	50	90	1	37.7
424	398.4	567	−22.9	51	50	0	−28.5
425	399.8	674	12.7	49	630	1	32.6
426	400.6	672	27.9	50	870	1	83.1
427	398.7	567	−16.5	50	160	0	−9.5
428	398.7	566	−21.5	50	80	0	−27.0
429	400.3	563	−27.7	50	0	0	−16.4
430	397.7	679	8.4	51	560	1	20.3
431	401.0	562	−34.6	51	980	0	−21.8
432	399.0	564	−25.6	50	820	0	−63.1
433	398.3	569	−32.5	49	930	0	−19.3
434	401.6	680	6.2	49	320	1	7.6
435	401.4	670	11.8	49	240	1	14.0
436	399.8	677	16.8	51	160	1	10.0
437	398.7	671	21.3	50	80	1	36.9
438	399.4	673	15.8	50	160	1	38.5
439	399.9	675	5.5	50	330	1	3.3
440	400.7	563	−22.1	50	60	0	−26.0
441	401.8	569	−10.8	50	240	0	−26.8
442	401.1	678	9.0	51	560	1	16.1
443	401.7	563	−14.9	50	190	0	−25.7
444	401.3	568	−15.8	50	180	0	−17.7
445	400.8	570	−12.0	51	230	0	−14.6
446	402.0	680	25.9	51	0	1	49.3
447	399.7	676	5.6	49	510	1	15.0
448	398.1	562	−21.3	49	80	0	−13.3
449	397.6	671	18.9	50	110	1	11.5
450	402.0	676	0.6	50	410	1	0.7
451	397.9	679	6.3	51	320	1	3.7
452	399.9	570	−25.0	51	810	0	−31.0
453	401.7	670	6.4	49	320	1	11.6
454	398.8	678	11.4	51	240	1	21.3
455	402.3	679	26.0	50	830	1	60.8
456	401.4	564	−12.2	51	230	0	−14.1
457	401.9	671	26.8	51	0	1	61.2
458	400.3	678	13.2	50	640	1	32.0
459	401.0	570	−20.0	50	90	0	−12.0
460	397.8	675	10.4	49	260	1	19.0
461	398.0	563	−22.6	51	780	0	−14.2
462	400.6	568	−17.8	51	690	0	−41.8
463	399.0	671	4.3	51	350	1	5.2
464	397.7	671	2.4	50	380	1	6.3
465	400.9	671	6.8	51	310	1	12.8

(Continued)

No.	Utility Side 3ϕ Voltage (V)	DC Bus Voltage (V)	Utility Side 3ϕ Current (A)	Utility Side 3ϕ Power Freq. (Hz)	Elevator Load (kg)	Travelling Direction [Up/ Down] (1/0)	Regen. Energy (Wh)
466	399.8	677	25.7	49	0	1	32.1
467	400.2	567	−16.1	51	170	0	−19.1
468	399.6	675	2.6	49	460	1	5.8
469	400.7	565	−20.3	50	110	0	−35.9
470	398.2	679	10.2	51	580	1	18.5
471	400.6	675	13.8	50	650	1	16.8
472	397.8	567	−13.2	49	210	0	−16.5
473	400.0	563	−15.9	50	170	0	−9.6
474	400.3	563	−13.1	51	210	0	−16.3
475	399.5	564	−25.4	49	810	0	−14.7
476	398.5	680	3.6	49	360	1	6.5
477	399.9	677	1.9	50	390	1	2.2
478	400.5	680	6.0	50	320	1	3.7
479	398.1	677	7.9	51	290	1	15.4
480	398.1	674	26.0	49	0	1	63.6
481	401.2	678	13.8	49	640	1	33.0
482	398.1	677	19.8	50	730	1	45.9
483	397.7	678	23.9	50	810	1	30.5
484	400.6	678	36.6	50	990	1	42.3
485	399.2	677	20.7	50	740	1	24.9
486	400.4	678	16.2	50	680	1	10.3
487	399.1	671	25.6	51	820	1	46.0
488	399.8	566	−23.9	50	40	0	−14.7
489	399.6	678	14.4	50	190	1	8.6
490	401.6	675	6.7	49	310	1	4.1
491	400.1	670	0.6	50	430	1	0.7
492	398.3	562	−19.7	51	740	0	−12.4
493	398.8	677	4.3	51	350	1	8.1
494	398.3	675	0.0	51	420	1	0.0
495	402.4	680	15.8	50	170	1	38.4
496	399.7	677	26.4	51	0	1	77.4
497	400.7	680	10.0	51	580	1	26.6
498	397.8	565	−12.2	51	230	0	−20.9
499	400.8	676	4.2	50	490	1	2.7
500	402.4	673	13.1	49	640	1	16.1
501	400.3	678	21.3	51	760	1	12.3
502	400.3	677	36.5	50	1000	1	65.2
503	400.9	678	6.0	50	320	1	3.9
504	400.0	670	3.1	50	370	1	3.9
505	399.2	672	11.0	50	240	1	13.9
506	399.0	673	12.6	50	210	1	16.0
507	398.2	674	4.4	50	350	1	7.6
508	399.4	676	18.4	49	130	1	38.9

(Continued)

No.	Utility Side 3ϕ Voltage (V)	DC Bus Voltage (V)	Utility Side 3ϕ Current (A)	Utility Side 3ϕ Power Freq. (Hz)	Elevator Load (kg)	Travelling Direction [Up/ Down] (1/0)	Regen. Energy (Wh)
509	400.6	677	12.6	49	210	1	15.5
510	402.2	568	−19.8	49	110	0	−11.6
511	399.5	676	33.4	50	970	1	86.6
512	399.5	678	14.2	50	640	1	25.2
513	402.3	677	18.6	50	720	1	47.4
514	398.4	671	28.4	50	880	1	49.8
515	401.8	679	11.8	50	240	1	6.5
516	400.8	678	16.7	49	160	1	29.3
517	398.0	673	11.6	50	240	1	21.3
518	399.6	673	26.3	51	0	1	45.6
519	400.5	673	5.8	50	330	1	14.0
520	401.8	672	16.8	51	150	1	10.6
521	401.3	565	−15.2	50	170	0	−36.6
522	402.4	563	−16.2	51	150	0	−48.0
523	398.8	567	−12.6	50	210	0	−7.6
524	401.8	673	16.7	49	690	1	30.1
525	399.2	679	4.3	50	490	1	2.8
526	398.0	563	−23.6	49	40	0	−14.4
527	399.7	677	22.2	50	80	1	12.8
528	402.2	671	10.7	50	250	1	19.9
529	402.1	676	15.2	51	170	1	38.3
530	398.2	678	18.6	50	110	1	11.3
531	399.9	675	25.2	50	0	1	80.7
532	398.6	566	−18.7	51	120	0	−34.6
533	402.2	564	−15.9	49	160	0	−28.8
534	398.5	676	23.0	50	780	1	56.7
535	401.9	563	−14.5	50	200	0	−26.2
536	398.2	674	7.0	50	310	1	16.8
537	398.2	676	10.8	50	240	1	13.4
538	400.9	676	14.7	50	180	1	18.1
539	397.5	671	11.6	50	230	1	7.2
540	400.0	567	−21.5	50	90	0	−50.6
Total regenerated energy per day by 1 elevator (Wh)							227.1
Total regenerated energy per day by all the 5 elevators (kWh)							1.1

Site Measured Elevator Data – Apartment Building Complex @ Boswell Place

No.	Utility Side 3ϕ Voltage (V)	DC Bus Voltage (V)	Utility Side 3ϕ Current (A)	Utility Side 3ϕ Power Freq. (Hz)	Elevator Load (kg)	Travelling Direction [Up/ Down] (1/0)	Regen. Energy (Wh)
1	401.5	677	11.8	50	490	0	45.6
2	398.7	679	14.5	51	530	0	35.3
3	400.2	672	0.5	51	260	0	0.3
4	404.2	679	4.3	50	340	0	3.0
5	402.7	563	−13.7	50	530	1	−60.1
6	395.1	678	1.0	49	230	1	1.3
7	398.1	679	7.7	51	90	1	23.2
8	399.5	679	1.0	50	270	0	1.2
9	403.2	680	7.7	49	410	0	33.5
10	395.0	678	3.5	49	320	0	4.0
11	403.4	677	14.8	50	550	0	18.4
12	400.2	676	6.2	49	380	0	4.1
13	396.2	679	1.5	51	220	1	4.7
14	402.6	565	−8.9	50	420	1	−5.5
15	400.9	569	−9.3	51	440	1	−18.0
16	402.3	671	1.0	51	230	1	1.2
17	398.3	566	−9.1	50	430	1	−11.3
18	395.6	677	5.2	51	350	0	8.8
19	404.3	560	−8.1	49	90	0	−5.5
20	403.3	670	11.0	51	470	0	47.7
21	399.0	679	2.0	51	210	1	3.8
22	400.4	673	14.6	49	540	0	17.0
23	399.1	675	11.4	50	490	0	14.6
24	400.8	671	6.8	49	390	0	4.7
25	403.1	680	6.8	50	110	1	48.1
26	395.2	679	13.9	50	520	0	41.3
27	395.3	674	11.5	50	470	0	27.5
28	398.3	677	2.0	49	290	0	1.4
29	399.5	679	2.0	49	210	1	2.3
30	402.6	565	−12.4	49	490	1	−36.7
31	399.2	565	−15.4	50	570	1	−27.6
32	402.4	678	5.7	49	130	1	11.0
33	401.4	675	10.8	50	460	0	12.1
34	400.7	676	10.5	49	470	0	13.1
35	397.3	561	−9.3	49	70	0	−6.1
36	398.3	560	−7.2	50	110	0	−12.8
37	395.2	674	4.6	50	340	0	5.7
38	402.5	677	10.6	49	460	0	12.4
39	404.8	673	1.5	51	280	0	1.0
40	397.0	671	5.8	50	360	0	3.6
41	400.0	678	1.5	51	220	1	5.2

(*Continued*)

No.	Utility Side 3ϕ Voltage (V)	DC Bus Voltage (V)	Utility Side 3ϕ Current (A)	Utility Side 3ϕ Power Freq. (Hz)	Elevator Load (kg)	Travelling Direction [Up/Down] (1/0)	Regen. Energy (Wh)
42	404.4	564	−10.8	50	470	1	−33.3
43	403.3	562	−13.9	50	520	1	−9.3
44	397.3	678	1.5	50	220	1	1.8
45	403.1	560	−7.6	49	100	0	−18.9
46	396.8	563	−9.5	49	50	0	−11.8
47	400.3	677	5.3	50	360	0	6.8
48	395.2	675	4.4	50	340	0	2.9
49	395.2	563	−8.7	50	80	0	−24.7
50	402.3	568	−11.4	49	470	1	−20.5
51	401.1	561	−18.6	51	610	1	−64.9
52	404.9	674	1.0	50	230	1	1.2
53	401.9	562	−15.1	50	560	1	−17.6
54	399.3	560	−14.5	50	550	1	−10.0
55	398.1	679	3.1	50	310	0	7.5
56	401.1	567	−9.8	50	50	0	−43.2
57	399.4	564	−15.0	50	560	1	−36.3
58	399.9	568	−13.8	51	520	1	−24.0
59	396.7	567	−15.5	49	570	1	−28.1
60	396.3	671	7.4	50	400	0	50.8
61	396.9	673	7.7	50	410	0	5.4
62	400.3	561	−4.8	51	150	0	−3.5
63	398.8	565	−8.9	49	420	1	−14.7
64	396.6	569	−13.1	50	520	1	−16.0
65	403.5	676	2.0	51	210	1	1.4
66	404.0	567	−11.4	50	480	1	−20.4
67	396.1	676	5.9	50	130	1	4.0
68	398.3	680	1.0	51	230	1	1.2
69	398.5	560	−10.6	49	470	1	−13.5
70	398.7	679	0.5	50	260	0	0.6
71	403.4	677	1.0	51	270	0	1.8
72	401.9	674	3.0	50	310	0	9.6
73	398.0	679	3.3	51	320	0	6.7
74	404.0	674	0.5	50	260	0	0.3
75	403.3	569	−11.9	49	480	1	−39.2
76	403.9	673	2.0	50	210	1	3.7
77	395.4	672	8.0	49	90	1	5.6
78	402.9	675	11.9	51	0	1	15.3
79	400.7	561	−13.8	50	520	1	−16.1
80	396.0	674	13.6	50	510	0	86.2
81	398.7	677	4.5	51	340	0	5.6
82	398.8	674	1.0	49	270	0	0.6
83	398.8	563	−10.3	50	450	1	−41.6
84	404.1	672	2.4	50	200	1	4.6

(Continued)

No.	Utility Side 3ϕ Voltage (V)	DC Bus Voltage (V)	Utility Side 3ϕ Current (A)	Utility Side 3ϕ Power Freq. (Hz)	Elevator Load (kg)	Travelling Direction [Up/ Down] (1/0)	Regen. Energy (Wh)
85	404.8	562	−11.8	51	490	1	−8.0
86	404.8	565	−15.7	49	550	1	−17.4
87	401.7	679	5.8	49	370	0	10.4
88	398.3	565	−8.3	50	80	0	−43.8
89	404.0	563	−18.0	50	600	1	−82.0
90	395.7	567	−12.1	50	490	1	−21.2
91	402.2	568	−9.4	50	70	0	−26.3
92	400.6	570	−6.2	50	130	0	−17.8
93	398.0	677	13.1	51	0	1	71.0
94	396.9	675	10.0	51	460	0	70.4
95	404.6	675	6.7	50	110	1	8.6
96	396.0	673	11.9	50	0	1	53.4
97	400.0	570	−12.9	49	500	1	−8.6
98	398.7	561	−13.2	51	520	1	−24.2
99	396.8	671	4.9	50	350	0	3.3
100	401.3	569	−7.7	50	100	0	−13.5
101	404.2	566	−12.1	51	500	1	−28.5
102	395.6	680	18.7	51	610	0	104.8
103	398.9	670	4.4	50	340	0	3.2
104	397.8	674	2.0	50	290	0	1.4
105	402.8	674	12.1	51	0	1	90.8
106	403.1	674	18.3	50	600	0	21.0
107	404.7	675	6.1	49	370	0	14.8
108	401.6	678	9.4	50	440	0	35.0
109	400.5	567	−12.3	49	500	1	−99.0
110	401.5	567	−7.8	49	100	0	−18.0
111	402.1	679	11.3	49	480	0	51.1
112	398.5	672	0.5	49	240	1	0.9
113	395.1	678	6.5	50	380	0	15.0
114	396.0	567	−9.0	51	430	1	−47.3
115	396.6	678	7.0	50	110	1	4.8
116	403.1	677	5.0	50	150	1	6.2
117	400.7	680	11.3	51	470	0	71.6
118	396.9	676	12.1	50	0	1	31.2
119	402.9	674	2.9	50	190	1	7.2
120	395.3	564	−9.8	51	50	0	−17.5
121	402.1	566	−6.4	50	120	0	−11.6
122	400.7	567	−8.2	49	80	0	−5.9
123	400.4	676	5.8	50	130	1	36.2
124	403.2	670	11.7	51	490	0	29.8
125	402.7	675	13.2	50	510	0	54.1
126	395.8	676	3.4	50	320	0	4.3
127	400.6	674	12.3	50	0	1	88.2

(Continued)

No.	Utility Side 3ϕ Voltage (V)	DC Bus Voltage (V)	Utility Side 3ϕ Current (A)	Utility Side 3ϕ Power Freq. (Hz)	Elevator Load (kg)	Travelling Direction [Up/ Down] (1/0)	Regen. Energy (Wh)
128	398.0	676	11.8	51	480	0	56.7
129	400.4	566	−18.0	51	600	1	−20.8
130	397.1	672	12.1	51	490	0	8.0
131	397.9	565	−9.4	51	440	1	−11.8
132	400.2	670	5.2	49	140	1	20.7
133	398.8	673	4.9	50	350	0	11.7
134	399.2	676	10.8	51	460	0	43.3
135	400.4	672	9.0	50	430	0	5.7
136	397.3	566	−11.0	49	480	1	−8.1
137	404.2	672	12.1	49	0	1	72.3
138	398.9	676	13.1	49	520	0	16.7
139	401.5	673	10.0	51	450	0	35.5
140	402.7	567	−13.8	50	540	1	−9.8
141	402.1	567	−14.8	50	560	1	−19.1
142	399.6	679	2.6	50	200	1	4.6
143	400.4	569	−4.5	51	160	0	−13.8
144	397.5	674	1.0	51	230	1	1.8
145	396.6	569	−16.0	51	580	1	−29.3
146	399.7	679	7.3	50	390	0	32.3
147	395.2	565	−15.7	49	560	1	−47.9
148	397.5	671	6.8	50	110	1	12.7
149	401.4	567	−11.5	50	490	1	−14.8
150	398.6	670	16.2	50	590	0	137.3
151	397.0	566	−9.1	50	430	1	−10.5
152	402.7	673	12.9	50	0	1	76.4
153	402.3	674	9.6	49	450	0	59.3
154	396.8	674	7.2	50	100	1	51.5
155	398.4	679	9.9	50	450	0	6.7
156	396.9	678	11.6	50	490	0	78.1
157	400.2	568	−6.8	51	110	0	−8.6
158	397.8	679	3.3	50	180	1	21.2
159	395.8	560	−14.8	50	540	1	−16.9
160	398.3	673	9.7	51	450	0	6.5
161	396.9	565	−9.1	50	70	0	−21.7
162	396.1	673	1.5	50	220	1	2.8
163	403.1	564	−8.1	50	420	1	−15.0
164	398.1	678	14.7	51	540	0	108.3
165	403.1	670	12.3	49	0	1	78.6
166	402.2	676	2.9	49	190	1	3.8
167	398.2	673	2.5	49	300	0	7.9
168	398.4	678	10.9	50	460	0	31.1
169	404.9	567	−9.8	50	450	1	−18.1
170	403.3	674	1.0	49	230	1	0.7

(Continued)

No.	Utility Side 3ϕ Voltage (V)	DC Bus Voltage (V)	Utility Side 3ϕ Current (A)	Utility Side 3ϕ Power Freq. (Hz)	Elevator Load (kg)	Travelling Direction [Up/ Down] (1/0)	Regen. Energy (Wh)
171	399.0	673	0.5	50	240	1	0.6
172	401.8	562	−8.1	49	420	1	−16.2
173	395.3	679	2.1	50	210	1	2.4
174	397.6	672	18.1	49	610	0	112.0
175	399.1	671	12.9	49	0	1	63.0
176	395.0	674	11.9	50	490	0	51.3
177	399.3	564	−15.7	51	570	1	−10.9
178	395.6	674	6.7	50	110	1	28.6
179	402.9	676	17.6	50	590	0	86.0
180	402.9	675	2.1	50	290	0	3.7
181	400.8	671	2.4	50	200	1	1.7
182	401.0	678	9.4	50	430	0	10.6
183	403.9	562	−11.0	50	470	1	−41.6
184	396.2	677	2.0	49	290	0	2.4
185	400.2	566	−15.1	49	540	1	−63.4
186	403.3	673	15.7	49	560	0	82.7
187	399.5	678	1.0	50	230	1	1.1
188	400.4	676	2.9	49	190	1	7.3
189	401.9	565	−12.7	50	500	1	−8.1
190	396.5	680	12.5	51	490	0	65.4
191	401.7	678	12.5	49	0	1	82.2
192	396.8	672	1.9	50	290	0	8.3
193	403.4	568	−13.1	51	510	1	−30.2
194	400.6	569	−12.0	49	500	1	−22.4
195	404.3	677	1.0	51	270	0	0.7
196	401.9	676	12.7	51	510	0	86.5
197	400.6	677	5.0	50	150	1	28.0
198	396.3	677	12.4	51	500	0	22.3
199	404.4	672	8.3	50	410	0	14.0
200	404.4	570	−18.1	50	620	1	−92.5
201	399.0	679	9.9	49	440	0	6.4
202	397.2	673	11.8	49	490	0	59.9
203	404.6	561	−8.6	50	420	1	−20.8
204	403.0	679	4.9	50	350	0	8.7
205	399.9	563	−12.8	50	510	1	−8.8
206	402.7	570	−15.0	51	560	1	−49.0
207	399.5	676	5.7	49	370	0	3.9
208	401.9	565	−8.3	50	90	0	−25.2
209	402.8	673	1.0	49	270	0	1.2
210	401.4	564	−18.2	50	600	1	−86.2
211	402.4	673	13.9	50	530	0	35.2
212	402.0	566	−5.4	51	140	0	−10.1
213	397.8	672	11.9	50	0	1	64.7

(Continued)

No.	Utility Side 3ϕ Voltage (V)	DC Bus Voltage (V)	Utility Side 3ϕ Current (A)	Utility Side 3ϕ Power Freq. (Hz)	Elevator Load (kg)	Travelling Direction [Up/Down] (1/0)	Regen. Energy (Wh)
214	395.4	561	−7.6	50	100	0	−26.5
215	401.1	675	6.4	49	120	1	23.0
216	402.7	674	3.1	49	190	1	3.7
217	396.0	679	5.5	49	360	0	33.6
218	403.4	674	0.5	50	240	1	2.7
219	397.5	679	10.5	50	470	0	76.4
220	404.1	563	−11.6	51	490	1	−62.3
221	402.5	672	0.5	49	240	1	0.4
222	403.2	672	17.2	51	610	0	42.5
223	395.5	566	−15.3	50	570	1	−10.7
224	395.9	675	10.2	51	50	1	41.4
225	397.0	564	−7.2	49	100	0	−14.0
226	398.6	673	14.1	50	520	0	72.0
227	403.0	566	−12.8	50	510	1	−79.8
228	399.2	567	−9.6	50	60	0	−11.6
229	395.5	672	2.9	50	310	0	7.4
230	397.8	677	4.6	50	340	0	5.7
231	395.5	564	−6.8	50	120	0	−12.2
232	404.0	678	12.1	50	0	1	31.2
233	399.2	567	−11.2	51	470	1	−19.8
234	395.5	567	−12.4	50	510	1	−15.2
235	398.5	565	−10.4	50	450	1	−24.1
236	397.0	672	2.0	49	290	0	7.5
237	397.6	565	−9.9	50	450	1	−18.1
238	398.5	568	−6.7	49	120	0	−7.5
239	403.3	676	11.2	50	470	0	33.2
240	397.2	671	3.0	50	310	0	3.7
241	402.6	679	0.5	51	260	0	0.3
242	400.1	568	−15.6	50	560	1	−108.2
243	395.3	674	3.4	49	320	0	12.2
244	396.9	676	11.4	50	480	0	42.7
245	400.4	566	−9.3	49	70	0	−6.3
246	401.2	564	−14.0	50	540	1	−9.2
247	403.7	570	−9.8	50	440	1	−40.1
248	396.5	677	4.8	51	350	0	3.3
249	395.1	564	−6.5	50	120	0	−4.2
250	400.3	675	9.2	49	430	0	31.3
251	398.6	569	−8.3	49	420	1	−36.6
252	400.2	566	−9.1	49	430	1	−22.6
253	401.0	562	−11.9	49	500	1	−23.2
254	403.0	680	7.7	51	400	0	21.4
255	395.6	566	−6.5	50	120	0	−23.1
256	395.0	566	−10.7	50	460	1	−20.1

(Continued)

No.	Utility Side 3ϕ Voltage (V)	DC Bus Voltage (V)	Utility Side 3ϕ Current (A)	Utility Side 3ϕ Power Freq. (Hz)	Elevator Load (kg)	Travelling Direction [Up/Down] (1/0)	Regen. Energy (Wh)
257	396.9	569	−11.0	49	470	1	−12.9
258	398.6	673	1.9	49	210	1	3.8
259	397.7	563	−15.2	49	560	1	−28.4
260	398.0	678	10.1	49	450	0	34.5
261	397.4	569	−9.6	49	440	1	−22.0
262	399.4	676	4.5	50	340	0	25.2
263	399.1	565	−9.9	49	60	0	−12.0
264	404.9	672	12.7	50	0	1	63.0
265	403.7	565	−14.6	50	540	1	−10.1
266	395.7	566	−16.7	50	580	1	−20.1
267	396.3	674	8.4	51	420	0	30.1
268	398.6	564	−15.3	50	570	1	−30.3
269	399.9	674	8.0	49	410	0	38.7
270	404.9	567	−14.2	51	530	1	−9.7
271	403.8	569	−13.4	49	520	1	−9.4
272	402.1	561	−15.0	51	550	1	−44.8
273	402.4	678	4.8	49	150	1	17.8
274	396.8	567	−6.3	50	130	0	−38.7
275	403.2	676	4.1	51	170	1	16.9
276	403.3	673	9.7	50	440	0	16.4
277	399.0	563	−11.4	49	480	1	−14.3
278	398.5	670	8.2	49	410	0	5.6
279	396.2	567	−7.2	50	100	0	−26.4
280	401.3	570	−16.8	50	570	1	−28.8
281	395.8	680	8.4	51	420	0	19.8
282	398.2	567	−10.3	50	460	1	−58.4
283	402.2	676	6.9	50	390	0	25.5
284	399.8	678	7.8	49	100	1	13.1
285	404.9	678	17.0	50	600	0	53.3
286	403.7	670	6.2	51	130	1	18.3
287	399.0	674	2.5	51	300	0	3.1
288	397.1	670	2.0	50	290	0	2.5
289	402.7	679	4.0	50	170	1	19.8
290	400.7	570	−15.7	51	560	1	−28.8
291	396.1	679	9.0	50	440	0	55.0
292	399.9	674	12.9	51	500	0	14.8
293	402.6	570	−7.6	50	100	0	−8.6
294	397.5	677	11.9	50	0	1	72.5
295	402.5	673	6.7	49	390	0	28.3
296	403.0	565	−11.8	51	490	1	−30.2
297	398.7	679	15.0	49	560	0	48.5
298	398.2	677	15.4	50	570	0	10.7
299	395.2	674	7.9	51	90	1	33.4

(*Continued*)

No.	Utility Side 3ϕ Voltage (V)	DC Bus Voltage (V)	Utility Side 3ϕ Current (A)	Utility Side 3ϕ Power Freq. (Hz)	Elevator Load (kg)	Travelling Direction [Up/ Down] (1/0)	Regen. Energy (Wh)
300	404.3	562	−11.5	50	480	1	−21.6
301	401.7	674	6.8	50	390	0	33.1
302	400.4	677	8.7	49	80	1	44.7
303	404.1	673	5.4	50	360	0	29.7
304	397.6	678	2.4	50	200	1	12.1
305	401.5	673	15.8	49	580	0	108.6
306	402.7	673	4.5	50	160	1	11.2
307	402.9	673	6.3	50	380	0	4.3
308	397.0	566	−12.3	49	500	1	−37.5
309	403.3	679	0.5	51	260	0	2.4
310	399.5	568	−10.4	51	450	1	−55.7
311	401.6	678	1.5	49	220	1	3.8
312	398.2	679	17.7	51	600	0	32.6
313	398.1	565	−8.3	51	80	0	−34.6
314	403.4	570	−7.7	50	100	0	−9.3
315	400.2	561	−11.5	50	490	1	−35.4
316	395.3	569	−8.6	51	430	1	−33.7
317	399.0	570	−9.6	49	440	1	−12.1
318	395.5	677	16.1	49	580	0	109.7
319	398.7	680	12.0	50	0	1	52.3
320	395.5	673	1.0	50	230	1	1.2
321	398.9	567	−7.7	51	90	0	−47.7
322	396.2	563	−15.4	50	550	1	−43.7
323	395.3	673	2.4	50	200	1	10.4
324	404.3	562	−7.1	51	100	0	−55.1
325	395.0	560	−7.0	50	390	1	−13.1
326	396.9	567	−14.6	50	530	1	−17.1
327	400.1	570	−16.6	50	590	1	−70.7
328	396.8	672	14.0	50	530	0	118.9
329	404.1	562	−12.7	51	510	1	−91.2
330	403.8	560	−13.1	50	510	1	−16.2
331	397.9	568	−5.3	50	140	0	−46.2
332	396.8	568	−13.6	50	530	1	−91.2
333	399.3	674	4.7	50	340	0	2.9
334	403.2	567	−6.9	51	110	0	−33.8
335	401.1	679	3.9	50	170	1	5.0
336	400.2	564	−12.4	51	490	1	−14.6
337	397.0	675	0.5	50	240	1	0.9
338	395.6	564	−5.1	49	150	0	−18.7
339	403.1	673	12.5	50	0	1	73.8
340	404.1	679	17.1	50	580	0	136.2
341	397.0	675	2.9	51	190	1	18.6
342	399.3	565	−9.6	51	60	0	−11.9

(*Continued*)

No.	Utility Side 3ϕ Voltage (V)	DC Bus Voltage (V)	Utility Side 3ϕ Current (A)	Utility Side 3ϕ Power Freq. (Hz)	Elevator Load (kg)	Travelling Direction [Up/Down] (1/0)	Regen. Energy (Wh)
343	396.4	678	5.2	50	350	0	3.3
344	397.3	568	–14.0	50	520	1	–54.2
345	397.7	671	7.9	51	410	0	23.7
346	398.5	565	–9.0	50	430	1	–22.3
347	403.1	675	12.6	50	500	0	15.3
348	399.0	561	–10.1	50	50	0	–12.0
349	400.2	562	–8.4	51	90	0	–29.8
350	403.2	560	–8.3	50	410	1	–19.5
351	397.4	561	–13.9	49	530	1	–25.8
352	398.7	678	11.6	49	480	0	13.6
353	399.1	562	–7.0	51	110	0	–20.3
354	402.7	671	15.1	51	550	0	27.9
355	404.2	565	–11.5	49	490	1	–82.8
356	398.2	679	4.1	50	330	0	9.9
357	404.3	677	8.3	50	410	0	19.2
358	398.5	564	–12.4	50	510	1	–56.7
359	396.8	679	2.9	50	190	1	5.6
360	396.6	679	6.8	49	380	0	39.6
361	395.3	566	–7.2	50	100	0	–17.9
362	403.9	567	–14.4	50	530	1	–75.0
363	395.5	675	1.9	50	290	0	1.3
364	399.9	568	–7.3	51	100	0	–4.9
365	395.4	678	4.4	51	160	1	8.3
366	403.5	570	–11.6	50	480	1	–26.2
367	404.8	568	–8.3	50	90	0	–10.0
368	396.9	676	13.3	49	510	0	91.2
369	403.1	676	12.8	49	0	1	74.3
370	397.3	679	0.5	49	260	0	1.3
371	403.7	679	5.1	50	350	0	3.5
372	404.6	672	5.2	51	350	0	3.4
373	401.4	679	8.5	50	80	1	35.2
374	404.4	674	11.8	50	480	0	75.2
375	399.0	568	–18.0	50	600	1	–11.1
376	401.7	678	2.4	49	200	1	14.5
377	398.8	680	4.2	50	330	0	23.4
378	398.7	566	–8.6	50	430	1	–37.2
379	400.4	561	–9.0	49	430	1	–10.5
380	403.0	679	12.4	51	510	0	32.5
381	402.6	675	1.0	49	270	0	1.9
382	401.5	565	–10.7	50	470	1	–41.2
383	398.3	678	4.8	50	150	1	9.1
384	400.6	678	5.7	50	360	0	31.8
385	398.2	679	12.8	51	0	1	57.6

(Continued)

No.	Utility Side 3ϕ Voltage (V)	DC Bus Voltage (V)	Utility Side 3ϕ Current (A)	Utility Side 3ϕ Power Freq. (Hz)	Elevator Load (kg)	Travelling Direction [Up/Down] (1/0)	Regen. Energy (Wh)
386	404.7	570	−16.1	50	560	1	−9.9
387	399.0	673	8.5	49	420	0	15.0
388	401.2	568	−9.5	49	60	0	−16.4
389	395.3	678	9.5	50	440	0	17.5
390	398.3	565	−13.5	50	530	1	−92.4
391	405.0	563	−6.8	51	110	0	−60.2
392	402.1	672	1.9	49	210	1	8.5
393	398.2	673	0.5	50	240	1	0.3
394	397.5	562	−13.1	49	520	1	−24.4
395	398.5	672	5.5	50	360	0	28.9
396	400.6	566	−6.7	50	110	0	−4.7
397	396.9	678	2.0	50	210	1	8.8
398	398.9	562	−11.7	50	480	1	−7.6
399	397.7	560	−10.5	50	450	1	−12.3
400	403.9	562	−11.1	50	470	1	−7.1
401	396.6	674	9.4	51	430	0	26.0
402	400.7	671	5.0	51	350	0	6.1
403	403.9	566	−9.1	49	70	0	−5.9
404	395.1	568	−6.9	50	110	0	−4.8
405	401.1	674	8.5	50	420	0	10.2
406	398.9	561	−8.7	50	70	0	−5.8
407	400.5	678	9.1	50	70	1	41.9
408	399.1	566	−10.4	51	460	1	−19.2
409	399.9	564	−9.9	51	450	1	−18.7
410	400.1	563	−8.3	50	90	0	−14.5
411	401.7	678	3.1	50	310	0	2.0
412	398.2	676	9.9	50	450	0	24.3
413	395.7	673	13.1	50	500	0	14.2
414	397.0	560	−5.6	50	140	0	−9.6
415	396.8	560	−7.2	49	100	0	−5.2
416	403.0	680	1.0	50	230	1	1.9
417	397.5	564	−9.6	49	450	1	−23.4
418	404.1	673	2.0	51	210	1	3.5
419	395.6	674	5.2	51	150	1	9.0
420	399.2	568	−9.7	50	60	0	−23.5
421	404.5	679	5.5	49	360	0	3.8
422	396.3	671	5.5	51	360	0	6.4
423	398.5	564	−6.2	51	120	0	−8.0
424	395.7	675	11.1	50	470	0	7.2
425	401.2	679	13.4	50	510	0	23.6
426	401.0	562	−10.1	50	450	1	−24.6
427	403.8	561	−9.2	51	430	1	−11.3
428	398.5	677	0.5	49	240	1	1.8

(*Continued*)

No.	Utility Side 3ϕ Voltage (V)	DC Bus Voltage (V)	Utility Side 3ϕ Current (A)	Utility Side 3ϕ Power Freq. (Hz)	Elevator Load (kg)	Travelling Direction [Up/Down] (1/0)	Regen. Energy (Wh)
429	404.8	678	11.9	50	500	0	14.7
430	404.6	567	−6.1	49	130	0	−11.2
431	400.5	672	13.5	50	510	0	8.5
432	400.9	673	11.7	50	490	0	29.5
433	397.7	679	1.4	49	280	0	1.8
434	396.4	679	1.0	51	230	1	3.1
435	401.3	677	0.5	50	240	1	0.3
436	399.7	565	−11.6	51	480	1	−14.2
437	395.4	675	12.5	51	0	1	21.7
438	397.8	568	−15.0	50	540	1	−18.2
439	400.6	676	13.2	51	510	0	16.1
440	397.6	674	9.0	50	440	0	10.9
441	404.6	676	1.4	50	280	0	1.1
442	396.4	678	8.0	50	410	0	15.2
443	398.4	676	11.3	49	480	0	21.6
444	395.3	672	5.0	51	350	0	3.4
445	404.7	562	−7.7	50	90	0	−5.4
446	404.1	568	−12.4	49	490	1	−22.0
447	398.6	564	−11.6	50	480	1	−34.3
448	403.9	677	2.0	51	210	1	2.4
449	398.6	568	−10.2	50	460	1	−18.9
450	402.2	568	−13.1	49	500	1	−8.3
451	398.0	676	9.3	50	440	0	33.7
452	399.3	678	9.4	51	440	0	23.4
453	402.9	566	−6.7	51	120	0	−7.5
454	400.8	568	−7.3	50	110	0	−8.7
455	400.6	566	−9.2	49	430	1	−16.0
456	397.6	671	12.8	49	0	1	51.7
457	399.6	672	2.5	51	200	1	4.5
458	398.2	673	8.9	49	430	0	10.4
459	402.4	673	6.8	49	390	0	8.4
460	405.0	671	6.5	50	380	0	4.3
461	397.5	676	12.0	51	490	0	14.2
462	397.9	561	−6.5	49	120	0	−11.9
463	401.6	677	5.5	49	360	0	6.6
464	403.2	671	3.1	49	310	0	1.9
465	404.3	563	−17.2	50	600	1	−62.7
466	404.1	565	−15.6	51	570	1	−10.8
467	399.1	676	1.0	50	230	1	1.7
468	404.2	570	−13.2	50	520	1	−9.3
469	400.9	678	0.5	50	240	1	0.6
470	399.0	565	−8.3	50	90	0	−9.7
471	397.5	674	9.2	51	440	0	16.5

(Continued)

No.	Utility Side 3ϕ Voltage (V)	DC Bus Voltage (V)	Utility Side 3ϕ Current (A)	Utility Side 3ϕ Power Freq. (Hz)	Elevator Load (kg)	Travelling Direction [Up/ Down] (1/0)	Regen. Energy (Wh)
472	400.5	569	−6.8	51	120	0	−11.7
473	404.9	676	5.0	50	350	0	6.0
474	401.4	673	6.3	51	380	0	4.2
475	402.1	565	−7.3	51	110	0	−8.7
476	396.9	567	−16.3	51	580	1	−19.6
477	399.3	675	4.8	50	350	0	6.2
478	403.3	673	12.9	51	0	1	46.2
479	395.9	561	−15.2	50	540	1	−17.6
480	399.0	570	−12.7	49	500	1	−14.6
481	396.0	671	12.1	49	490	0	74.6
482	404.2	673	6.8	49	110	1	20.8
483	395.4	679	6.2	51	130	1	20.7
484	396.5	562	−10.3	50	40	0	−12.3
485	396.8	671	4.1	50	330	0	7.1
486	401.6	671	12.3	51	490	0	8.0
487	402.2	675	3.5	51	320	0	6.3
488	404.4	673	16.9	49	590	0	20.6
489	397.7	563	−13.0	51	500	1	−38.3
490	399.8	568	−11.2	50	480	1	−34.4
Total regenerated energy per day (Wh)							1,747.0

Site Measured Elevator Data – Apartment Building Complex @ Moore's Road

No.	Utility Side 3ϕ Voltage (V)	DC Bus Voltage (V)	Utility Side 3ϕ Current (A)	Utility Side 3ϕ Power Freq. (Hz)	Elevator Load (kg)	Travelling Direction [Up/ Down] (1/0)	Regen. Energy (Wh)
1	401.6	569	−11.1	51	460	1	−65.2
2	402.5	567	−7.0	50	110	0	−30.0
3	397.7	671	15.1	50	560	0	18.7
4	406.0	670	9.0	49	70	1	21.2
5	404.4	679	1.5	51	220	1	2.9
6	402.4	679	6.8	50	390	0	20.5
7	404.7	570	−13.0	50	520	1	−47.9
8	403.2	678	14.6	49	550	0	36.3
9	405.8	568	−15.4	49	550	1	−27.0
10	404.5	673	12.9	51	510	0	15.5
11	402.0	567	−11.4	49	480	1	−20.6
12	397.7	679	4.2	49	330	0	12.2
13	400.3	568	−10.7	49	470	1	−20.1
14	400.7	565	−13.4	51	510	1	−24.2

(Continued)

No.	Utility Side 3ϕ Voltage (V)	DC Bus Voltage (V)	Utility Side 3ϕ Current (A)	Utility Side 3ϕ Power Freq. (Hz)	Elevator Load (kg)	Travelling Direction [Up/ Down] (1/0)	Regen. Energy (Wh)
15	399.3	670	8.9	50	420	0	9.9
16	399.7	676	5.6	50	360	0	13.5
17	401.1	670	1.0	51	270	0	2.5
18	404.3	672	6.7	50	110	1	21.4
19	402.2	674	17.3	50	580	0	52.2
20	400.8	679	12.7	50	0	1	84.1
21	398.4	671	1.4	51	280	0	4.4
22	404.2	675	0.5	50	260	0	1.5
23	403.9	570	−11.4	50	480	1	−27.5
24	400.0	671	3.7	50	180	1	8.8
25	402.5	676	15.5	50	560	0	54.1
26	398.8	677	11.2	50	480	0	21.1
27	399.2	676	2.0	50	210	1	1.3
28	404.0	565	−13.4	50	510	1	−40.0
29	401.2	672	4.2	50	170	1	4.9
30	398.3	677	3.5	50	180	1	6.5
31	396.2	676	3.4	50	320	0	4.0
32	396.5	568	−9.8	50	60	0	−41.3
33	402.7	565	−15.7	50	570	1	−30.0
34	403.4	678	5.3	49	150	1	6.2
35	400.0	673	6.4	50	380	0	19.2
36	405.7	567	−9.1	50	430	1	−48.7
37	403.1	567	−8.8	49	80	0	−15.6
38	400.9	672	14.9	51	540	0	17.3
39	401.3	672	7.7	51	400	0	18.7
40	396.5	678	8.8	51	420	0	9.8
41	403.6	674	2.1	50	210	1	6.1
42	399.5	561	−14.2	49	540	1	−18.1
43	399.9	674	5.6	49	140	1	10.5
44	404.0	680	12.0	51	480	0	35.5
45	401.9	674	18.8	49	610	0	21.4
46	399.8	677	7.8	50	400	0	5.2
47	400.8	565	−11.4	51	470	1	−47.4
48	404.8	566	−9.1	50	70	0	−45.0
49	402.7	673	6.2	49	130	1	18.1
50	405.8	674	0.5	50	240	1	1.6
51	400.2	678	12.2	51	490	0	43.7
52	398.5	672	0.5	50	240	1	1.3
53	399.6	562	−6.0	51	130	0	−6.9
54	405.2	672	7.8	50	410	0	24.8
55	396.3	565	−15.0	50	560	1	−75.3
56	401.5	565	−7.0	49	110	0	−13.1
57	402.9	672	3.1	50	310	0	11.5

(Continued)

No.	Utility Side 3ϕ Voltage (V)	DC Bus Voltage (V)	Utility Side 3ϕ Current (A)	Utility Side 3ϕ Power Freq. (Hz)	Elevator Load (kg)	Travelling Direction [Up/ Down] (1/0)	Regen. Energy (Wh)
58	396.6	563	−15.9	51	560	1	−28.4
59	405.8	679	6.2	51	120	1	16.1
60	403.7	566	−15.0	50	560	1	−19.8
61	401.2	563	−6.4	49	120	0	−4.6
62	405.6	680	10.7	51	460	0	51.4
63	398.7	564	−14.4	50	530	1	−76.3
64	401.2	678	8.8	51	430	0	51.1
65	401.2	567	−11.5	50	480	1	−56.1
66	404.4	567	−14.0	49	520	1	−16.7
67	398.0	670	9.1	50	440	0	64.4
68	396.3	674	1.5	49	220	1	2.7
69	404.9	564	−12.7	50	510	1	−32.2
70	403.3	675	2.0	49	290	0	1.3
71	401.4	565	−5.0	50	150	0	−9.0
72	404.8	561	−15.8	50	560	1	−18.5
73	397.6	569	−13.2	50	510	1	−46.9
74	400.8	670	1.5	50	280	0	6.6
75	399.7	561	−11.8	49	490	1	−28.6
76	399.6	567	−6.5	50	120	0	−24.6
77	402.7	674	0.5	50	260	0	0.3
78	403.7	561	−11.3	49	470	1	−14.1
79	398.9	565	−14.1	50	530	1	−40.7
80	403.0	679	2.0	51	290	0	5.1
81	404.0	569	−8.9	51	420	1	−10.1
82	404.1	672	5.4	49	360	0	10.5
83	405.4	673	4.0	49	330	0	2.7
84	400.3	565	−11.2	49	470	1	−45.3
85	401.6	560	−9.0	50	430	1	−11.3
86	405.9	676	15.5	49	550	0	104.9
87	405.7	566	−14.4	50	530	1	−43.2
88	399.0	676	1.4	51	220	1	4.6
89	397.8	676	10.7	50	470	0	52.0
90	404.1	567	−11.1	50	470	1	−39.6
91	398.6	675	12.6	50	490	0	21.2
92	400.4	674	9.6	49	60	1	11.5
93	400.4	671	16.2	50	560	0	48.1
94	400.5	676	2.5	49	200	1	1.7
95	405.2	568	−9.4	49	440	1	−36.4
96	403.4	674	6.9	50	390	0	38.5
97	399.5	564	−13.0	51	500	1	−31.0
98	397.3	563	−14.8	51	550	1	−18.6
99	396.8	675	3.0	49	310	0	2.0
100	404.7	565	−16.3	50	560	1	−28.9

(Continued)

No.	Utility Side 3ϕ Voltage (V)	DC Bus Voltage (V)	Utility Side 3ϕ Current (A)	Utility Side 3ϕ Power Freq. (Hz)	Elevator Load (kg)	Travelling Direction [Up/Down] (1/0)	Regen. Energy (Wh)
101	399.2	671	9.3	49	430	0	42.0
102	400.6	678	4.4	50	160	1	30.6
103	400.9	671	2.5	51	300	0	5.9
104	399.9	673	13.8	49	520	0	58.9
105	400.0	567	−13.1	50	500	1	−15.8
106	399.1	671	2.5	50	300	0	1.6
107	396.7	568	−14.4	49	530	1	−41.9
108	403.6	673	8.9	51	420	0	21.8
109	405.1	563	−12.1	49	490	1	−22.5
110	400.0	674	4.0	50	330	0	2.6
111	397.0	563	−13.1	49	510	1	−29.9
112	396.2	678	7.1	50	390	0	34.5
113	403.9	568	−6.7	51	390	1	−12.8
114	405.3	568	−9.9	49	450	1	−24.6
115	397.8	674	12.0	51	490	0	14.3
116	400.3	565	−9.6	50	440	1	−6.3
117	403.9	671	5.5	50	140	1	6.5
118	401.9	568	−15.5	49	570	1	−20.4
119	396.3	671	15.7	51	550	0	89.5
120	402.5	562	−16.6	49	580	1	−30.7
121	401.7	563	−15.2	50	540	1	−25.3
122	400.7	564	−14.9	49	540	1	−17.5
123	399.6	568	−7.1	50	110	0	−4.8
124	398.9	677	8.9	49	420	0	25.5
125	405.1	565	−7.7	49	90	0	−5.6
126	400.9	569	−12.0	51	480	1	−34.0
127	397.8	678	13.7	49	510	0	37.9
128	397.5	560	−8.3	51	420	1	−31.0
129	396.9	675	5.8	49	370	0	26.6
130	400.1	562	−11.4	50	480	1	−27.8
131	397.0	670	5.7	50	140	1	13.6
132	398.3	564	−7.7	49	100	0	−28.5
133	404.8	679	5.9	49	370	0	7.3
134	401.6	671	1.5	49	220	1	5.6
135	396.8	563	−9.8	50	60	0	−11.6
136	404.8	675	4.4	50	160	1	16.2
137	396.5	676	3.9	51	330	0	4.8
138	397.4	672	1.5	50	280	0	5.2
139	404.7	561	−7.6	50	100	0	−5.2
140	396.4	562	−15.2	49	550	1	−10.3
141	399.1	563	−11.5	51	480	1	−21.6
142	402.1	673	2.5	50	300	0	5.8
143	401.0	675	6.1	50	130	1	18.4

(Continued)

No.	Utility Side 3ϕ Voltage (V)	DC Bus Voltage (V)	Utility Side 3ϕ Current (A)	Utility Side 3ϕ Power Freq. (Hz)	Elevator Load (kg)	Travelling Direction [Up/Down] (1/0)	Regen. Energy (Wh)
144	402.4	672	6.3	51	130	1	7.4
145	396.0	566	−8.1	50	90	0	−14.9
146	398.6	680	10.5	50	460	0	18.8
147	400.8	678	2.4	51	200	1	7.6
148	401.7	567	−9.8	51	450	1	−12.1
149	403.9	679	4.4	50	340	0	10.8
150	396.2	561	−15.3	51	560	1	−44.4
151	402.9	677	2.0	49	290	0	5.1
152	396.2	568	−9.4	50	430	1	−28.1
153	405.8	567	−6.6	51	120	0	−15.3
154	396.8	678	1.0	50	230	1	0.6
155	400.8	673	11.5	50	480	0	20.3
156	404.0	671	13.7	50	510	0	15.8
157	396.7	678	1.0	50	270	0	1.8
158	398.1	560	−11.6	50	490	1	−42.3
159	399.3	561	−15.6	50	550	1	−47.1
160	399.4	673	9.2	50	430	0	11.4
161	404.3	567	−16.7	50	570	1	−11.2
162	397.8	675	13.8	51	530	0	58.0
163	403.2	566	−11.9	50	480	1	−27.8
164	399.0	679	6.1	50	370	0	22.0
165	397.9	560	−14.2	50	520	1	−32.8
166	402.9	564	−8.1	50	90	0	−20.1
167	396.2	670	13.2	50	0	1	51.7
168	400.5	673	16.4	49	570	0	51.1
169	400.0	675	3.2	50	190	1	5.6
170	401.7	563	−9.8	50	440	1	−6.5
171	396.0	563	−8.7	51	430	1	−10.6
172	397.2	565	−16.6	49	590	1	−20.4
173	405.2	677	13.9	50	540	0	51.4
174	405.4	675	9.8	50	450	0	18.7
175	396.0	671	4.4	50	160	1	5.5
176	398.8	678	7.8	51	90	1	23.4
177	405.0	671	7.3	49	400	0	14.0
178	405.7	678	4.5	50	340	0	3.1
179	398.7	673	2.5	50	200	1	4.7
180	405.6	676	9.1	50	440	0	30.0
181	402.2	672	4.1	50	170	1	15.4
182	402.0	679	5.4	51	360	0	6.9
183	399.4	673	8.3	51	410	0	29.6
184	402.1	676	12.3	50	0	1	78.0
185	403.9	677	4.1	49	330	0	7.7
186	399.0	673	1.1	49	270	0	4.3

(Continued)

No.	Utility Side 3ϕ Voltage (V)	DC Bus Voltage (V)	Utility Side 3ϕ Current (A)	Utility Side 3ϕ Power Freq. (Hz)	Elevator Load (kg)	Travelling Direction [Up/Down] (1/0)	Regen. Energy (Wh)
187	397.8	567	−14.2	50	540	1	−9.6
188	405.8	677	0.5	51	240	1	1.6
189	400.3	680	2.5	50	300	0	3.2
190	404.0	561	−11.0	50	470	1	−42.2
191	396.3	675	17.3	50	590	0	88.7
192	398.8	671	5.8	50	130	1	19.0
193	398.7	674	5.3	49	360	0	13.5
194	405.7	678	11.6	49	490	0	8.4
195	399.7	677	9.6	50	440	0	11.8
196	399.9	670	9.0	51	70	1	37.0
197	401.6	677	1.1	50	270	0	1.2
198	400.5	678	3.6	50	320	0	2.4
199	403.0	569	−12.8	50	500	1	−40.1
200	404.2	678	1.5	51	220	1	1.0
201	401.4	679	9.3	49	440	0	23.2
202	397.7	679	7.4	51	390	0	4.7
203	398.7	674	6.6	51	120	1	11.6
204	397.9	566	−13.0	51	510	1	−16.1
205	402.4	563	−8.3	51	90	0	−15.3
206	397.5	676	11.4	50	470	0	48.4
207	404.3	677	7.3	51	100	1	32.4
208	403.0	671	1.0	50	270	0	2.4
209	398.6	566	−11.6	50	480	1	−20.8
210	404.9	679	13.6	51	530	0	17.6
211	400.5	566	−11.6	50	490	1	−22.4
212	405.1	677	8.8	49	430	0	6.2
213	401.7	570	−9.0	50	70	0	−21.3
214	404.3	671	12.2	51	0	1	55.5
215	405.7	565	−7.9	49	100	0	−17.9
216	404.5	673	0.5	50	240	1	0.6
217	399.2	678	15.5	50	560	0	66.8
218	396.5	679	4.1	49	170	1	12.2
219	402.9	675	1.0	50	230	1	1.9
220	404.8	674	5.8	49	130	1	7.1
221	404.9	564	−10.7	49	40	0	−19.6
222	401.4	673	9.9	51	450	0	37.5
223	398.9	672	13.0	50	0	1	63.3
224	405.8	675	3.1	50	310	0	2.0
225	398.8	565	−11.5	49	480	1	−21.0
226	401.5	679	14.1	49	530	0	52.7
227	398.2	675	1.5	49	280	0	1.0
228	399.5	676	8.8	50	80	1	35.7
229	399.7	673	6.3	50	380	0	20.1

(*Continued*)

No.	Utility Side 3ϕ Voltage (V)	DC Bus Voltage (V)	Utility Side 3ϕ Current (A)	Utility Side 3ϕ Power Freq. (Hz)	Elevator Load (kg)	Travelling Direction [Up/Down] (1/0)	Regen. Energy (Wh)
230	398.6	570	−12.3	50	490	1	−22.1
231	403.7	564	−10.1	49	50	0	−23.7
232	396.4	563	−11.9	51	490	1	−45.1
233	398.5	673	14.9	50	550	0	87.1
234	396.7	679	2.5	50	200	1	1.7
235	402.4	562	−6.6	50	380	1	−8.2
236	400.7	562	−9.2	50	430	1	−16.2
237	399.7	671	10.1	50	450	0	6.8
238	402.1	564	−10.4	51	450	1	−18.6
239	397.1	671	5.3	51	360	0	6.3
240	404.2	564	−13.0	51	510	1	−8.9
241	405.0	676	11.8	50	490	0	49.3
242	405.9	674	12.6	50	0	1	74.1
243	396.0	672	13.0	49	500	0	64.7
244	397.4	566	−7.2	51	390	1	−13.3
245	398.4	568	−13.7	50	520	1	−33.7
246	397.9	680	16.2	49	570	0	80.5
247	400.4	676	5.5	50	140	1	23.4
248	401.1	670	4.1	49	330	0	14.0
249	401.8	565	−14.4	50	530	1	−9.8
250	398.4	673	1.0	49	230	1	4.9
251	398.2	678	5.4	49	360	0	19.6
252	405.0	676	10.9	49	470	0	7.3
253	398.1	677	1.0	50	230	1	2.4
254	396.6	680	14.1	49	520	0	25.0
255	398.3	675	6.3	50	130	1	22.0
256	397.8	676	17.0	49	580	0	41.0
257	404.3	569	−10.6	51	460	1	−13.5
258	401.2	676	4.7	50	340	0	8.2
259	404.0	677	12.6	50	490	0	35.9
260	399.3	675	4.5	50	160	1	14.3
261	397.4	564	−6.2	50	120	0	−15.2
262	400.5	671	8.9	50	420	0	5.5
263	397.8	672	8.9	50	70	1	20.9
264	403.8	678	1.5	50	280	0	1.8
265	402.2	674	5.1	51	150	1	17.9
266	401.3	674	1.0	51	230	1	0.7
267	405.9	680	15.5	49	560	0	38.0
268	398.7	678	7.9	51	410	0	19.0
269	401.3	678	9.0	50	430	0	10.7
270	402.4	680	4.5	51	160	1	24.2
271	396.9	672	15.8	50	570	0	50.3
272	402.6	674	5.4	49	140	1	6.7

(Continued)

No.	Utility Side 3ϕ Voltage (V)	DC Bus Voltage (V)	Utility Side 3ϕ Current (A)	Utility Side 3ϕ Power Freq. (Hz)	Elevator Load (kg)	Travelling Direction [Up/ Down] (1/0)	Regen. Energy (Wh)
273	396.5	569	−10.4	50	450	1	−23.3
274	397.8	676	15.1	50	540	0	59.2
275	399.0	562	−10.2	50	450	1	−19.1
276	402.7	677	0.5	50	240	1	0.9
277	400.6	677	2.6	50	300	0	6.4
278	403.7	568	−8.8	51	420	1	−15.8
279	405.5	561	−15.3	50	550	1	−27.0
280	400.3	675	6.7	51	380	0	7.6
281	401.5	678	18.0	49	590	0	92.5
282	402.0	679	3.4	50	180	1	15.2
283	402.8	680	10.4	51	450	0	35.4
284	396.8	674	1.5	49	220	1	3.6
285	402.7	568	−7.3	51	110	0	−8.8
286	396.8	568	−9.8	50	440	1	−16.3
287	404.6	561	−12.4	49	500	1	−15.8
288	404.7	671	16.8	51	570	0	76.1
289	397.7	675	0.5	51	240	1	0.9
290	397.9	672	8.8	50	80	1	10.6
291	396.4	677	10.8	50	470	0	7.4
292	398.5	566	−7.7	49	410	1	−5.2
293	399.0	563	−16.1	49	560	1	−10.8
294	401.8	569	−10.5	51	450	1	−30.1
295	400.3	670	16.5	49	570	0	94.4
296	400.6	674	2.1	49	210	1	8.6
297	399.0	678	12.3	50	490	0	21.8
298	403.8	568	−10.5	49	450	1	−6.9
299	401.5	560	−13.2	51	520	1	−16.1
300	399.0	677	7.8	50	100	1	13.4
301	399.7	670	14.5	51	540	0	93.2
302	398.9	566	−9.2	50	430	1	−16.9
303	398.4	671	2.1	50	210	1	7.5
304	401.3	676	13.6	49	530	0	49.1
305	403.4	674	3.7	50	320	0	2.4
306	404.6	674	12.7	49	0	1	68.6
307	397.0	676	12.2	50	490	0	79.2
308	397.6	671	4.5	50	160	1	22.7
309	404.7	671	2.9	50	310	0	7.6
310	396.0	566	−12.0	50	480	1	−13.5
311	405.9	679	8.2	50	410	0	20.4
312	405.1	568	−12.7	51	490	1	−37.1
313	399.3	672	6.9	50	380	0	11.8
314	397.3	563	−7.0	50	110	0	−12.7
315	401.2	563	−10.3	49	460	1	−38.1

(Continued)

No.	Utility Side 3ϕ Voltage (V)	DC Bus Voltage (V)	Utility Side 3ϕ Current (A)	Utility Side 3ϕ Power Freq. (Hz)	Elevator Load (kg)	Travelling Direction [Up/Down] (1/0)	Regen. Energy (Wh)
316	400.8	564	−9.2	49	430	1	−17.0
317	397.8	561	−7.6	49	100	0	−13.9
318	398.5	679	13.5	51	510	0	46.4
319	398.4	566	−14.2	51	530	1	−51.6
320	399.4	674	1.0	49	230	1	2.5
321	403.9	674	10.7	51	460	0	12.9
322	398.0	563	−9.8	50	60	0	−11.2
323	397.5	672	3.1	51	310	0	3.7
324	396.7	678	4.6	49	340	0	8.2
325	399.2	566	−13.0	49	510	1	−16.3
326	399.8	566	−13.5	49	520	1	−31.9
327	405.5	562	−12.5	50	490	1	−22.9
328	398.7	679	6.0	49	370	0	32.3
329	401.6	569	−10.1	50	460	1	−50.5
330	398.1	676	2.4	49	300	0	8.7
331	397.7	672	7.5	50	400	0	9.1
332	404.5	565	−12.1	50	500	1	−38.0
333	400.5	672	10.9	50	460	0	32.1
334	396.9	564	−15.4	50	570	1	−20.0
335	397.4	568	−12.6	50	510	1	−56.2
336	402.3	678	16.7	51	590	0	116.6
337	401.8	562	−14.4	50	550	1	−27.6
338	401.8	563	−12.0	51	490	1	−7.8
339	399.2	670	4.6	49	340	0	5.4
340	402.3	565	−13.0	50	500	1	−29.5
341	402.7	565	−9.9	51	440	1	−16.9
342	398.9	676	6.6	51	380	0	35.2
343	396.4	568	−10.2	51	460	1	−32.8
344	397.8	677	7.9	49	90	1	24.4
345	399.6	676	5.2	50	150	1	3.4
346	404.0	673	5.8	51	360	0	20.5
347	404.6	670	2.0	49	290	0	4.8
348	406.0	674	12.1	50	0	1	54.3
349	403.3	568	−14.7	51	530	1	−17.1
350	396.4	561	−9.5	50	70	0	−21.1
351	397.6	679	4.9	49	150	1	8.9
352	399.9	670	9.9	50	450	0	53.3
353	404.0	562	−14.0	50	520	1	−17.3
354	400.8	679	11.0	50	470	0	13.1
355	400.7	677	2.1	50	210	1	8.4
356	398.9	679	6.2	50	130	1	11.2
357	396.4	673	4.1	50	330	0	12.3
358	404.8	569	−12.8	49	500	1	−22.5

(Continued)

No.	Utility Side 3ϕ Voltage (V)	DC Bus Voltage (V)	Utility Side 3ϕ Current (A)	Utility Side 3ϕ Power Freq. (Hz)	Elevator Load (kg)	Travelling Direction [Up/Down] (1/0)	Regen. Energy (Wh)
359	397.7	564	−14.8	49	540	1	−26.0
360	405.6	678	3.0	49	310	0	12.4
361	396.4	568	−13.4	49	510	1	−23.4
362	403.3	561	−11.5	51	480	1	−14.4
363	405.4	564	−13.7	49	520	1	−8.9
364	396.6	671	2.5	50	300	0	7.3
365	397.8	565	−11.2	50	470	1	−19.9
366	400.7	677	0.5	51	260	0	0.9
367	404.8	675	5.4	50	140	1	13.7
368	397.4	677	4.5	50	340	0	11.1
369	397.6	568	−12.1	51	480	1	−34.8
370	398.7	677	1.5	51	280	0	1.8
371	405.8	567	−7.6	51	100	0	−18.3
372	398.4	569	−7.6	50	400	1	−22.4
373	403.6	567	−4.9	50	150	0	−26.6
374	401.6	562	−7.7	49	410	1	−23.9
375	404.5	676	8.4	49	410	0	18.8
376	401.2	676	1.4	51	220	1	4.8
377	403.5	673	8.0	49	90	1	9.6
378	399.0	671	4.9	51	150	1	6.0
379	396.4	670	13.7	49	520	0	24.9
380	398.9	563	−10.0	50	450	1	−23.5
381	399.8	676	5.3	49	360	0	34.3
382	396.8	567	−10.0	49	450	1	−35.1
383	397.0	677	18.7	50	610	0	11.5
384	404.0	680	1.0	50	230	1	1.9
385	403.7	675	9.7	51	440	0	23.7
386	401.4	564	−16.7	50	580	1	−19.1
387	397.1	567	−9.6	49	440	1	−18.0
388	400.1	560	−6.4	49	120	0	−19.8
389	405.2	677	2.6	51	300	0	3.2
390	397.0	678	7.7	50	410	0	5.4
391	404.6	561	−9.5	50	440	1	−33.7
392	400.6	671	11.7	50	490	0	60.3
393	398.9	680	9.5	49	70	1	56.3
394	398.9	680	1.6	51	280	0	7.4
395	403.5	562	−8.5	50	420	1	−31.3
396	399.9	678	2.1	51	290	0	3.5
397	402.8	678	2.5	49	300	0	7.9
398	398.7	567	−15.8	50	550	1	−17.6
399	400.6	561	−14.6	50	530	1	−41.3
400	401.9	672	3.5	50	320	0	4.4
401	397.5	671	9.7	50	440	0	6.1

(Continued)

No.	Utility Side 3ϕ Voltage (V)	DC Bus Voltage (V)	Utility Side 3ϕ Current (A)	Utility Side 3ϕ Power Freq. (Hz)	Elevator Load (kg)	Travelling Direction [Up/Down] (1/0)	Regen. Energy (Wh)
402	398.0	567	−12.5	51	510	1	−39.3
403	401.2	566	−9.2	51	60	0	−17.8
404	405.8	561	−14.0	50	540	1	−34.1
405	404.7	676	6.3	49	380	0	25.0
406	406.0	673	0.5	49	260	0	0.9
407	400.6	566	−8.2	49	410	1	−14.2
408	404.2	569	−15.6	51	550	1	−27.1
409	404.0	673	8.2	50	420	0	25.6
410	401.0	565	−14.4	49	540	1	−25.3
411	404.5	678	1.6	50	220	1	1.0
412	397.0	565	−10.3	50	460	1	−18.7
413	402.5	671	10.5	50	470	0	33.2
414	397.9	677	13.0	50	520	0	8.8
415	405.6	562	−10.5	49	470	1	−13.4
416	401.4	565	−14.5	50	540	1	−9.8
417	400.9	562	−13.9	50	530	1	−16.8
418	401.2	567	−9.8	51	450	1	−11.8
419	397.1	679	7.5	51	400	0	14.0
420	402.4	676	5.4	49	360	0	16.2
421	404.8	567	−13.5	51	510	1	−9.2
422	405.4	672	2.0	50	290	0	3.5
423	405.3	677	6.7	50	110	1	34.0
424	397.0	675	4.5	50	160	1	5.7
425	403.4	679	15.3	50	540	0	81.6
426	401.8	680	12.0	50	0	1	76.1
427	397.6	671	12.3	50	490	0	44.2
428	399.7	564	−12.1	50	480	1	−13.9
429	399.9	674	2.0	49	210	1	2.3
430	405.3	565	−8.9	50	70	0	−16.5
431	396.1	672	16.1	50	560	0	48.7
432	403.0	678	9.0	50	70	1	36.7
433	400.9	670	6.1	50	370	0	17.9
434	399.0	671	12.4	50	490	0	14.9
435	399.9	677	10.2	50	450	0	7.0
436	399.0	566	−15.2	50	550	1	−36.5
437	405.7	568	−14.0	49	530	1	−16.9
438	399.3	674	7.1	50	390	0	17.1
439	405.6	673	4.6	51	160	1	14.0
440	396.4	565	−13.8	51	530	1	−9.3
441	400.2	678	0.5	50	260	0	1.9
442	397.9	678	3.4	49	180	1	18.6
443	403.1	679	2.0	50	290	0	2.4
444	403.8	678	6.0	50	370	0	25.0

(*Continued*)

No.	Utility Side 3ϕ Voltage (V)	DC Bus Voltage (V)	Utility Side 3ϕ Current (A)	Utility Side 3ϕ Power Freq. (Hz)	Elevator Load (kg)	Travelling Direction [Up/Down] (1/0)	Regen. Energy (Wh)
445	402.1	673	4.5	50	160	1	14.4
446	403.7	569	−18.1	50	600	1	−20.6
447	404.8	675	8.2	50	410	0	29.0
448	402.7	563	−10.0	50	440	1	−27.9
449	398.8	563	−6.5	50	120	0	−7.7
450	400.9	567	−13.7	51	530	1	−26.3
451	402.7	675	11.7	49	490	0	28.6
452	404.8	675	8.8	50	430	0	11.1
453	397.2	570	−6.5	49	120	0	−7.8
454	398.7	561	−15.6	49	550	1	−75.9
455	396.4	564	−6.9	50	120	0	−7.6
456	402.7	673	0.5	51	240	1	0.9
457	402.3	680	12.1	51	490	0	53.2
458	398.4	679	6.5	50	120	1	31.7
459	400.1	565	−6.7	50	120	0	−19.3
460	399.7	674	1.0	50	230	1	1.8
461	401.0	670	8.8	51	430	0	10.8
462	396.1	672	9.3	51	70	1	20.9
463	403.7	562	−5.8	49	130	0	−25.0
464	396.4	564	−12.7	50	490	1	−21.3
465	403.8	565	−8.7	49	430	1	−6.2
466	400.4	671	5.8	49	370	0	22.8
467	400.9	567	−10.5	49	460	1	−44.0
468	397.4	673	3.6	50	320	0	14.9
469	405.2	565	−12.8	50	500	1	−22.8
470	404.3	677	9.4	50	440	0	30.3
471	396.4	672	3.4	50	180	1	12.4
472	398.8	569	−14.6	50	540	1	−25.5
473	399.3	671	5.5	50	360	0	20.7
474	396.0	674	2.0	51	290	0	3.8
475	399.8	678	12.3	51	0	1	80.5
476	398.6	678	11.4	49	470	0	38.9
477	401.4	561	−16.8	50	580	1	−38.4
478	405.6	565	−9.8	49	440	1	−11.2
479	401.1	677	16.6	51	570	0	109.7
480	401.7	674	0.5	49	240	1	1.0
481	397.3	564	−8.4	50	90	0	−9.4
482	403.8	564	−8.9	50	430	1	−48.9
483	401.3	676	11.1	51	460	0	45.3
484	398.8	565	−18.5	51	600	1	−31.9
485	404.8	564	−10.1	50	450	1	−18.6
486	396.5	562	−9.3	50	440	1	−11.4
487	402.3	677	8.2	50	420	0	10.6

(Continued)

No.	Utility Side 3ϕ Voltage (V)	DC Bus Voltage (V)	Utility Side 3ϕ Current (A)	Utility Side 3ϕ Power Freq. (Hz)	Elevator Load (kg)	Travelling Direction [Up/ Down] (1/0)	Regen. Energy (Wh)
488	402.2	670	9.1	50	430	0	6.2
489	396.4	678	16.6	49	570	0	38.3
490	396.2	564	−9.2	49	430	1	−16.2
Total regenerated energy per day (Wh)							1,882.0

Site Measured Elevator Data – Apartment Building Complex @ Frankfort Place

No.	Utility Side 3ϕ Voltage (V)	DC Bus Voltage (V)	Utility Side 3ϕ Current (A)	Utility Side 3ϕ Power Freq. (Hz)	Elevator Load (kg)	Travelling Direction [Up/ Down] (1/0)	Regen. Energy (Wh)
1	406.9	680	12.5	50	620	0	15.1
2	399.9	566	−12.6	49	610	1	−21.6
3	399.7	677	13.4	49	0	1	25.3
4	404.8	673	10.9	51	560	0	12.7
5	403.5	678	4.6	51	210	1	8.8
6	402.5	678	19.1	50	780	0	88.2
7	399.0	679	9.7	49	90	1	23.7
8	399.4	672	1.7	49	360	0	2.2
9	404.3	561	−15.8	49	700	1	−10.6
10	403.8	570	−10.9	49	60	0	−13.6
11	406.7	565	−10.0	51	550	1	−18.1
12	399.0	671	5.9	50	180	1	3.9
13	403.8	673	4.0	49	410	0	6.8
14	401.9	680	1.7	51	280	1	5.2
15	399.8	672	6.6	50	470	0	15.0
16	401.2	677	6.6	51	470	0	4.3
17	401.4	567	−4.9	49	200	0	−3.4
18	406.3	676	10.4	49	80	1	19.2
19	403.0	679	14.6	51	650	0	34.5
20	401.1	673	13.7	49	0	1	50.3
21	406.5	672	11.0	50	570	0	7.5
22	402.6	566	−6.6	50	160	0	−4.6
23	401.8	564	−15.4	49	670	1	−26.6
24	406.2	674	1.3	50	350	0	1.5
25	401.8	566	−7.2	50	160	0	−8.2
26	402.0	562	−10.5	49	80	0	−6.8
27	401.4	676	3.6	50	400	0	4.1
28	399.5	564	−18.2	49	740	1	−21.4
29	403.7	564	−13.5	50	650	1	−9.2
30	406.7	677	13.9	49	0	1	24.4

(Continued)

No.	Utility Side 3ϕ Voltage (V)	DC Bus Voltage (V)	Utility Side 3ϕ Current (A)	Utility Side 3ϕ Power Freq. (Hz)	Elevator Load (kg)	Travelling Direction [Up/Down] (1/0)	Regen. Energy (Wh)
31	400.2	671	0.8	50	340	0	0.6
32	406.4	674	15.4	50	680	0	38.1
33	404.7	678	1.7	49	360	0	1.2
34	400.0	563	−9.4	51	530	1	−16.4
35	405.6	568	−10.1	49	80	0	−12.1
36	403.8	671	5.0	50	210	1	11.1
37	398.6	670	14.8	50	670	0	18.8
38	404.4	677	4.2	49	420	0	5.5
39	398.1	672	13.6	50	0	1	42.7
40	405.2	675	2.9	50	250	1	2.1
41	405.2	672	8.0	51	510	0	9.6
42	402.6	671	3.7	51	410	0	4.6
43	399.6	673	6.3	49	470	0	11.2
44	405.7	569	−11.7	51	600	1	−8.5
45	397.1	680	3.9	49	230	1	6.9
46	406.6	671	17.4	49	720	0	11.6
47	404.4	569	−13.2	50	630	1	−34.0
48	399.6	671	0.8	50	340	0	3.0
49	406.2	676	7.2	50	150	1	5.2
50	406.4	671	14.2	51	660	0	18.1
51	397.3	680	13.9	51	0	1	42.4
52	405.3	677	9.0	50	520	0	10.5
53	399.2	561	−13.2	49	630	1	−33.8
54	400.6	566	−8.9	49	110	0	−16.6
55	397.5	564	−16.6	49	690	1	−19.1
56	402.4	679	14.4	49	650	0	25.2
57	405.0	677	3.8	51	410	0	2.6
58	403.1	563	−10.9	49	580	1	−21.4
59	400.1	567	−10.9	49	70	0	−7.0
60	399.0	676	5.7	50	190	1	6.5
61	406.4	670	10.4	49	550	0	17.7
62	401.0	565	−8.9	49	120	0	−10.0
63	402.1	672	2.2	50	270	1	3.8
64	398.9	568	−12.5	50	40	0	−28.1
65	405.2	566	−19.8	51	760	1	−33.5
66	401.0	672	6.2	49	180	1	14.7
67	401.3	561	−6.4	50	170	0	−7.6
68	399.6	563	−9.7	51	90	0	−18.7
69	406.6	676	11.8	50	600	0	15.5
70	401.6	568	−13.6	49	640	1	−31.9
71	401.7	568	−15.2	50	660	1	−25.4
72	403.2	672	7.7	49	500	0	9.5
73	404.6	563	−10.3	49	70	0	−19.5

(Continued)

No.	Utility Side 3ϕ Voltage (V)	DC Bus Voltage (V)	Utility Side 3ϕ Current (A)	Utility Side 3ϕ Power Freq. (Hz)	Elevator Load (kg)	Travelling Direction [Up/ Down] (1/0)	Regen. Energy (Wh)
74	397.0	674	4.5	51	220	1	2.8
75	405.2	679	9.9	50	540	0	17.9
76	404.6	568	−15.9	50	690	1	−18.8
77	402.9	678	6.0	51	180	1	7.1
78	397.4	671	1.3	51	290	1	0.9
79	399.9	671	3.1	50	390	0	3.8
80	400.5	565	−6.5	51	170	0	−12.1
81	404.3	565	−13.8	49	630	1	−31.8
82	398.8	673	14.8	50	680	0	27.2
83	397.8	565	−11.4	50	590	1	−13.7
84	399.2	677	12.0	51	590	0	21.6
85	402.1	674	14.2	50	0	1	59.2
86	406.4	675	12.1	51	600	0	8.4
87	397.7	568	−9.2	50	110	0	−25.8
88	398.7	568	−10.0	49	560	1	−30.7
89	402.6	678	3.4	50	400	0	4.2
90	405.4	679	2.2	51	370	0	1.4
91	406.6	672	1.2	50	290	1	1.7
92	398.6	568	−11.9	51	590	1	−14.3
93	400.4	561	−5.6	50	190	0	−16.7
94	397.1	566	−12.7	51	630	1	−33.0
95	402.3	671	7.5	49	500	0	9.0
96	401.0	562	−9.6	49	100	0	−11.5
97	399.8	674	2.7	49	380	0	3.2
98	397.9	671	8.7	50	110	1	36.2
99	398.7	672	19.5	51	760	0	69.2
100	406.4	674	4.0	49	230	1	9.6
101	399.0	679	1.7	50	360	0	5.2
102	397.6	679	11.8	51	60	1	7.8
103	397.7	560	−13.8	50	650	1	−9.6
104	402.4	672	10.8	50	70	1	19.6
105	404.3	672	3.1	51	390	0	9.6
106	404.4	672	10.0	51	80	1	12.8
107	402.6	567	−14.4	50	640	1	−17.2
108	401.9	677	3.5	51	400	0	2.4
109	404.9	671	0.4	49	310	1	0.5
110	404.4	563	−16.9	51	700	1	−10.7
111	404.0	569	−6.1	50	180	0	−7.2
112	403.8	562	−7.3	50	150	0	−17.3
113	401.4	680	13.6	49	0	1	49.1
114	403.5	564	−6.2	49	180	0	−4.3
115	399.4	678	5.9	51	460	0	14.3
116	406.6	567	−10.9	50	570	1	−19.2

(Continued)

No.	Utility Side 3ϕ Voltage (V)	DC Bus Voltage (V)	Utility Side 3ϕ Current (A)	Utility Side 3ϕ Power Freq. (Hz)	Elevator Load (kg)	Travelling Direction [Up/ Down] (1/0)	Regen. Energy (Wh)
117	406.7	565	−7.5	50	150	0	−9.4
118	402.4	674	12.4	49	600	0	8.5
119	400.8	672	7.5	51	150	1	26.5
120	400.3	675	3.9	51	410	0	11.8
121	405.7	670	7.5	50	490	0	5.2
122	398.0	677	3.5	51	240	1	8.2
123	401.3	675	9.2	50	110	1	10.9
124	406.3	566	−7.2	51	150	0	−12.8
125	406.7	677	14.4	49	650	0	36.5
126	401.8	565	−12.2	51	590	1	−20.7
127	397.9	678	11.2	49	580	0	13.6
128	398.2	562	−12.9	49	630	1	−23.3
129	398.1	674	14.0	49	630	0	32.4
130	401.6	566	−13.2	49	620	1	−16.3
131	401.5	570	−12.1	51	610	1	−22.2
132	404.8	566	−11.1	49	570	1	−13.5
133	401.4	678	11.6	50	600	0	51.0
134	401.0	676	7.6	51	150	1	4.9
135	399.9	569	−13.2	49	620	1	−15.2
136	404.5	674	3.9	50	230	1	2.7
137	397.6	676	5.6	50	190	1	6.4
138	401.1	673	10.2	50	560	0	24.3
139	402.1	674	14.3	51	0	1	42.9
140	399.4	680	6.6	51	470	0	20.4
141	398.9	563	−12.8	49	620	1	−23.9
142	402.4	673	17.7	51	720	0	51.7
143	397.5	674	1.8	51	280	1	2.0
144	400.6	679	4.0	49	230	1	9.6
145	403.5	679	3.9	51	410	0	4.8
146	398.8	676	9.0	50	120	1	15.8
147	397.2	678	2.5	49	380	0	6.0
148	398.0	562	−8.9	50	120	0	−5.9
149	404.4	675	9.4	51	530	0	11.3
150	402.4	567	−7.8	50	500	1	−5.2
151	406.3	676	5.8	51	190	1	14.3
152	404.0	563	−13.7	51	640	1	−9.0
153	407.0	560	−11.7	50	50	0	−21.2
154	405.7	678	0.8	49	340	0	1.6
155	402.8	568	−15.4	49	680	1	−19.2
156	398.7	672	5.9	51	180	1	17.3
157	406.4	673	10.1	50	560	0	13.3
158	397.4	560	−15.1	50	680	1	−10.5
159	398.5	561	−8.2	50	130	0	−19.2

(*Continued*)

No.	Utility Side 3ϕ Voltage (V)	DC Bus Voltage (V)	Utility Side 3ϕ Current (A)	Utility Side 3ϕ Power Freq. (Hz)	Elevator Load (kg)	Travelling Direction [Up/ Down] (1/0)	Regen. Energy (Wh)
160	401.5	672	6.3	51	180	1	7.7
161	401.9	672	9.0	50	520	0	10.7
162	403.1	563	−8.5	49	520	1	−21.9
163	399.4	673	2.2	51	270	1	1.4
164	403.7	675	15.1	50	680	0	54.6
165	401.6	678	3.7	51	230	1	7.1
166	404.2	679	10.1	50	560	0	6.9
167	397.0	677	7.3	50	150	1	13.6
168	397.2	676	0.4	50	330	0	1.0
169	397.4	564	−12.6	49	610	1	−30.2
170	402.7	674	7.8	50	500	0	23.7
171	403.0	680	13.6	50	0	1	50.7
172	406.7	678	3.1	49	390	0	13.5
173	400.2	677	8.5	50	130	1	20.2
174	402.9	563	−17.2	49	710	1	−11.8
175	405.8	563	−8.4	51	120	0	−25.8
176	397.1	673	7.1	50	160	1	16.7
177	399.4	680	2.7	49	380	0	6.0
178	406.0	568	−13.2	50	620	1	−15.2
179	399.0	563	−15.6	49	690	1	−10.3
180	402.4	672	14.4	51	660	0	27.2
181	403.6	676	4.5	49	220	1	5.4
182	402.9	676	3.7	50	230	1	4.6
183	404.7	569	−8.1	51	130	0	−19.4
184	404.1	677	11.1	49	60	1	26.8
185	398.6	672	5.8	50	450	0	9.9
186	403.5	671	5.4	51	190	1	17.1
187	406.1	676	12.3	49	610	0	22.8
188	400.7	562	−12.1	51	610	1	−8.1
189	399.4	678	10.6	51	570	0	7.0
190	397.9	675	7.8	50	500	0	14.0
191	403.4	673	13.9	51	0	1	51.0
192	402.7	675	8.6	50	510	0	10.1
193	404.8	673	15.5	49	690	0	38.6
194	403.0	675	9.7	50	90	1	31.1
195	399.1	674	4.7	49	210	1	5.9
196	404.2	674	3.4	51	400	0	6.3
197	405.1	680	4.1	51	420	0	10.2
198	406.3	675	7.8	49	140	1	24.2
199	397.6	676	16.7	50	720	0	41.1
200	402.1	673	4.6	49	210	1	5.6
201	398.1	569	−10.8	50	580	1	−7.7
202	406.9	676	7.1	49	160	1	8.7

(Continued)

No.	Utility Side 3ϕ Voltage (V)	DC Bus Voltage (V)	Utility Side 3ϕ Current (A)	Utility Side 3ϕ Power Freq. (Hz)	Elevator Load (kg)	Travelling Direction [Up/Down] (1/0)	Regen. Energy (Wh)
203	397.4	675	17.4	51	710	0	62.0
204	404.3	673	14.1	50	0	1	42.8
205	398.3	678	7.9	49	500	0	17.8
206	405.3	566	−10.0	51	550	1	−12.7
207	406.0	671	0.4	50	310	1	1.0
208	401.1	676	5.7	51	450	0	10.1
209	406.7	679	2.6	51	380	0	3.0
210	401.2	570	−11.8	49	600	1	−22.9
211	401.3	676	0.4	51	330	0	0.8
212	404.6	673	8.2	49	130	1	20.5
213	399.5	674	6.0	49	460	0	7.1
214	398.4	674	10.4	49	80	1	6.7
215	400.6	674	13.8	50	630	0	15.5
216	399.9	568	−11.7	49	590	1	−7.5
217	400.5	674	10.2	50	560	0	12.6
218	403.9	674	14.1	50	640	0	17.1
219	405.3	670	14.1	50	0	1	53.0
220	401.0	674	4.9	51	440	0	6.3
221	403.1	679	17.7	51	720	0	30.9
222	404.7	561	−10.2	50	550	1	−11.7
223	401.6	563	−9.5	50	550	1	−11.9
224	401.7	676	20.7	50	780	0	59.3
225	398.3	564	−9.8	49	550	1	−11.9
226	406.4	671	3.6	49	400	0	4.1
227	400.8	672	8.7	51	120	1	16.4
228	405.8	561	−10.6	50	570	1	−20.4
229	401.1	672	13.0	50	620	0	40.0
230	404.8	680	2.1	51	270	1	4.0
231	400.0	673	0.8	49	300	1	1.6
232	404.1	679	8.5	49	520	0	5.8
233	404.7	674	5.3	49	440	0	6.6
234	398.4	671	8.6	49	520	0	10.9
235	400.2	561	−10.4	49	570	1	−19.1
236	405.9	680	19.9	49	760	0	47.1
237	401.9	565	−14.3	50	650	1	−16.6
238	401.5	560	−11.2	51	590	1	−21.4
239	402.6	565	−11.0	50	580	1	−7.9
240	397.2	670	7.4	51	500	0	18.2
241	402.5	676	0.4	49	330	0	0.7
242	399.0	560	−14.0	51	650	1	−9.9
243	404.3	675	14.2	51	0	1	48.7
244	405.9	671	9.5	50	530	0	11.5
245	402.1	676	3.8	50	410	0	4.8

(Continued)

No.	Utility Side 3ϕ Voltage (V)	DC Bus Voltage (V)	Utility Side 3ϕ Current (A)	Utility Side 3ϕ Power Freq. (Hz)	Elevator Load (kg)	Travelling Direction [Up/Down] (1/0)	Regen. Energy (Wh)
246	398.5	674	18.1	50	720	0	29.8
247	398.3	670	5.6	51	190	1	13.7
248	401.2	679	1.7	51	360	0	3.1
249	399.2	676	4.7	50	210	1	11.3
250	398.8	673	9.4	50	110	1	10.8
251	398.5	677	16.7	50	690	0	66.5
252	400.1	672	3.1	50	250	1	2.0
253	397.8	673	7.3	49	150	1	17.7
254	402.3	671	13.6	51	640	0	32.1
255	402.0	561	−12.7	50	630	1	−16.6
256	405.5	561	−9.1	50	530	1	−22.2
257	399.5	672	7.5	49	490	0	8.7
258	398.1	674	4.9	49	210	1	5.6
259	400.9	679	4.4	51	420	0	7.7
260	404.5	670	13.8	50	630	0	16.2
261	397.0	560	−8.3	50	130	0	−9.8
262	400.8	675	8.1	49	140	1	13.9
263	404.7	670	1.3	50	290	1	0.9
264	398.0	566	−11.6	49	590	1	−7.6
265	403.8	675	15.3	50	670	0	18.5
266	399.2	680	2.7	51	380	0	3.2
267	401.8	568	−11.9	50	590	1	−21.8
268	406.9	676	3.7	51	410	0	4.6
269	402.9	672	3.3	49	240	1	6.4
270	398.9	563	−16.4	49	700	1	−11.0
271	405.2	676	11.3	51	580	0	42.9
272	406.7	671	3.0	50	250	1	2.2
273	403.4	676	7.5	49	140	1	27.2
274	401.2	677	13.9	49	630	0	49.2
275	402.1	569	−10.2	49	560	1	−7.1
276	400.8	679	13.6	50	0	1	16.8
277	401.1	678	11.1	50	590	0	21.9
278	406.3	564	−12.3	49	610	1	−14.8
279	397.7	675	10.2	51	550	0	17.4
280	404.6	672	0.4	50	310	1	0.3
281	404.0	564	−16.1	50	680	1	−18.5
282	398.0	560	−16.9	50	700	1	−19.4
283	398.3	671	10.5	50	570	0	19.0
284	402.9	568	−9.8	50	550	1	−12.4
285	400.4	673	8.0	50	140	1	14.6
286	401.6	677	8.4	50	520	0	37.6
287	401.4	677	4.4	51	220	1	10.0
288	400.0	561	−11.2	49	590	1	−13.8

(Continued)

No.	Utility Side 3ϕ Voltage (V)	DC Bus Voltage (V)	Utility Side 3ϕ Current (A)	Utility Side 3ϕ Power Freq. (Hz)	Elevator Load (kg)	Travelling Direction [Up/ Down] (1/0)	Regen. Energy (Wh)
289	404.9	568	−5.2	49	200	0	−6.1
290	406.1	679	9.0	49	530	0	17.1
291	401.3	679	12.7	49	610	0	8.7
292	402.6	671	14.3	50	0	1	51.3
293	405.8	670	9.7	50	550	0	23.3
294	399.7	569	−11.2	51	580	1	−34.3
295	401.2	676	0.8	49	340	0	1.6
296	405.1	679	8.4	50	520	0	15.6
297	400.6	676	5.4	49	190	1	10.1
298	404.3	674	3.3	51	400	0	2.3
299	397.5	563	−11.7	51	600	1	−22.5
300	401.3	674	8.6	49	520	0	20.0
301	399.3	670	3.9	49	230	1	7.0
302	406.3	560	−8.2	49	120	0	−26.9
303	403.4	673	10.1	50	80	1	37.0
304	402.8	564	−8.6	51	130	0	−10.2
305	401.1	672	3.8	49	410	0	9.6
306	403.0	565	−14.0	50	630	1	−16.2
307	400.9	678	8.8	51	110	1	22.8
308	402.9	673	1.3	51	350	0	2.3
309	404.2	567	−11.7	51	600	1	−15.3
310	404.4	673	17.2	49	720	0	50.4
311	405.0	673	13.9	50	0	1	33.1
312	403.8	562	−9.9	49	540	1	−17.9
313	397.5	676	8.5	49	520	0	5.7
314	405.9	670	5.8	51	450	0	10.5
315	402.2	565	−10.9	50	570	1	−12.6
316	401.4	680	12.0	50	610	0	8.1
317	400.5	563	−9.2	51	530	1	−11.4
318	397.4	568	−9.4	49	100	0	−11.5
319	400.5	677	13.0	50	610	0	29.8
320	397.8	567	−12.8	49	620	1	−8.3
321	403.0	674	10.6	50	70	1	38.2
322	404.4	676	8.9	49	530	0	21.2
323	402.5	677	10.2	51	560	0	13.1
324	406.7	671	8.2	49	120	1	25.8
325	402.9	673	5.2	49	440	0	6.0
326	403.7	674	11.6	50	580	0	27.2
327	405.1	567	−10.3	51	560	1	−6.7
328	402.2	678	4.7	51	210	1	3.2
329	397.9	676	7.0	51	160	1	16.5
330	405.4	566	−15.3	51	660	1	−10.2
331	398.0	679	8.6	51	520	0	27.0

(*Continued*)

No.	Utility Side 3ϕ Voltage (V)	DC Bus Voltage (V)	Utility Side 3ϕ Current (A)	Utility Side 3ϕ Power Freq. (Hz)	Elevator Load (kg)	Travelling Direction [Up/Down] (1/0)	Regen. Energy (Wh)
332	405.1	676	2.1	50	370	0	2.8
333	398.8	565	−14.8	49	680	1	−10.3
334	398.3	562	−12.7	49	610	1	−14.9
335	401.2	567	−12.9	49	610	1	−14.6
336	406.7	672	0.9	50	340	0	2.6
337	406.0	671	14.2	49	0	1	48.6
338	404.7	677	7.8	51	500	0	14.3
339	399.6	675	2.5	49	260	1	3.1
340	403.1	562	−14.8	51	660	1	−18.1
341	404.9	567	−11.3	51	70	0	−34.1
342	399.0	673	10.3	50	550	0	11.9
343	400.9	673	10.3	50	90	1	35.1
344	406.0	675	3.5	51	400	0	2.2
345	398.3	564	−7.1	51	160	0	−16.6
346	400.9	677	2.2	50	270	1	3.8
347	403.9	680	8.0	50	510	0	10.4
348	400.2	566	−11.6	49	590	1	−8.2
349	405.6	672	3.3	50	240	1	4.1
350	400.5	679	17.8	49	720	0	53.8
351	401.9	678	4.5	51	220	1	13.5
352	405.4	676	6.4	49	170	1	4.4
353	405.1	676	15.5	50	690	0	51.2
354	402.3	563	−15.7	50	690	1	−28.7
355	399.1	566	−12.5	49	600	1	−8.5
356	402.3	676	12.6	49	600	0	35.9
357	399.7	568	−18.9	50	750	1	−34.8
358	401.3	673	1.2	51	290	1	1.5
359	397.4	675	2.9	51	250	1	3.7
360	398.2	670	3.6	50	400	0	8.2
361	402.6	567	−9.4	50	110	0	−5.8
362	401.2	677	7.6	50	150	1	18.6
363	403.4	674	5.9	50	450	0	16.8
364	398.6	675	2.2	49	270	1	2.6
365	397.6	675	8.4	49	510	0	14.1
366	401.0	673	10.5	50	80	1	31.0
367	406.1	671	2.2	50	370	0	3.9
368	401.2	565	−17.5	49	740	1	−33.4
369	397.7	672	0.4	49	330	0	0.5
370	398.5	564	−14.7	49	660	1	−26.2
371	401.5	670	5.2	50	440	0	19.2
372	402.4	674	13.3	50	0	1	48.7
373	401.0	674	0.9	50	340	0	1.5
374	397.8	677	0.8	51	300	1	1.1

(Continued)

No.	Utility Side 3ϕ Voltage (V)	DC Bus Voltage (V)	Utility Side 3ϕ Current (A)	Utility Side 3ϕ Power Freq. (Hz)	Elevator Load (kg)	Travelling Direction [Up/ Down] (1/0)	Regen. Energy (Wh)
375	406.6	671	5.2	50	440	0	9.8
376	399.9	676	3.1	50	390	0	2.1
377	405.1	679	4.7	51	210	1	15.0
378	399.6	675	11.0	50	580	0	39.1
379	398.2	560	−9.8	49	550	1	−40.6
380	402.0	676	6.3	51	470	0	11.4
381	404.2	672	14.9	50	680	0	27.4
382	399.0	568	−12.5	49	620	1	−14.8
383	397.9	680	7.1	50	160	1	8.4
384	403.1	568	−9.8	51	540	1	−6.2
385	397.1	678	18.8	50	740	0	65.3
386	398.2	561	−15.2	49	690	1	−30.2
387	400.1	677	8.9	51	110	1	22.5
388	400.6	677	13.1	50	630	0	31.1
389	405.2	671	2.9	50	250	1	5.3
390	399.6	679	1.3	51	290	1	0.9
391	402.7	670	7.9	51	510	0	25.8
392	402.3	674	10.8	51	80	1	12.8
393	406.7	673	7.9	51	140	1	9.2
394	402.2	675	10.0	50	560	0	36.7
395	399.0	563	−12.9	50	620	1	−15.0
396	403.5	672	5.2	49	440	0	3.6
397	397.5	677	0.5	49	310	1	0.5
398	400.1	564	−13.9	51	650	1	−9.5
399	400.3	680	7.2	51	490	0	8.6
400	398.6	568	−10.3	51	560	1	−30.8
401	401.1	675	9.3	51	530	0	32.3
402	405.1	671	2.6	50	260	1	7.5
403	404.4	674	8.0	50	510	0	23.9
404	403.8	673	3.5	49	240	1	4.3
405	404.7	570	−11.3	50	590	1	−22.1
406	402.7	674	10.7	49	560	0	25.6
407	398.2	564	−15.2	50	680	1	−28.0
408	401.2	671	6.0	50	460	0	17.7
409	402.4	679	5.6	49	190	1	10.7
410	402.0	563	−11.7	49	600	1	−30.7
411	403.5	679	17.9	51	730	0	76.3
412	406.3	677	9.5	51	110	1	31.9
413	399.3	673	6.6	49	470	0	15.3
414	398.7	567	−10.7	50	70	0	−12.4
415	398.0	569	−13.5	51	630	1	−15.6
416	400.1	675	10.4	50	550	0	6.8
417	404.4	561	−13.1	50	610	1	−30.7

(Continued)

No.	Utility Side 3ϕ Voltage (V)	DC Bus Voltage (V)	Utility Side 3ϕ Current (A)	Utility Side 3ϕ Power Freq. (Hz)	Elevator Load (kg)	Travelling Direction [Up/ Down] (1/0)	Regen. Energy (Wh)
418	398.1	676	19.2	51	770	0	60.2
419	398.8	671	9.4	50	90	1	35.4
420	403.0	672	7.1	49	480	0	17.0
421	404.6	568	−14.1	51	660	1	−34.8
422	399.7	565	−15.4	51	680	1	−10.4
423	404.0	677	16.2	51	690	0	39.7
424	403.1	679	3.8	50	410	0	4.9
425	400.5	561	−12.4	49	620	1	−23.3
426	397.4	568	−9.5	50	550	1	−18.2
427	406.5	676	13.1	49	620	0	31.2
428	404.7	671	18.1	51	740	0	32.7
429	401.9	565	−12.1	50	610	1	−15.6
430	402.8	562	−10.5	49	570	1	−7.1
Total regenerated energy per day (Wh)							2,703.7

Index

Note: **Bold** page numbers refer to tables and *italic* page numbers refer to figures.

F

G

H

I

K

L

M

N

O

T

U

V

W

X

Z